Physiographic Regions

of

ANGLO-AMERICA

Anglo-America

A SYSTEMATIC AND REGIONAL GEOGRAPHY

2nd Edition

Anglo-America

A Systematic and Regional Geography

Paul F. Griffin, Ph.D.
Professor of Geography
Oregon College of Education
Monmouth, Oregon

Ronald L. Chatham, Ph.D.
Professor of Geography
Oregon College of Education
Monmouth, Oregon

Robert N. Young, Ph.D.
Executive Director
State Planning Commission
Baltimore, Maryland

Cartography and artwork
by **Jay B. Vanderford**

37220

·EARON PUBLISHERS //P Palo Alto, California

To
ELLIS STEBBINS
honor, service, dedication

Preface

Anglo-America (the United States and Canada) is a cultural realm based on English as the common spoken language (with the French-speaking population of Canada a notable exception) and on the prevalence, historically, of northern European folkways and customs. The term "Anglo-America" readily designates a particular geographical area in the Western and Northern Hemispheres, setting it apart from Latin America, which has strong Hispanic traditions, greater ethnic diversity, and a different cultural heritage.

Many changes have occurred in the United States and Canada since the first edition of *Anglo-America, a Regional Geography of the United States and Canada* was published in 1962. Since that time, we have revisited all the regions of Anglo-America to gather new data, to analyze trends, to reaffirm previous convictions where evidence continues to support them, and to eliminate ideas that are no longer valid.

This new edition is more than a revision. Not only has the book been completely rewritten, but it has undergone total reorganization. The first eight chapters (Part I) are entirely new. They are designed to give the student greater breadth by treating the major patterns of Anglo-America in a systematic, or topical, framework. Part II deals with 10 major regions and 23 subregions. This change from the 22 regions and 36 subregions of the first edition is in response to suggestions from colleagues and students. The consolidation of some regions, elimination of much pure factual data, and greater emphasis on analysis and synthesis should facilitate student understanding and make the book far more appealing.

More than 400 maps, graphs, drawings, and photographs have been prepared especially for this new edition. They have been designed to clarify concepts, to systematize data, and to enable the student to grasp difficult material.

We are indebted to many people who have supplied materials, ideas, and criticisms. We owe special thanks to the many colleagues who have contributed to the literature of Anglo-America, for the regional geographer must, of necessity, draw much of his data from both the natural and social sciences. We wish especially to thank the following geographers who read the manuscript critically and contributed ideas that have helped to improve the text greatly: James Goodman, for his careful reading of Chapter 1; David Wilcoxson, who reviewed Chapters 2, 3, and 6; Philip Vogel, for his many helpful suggestions on Chapters 4, 5, 7, and 8; Charles Johnson, for his valuable contributions to Part II; Wayne White, for his careful editing of Chapter 11; John Augelli, who made several helpful suggestions regarding the basic organization of the text; George Vuicich, for his helpful suggestions on Chapter 8; Allen Schmieder and Peter Greco who made helpful suggestions on Part I; James Gallagher, for his contributions to Chapter 12; John Sherman, who reviewed many of the illustrations; and Jay Vanderford, who was responsible for selecting and compiling or executing all of the maps, graphs, drawings, and photographs. Last, but not least, we wish to thank our students, who served as our patient critics.

Monmouth, Oregon
January, 1968

PAUL F. GRIFFIN
RONALD L. CHATHAM
ROBERT N. YOUNG

Contents

11 APPALACHIAN-OZARK REGION

12 INTERIOR LOWLANDS REGION

285

13 GREAT PLAINS REGION

317

14 ROCKY MOUNTAIN REGION

337

15 INTERMONTANE BASINS AND PLATEAUS REGION

Part I *Anglo-America: A Systematic Appraisal*

In recent years, the concept and scope of geography have undergone such considerable change that it is highly unlikely that a definition of this science would satisfy everyone. Most geographers are agreed that geography comprises the study of the earth's surface in its areal differentiation as the home of man. How much of geography is a "science of distributions," physical and human; how much man in his spatial setting is its focus; and how much importance can be ascribed to regional study—all are matters for debate. The geographer seeks to describe diverse features of the earth's surface, to explain, if possible, how these features have come about, and to discuss how they influence the distribution of man. Geography occupies a central yet transitional position between the natural sciences, the social sciences, and the humanities; thus, in its concept and content, it is an integrated whole.

Not only have geographers quarreled among themselves for years regarding the nature of the subject matter in their discipline, but the method of approach to the subject has also been in dispute. Geographers once identified themselves as either physical geographers or human geographers, a natural carry-over from the 19th century, when geology and physical geography so dominated the discipline that the humanistic tradition became submerged. About the beginning of this century, however, geographers began to identify themselves as belonging to either the systematic (topical) or the regional (specific) approach to the teaching of the subject. But these two approaches are not separable. Most studies in geography require the use of both systematic and regional analyses. Thus, when used by contemporary geographers, the term "region" refers to "an area of specific location which is in some way distinctive from other areas and which extends as far as that distinction extends."[1] Systematic geography, on the other hand, investigates "a particular group of features produced by one kind of process wherever these features may occur in the world."[2]

[1] Richard Hartshorne, *Perspective on the Nature of Geography* (Chicago: Rand McNally, 1959), p. 130.

[2] P. E. James, "American Geography at Mid-century," *New Viewpoints in Geography*, Twenty-ninth Yearbook of the National Council for the Social Studies (Washington, D. C.: The Council, 1959), p. 10.

In "Anglo-America: A Systematic Appraisal," broad patterns or topics are discussed in order to present a broad over-all view of the major components of Anglo-America. We believe this treatment will provide the student with a more meaningful framework for study of Part II, "Anglo-America: A Regional Appraisal." It is hoped that this addition to the first edition of *Anglo-America, a Regional Geography of the United States and Canada* will make the text more useful and appealing to both teachers and students.

1 *The Physical Pattern*

Anglo-America occupies a strategic position in the world's land mass because of its location in the Western and Northern Hemispheres, its vast natural resources, the unsurpassed intensity of its industrial growth, its role in regional and world organizations, and the distinctive national characteristics and traditions that its people have developed (*Fig. 1-1*).

In a sense Anglo-America might be thought of as a great island. On the west, it is bounded by thousands of miles of ocean; on the north, except for a narrow strip of habitable land, by a vast expanse of uninhabited wilderness of Canadian forest and tundra; on the east and southeast, by a second vast ocean; and on the southwest, by the deserts of northern Mexico.

With a total of 7,467,020 square miles, Anglo-America is nearly twice the size of the continent of Europe and slightly more than one-tenth larger than South America. Shaped like a distorted parallelogram, its westernmost mainland point is Cape Prince of Wales, Alaska (168° 4′ W.), only 55 miles across the Bering Strait from Cape Dezhnev, U.S.S.R. Its easternmost mainland point is the Labrador coast (55° W.). The greatest length of mainland is about 4,500 miles; the greatest width, about 3,380 miles.

In the past, the compact shape of mainland Anglo-America has been a great military asset, especially to the United States. In addition, this compactness has greatly facilitated development of the United States and materially enhanced its political and economic unity and strength.

Surface Features

Physically, Anglo-America is an area of great diversity. Elevations range from 20,300 feet in Alaska (Mt. McKinley) to 282 feet below sea level in California (Death Valley); rainfall varies from less than 2 inches annually (southeastern California) to more than 450 inches (Mt. Waialeale, Hawaiian Islands). Similar contrasts are found in soil and vegetation types.

PHYSIOGRAPHIC REGIONS

There are three main physiographic regions of Anglo-America: (1) Western Mountains, Basins, and Plateaus, (2) Central Interior and Eastern Coastal Plains, and (3) Eastern Highlands (*Fig. 1-2*).

Western Mountains, Basins, and Plateaus. This region comprises the complex of young folded and igneous mountains and high intermontane basins and plateaus that occupy the western third of the continent. (The mountain system

FIGURE 1-1. *Anglo-America's global position.*

itself begins as a single chain through Central America to southern Mexico. There it divides into two major ranges with an intermountain plateau between them.) The interior ranges are separated by long, narrow valleys, broken occasionally by buttes, or expanding into broad flat plains or basins (*Fig. 1-3*). The westernmost ranges are not always continuous, as in the case of the peninsula of Lower California, which is essentially a part of the Sierra-Cascade chain. The Coast Range, which extends from

southern California to Vancouver Island, breaks down into a string of off-shore islands along the British Columbia coast. As a barrier the Western Mountain system is impressive, although not so high nor so lacking in passageways as the Andes in South America. Three great rivers cross from the intermountain section to the coast: the Fraser River of British Columbia, the Columbia River, and the Colorado River (*Fig. 1-4*). The Sacramento River allows access through the Coast Range of

FIGURE 1-2. *The three major physiographic regions of Anglo-America.*

California to the Central Valley of California. There are also several passes through the Rocky Mountains to the Central Plains.

The Central Interior and Eastern Coastal Plains. This region extends from the Arctic Ocean to the Gulf of Mexico and includes the St. Lawrence Lowlands and the Atlantic Coastal Plain. To the north and west, the plain is drained by the MacKenzie River into the Arctic Ocean. In southern Canada a small por-

tion of the plain is drained by the Saskatchewan and Nelson rivers into Hudson Bay. South of the Canadian border, the drainage system of the Mississippi River causes all of the water to flow ultimately into the Gulf of Mexico. The St. Lawrence River drains the Great Lakes region to the north and east. The Central Interior Plain constitutes the heart of Anglo-America and contains the richest farming regions of the continent. It is made up mainly of sediments that are nearly flat-lying (*Fig. 1-5*) and, for

FIGURE 1-3. *A scene in south-central Utah. Buttes are typical landforms of horizontal strata evolving in an arid climate. (C. B. Hunt, U.S. Geological Survey)*

FIGURE 1-4. *Aerial view of the Columbia River Gorge where the river cuts through the Cascade Mountains east of Portland, Oregon. (Oregon State Highway Dept.)*

FIGURE 1-5. *The flat landscape of the Central Interior Plains is well illustrated in this aerial view taken over Kirwin Dam and Reservoir in Kansas. (Bureau of Reclamation)*

the most part, is below 2,000 feet in elevation. There are many parts of this great lowland that can be set apart as natural regions on the basis of minor physiographic features, the climate, and the natural vegetation. These divisions will be treated in more detail in Part II, "Anglo-America: A Regional Appraisal."

The Eastern Highlands. There are two natural divisions in this region: (1) the Canadian Shield, and (2) the Appalachian Chain.

The Canadian Shield, which covers most of northeastern Canada as far south as the Great Lakes and includes much of New England, is made up of very old crystalline rocks that have been worn down by erosion until they present a very subdued appearance. There are no great ranges, but the area constitutes an upland of very low relief (*Fig. 1-6*). The rivers appear almost as spillways between the numerous lakes dotting the area: Great Bear Lake, Great Slave Lake, Lake Athabaska, Lake Winnipeg, Lake of the Woods, and the Great Lakes. The entire area was glaciated during the Ice Age and virtually stripped of all soil; thus, the higher portions are almost barren and the forests are to be found in the depressions around the lakes and rivers.

The Appalachian Chain is made up primarily of a great series of tightly folded sedimentary rocks. The range is old and has been subjected to erosion for so many geological periods that it now has a corrugated appearance, with the corrugations nearly parallel and almost continuous from northern Alabama and Georgia to the Catskills in New York (*Fig. 1-7*). At the northern end, between the Catskills and the Adirondack Mountains in New York, is an east-west trench or corridor, the Mohawk Valley (or Mohawk Trench), which allows easy transportation around the northern end of the Appalachian Chain. This trench joins at right angles with the north-south trench of the Hudson and Champlain Valleys, which extend from New York City northward to Montreal on the St. Lawrence River. The famous Cumberland Gap, a water gap on the Potomac lying between extreme southwestern Virginia and southeastern Kentucky, permits passage across the barrier of corrugated ranges between the Atlantic Coastal Plain and the Central Lowlands to the west. The Chickasaw Trail through Georgia and Alabama is a passageway around the southern end of the Appalachian Chain. The mountains are not high when compared with the Rockies or the Andes, but the relief is great. The range gives the appearance of grained wood that has been etched out by sandblasting. The northeastern and southwestern direction of its valleys and their great length caused the western migrations from Pennsylvania, Maryland, and Virginia to be deflected to the southwest into Kentucky, Tennessee, and Alabama so that this region was explored and occupied long before the nearby region of Ohio.

EFFECTS OF THE ICE AGE

The Ice Age materially altered the surface features of large sections of Anglo-America. Great continental ice sheets, similar to those of Greenland and Antarctica today, developed in three centers: (1) eastern Canada, (2) over central Canada near the southwestern shore of Hudson Bay, and (3) over the Canadian Rockies in the west (*Fig. 1-8*). In each case the ice began to accumulate in masses from 5,000 to 8,000 feet thick, and spread out laterally, principally toward the south and warmer climates. The terminus of the ice movement was determined by the point where the rate of melting equaled the rate of advance. Beneath this terrific weight of ice all loose soil and fragmental material was picked up and carried away from the focal centers of the ice sheets, leaving behind a denuded region with little soil and rocky ridges that have been rounded

FIGURE 1-6. *The Canadian Shield area in the vicinity of Indian House Lake, Quebec. Scattered lakes, clumps of trees, muskegs, erratics, and morainal material are characteristic features. (Geographical Branch, Canadian Dept. of Mines and Technical Surveys)*

FIGURE 1-7. *Cross-section of the eastern United States.*

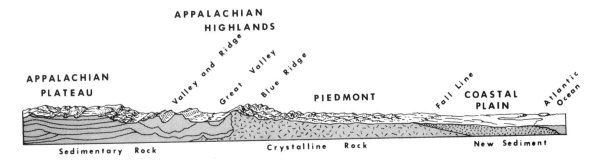

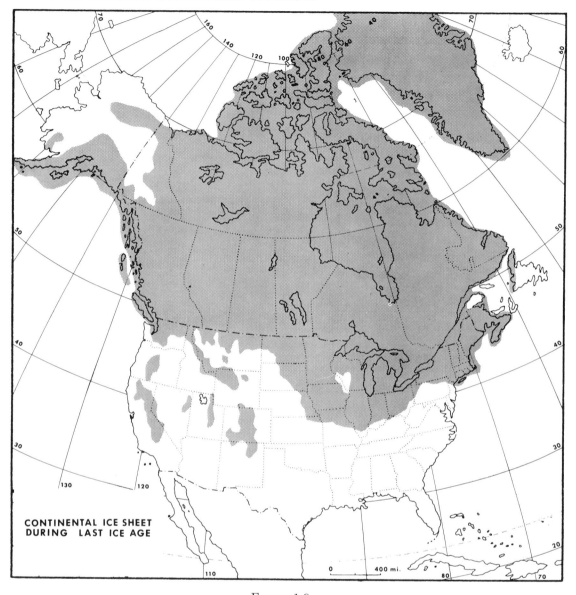

CONTINENTAL ICE SHEET
DURING LAST ICE AGE

FIGURE 1-8.

and scoured by the action of the moving ice. These regions are called *ice-scoured plains.*

Eastern Canada has been scoured and denuded of its soil, and the region of denudation extends across the Maritime Provinces. Ancient volcanic rocks of a granitic or crystalline nature make up eastern Canada, while the plains to the south are composed of sedimentary rocks, such as sands, clays, and limestones. The movement of the ice sheet has brought vast quantities of volcanic materials southward and deposited them on these sedimentary plains.

Some of the glacial drift is so fresh that it has not been broken down into soil by the agents of weathering. In certain sections, however, particularly on the outwash plains, the glacial materials have been mixed with the residual soils of the region to produce very fertile soils. The finest soils of Anglo-America are to be found in the regions of the southern extension of the ice sheets.

The ice also overrode New England and extended into the ocean; Long Island is a part of the terminal moraine. In the central part, the

Great Lakes region was covered and the ice extended as far south as Cairo, Illinois. In the west, the ice sheets advanced into the ocean along the coasts of British Columbia and Alaska, gouging out canyons and leaving numerous deep inlets called fiords, similar to those along the coast of Norway. The ice extended southward into the Puget Sound area, coming as far south as Chehalis, Washington. East of the Cascades it moved southward into the Grand Coulee country, and the dry washes that are now so characteristic of the Scablands were caused when ice dammed the Columbia River and deflected it across this region through many channels (*Fig. 1-9*). Since the melting of the ice, the Columbia has abandoned the channels across the Scablands and returned to its original channel.

EAST-WEST TRAVERSE
OF THE UNITED STATES

Figure 1-10 shows a cross-sectional traverse of the United States. As we look westward from the shores of the Atlantic Ocean, the fairly narrow Atlantic Coastal Plain is first sighted. This widens to the south, and finally merges into the Gulf Coastal Plain. Breaking the Atlantic Coastal Plain are the valleys of many rivers, such as the Connecticut, the Hudson, the Delaware, and the James. Only one of these, the Hudson, shows its sea level connection to the Great Lakes along the Mohawk depression. The New England Lowlands continue north-eastward into the Canadian Maritime Provinces.

At the inland edge of the Coastal Plain, the fall line and the Piedmont mark the end of nav-igation on all rivers except the Hudson. Rising from the Piedmont, the old worn Appalachian Highlands stretch toward the northeast from central Alabama to the Gaspé Peninsula at the mouth of the St. Lawrence River. Beyond the St. Lawrence, eastern Quebec and Newfoundland continue this upland pattern.

West of the Appalachian barrier, the Central Plains dip toward the Great Lakes on the north and the Mississippi River on the south, and encompass the lowlands surrounding Hudson Bay. The South Atlantic-Gulf Plain takes in all of Florida, goes around the Gulf of Mexico in southern Alabama, and then extends northward along the Mississippi River for some 500 miles. West of the Mississippi River this Gulf Plain continues in Louisiana, Arkansas, and Texas.

Beyond the Mississippi River the flat plains begin to rise gradually with an average increase in elevation of about ten feet per mile.

FIGURE 1-9. *Steamboat Rock was left standing in the middle of the upper Grand Coulee as a retreating Ice Age waterfall cut its way around each side. (Bureau of Reclamation)*

FIGURE 1-10. *Cross-sectional traverse of the United States.*

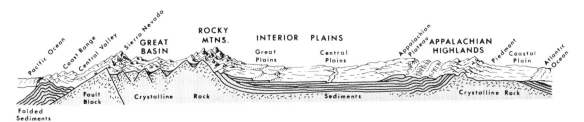

This almost imperceptible land rise continues across the Great Plains to the base of the Rocky Mountain system. The latter, trending slightly west of north, thrusts its ramparts high above the surface, with many peaks exceeding 14,000 feet.

Between the Rocky Mountains on the east and the Sierra Nevada and Cascades on the west within the conterminous[1] United States from north to south are the Columbia and Colorado Plateaus and the Basin and Range subregion, characterized by interior drainage, playas, and salt-encrusted flats. The Columbia Plateau on the north abuts the Canadian Rockies, a complex of north-south trending ranges.

Finally, the bold scarp of the Sierra Nevada in eastern California forms the western boundary of the Basin and Range subregion. The Cascade Range, beginning in northern California and extending through Oregon and Washington into Canada, marks the western edge of the Intermontane Plateau Region. Many peaks within these ranges exceed 10,000 feet, with Mt. Whitney, the highest point in the conterminous United States, rising 14,496 feet above sea level. Outstanding among the peaks of the high Cascades are Mt. Shasta, Mt. Hood, and Mt. Rainier.

In the south, the land drops from the Sierra Nevada to the Central Valley of California, and in the north, from the Cascades to the Willamette-Puget Lowland. Both valleys run to the coastal shelf of the Pacific, which is fringed by coast ranges and notched at San Francisco Bay, the Columbia River, and the Strait of Juan de Fuca. North of British Columbia, the Alaska Range marks the southern boundary of the Yukon Plateau, an area of low relief bounded by the Brooks Range on the north. A narrow coastal plain adjoins the Arctic Ocean north of the Brooks Range. The Aleutian Islands (about 150 in number) extend west-southwest from Alaska for 1,200 miles toward the Asiatic peninsula of Kamchatka. The chain is a continuation of the main Alaskan mountain range and contains many volcanic peaks 4,000 to 8,000 feet high. Far to the north, the islands of the Arctic Archipelago stand in a partially frozen sea.

Hawaii, a chain of islands in the mid-Pacific aligned northwest-southeast between 19° and 22° N. latitude, consists of eight main islands and 15 small, uninhabited islands. The four large islands, Hawaii, Maui, Oahu, and Kauai, have great strategic importance to the United States. They lie near the northern limits of the tropics, directly south of the Alaska Peninsula about 2,100 miles west-southwest of San Francisco. The islands are the upper parts of great volcanoes rising from the Pacific floor, and thus are composed of lava and other volcanic ejecta piled up in mountain masses. Debris has been transported downward by torrential rains and has formed fertile alluvial valley bottoms and tracts around the coasts, especially on Oahu, Kauai, and Maui (*Fig. 1-11*). Broken ravine-cut highlands flanking the parent volcanoes form the greater part of the four larger islands.

FIGURE 1-11. *Waipio, on the island of Hawaii, one of a number of great, virginal valleys found in the Hawaiian Islands. (Bank of Hawaii, Werner Stoy/ Camera House)*

[1] "Conterminous," a term coined by the American Geographical Society to distinguish the land area before the admission of Alaska and Hawaii to statehood, refers to the first 48 states.

There are 15 volcanoes, active or extinct; the two highest, Mauna Kea (13,805 feet) and Mauna Loa (13,675 feet), are on the largest island, Hawaii. Mauna Loa is active, as is Kilauea on its east flank. Many short and swift streams radiate from the mountain heights, flowing in deep canyons in their upper courses and in wide, fairly level valleys near the sea.

Climate

CLIMATE CONTROLS

Because of its large size and latitudinal extent, Anglo-America has a wide range of climates (*Fig. 1-12*). In general, the following climatic controls are instrumental in develop-

FIGURE 1-12.

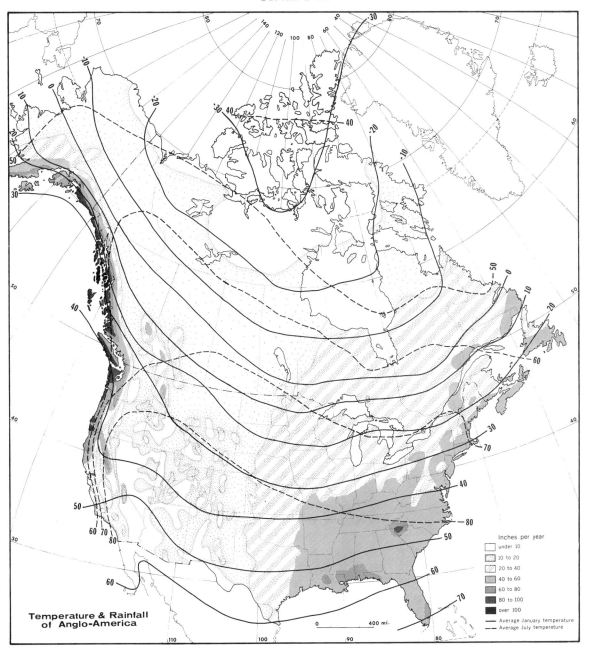

Temperature & Rainfall of Anglo-America

Inches per year
under 10
10 to 20
20 to 40
40 to 60
60 to 80
80 to 100
over 100

—— Average January temperature
- - - Average July temperature

0   400 mi.

ing the varied climates of the region: (1) latitude, (2) mountain barriers, (3) water bodies, (4) ocean currents, (5) prevailing winds, (6) air masses, and (7) altitude.

Latitude. Generally, the farther poleward from the equator, the lower the average *annual* temperatures. Anglo-America, extending from approximately 25° north latitude in southern Florida to about 83° north latitude in Canada, follows this general rule. Canadian winters, for example, are more severe than those of the conterminous United States. Snag, in the Yukon, has a recorded low of −86° F., while Montana's lowest is −69.7° F.

Mountain barriers. Altitude qualifies as an important climatic control because of the effect of the vertical temperature and pressure gradients. For instance, the Rocky Mountains act as effective barriers to the movement of maritime polar air from the North Pacific. Perhaps the most noteworthy effect of mountain barriers on climate, however, is in the distribution of precipitation. More rain falls on the windward side of mountains than on the leeward side. The rainfall along the North Pacific Coast is quite heavy, but the high mountains rob the air currents of most of their moisture so that the region east of the Cascades is arid (*Fig. 1-13*).

Water bodies. In winter, water bodies are warmer than the land. They absorb heat during the period of high sun and retain it over a longer period of time than land bodies, which heat up or cool off rapidly with the ascent or descent of the sun. In summer the reverse is true—the land warms up more rapidly, and the cooler, denser air over the ocean moves inland over water bodies to replace the warmer, lighter, land air. Thus water bodies are great modifiers of the climate of their surrounding regions. The south and east shores of the Great Lakes, for example, have much milder winter temperatures than inland areas far removed from their ameliorating influence.

Ocean currents. The shores of Anglo-America are bathed by several ocean currents whose temperatures modify that of the adjoining land masses (*Fig. 1-14*). The North Pacific Drift, propelled by the Westerlies, meets the west coast of Anglo-America near the mouth of the Columbia River. There it divides, with one branch going north and the other south. The northern branch gives British Columbia and the coast of Alaska mild winters for the latitude. The southern branch becomes the cool California Current and greatly modifies the climate of the coast, bringing lower temperatures, scanty rainfall, but much fog.

FIGURE 1-13. *An example of orographic precipitation in western North America.*

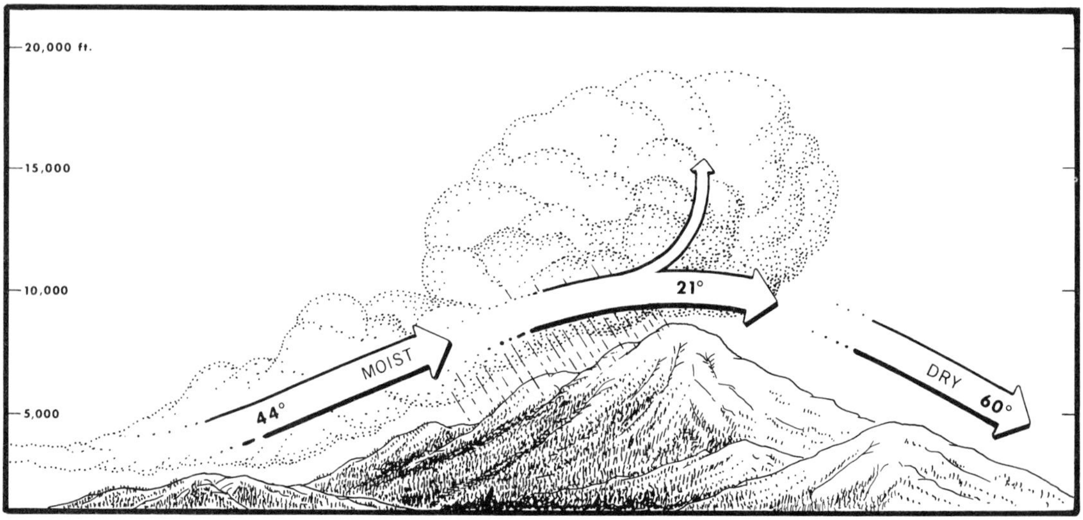

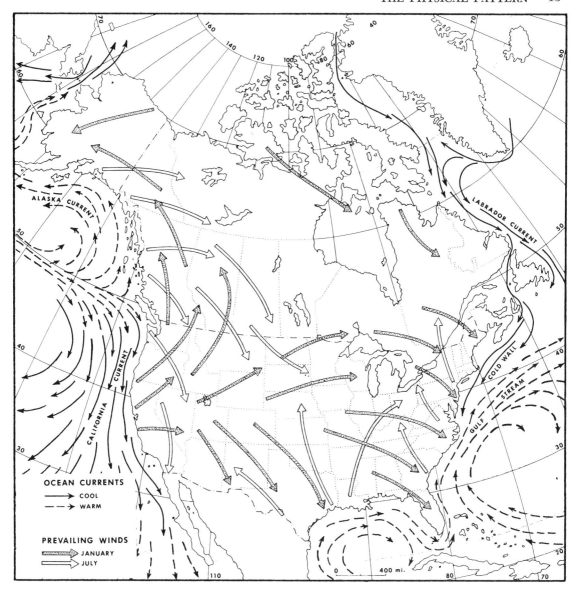

FIGURE 1-14. *The ocean currents surrounding Anglo-America, and the air masses affecting Anglo-America.*

The cold Labrador Current in the North Atlantic flows along the coasts of Labrador and Newfoundland and imparts a cold, damp climate to this region. Hence, northern New England, Nova Scotia, New Brunswick, and Quebec have severe winters, frequently accompanied by great depths of snow, and short, warm summers. During the summer the warm air from the southeast and south flows over the cold wedge of the Labrador Current and produces one of the foggiest regions on the globe.

The Gulf Stream is the only well-defined warm current having far-reaching effects in the Atlantic Ocean. A Florida Current has been identified, but it is limited in area, and eventually merges with the Gulf Stream. Anglo-America derives less benefit from the Gulf Stream than might be expected, for, in winter, when a warm current can have most effect, the prevailing winds are offshore. In summer the onshore winds are hot and moist, and when these qualities are especially pronounced, they form heat waves, an unpleasant element in the climate of the southeastern and eastern states.

Prevailing winds. Although the great latitudinal extent of Anglo-America puts it within the influence of several wind systems, one system in particular is important because of its location. Between 30° and 60° north latitude, where most of the population of Anglo-America is concentrated, lies the zone of the prevailing Westerlies. These winds blow across the country from west to east, carrying with them the cyclonic and anticyclonic systems that produce a broad variety of weather conditions, especially during the winter season.

Air masses. Anglo-America is the meeting ground for the various air masses of the North American continent and adjacent ocean bodies. These masses include both cold and warm air. Cold masses of air that influence climate are the Polar Pacific in the North Pacific, the Polar Continental in north-central Canada, and the Polar Atlantic in eastern Canada and the northeastern United States. Warm air masses include the Tropical Continental from northern interior Mexico; the Tropical Gulf, a major source of tropical air in the southeastern United States; and the Tropical Atlantic, which has only a small effect on Anglo-America (*see Fig. 1-14*).

In the winter months, masses of cold air move southward from the permanent high-pressure centers in polar regions or from the cold interior of the continent, forming an anticyclonic center, with low temperatures and a low relative humidity. Winds blow outward from the center at a speed that varies according to the rate at which the pressure changes in a given distance over the surface of the earth. At the same time, the winds over the oceans and the bordering lands are composed of air coming from warmer, lower latitudes, and circling about permanent high-pressure centers in the ocean.

On the lee side of these masses of continental cold air, cyclonic eddies, or cyclones, develop, into which blows warm, humid air from equatorial regions on one side, and cold polar air from the other. Cyclones form in front of the anticyclonic polar air masses and move eastward across Anglo-America (*see Fig. 1-14*). On the easterly side of the cyclonic low pressure center, the warm, humid air usually causes precipitation as it is cooled by rising and mixing with the cold air blowing into the eddy from the opposite direction.

The approach of a cyclone is first indicated by a barometric drop and by a shift of the wind in an easterly direction. Cloudiness steadily increases, and rain or snow usually follows. A cyclone may be from 300 to 1,000 miles in diameter; and, in the winter months, the center moves forward about thirty miles an hour on the average.

Cyclonic and anticylonic areas are better developed in the winter than in the summer months; therefore, storms are generally more severe in winter, and weather changes are more rapid and extreme. In winter, a great polar air mass may spread southward and eastward over eastern Anglo-America and cause a period of extreme cold lasting for several days. The weather is coldest during the calm that marks the center of the anticyclone.

During the summer, when the interior of the continent is warm and cyclonic and anticyclonic centers are less well developed, a long period of warm, humid weather may occur.

Most of the winter precipitation over eastern Anglo-America occurs during the passage of cyclones. Much of the summer precipitation results from local convectional movements in thunderstorms, which are caused by the superheating of the humid surface air.

Altitude. The air resting on highlands is less dense and contains less water vapor than that resting on lowlands. Hence, it has fewer molecules to absorb the heat of the sun by day or the heat given off by the earth at night.

The exposure, or direction of slope, in hilly country has a great influence on the amount of heat imparted to the ground and, therefore, upon the weather. In the Northern Hemisphere the southern slopes are warmer than other slopes because they receive the rays of the sun for a longer time each day and the rays are more nearly perpendicular.

The rate at which air becomes cooler with increasing altitude varies at different places and at different times. The general average is one degree for each 300 feet of ascent (*Fig 1–15*). On the ordinary slopes of nonmountain regions, such as those of the Mississippi Valley, the average rate is about one degree for each 450 feet of ascent. The rate is most rapid in summer and on the warm side of a mountain.

When air is forced to ascend and go over mountains, extensive precipitation may result on the windward side, while clear weather prevails on the leeward side (*see Fig. 1-13*).

CLIMATIC REGIONS

The interaction between the various modifiers of climate introduces a variety of climatic types in Anglo-America (*Fig. 1-16*).

Polar continental. In the far northern islands of Canada and on the shoreline of the Arctic in both Canada and Alaska, a *polar continental* (Köppen E[2]) climate is present. Here the warmest month is below 50° F., and the summer is very short. The ground is frozen for nine or ten months, and, during the summer, the surface thaws only to a depth of a few inches.

Subarctic. To the south, stretching in a band 500 to 1,000 miles wide from south-central Alaska to Newfoundland, is found a *subarctic*

[2] Under the Köppen classification of climate, there are five major climates; they are given symbols in the form of capital letters: **E** is for polar climates; **D**, microthermal climates; **C**, mesothermal climates; **B**, dry climates; **A**, tropical climates. A subclassification (for the D, C, and A climates) uses a small letter symbol for the distribution of precipitation over the seasons: **s** is for summer dry, with rain in other seasons, often winter; **w**, winter dry, with rain in other seasons, often summer; **f**, humid, with rain in all seasons; **m**, transitional (monsoon-like). A further subclassification for the C and D climates uses a small letter symbol: **a** is for summer hot; **b**, summer moderate; **c**, summer cool and short, winter severe and long; **d**, summer cool and short, winter very cold and long. The B climates are subdivided into **BW** representing desert and **BS** representing steppe, with further subdivision using the small letter symbol **h** indicating hot and **k** indicating cold. The polar climate E is further subdivided into **ET** (with vegetation) and **EF** (without vegetation, e.g., ice).

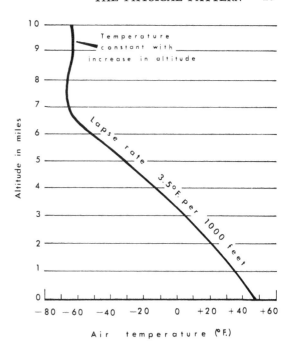

FIGURE 1-15. *Moist adiabatic temperature lapse rate.*

(Köppen Dcf) regime, with mean temperatures above 50° F. for the warmest month of summer and below 26° F. for the coldest month of winter. Precipitation is usually in the form of snow, with cool rains in summer. The precipitation is well distributed throughout the year, with the zone of heaviest rainfall on the western margin, gradually diminishing eastward. The winter precipitation is frozen and is held in place until the warm days of spring when thawing releases the moisture of the snow and ice. This region in winter is physically dry, but meteorologically humid. The region has a great temperature range throughout the year. Temperatures are relatively high during summer months because of the long hours of sunlight, and considerably below zero for long periods in winter because of the very long nights.

Humid continental. The northeastern and north-central sections of the United States and the southeastern and south-central parts of Canada have a *humid continental* (Köppen Daf, Dbf) climate, with cool, short summers in the north and hot, long summers in the south. In this area the weather is characterized by

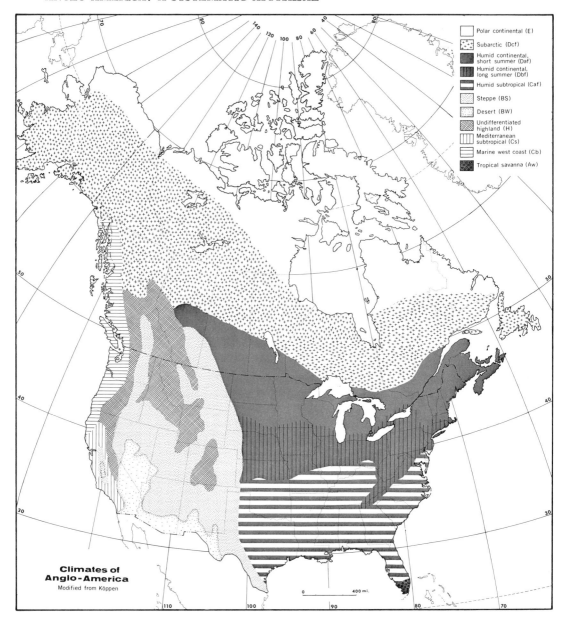

FIGURE 1-16.

wide seasonal ranges of temperature and rapid changes in wind direction, precipitation, humidity, and air pressure. It is not unusual to have temperatures above 100° F. in the summer and an average temperature below freezing one to three months during the winter season. The annual rainfall averages between 20 and 50 inches. Since a minimum of 20 inches of rainfall is essential for agriculture without irrigation and 30 to 50 inches are required for ideal soil moisture, conditions for farming in this belt are most favorable. As a result, this area contains some of the most productive agricultural sections in the world. It has also become one of the world's greatest industrial and manufacturing centers.

Humid subtropical. The southeastern and south-central United States has a *humid subtropical* (Köppen Caf) climate characterized by hot, humid summers and mild, cool winters. (An exception is the southern tip of Florida, which has a *tropical savanna* climate.) Rainfall is distributed through all months of the year, although it is heaviest in the summer season. Sharp, quick thundershowers occur during the summer because of the almost tropical heat; but during the winter, rain occurs over periods of several days, alternating with dry, sunny weather. Light snow may fall occasionally, and periods of fairly cold weather may be expected during midwinter. Thus, the growing season is limited to a period of seven to eleven months. Cloudiness and relative humidity are high most of the year.

Stations along the southeastern coast of the United States show colder temperatures in winter than west coast stations of the same latitude because of offshore winds. For example, the mean for January in Norfolk, Virginia (37° N.) is 40° F.; the mean for January in San Francisco (38° N.) is 49° F. On the other hand, the temperature is cooler in summer at west coast stations than at east coast stations; the July mean for Norfolk is 78° F., and for San Francisco, 57° F. Thus, it is apparent that the climate of the east coast is considerably more continental than the west.

Steppe and desert. The western interior of the United States and Canada experiences a variety of dry climates—either *steppe* (Köppen BS) or *desert* (Köppen BW)—except at the higher elevations, where an *undifferentiated highland* climate prevails. The most striking climatic features of the western interior are the high percentage of sunshine, the low rainfall in the valleys, and the high evaporation rate in the more southerly portion of the region.

Nearly all of the region's rainfall is caused by the interaction of great masses of cold, dry, and heavy air (polar continental) originating over the vast arctic tundra of northern Canada, and masses of warm, moist, and light air (tropical maritime) that originate over the Gulf of Mexico and the Atlantic between Bermuda and the Bahamas. At irregular intervals, the polar continental air masses advance south and east across the Great Plains, where they generally encounter maritime air moving northward from the Gulf of Mexico or the Atlantic. The tropical air masses that flow

northward across the plains generally come from the dry plateau of Mexico; they are warm but contain little water vapor. When this tropical air comes in contact with the cold, heavy air from the north, it is forced up; but little precipitation results from the consequent cooling. The farther the tropical air has traveled from its sources of moisture, the drier it becomes and the lighter is the precipitation that results from its cooling. The result is a gradual decrease in annual average precipitation from approximately 20 inches in southern Texas to less than 12 inches in northern Canada.

Precipitation, in addition to being generally light, is also extremely variable, following a pattern of successive wet and dry periods, rather than a heterogeneous occurrence of single wet and dry years. Rain comes mainly in summer in the form of local thundershowers that produce rain over a small area at a time. The amount of rainfall is rather irregular and undependable; some places may suffer from drought while places a few miles away receive ample rain. Some parts of this region are real desert, recording less than 8 inches of precipitation per year; other parts are semiarid, receiving up to 20 inches annually. Winters are rather dry, but a few light snows may fall during this season. Generally, sunny skies prevail much of the time. Sometimes warm winds (chinooks) occur in mid-winter, raising the local temperature 50 to 60 degrees in a few hours. Cold waves, blizzards, and "northers" may occur in the autumn or the spring.

Over most of the western interior the summers are hot and the winters are cold. The average maximum temperatures range from more than 100° F. on the floors of the desert basins to less than 50° F. at higher elevations. Temperatures below zero occur quite frequently in winter. Because of the high altitude and extreme dryness and clearness of the air, there is rapid nocturnal radiation of heat, which results in wide daily ranges in temperature. In extreme instances, the daily range may be as great as 50 to 60 degrees. Humidity is normally low, and the dryness of the air makes both the summer heat and the winter cold less disagreeable.

Mediterranean subtropical. Central- and south-coastal and a good part of interior California possess a *Mediterranean subtropical* (Köppen Cs) climate, with warm to hot, dry summers and cool, rainy winters. The growing season is nearly twelve months long; for while the nights of the three-month cool season are often frosty, killing frosts are rare. The other nine months are warm to hot. The cool season is characterized by the prevalence of rain, fogginess, cloudiness, and high humidity. Although rain may fall very heavily in storm centers, the weather soon brightens and the sun shines more brilliantly through air that has been washed by rain. During the rest of the year, there is low humidity and almost unbroken sunshine.

Bordered by desert lands on the equatorward margin, California's Mediterranean subtropics experience the poleward edge of the dry trade winds during the summer season. These winds blow strong and fresh from the belt of subtropical high pressure (colder, more dense air) toward the equator (warmer and lighter air). In their procession toward the Tropical Zone, these winds expand as they become warmer, thus increasing their capacity to absorb moisture. Unless they are forced to rise and cool, they give off little or no moisture during the summer period. Consequently, during the summer, the deep-blue sky is almost cloudless, the air is dry, and rain is very rare. The only showers are on the higher mountains, which receive rain all through the dry summer. Streams descending to the lowlands from these mountains are used for irrigation on the deltas, alluvial fans, and valleys. During the winter, the trade winds shift equatorward, allowing rain-bearing cyclonic storms to move in from the ocean, bringing spells of rainy, cloudy weather. The rain usually falls as a gentle, light drizzle. In spring and autumn, this region lies in the belt of tropical calms, and these periods are characterized by light variable winds and occasional fogs.

The southern part of California has only about seven per cent of the annual precipitation that northern California coastal regions have. Temperatures vary from south to north and from the coast inland. Relative to inland areas, the coast is warm in winter and cool in summer. There is a great deal of advection fog[3] over the coast in summer and radiational fog[4] over the inland valleys in winter.

Marine west coast. The Pacific coastal region from northern California through southern Alaska has a *marine west coast* (Köppen Cb) climate. Although this region is in the same latitude as the humid continental climate, it is much more moderate in temperature. This moderation results from cool winds prevailing from the ocean in summer and relatively warm winds from the ocean in winter.

The climate is both equable and changeable. Extremes of heat and cold or of drought and heavy rain are rare, but the weather seldom remains the same for longer than ten days or so at a time. As is usual in oceanic climates, winter tends to be prolonged into spring—a treacherous, uncertain season—and summer prolonged into autumn. The growing season is long and variable; for example, it varies from 180 to 210 days in the Pacific Northwest of the conterminous United States.

On the average, more than 80 per cent of the annual precipitation occurs during the period from October 15 to May 15. Having maximum rainfall in winter is one of the features that distinguishes a marine climate from a continental climate, which has its maximum rainfall in summer. In winter, the land is cooler than the ocean. Hence, the ocean's moist winds are cooled, water vapor is condensed out of them, and rain almost certainly results. Although a general mildness results from the proximity of the ocean, much of the remarkable winter mildness occurs when the usual track of the low pressure storms that produce rain is so far to the poleward that warm southerly winds prevail over the region. When the

---

[3] Formed when a warm, moist air stream moves horizontally over a cooler land or sea surface, thus reducing the temperature of the lower layers of the air below the dew point.

[4] A shallow layer of white fog (often called ground fog), formed during settled weather in low-lying areas. The surface of the ground, itself cooled by radiation at night, cools the layer of air resting on it, which, in turn, flows down into hollows by gravity and is cooled to the dew point, causing condensation.

track is so far equatorward that northerly winds predominate, the weather is generally clear. If unusually high pressure should prevail with northerly winds, the weather becomes severe. In brief, rain and mild weather occur with southerly winds (southeast, south, or southwest), and clear, cold weather—and snowfall in the valleys under certain conditions—occurs with northerly winds (northwest, north, or northeast).

In the summer months, no well-defined low pressure storms move over the region. During this period, high pressure usually predominates, causing dry weather, with very infrequent showers; the nights and forenoons are cool, and the afternoons are pleasantly warm.

Natural Vegetation

The natural vegetation of Anglo-America is as varied as its climatic regions (*Fig. 1-17*).

FIGURE 1-17.

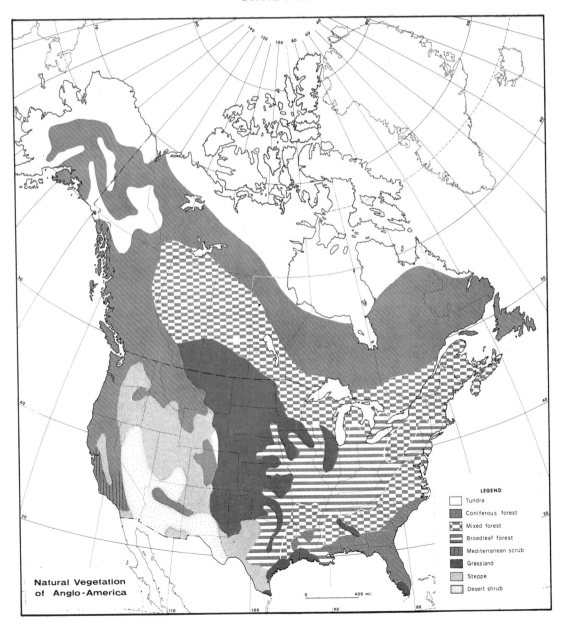

LEGEND

Tundra
Coniferous forest
Mixed forest
Broadleaf forest
Mediterranean scrub
Grassland
Steppe
Desert shrub

Natural Vegetation
of Anglo-America

0   400 mi.

Northern Canada and most of Alaska, with the exception of the Panhandle and the central portions, possess a tundra vegetation of mosses, lichens, and flowering plants. Central Alaska, the Panhandle area, and nearly all of central and southern Canada, with the exception of the Prairie Provinces, are composed of coniferous forests, with the thickness of the forest area varying from place to place. The northeastern part of the United States has both broadleaf deciduous trees and coniferous forests(mixed). The White, the Taconic, the Appalachian, and other mountain ranges in this section show a predominance of coniferous trees, however. The southeastern United States follows a similar pattern of mixed broadleaf and coniferous forests that gradually give way to purely coniferous forests in southern Georgia, Alabama, Mississippi, North and South Carolina, and all of Florida but the southern tip (*Fig. 1-18*). The interior plains of the United States and Canada are the home of grasslands, with tall prairie grass in the east and short steppe grass in the west as a response to variance in precipitation and evaporation rate. The Rocky Mountains of Canada and Alaska and the Sierra Nevada, the Cascades, and the Coast Ranges of northern California, Oregon, Washington, British Columbia, and Alaska have coniferous vegetation. The Basin and Range subregion of the western and southwestern United States shows a desert shrub complex (*Fig. 1-19*). The central portion of

FIGURE 1-19. *These saguaro cacti in southern Arizona are typical of desert vegetation. (U.S. National Park Service)*

the Intermontane Basins and Plateaus Region and the Central Valley of California possess steppe vegetation, and the Coast Ranges of central and southern California are primarily the home of Mediterranean scrub forests—with chamise, chaparral, and other characteristic species. The Hawaiian Islands display a mixed assemblage—tropical rain forest vegetation in some areas, and shrubs, grasses, and brush in other areas.

Soils

Soils result from the breaking down of the underlying rock by the agents of weathering. Each drop of water that falls upon land dissolves away a portion of the rock surface or loosens small particles and, under the influence of gravity, carries the loosened part downhill.

The soil of any place is the product of all the local physical forces, and since there are a

FIGURE 1-18. *A stand of 40-year-old longleaf pine in North Carolina. (U.S. Forest Service)*

great number of combinations of biological, geological, and climatic conditions in Anglo-America, there are a great many types of soil (*Fig. 1-20*).

Northern Canada and northern and western Alaska possess poor tundra soils of little value for agricultural use. Central and southeastern Canada and central Alaska are made up predominantly of podzol soil that has developed under coniferous forests. It is acid, thin in cover, and generally regarded as poor soil. The northeastern United States is principally an area of gray-brown podzolic soils that have a fair rating in terms of crop potential. The southeastern United States is a land of red and yellow podzolic-latosolic soils, soils that have been leached of much of their nutrients by rainfall. These soils need heavy applications of fertilizers. In the central part of the United States are found the fertile prairie soils. This group, with

FIGURE 1-20.

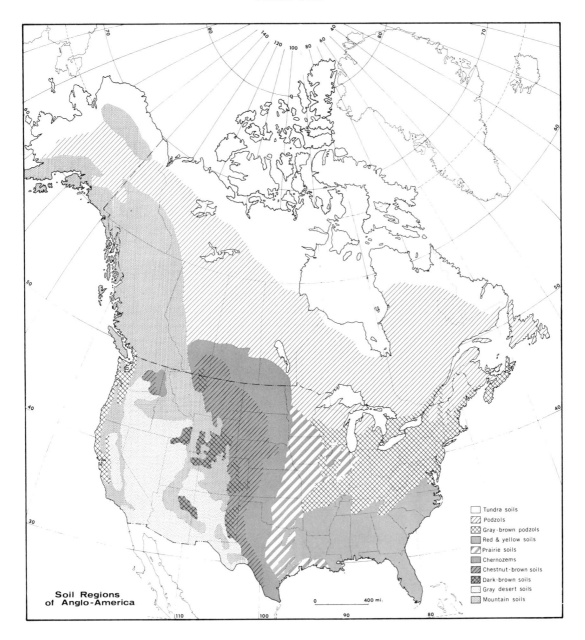

Soil Regions of Anglo-America

0   400 mi.

Tundra soils
Podzols
Gray-brown podzols
Red & yellow soils
Prairie soils
Chernozems
Chestnut-brown soils
Dark-brown soils
Gray desert soils
Mountain soils

a north-south extent centering on approximately 95° west longitude, makes up one of the great agricultural soils of the world. To the west of the prairie soils, also stretching along a north-south axis, is a narrow band of chernozem, or black earth soils. Like the prairie soils, these are extremely fertile and are generally rated among the finest soil groups in the world for crop production, although the area is marginal in terms of adequate precipitation. The western interior section of the United States is composed of various soil groups, ranging from chestnut and brown steppe soils, which are considered fair, to desert soils and soils of the mountainous region, which vary in fertility and chemical composition. The soils of the Pacific Coast of Anglo-America are mostly mountain soils, although the valleys of the Sacramento, San Joaquin, Willamette, Puget Sound, and the smaller coastal valleys contain alluvial soils. The soils of Hawaii are derived mainly from volcanics, although some parent material was alluvium or marine sediment.

Drainage

Anglo-America has five great drainage basins: (1) the Atlantic Basin—rivers draining the eastern coast—for the most part short, rapid rivers, but including such large systems as the St. Lawrence; (2) the Gulf of Mexico Basin— rivers flowing toward the Gulf of Mexico, including such master streams as the Mississippi, the Missouri, the Ohio, the Arkansas, and the Tennessee; (3) the Pacific Basin, with such master streams as the Colorado, the Sacramento-San Joaquin, and the Columbia, which flow into the Pacific Ocean, and the Yukon-Kuskokwim, which enters the Bering Sea; (4) Arctic Basin, including the MacKenzie-Peace system, and (5) the Hudson Bay Basin, which includes the Red, Nelson, Thelon, and Churchill Rivers (*Fig. 1-21*).

Selected References

ATWOOD, WALLACE W., *The Physiographic Provinces of North America*, Boston: Ginn & Co., 1940.

BENNETT, M. K., "The Isoline of Ninety Frost-free Days in Canada," *Economic Geography*, Vol. 35, January, 1959, pp. 41–50.

CAMU, PIERRE, WEEKS, E. P., and SAMETZ, Z. W., *Economic Geography of Canada*, Toronto: Macmillan of Canada, 1964, pp. 9–32.

COURT, ARNOLD, "Temperature Extremes in the United States," *The Geographical Review*, Vol. 43, January, 1953, pp. 39–49.

COURT, ARNOLD, and GERSTON, RICHARD, "Fog Frequency in the United States," *The Geographical Review*, Vol. 56, October, 1966, pp. 543–550.

FENNEMAN, NEVIN M., *Physiography of Eastern United States*, New York: McGraw-Hill Book Co., Inc., 1938.

———, *Physiography of Western United States*, New York: McGraw-Hill Book Co., Inc., 1931.

HADEN-GUEST, STEPHEN, WRIGHT, J. K., and TECLAFF, E. M., *A World Geography of Forest Resources*, New York: The Ronald Press Co., 1956, pp. 115–182.

HORN, LYLE H., and BRYSON, REID A., "Harmonic Analysis of the Annual March of Precipitation over the United States," *Annals of the Association of American Geographers*, Vol. 50, June, 1960, pp. 157–171.

HUDSON, F. S., *North America*, London: Macdonald & Evans, Ltd., 1962, pp. 1–15, 25–31, 141–149.

HUNT, CHARLES B., *Physiography of the United States*, San Francisco: W. H. Freeman & Co., 1967.

KENDREW, W. G., *The Climates of the Continents*, London: Oxford University Press, 1961, pp. 389–464.

KENDREW, W. G., and CURRIE, B. W., *The Climate of Central Canada*, Ottawa: Queen's Printer, 1955.

KIMBLE, GEORGE H. T., *Our American Weather*, New York: McGraw-Hill Book Co., Inc., 1955.

KROEBER, A. L., *Cultural and Natural Areas of Native North America*, Berkeley: University of California Press, 1963.

LEGGET, R. F., *et. al.*, *Soils in Canada: Geological, Pedological and Engineering Studies*, Toronto: University of Toronto Press and Royal Society of Canada, 1961.

LOBECK, A. K., *Physiographic Diagram of North America*, New York: C. S. Hammond & Co., Inc., 1950.

LOOMIS, F. B., *Physiography of the United States*, New York: Doubleday & Co., Inc., 1937.

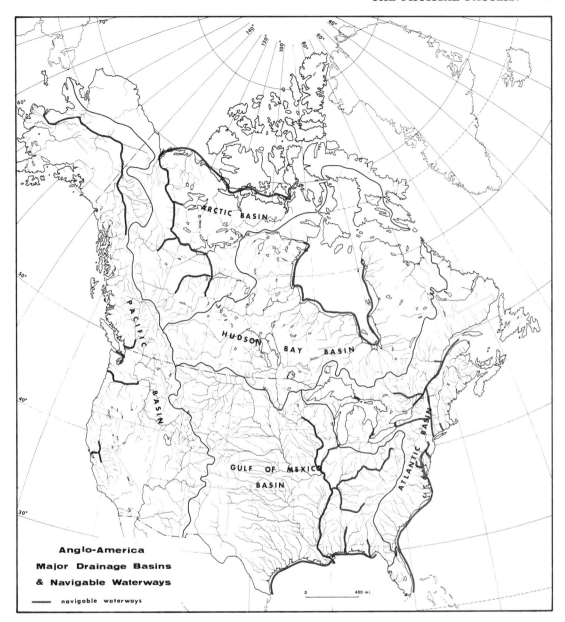

FIGURE 1-21.

MEAD, W. R., and BROWN, E. H., *The United States and Canada, a Regional Geography*, London: Hutchinson Educational, Ltd., 1962, pp. 23–96.

MILLER, G. J., PARKINS, A. E., and HUDGINS, B., *Geography of North America*, New York: John Wiley & Sons, Inc., 1954, pp. 3–31.

PARKER, W. H., *Anglo-America, a Systematic Regional Geography*, London: University of London Press, 1962, pp. 1–36.

PATERSON, J. H., *North America, a Geography of Canada and the United States*, London: Oxford University Press, 1965, pp. 1–45.

PRESTON, RICHARD, *North American Trees*, Cambridge: Massachusetts Institute of Technology Press, 1966.

SABBAGH, MICHAEL E., and BRYSON, REID A., "Aspects of the Precipitation Climatology of Canada Investigated by the Method of Harmonic Analysis," *Annals of the Association of Ameri-*

can Geographers, Vol. 52, December, 1962, pp. 426–440.

SAUER, CARL O., "The End of the Ice Age and Its Witnesses," *The Geographical Review,* Vol. 47, January, 1957, pp. 29–43.

SHELFORD, VICTOR E., *The Ecology of North America,* Urbana: University of Illinois Press, 1963.

SHIMER, J. A., *This Sculptured Earth: The Landscape of America,* New York: Columbia University Press, 1959.

STAMP, L. D., and HARE, F. K., *Physical Geography of Canada,* Toronto: Longmans, 1953.

SUMNER, ALFRED R., "Standard Deviation of Mean Monthly Temperatures in Anglo-America," *The Geographical Review,* Vol. 43, January, 1953, pp. 50–59.

TERJUNG, WERNER H., "Physiologic Climates of the Conterminous United States: A Bioclimatic Classification Based on Man," *Annals of the Association of American Geographers,* Vol. 56, March, 1966, pp. 141–179.

THORNBURY, W. D., *Regional Geomorphology of the United States,* New York: John Wiley & Sons, Inc., 1965.

WILLIAMS, LLEWELYN, "Regionalization of Freeze-thaw Activity," *Annals of the Association of American Geographers,* Vol. 54, December, 1964, pp. 597–611.

Yearbook of Agriculture, Washington, D.C.: United States Department of Agriculture, Government Printing Office, 1938, 1941, 1943–47, 1948, 1949, 1951, 1952, 1955, 1957, 1958.

2 *The Settlement Pattern*

The history and culture of a people are inseparable from the land area they occupy. What people do, where they settle, how they earn a living, govern themselves, and relate to other peoples in different places of the world are as vital to an understanding of their actions as is the knowledge of their physical environment. Recognizing this interrelationship, Peter Heylyn wrote more than 300 years ago:

As Geography without History hath life and motion, but at randome and unstable: So History without Geography, like a dead carkasse hath neither life nor motion at all: and as the exact notice of the place addeth a satisfactorie delight to the action: so the mention of the action, beautifieth the notice of the place. Geography therefore and History, like the two firelights *Castor and Porlux,* seem together, a crowne our happinesse; but parted asunder menace a shipwracke of our content: and are like two sisters intirely loving each other, and not without great pitty to be divided; So as that which Sir Philip Sidney said of *Argolus* and *Partheria:*

> Her beeing was in him alone.
> And she not being, he was none.

I may justly say of these two *Gemini,* History and Geography.[1]

---

[1] Peter Heylyn, *Microcosmos, a Little Description of the Great World* (5th ed.; Oxford: William Turner and Robert Allot, 1631), p. 16.

The story of Anglo-America is the story of the impact of an old culture upon a wilderness environment. Anglo-America skipped, as it were, the first six thousand years of history and arrived upon the historical scene bold and mature, for the first European settlers were civilized men, and they transplanted a culture centuries old. Yet the New World was never merely an extension of the Old. The unconquered wilderness confronting the pioneer profoundly modified inherited institutions, and the intermixture of peoples and of races modified inherited cultures. Anglo-America became the most ambitious experiment ever undertaken in the intermingling of peoples, religious toleration, social equality, economic opportunity, and political democracy.

The history of Anglo-America, written largely in terms of expansion upon the North American continent, shows physiographic influences at every phase. Because of its proximity to Europe and its contour, the eastern seaboard became the place of first settlement; the river valleys and the water and wind gaps pointed the routes westward, and the land formation and its products aided in determining the occupation of the new settler. These factors, added to a favorable climate, an abundance of natural resources, and the peoples' initiative, have contributed greatly to the development of Anglo-America.

Anglo-America in Pre-Columbian Times

The Indians who occupied the Americas were of Asiatic origin. They migrated to this hemisphere in a series of waves, probably a few at a time. They undoubtedly came from different parts of Asia. Most anthropologists believe that they migrated by way of the Bering Strait between Alaska and Siberia, and that the majority moved southward through the Central Plains. Some pushed southward between the great mountain ranges and some down along the tortuous west coast (*Fig. 2-1*).

Sauer suggests that the optimum passage would have been during the development of the Illinoian glaciation (the next to the last ice advance), when genial weather, varied biota, and low sea level existed.

Thus, about a third way back through the Ice Age the same invitation to pass at leisure through an easy gateway was available to animals, plants, and man. Well before this time man had become distributed to pretty far ends of the Old World Continents. No reason has been offered as to why he should not have gone where went bear, bison, and deer, and I see no reason why he should not have availed himself of the same favorable opportunity to colonize the New World.[2]

When Columbus arrived, the Americas were inhabited from the Arctic pastures of North America south to the island of Tierra del Fuego at the extreme tip of South America. The Indians differed considerably as to physical features from one region to another, though all are believed to have belonged to the same racial stock. (*Fig. 2-2*).

NATURAL FOOD AREAS

There were seven major natural food areas in Anglo-America: (1) caribou area, (2) salmon area, (3) wild seed area, (4) bison area, (5) eastern maize area, (6) area of intensive agriculture, and (7) the game area (*Fig. 2-3*).

[2] Carl O. Sauer, *Agricultural Origins and Dispersals* (New York: The American Geographical Society, 1952), pp. 8–9.

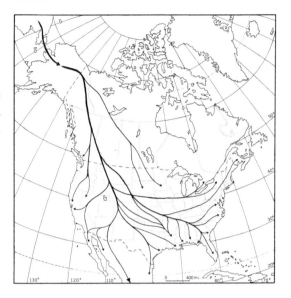

FIGURE 2-1. *Indian migration routes in Pre-Columbian Anglo-America.*

The utilization of these food areas by rather primitive Indian groups roughly delimits the major cultural areas existing in Anglo-America in pre-Columbian times and will be used as the key to regional differentiations.

Caribou area. Most of the Eskimos of Alaska and Canada and many present-day Indians of the subarctic pastures of Canada dwell in this area. Their lives revolve largely about the caribou.[3] This is especially true of the Nunamiut Eskimos of Anaktuvuk Pass in the Brooks Range of Alaska and the Canadian Indians of the Northwest Territories. The caribou range widely from winter to summer, and the Indian tribes follow them, preying upon the herds at all times. A constant source of food, the caribou also supplies clothing, leather for boots and dog harnesses, and a covering for their houses. Through necessity, the Indians are nomadic, living in small bands of several families each. There is little, if anything, in the way of government except that practiced by chieftains, and there are very few social orders or religious societies. Because they are nomadic,

[3] Other game animals also provide a source of food, clothing, and shelter. For example, the seal is important in the Bering Sea area, and upland game furnishes sustenance for many Indians of the Canadian northland.

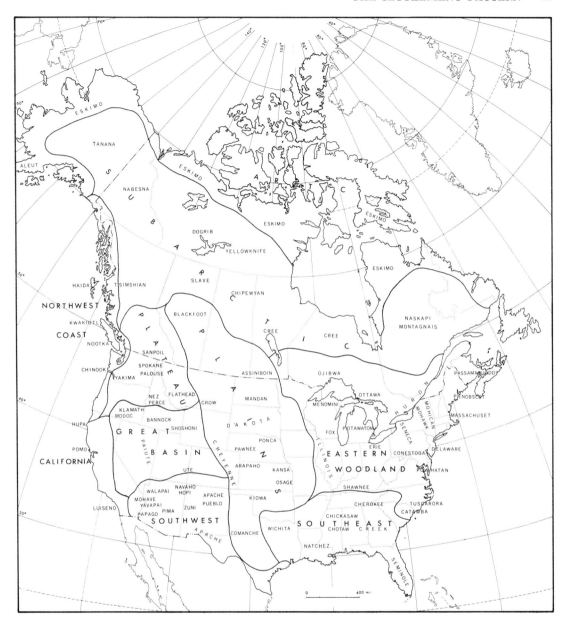

FIGURE 2-2. *The Indian tribes of Pre-Columbian Anglo-America.*

their houses must be easily transported and their goods kept at an absolute minimum. The dog is necessary to their life, for he is a beast of burden, drawing sleds in winter and the travois[4] in summer. The food cache was an invention of these people for preserving sur-

plus food until needed. It is usually a stanchion of poles where the frozen meat is placed so that it will be safe from wild animals. Canoes are used for river transportation during the summer months in this well-watered country.

The Eskimos are less nomadic than the Canadian Indians. They remain on the shores of the Arctic Ocean during the long winter season, living in houses built of driftwood and sod.

[4] A primitive vehicle consisting of two trailing poles serving as shafts for dogs, and bearing a platform, or net, for the load.

Natural Food Areas of
Pre-Columbian Anglo-America

FIGURE 2-3.

During summer they often move southward to meet the herds of caribou, from which they secure a great deal of food as well as hides for clothing and other purposes.

Salmon area. The highest culture of this area occurred along the southern coast of Alaska and the coast of British Columbia. With the possible exception of a few Eskimo tribes, the Indians living here had closer affinities with Asia than any others *(see Fig. 2-1)*. Salmon was the principal food of these Indians, and they directed their skills toward catching this fish. Spears, harpoons, hooks, and nets were used. They built large dugout canoes for fishing purposes and used them also for war. Some canoes would hold fifty men and were made from a single log. Their fishing skill was sufficiently well developed that they hunted and killed the whale from these small boats.

Tribes dwelt in one location for generations in this heavily timbered area, building permanent houses out of split cedar and spruce logs. Often the houses were of sufficient size to house several families, with benches along the sides for sleeping purposes and a smoke hole in the roof to allow the escape of the smoke from their cooking fires. Their diet was supplemented by numerous berries, herbs, and roots in season, and by deer and small game.

The climate of the salmon area is very mild; thus, Indian clothing was quite scanty, usually consisting of little more than a blanket. These Indians wove the Chilkat blanket by the method known as finger-weaving. The abundance of easily worked wood caused them to turn to wood carving for artistic expression. Fine totem poles and well-carved and colored ceremonial masks are the best examples of this woodcarving art. As is true of many people who live in a permanent village, their culture principally revolved about religion. Their most outstanding ceremony is the potlatch, an ostentatious display of wealth involving the host's lavish destruction of personal property and an almost endless giving of gifts requiring elaborate reciprocation. Captured members of enemy tribes were enslaved—and were sometimes offered as human sacrifice during the potlatch ceremony.

The greatest inland penetration of this culture occurred along the rivers where the salmon could be taken. For example, the culture area spread into the inland areas of Oregon and Washington via the Columbia River, and all of the coastal river areas as far south as the Klamath River in California show evidence of this culture.

Wild seed area. In the uplands of southern California the basic food was wild acorns. Raw acorns are unpalatable, because they contain large amounts of tannic acid. This was eliminated, however, by crushing the nuts in stone mortars to form a sort of flour. Then this flour was leached with hot water and made into a form of bread or cake. Elsewhere in the area the wild seeds of many plants were gathered and used as a basic food supply; shellfish supplemented the diet along the coastal region. In Nevada the grasshopper often was a source of food.

Of all the regions in Anglo-America, the wild seed area is considered the lowest in culture. Housing usually consisted of nothing more than a hut of brush as shelter against the wind and sun. Clothing, too, was of minor importance. Very little in the way of weapons was used; the bow and arrow were found in the area but were of low standard. River travel was accomplished by tying a bunch of tule stalks together into a crude raft. Reed basketry was of a high order, however, and baskets had many uses. Tightly woven baskets were used to hold water, and heating was accomplished by dropping hot stones into the water. Seeds and nuts for cooking were stored in baskets. One of the finest types of baskets used by these Indians was a large funnel-shaped affair, which was worn on the back and employed to hold berries and nuts as they were being picked.

Bison area. This area corresponded to the buffalo range on the Great Plains from Texas northward into Canada. The intermountain regions to the west were transitional zones between the bison area and the coastal types of culture. The area extended eastward to the edge of the high prairie grass, not too far west of the Mississippi River. In many respects this region was somewhat similar to the caribou area, except that the culture was of a higher order, the tribes were larger, and there was a greater development of ritualism and societies.

The Indians of this area were nomadic, following the buffalo herds as they migrated with the seasons. Because of the necessity for travel, they used the skin-covered tepee, which was easily dismantled and transported, for a house. All personal and household articles were kept at a minimum. Some basketry was used, but there was no evidence of pottery. Buffalo hides were made into clothing, shoes, and dog harnesses for travois. The clothing was tailored to fit, but there was little or no weaving of any sort of cloth. There was considerable use of rawhide, too. The parfleche bag, a round cylindrical object made from rawhide, was used to carry meat and berries that were preserved in tallow, making a type of pemmican. Highly developed bows and arrows were the principal hunting and war weapons of these Indians, whose hair was worn in the distinctive scalp lock. Knives and arrowheads were made of flint; there was no use of metal. Land ownership of a limited type was exercised, since each tribe claimed certain ranges as its hunting ground and fought other tribes to protect these rights.

Eastern maize area. The eastern maize area was so named because of the almost universal use of corn as the diet staple. Other things also were raised, such as beans, squash, melons, wild vegetables, and tobacco, but corn was the primary crop. Deer, bear, rabbit, fowl of all sorts, and occasionally fish supplemented the menu. Raising cultivated crops necessitated a permanent residence, at least during the growing season, and villages were erected near the cleared crop lands. The dwelling was often a bark house for summer and a dome-shaped, mat-covered lodge for winter.

The field work was done by the women of the tribes while the men hunted. Bows and arrows were the principal weapons, but were supplemented by flint knives and tomahawks. In the south the blow-gun was used occasionally, and fish poisoning was practiced. Toboggans, birch canoes, and snowshoes were commonly used for transportation in the north; the dugout canoe, in the south. The men often hunted in large parties, and the hunting party soon developed into a war party. The Iroquois Indians of New York were probably the best skilled in war. They overcame neighboring tribes and welded the "six nations" together into a unit, which was the first step toward political statehood.

Area of intensive agriculture. There was a long, narrow region, extending from Arizona, New Mexico, and southwestern Texas southward through the Mexican Plateau, through Central America, and along the parallel valleys of the western slopes of the Andes to central Chile, in which agriculture was the predominant occupation. The regions of highest culture were in southern Mexico and the Andes of Ecuador and Peru. In the southwestern United States was a third zone of high culture, the region of the Pueblo Indians. Their culture was much higher than any to be found elsewhere in the United States, but, at the same time, it was considerably lower than that found in southern Mexico and the Andes.

For the most part, the Pueblo Indians lived in large dwellings made up of several stories of single-room apartments that were all joined together in one large unit. The whole tribe lived in the one structure. The stories were stair-stepped, and entrance to the rooms was accomplished by means of ladders through a hole in the ceiling of each room; there were no windows or doors. The buildings were always situated in defense sites, on top of mesas or under overhanging cliffs for protection. The outside ladders could be drawn up on top of the buildings at night. The structural material was adobe (sun-dried brick and small logs with a mud plaster), and the roofs were flat and covered with sod, which was more than adequate for the dry subtropical climate in which they lived.

There were many societies, secret and otherwise, with ritualistic dances being quite common among these peoples. In some tribes as many as 180 days of dancing or other forms of pageantry were held during the year. Offices and other stations were determined by matrilineal descent, and the highest position within the tribe was that of the priest. Both men and women worked the corn fields that often were located several miles from the pueblos. Cornmeal was ground in stone mortars or on the stone metate and baked in flat sheets into a hard, brittle corn bread. To supplement the diet, small game was procured by community hunts in the form of a drive. There was a taboo on the eating of fish of any sort. Pottery was used extensively for cooking and for storing meal and water, which often had to be carried long distances from its source.

Game area. The inhabitants of the northeastern woodland were semi-nomadic hunters. They knew something of agriculture, though they practiced it hardly at all, with the result that the yield of the soil was never great enough to relieve dependence on the chase or on fishing. This was an area in which small tribes predominated, although the majority of them belonged to the extensive Algonquin linguistic family.

The Coming of the Europeans

With less than a million inhabitants in all North America north of Mexico, Europeans in this part of the continent found it comparatively easy to replace the "natives" with immigrants from the Old World and their descendants. Today, people of European, African, and Asian descent have displaced the native inhabitants in nearly every one of their natural food areas, with the exception of parts of Alaska and northern Canada. Even in those areas, however, the number of native people are few, and not many live in the primitive state of their ancestors.

THE DISCOVERY OF AMERICA

There are three possible routes for sailing vessels to reach the two Americas from Europe: (1) by the North Atlantic "stepping stones" from the British Isles to the Shetland Islands to the Faeroe Islands to Iceland to Greenland to Labrador or Newfoundland (Newfoundland or Labrador would undoubtedly be the first landfall on this route); (2) by drifting with the trade winds from the Azores or the Madeira Islands to the West Indies (the route followed by the Portuguese and Spanish); and (3) from west Africa to Brazil, again drifting with the trade winds.

Records show that Iceland was occupied by the Irish in the latter part of the ninth century. By A.D. 930 the Norsemen had displaced the Irish and established the first parliament in Iceland. In 982 Eric (the Red) discovered the east coast of Greenland. The west coast of Greenland was occupied in 986; twelve fishing villages were established with twelve churches. Godthaab was the main town. The settlement lasted until 1347, when it disappeared for some unknown reason. The region was soon reoccupied by Eskimos, who had just reached it in their eastward migration. In 1000 Leif Ericson of Iceland sailed with his Norsemen to what is believed to have been the coast of New England. Bronze battle axes have been found among Indian artifacts in Wisconsin. These are medieval European axes, and it is possible that either the Norsemen penetrated that far inland, following the waterways, or that the axes were traded inland by the Indians. Norse chronicles described the newly discovered lands. Helluland had a shore composed of flat rocks, and Labrador answers this description. Markland, or the land of the trees, was mentioned, and it could be Newfoundland. Vinland, the marshy land, was described, and the only marshy land is on the southern shore of the St. Lawrence north of Maine.

Columbus is given credit for discovering the island of San Salvador in the Bahamas in 1492; but twenty years before Columbus' voyage, King Christian of Denmark sent out a ship under Pothorst, who reported land of a fiorded character that undoubtedly was Labrador. After Columbus, in 1497 and 1498, John Cabot sailed along the Canadian coast; he planted the standard of England on the shores of Newfoundland, and this became the basis of Great Britain's claim to America. By 1513, Ponce de León had landed in Florida, and in 1519 the Spanish conquest of Mexico had begun under Cortéz. By 1530 the west coast of the continents was known, and in 1531 Pizarro started his conquest of the Inca Empire that was to lead to the addition of Peru to the Spanish realm.

FIGURE 2-4. *Major voyages of exploration to the northern Western Hemisphere.*

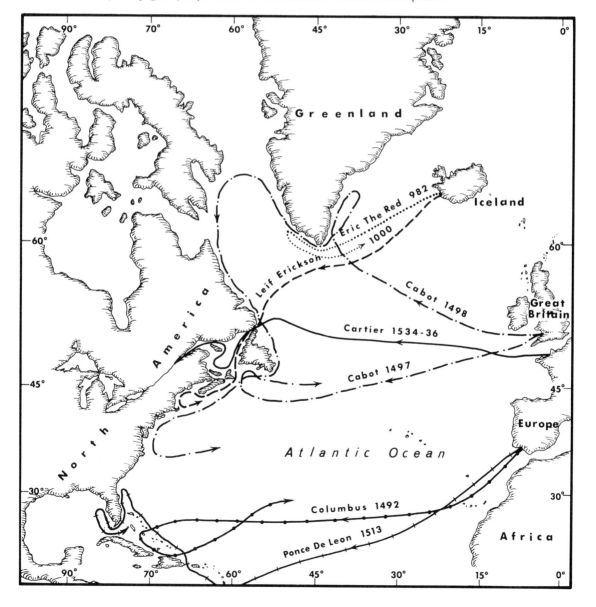

THE SETTLEMENT OF NORTH AMERICA

Spanish. Spanish interest centered mainly in Mexico because of the great hoards of gold to be found there. Much gold was taken from the area and shipped to Spain. Then the Spanish looked for new fields to conquer. Coronado marched from Mexico City northward to what is now Kansas, looking for the Seven Cities of Cibola, which were said to have streets paved with gold. By 1769 the Spanish had marched up the west coast of North America, and in that year a mission was established in southern California at San Diego; by 1776 missions had been established as far north as San Francisco. Permanent Spanish settlement of Florida began in the late sixteenth century.

FIGURE 2-5. *European colonies in Anglo-America.*

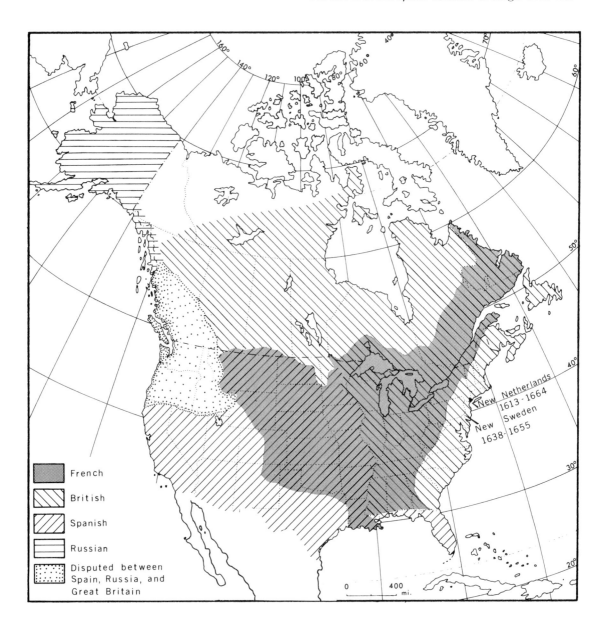

Canada. Within ten years after Cabot's visit in 1498, fishermen—English, Basque and Breton—began to visit the cod banks off New England and Canada in great numbers. French explorers entered Canada early in the sixteenth century, and the energy and good fortune of the French allowed them, for a time, to outstrip the British in the newly-found territory. In 1534 Jacques Cartier of St. Malo, in the service of the French King, landed at Gaspé Harbor and discovered the St. Lawrence River, which he explored the next year. The opening of the country was begun by Samuel de Champlain, and for a century and a half the development of "New France" remained chiefly in French hands. Champlain founded Port Royal (Annapolis, Nova Scotia) in 1605 and Quebec in 1608. The colony of Acadia roughly comprised Nova Scotia, New Brunswick, and Prince Edward Island.

Within a few short years, the French, in pursuit of their fur trade with the Indians, had penetrated inland along the St. Lawrence to the Great Lakes; from there they portaged to the Wisconsin River and the Mississippi, reaching the mouth of the latter in 1682. Thus, the great interior of the continent and what is now Canada became French. It was a vast expanse that was loosely held and hard to control. The principal French cities were Quebec, Montreal, and New Orleans.

The history of the French colonies in North America was one of continuous rivalry and intermittent strife with Great Britain and the British colonies to the south. The Hudson's Bay Company, from its foundation in 1670, laid active claim to the vast territories of the Hudson Bay watershed. In 1713, the Treaty of Utrecht ceded these territories, together with the peninsula of Acadia (the mainland of Nova Scotia), to Great Britain. During the next half century, English settlements centered on Halifax gradually supplanted most of the French Atlantic settlements. The colonial wars between the mother countries ended in 1763, when the Treaty of Paris gave all French territories in Canada to Great Britain. Another treaty gave Spain title to the rest of France's North American possessions.

British explorers succeeded French in the task of pushing back Canadian frontiers. By 1793 Alexander Mackenzie had voyaged north to the Arctic Ocean, along the great river that bears his name, and west to the Pacific Ocean. His work was continued by Simon Fraser and David Thompson. The opening up of Manitoba started in 1811, when Lord Selkirk established a small Scottish settlement in the Red River Valley.

The Act of Union (1840) united Upper and Lower Canada. In the resulting province of Canada, responsible government was firmly established as early as 1849. During these years, the idea of political union of all British North America was in the air. Rapid economic development laid the foundation for such a federation. Growing railways linked the provinces and required joint financial support. Improved transportation and communication paved the way for the opening of the west and stimulated visions of a transcontinental dominion. Immigration, too, added impetus to expansion. The population rose from under a half million in 1815 to nearly three million by 1850.

The growth and spread of population, the expansion of industry, the increasing burdens on local government, and the changing economic pattern—in short, the stirrings of a national life—all pointed to the urgent need for a political unit larger than the existing provinces. The idea of union was further recommended to Canadian and British opinion by the American Civil War, which gravely strained the relations between Great Britain and the United States and reawakened fears of annexation. Provincial statesmen were coming to regard federation as not only possible, but even necessary for survival.

In 1867, therefore, the provinces of Canada, Nova Scotia, and New Brunswick united in a federation. The new nation's constitution was embodied in the British North American Act. The Province of Canada was immediately divided into Ontario and Quebec, the name Canada thereafter being applied to the country as a whole.

Confederation was the signal for a rapid ex-

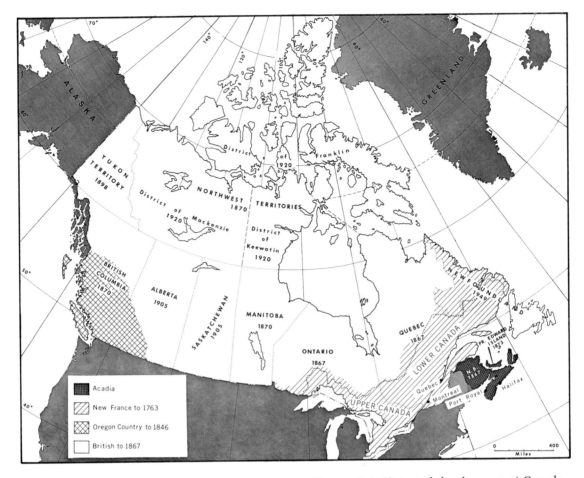

FIGURE 2-6. *Historical development of Canada.*

pansion of Canadian national life. Manitoba entered in 1870, British Columbia in 1871, and Prince Edward Island in 1873. In 1905 two new provinces, Alberta and Saskatchewan, were carved out of the prairies. Canada thus began the twentieth century with its present geographic outlines, except for Newfoundland (including Labrador), which did not enter the Confederation until 1949.

A declaration, drawn up at the Imperial Conference of 1926, defined the sovereign independence of Commonwealth members, which Canada had, in practice, already exercised on previous occasions. The Statute of Westminster (1931) formally recognized Canada's full autonomy and equality with the United Kingdom and other members of the Commonwealth.

Most of Canada's population is concentrated in a belt 200 miles wide just north of the Great Lakes and extending eastward along the St. Lawrence River. About one million square miles, or a third of Canada, lie north of this belt, and there are only about 10,000 Canadians living there—one person to each 100 square miles (*Fig. 2-11*).

Four centuries have seen Canada grow from a handful of scattered fishing settlements and trading posts into a modern industrialized state of more than 20 million people covering half a continent and ranking among the leading trading nations of the world.

The United States. The English found that the French had occupied the St. Lawrence district, and that the Spanish had occupied the Caribbean shores, including Florida, so they chose the region in between for a site of colonization, centering upon the lands bordering on Chesapeake Bay and the Delaware River. In 1606 they accidentally landed in Boston Harbor, but no permanent settlement was made until the landing of the Pilgrims at Plymouth, Massachusetts, in 1620.

In the early 1600's, what was later to become the nucleus of the United States of America consisted of a line of seaboard colonies that were mere extensions of Great Britain, the Netherlands, and Sweden—and soon only Great Britain—across the North Atlantic. Colonial settlers were Europeans, and their outlook was eastward, back toward Europe. The forest, the native Stone Age Amerindians, and the rugged Appalachian hill country all combined to produce a barrier that prevented westward expansion for 150 years. Only when a new type of man was bred on the western frontier did the colonies break their barriers and spill westward. This man was principally a mixture of English, Scottish, Scotch-Irish, Dutch, German, and French, with a dash of several other nationalities thrown in. He was at home in the forest, was strong and resourceful, and usually equaled or excelled the aborigines in nature craft.

There were two major areas, the northern and the southern. The northern area was largely interested in fishing and maritime affairs, and thus was the source of naval strength; the southern region was primarily concerned with land ownership under the plantation system. After considerable antagonism between these two core areas, a plan for integrating them into a nation was designed. The result, after the American Revolution, was thirteen sovereign states bound together under a federal government to which certain powers and rights were delegated, with the provision that additional powers could be delegated as the necessity arose.

The next phase of national growth was a transcontinental spread. In the South, planters and their Negro slaves, accompanied by a fringe of poor white farmers, artisans, and town builders, and augmented by hordes of immigrants, rolled westward. The southern

FIGURE 2-7. *Historical development of the United States, to 1783.*

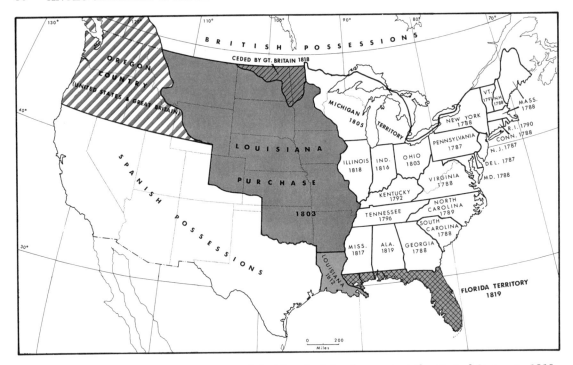

FIGURE 2-8. *Historical development of the United States, to 1819.*

planters had to cross no major barriers and therefore reached the borders of the Texas country very early. In the northern areas, the Appalachian hill country was so rugged that the pace of settlement was slower.

Florida was purchased from Spain and the Louisiana Territory from France, which had regained it from Spain. After these purchases, pressure from the South resulted in the annexation of Texas. Pressure from the East and Middle West resulted in the occupation of the Oregon Country. Finally, pressure from all sides resulted in the Mexican War and the resulting gain of California and the rest of the western United States.

Competition developed between the yeoman farmer and the industrial interests on the one side, and the plantation owner and the cotton trader on the other. It was a contest as to who would be the first to spread into and possess these vast new domains west of the Mississippi. Whoever settled and possessed these new lands would organize and settle additional sovereign states. As these were admitted to the Union, their votes would change the balance of power.

There followed a long series of arguments, tensions, compromises, border incidents, and the like. Finally, in 1861, eleven southern states withdrew from the Union and set up a loose federation of their own. The right to withdraw from a federal union would seem to be implied by the Constitution. But such withdrawal was thought to destroy the federal government, or at least to weaken it to such an extent that an outside power might destroy it. Thus, the government resisted the secessionist movement, and the Civil War resulted (1861-1865).

Before the Civil War, the slave-supported plantation economy in the South had made possible a social class with money and leisure enough to pursue the art of settlement and local self-government on a relatively informed ethical level. The influence of this factor was great enough to produce a demand for local and state responsibility for governmental programs, as well as a resistance to the growth and encroachment of federal paternalism and the bureaucracy accompanying it. War ruined the southern governing class, however, and broke down its resistance to governmental paternal-

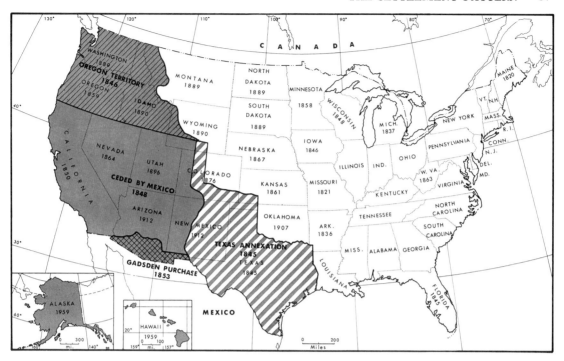

Figure 2-9. *Historical development of the United States, to 1959.*

Figure 2-10. *Centers of population for the conterminous United States, 1790-1960.*

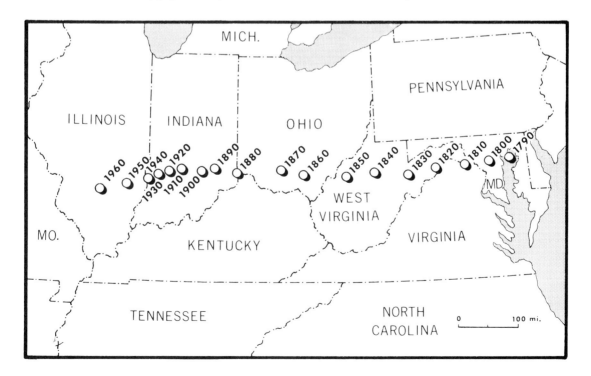

ism. It left many localities so devastated that the South has not yet fully recovered economically and socially.

After the Civil War, the American people rapidly completed the settlement of the country. By 1912 all of the conterminous United States stood completed. Industrialization became so accelerated that the U.S. rapidly pushed into the front rank of the great economic powers.

FIGURE 2-11.

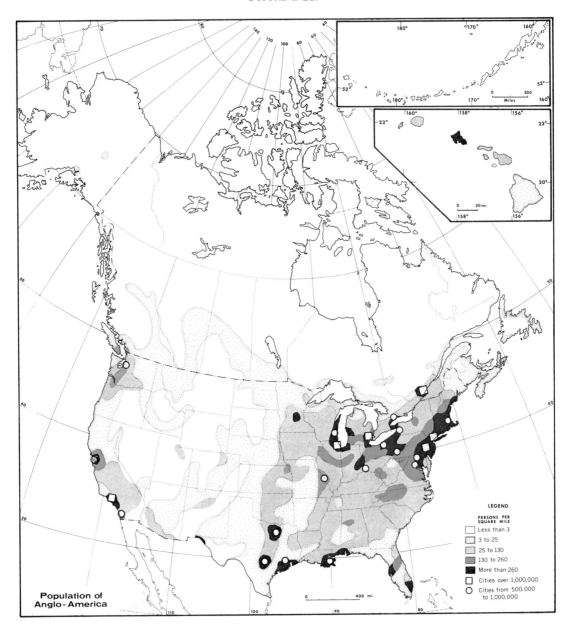

LEGEND

PERSONS PER
SQUARE MILE

☐ Less than 3
☐ 3 to 25
☐ 25 to 130
☐ 130 to 260
■ More than 260
☐ Cities over 1,000,000
○ Cities from 500,000
   to 1,000,000

Population of
Anglo-America

Selected References

ANDREWS, JOHN H., "Anglo-American Trade in the Early Eighteenth Century," *The Geographical Review*, Vol. 45, January, 1955, pp. 99–110.

BIRD, J. BRIAN, "Settlement Patterns in Maritime Canada, 1687–1786," *The Geographical Review*, Vol. 45, July, 1955, pp. 385–404.

BROWN, RALPH H., *Historical Geography of the United States*, New York: Harcourt, Brace & World, Inc., 1948.

BROWNE, WALTER A., *The American Development*, Kirksville, Mo.: The Simpson Printing and Publishing Co., 1964.

CLARK, ANDREW H., "Old World Origins and Religious Adherence in Nova Scotia," *The Geographical Review*, Vol. 50, July, 1960, pp. 317–344.

CLAWSON, MARION, "Factors and Forces Affecting the Optimum Future Rural Settlement Pattern in the United States," *Economic Geography*, Vol. 42, October, 1966, pp. 283–293.

DRIVER, HAROLD E., *Indians of North America*, Chicago: The University of Chicago Press, 1961.

KERSTEN, EARL W., JR., "The Early Settlement of Aurora, Nevada, and Nearby Mining Camps," *Annals of the Association of American Geographers*, Vol. 54, December, 1964, pp. 490–507.

KNIFFEN, FRED, "Folk Housing: Key to Diffusion," *Annals of the Association of American Geographers*, Vol. 55, December, 1965, pp. 549–577.

KNIFFEN, FRED, and GLASSIE, HENRY, "Building in Wood in the Eastern United States: A Time-place Perspective," *The Geographical Review*, Vol. 46, January, 1966, pp. 40–66.

KOELSCH, WILLIAM A. (ed.), *Lectures on the Historical Geography of the United States as Given in 1933* (by Harlan H. Barrows), Chicago: University of Chicago, Department of Geography Professional Paper Number 7, 1962.

KROEBER, A. L., *Cultural and Natural Areas of Native North America*, Berkeley: University of California Press, 1963.

LEIGHLY, JOHN, "John Muir's Image of the West," *Annals of the Association of American Geographers*, Vol. 48, December, 1958, pp. 309–318.

MATHER, EUGENE C., and HART, J. FRASER, "Fences and Farms," *The Geographical Review*, Vol. 44, April, 1954, pp. 201–223.

PATTISON, WILLIAM D., "The Pacific Railroad Rediscovered," *The Geographical Review*, Vol. 52, January, 1962, pp. 25–36.

SIBBS, JACK P., "The Evolution of Population Concentration," *Economic Geography*, Vol. 39, April, 1963, pp. 119–129.

SONNEFELD, J., "Changes in an Eskimo Hunting Technology, an Introduction to Implement Geography," *Annals of the Association of American Geographers*, Vol. 50, June, 1960, pp. 172–186.

SPENCER, ROBERT F., and JENNINGS, JESSE D., *The Native Americans*, New York: Harper & Row, Publishers, 1965.

STIRLING, MATTHEW W., *Indians of North America*, Washington, D. C.: The National Geographic Society, 1961.

VANCE, JAMES E., JR., "The Oregon Trail and Union Pacific Railroad: A Contrast in Purpose," *Annals of the Association of American Geographers*, Vol. 51, December, 1961, pp. 357–379.

WARNTZ, WILLIAM, "A New Map of the Surface of Population Potentials for the United States, 1960," *The Geographical Review*, Vol. 44, April, 1964, pp. 170–184.

WEBB, WALTER PRESCOTT, "Geographical-Historical Concepts in American History," *Annals of the Association of American Geographers*, Vol. 50, June, 1960, pp. 85–93.

WHITNEY, HERBERT A., "Estimating Precensus Populations: A Method Suggested and Applied to the Towns of Rhode Island and Plymouth Colonies in 1689," *Annals of the Association of American Geographers*, Vol. 55, March, 1965, pp. 179–189.

ZELINSKY, WILBUR, "Changes in the Geographic Patterns of Rural Population in the United States," *The Geographical Review*, Vol. 52, October, 1962, pp. 492–524.

———— "The Log House in Georgia," *ibid.*, Vol. 43, April, 1953, pp. 173–193.

3 The Resource Base and Its Current Utilization

Few, if any, areas of the world were as generously endowed as Anglo-America in original supply of natural resources—soils, minerals, water, and forest—and favorable climates for agricultural production. The utilization of these resources has given the people of Anglo-America the highest material standard of living in the world (*Fig. 3-1*)[1] The United States was particularly favored with an abundance of basic natural resources. Situated in an area of favorable climate and sufficient rainfall, the nation is virtually assured, assuming astute management, of an immense variety of crops, livestock, and forest products. With the possible exception of the Soviet Union, no other nation in the world has so great an abundance and variety of mineral resources immediately available within its boundaries. However, although the United States has a sufficient supply of petroleum, coal, iron ore, and other materials, it does not have an adequate supply of manganese, nickel, tungsten, chromite, tin, copper, lead, and zinc.

An adequate, dependable, and continuing supply of raw materials is indispensable to the United States and Canada and their industries in meeting the needs of an expanding population, maintaining a rising standard of living, and dealing with the demands of national security. Latest resource inventories of present and future needs suggest little likelihood of acute shortages in Anglo-America during the present century providing there is: (1) wise production and utilization of mineral resources, (2) discovery and development of new sources of mineral supply, (3) maintenance of mineral reserves and stocks at adequate levels, (4) fostering of a productive and processing industrial capacity large and effective enough to exploit the domestic mineral resources consistent with foreseen requirements, and (5) assurance of access to foreign mineral supply to supplement domestic output as needed. The possibilities of using lower grades of raw material, of substituting plentiful materials for scarce ones, of importing things from other countries, and of making multiple use of land and water resources seem to be sufficient guarantee against across-the-board shortage.

[1] Early man in America made few changes in the natural environment. Only since the advent of the machine age and modern technology have large inroads been made on the resource base. Consequently, even though the resource base is normally treated with the physical pattern, the emphasis here is on its current utilization as it affects the industrial and urban patterns of Anglo-America.

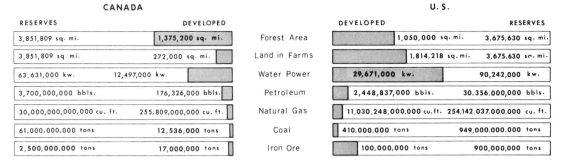

CANADA				U. S.		
RESERVES	DEVELOPED			DEVELOPED	RESERVES	
3,851,809 sq. mi.	1,375,200 sq. mi.	Forest Area		1,050,000 sq. mi.	3,675,630 sq. mi.	
3,851,809 sq. mi.	272,000 sq. mi.	Land in Farms		1,814,218 sq. mi.	3,675,630 sq. mi.	
63,631,000 kw.	12,497,000 kw.	Water Power		29,671,000 kw.	90,242,000 kw.	
3,700,000,000 bbls.	176,326,000 bbls.	Petroleum		2,448,837,000 bbls.	30,356,000,000 bbls.	
30,000,000,000,000 cu. ft.	255,809,000,000 cu. ft.	Natural Gas		11,030,248,000,000 cu. ft.	254,142,037,000,000 cu. ft.	
61,000,000,000 tons	12,536,000 tons	Coal		410,000,000 tons	949,000,000,000 tons	
2,500,000,000 tons	17,000,000 tons	Iron Ore		100,000,000 tons	900,000,000 tons	

FIGURE 3-1. *Resource development of Anglo-America.*

Mineral Resources

Mineral deposits are of paramount importance in providing a nation with the margin of wealth needed for a strong domestic economy and for world power (*Fig. 3-2*). Valuable minerals may be concentrated in great quantities within a small area—a characteristic not equally true in the case of other resources. The demand for individual minerals varies greatly. Some minerals, such as coal, are not only extremely vital but also are required in vast quantities. Others, although equally essential, may be used only in small quantities.

IRON ORE

Iron ore, in addition to supplying the metal for iron and steel products, is used in paint pigments, cement, basic refractories, as a fluxing agent in nonferrous smelting, and as a constituent of some catalytic agents.

The United States is by far the world's principal iron ore producer. Domestic production has averaged over 100 million gross tons annually since 1950. More than 30,000 men are directly engaged in producing iron ore, and many times that number are employed in turning it into finished products. Integrated iron and steel companies control 70 to 80 per cent of the domestic iron mining industry, and several of the larger companies either control or have an interest in iron mines in Venezuela, Australia, Chile, Peru, Liberia, and Canada.

In an emergency, the United States could be self-sufficient at the 1957 rate of consumption (100 million tons) for a period of 3 to 7 years. After that, depletion of the open-pit mining reserve on the Mesabi Range in Minnesota would probably reduce the number of mines so that a high rate of production could not be maintained. This does not mean, however, that there will not be enough high-grade iron ore in the country to supply our needs; only that its geographic distribution will be such that the output cannot be easily increased.

Iron ore is essential to the economic well-being and safety of the United States. A protracted interruption in its supply would affect the lives of everyone in the country. The principal danger to supply is vulnerability of the transportation system. Most of the Lake Superior district iron ore moves to markets through the Great Lakes. This movement is essential if the country is to have an adequate supply of iron ore, because railroads do not have enough capacity to replace this transportation system. Furthermore, the St. Lawrence Seaway carries 10 to 15 million tons of iron ore from Canada to the steel-producing centers on the lower Great Lakes. Since the United States is partially dependent on iron ore from South America and Africa, an even greater problem is created because this ore is subject to all the dangers of open ocean traffic. To date, however, stockpiling iron ore has been deemed impractical.

Since World War II, private industry has been heavily engaged in iron ore research, principally to develop ore-dressing techniques for beneficiating the taconites of Minnesota and the jaspilites of Michigan. (Taconite is

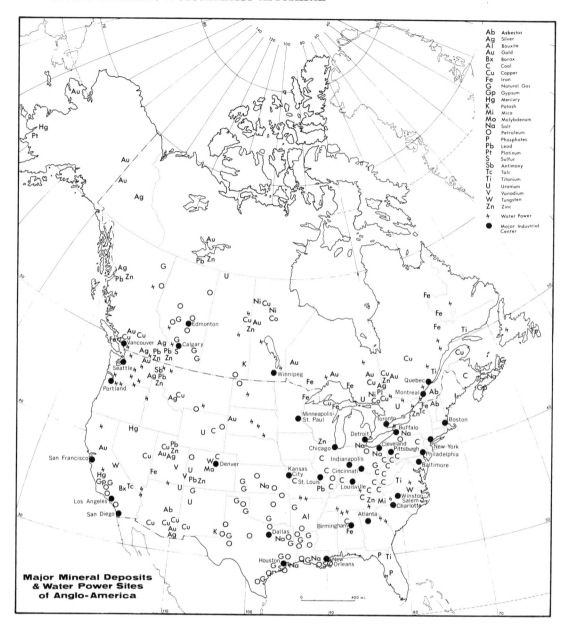

FIGURE 3-2. *Major deposits of minerals and sources of water power in Anglo-America.*

formed of deposits of iron oxides mixed with sand, rock material, and other minerals, and containing about one-third iron. Jaspilite is similar to taconite but has a slightly higher iron content.) The industry supports five research laboratories, with a total annual budget estimated at $5 million. Total industry expenditure for iron ore and associated research is believed to range between $15 and $20 million annually. The federal and state annual total is about $750,000.

There is relative agreement among those concerned with supplying the United States with its iron ore requirements that, in the next 20 years, domestic production will not exceed 90 to 100 million tons annually, and that the remaining requirements will be imported principally from Canada and South America. Figure 3-4 shows United States iron ore supply by major sources projected through 1975.

Canada, with estimated reserves approaching five billion tons of iron ore, ranks quite high in the world picture. Despite Canada's rapidly expanding iron mining industry, nearly two-thirds of the iron ore consumed in that country is imported from the United States, mainly because Canadian consumers participated in the development of United States mines or established commercial ties with United States merchant companies prior to 1950, when little iron ore was being mined in Canada and importation was an economic necessity.

Canadian iron mining is carried on in various places in Ontario, northeastern Newfoundland, on the Quebec-Labrador border, and in British Columbia.

FIGURE 3-3. *Major iron ore areas and major steel centers of Anglo-America.*

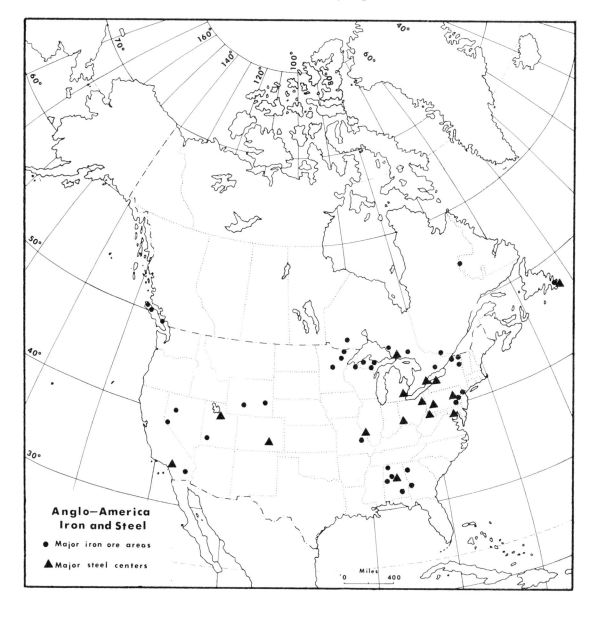

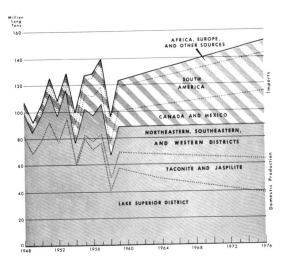

FIGURE 3-4. *Major sources of U.S. iron ore, 1948-1966, and predicted sources, 1967-1976.*

ENERGY SOURCES

Coal, petroleum, natural gas, and running water are the four outstanding sources of energy; consequently, they are extremely important to a dynamic economy. No nation can now be considered truly great if it does not rank high in at least one of these.

Industrial nations need power in abundance; but hydroelectric power cannot be sent across oceans, and the transportation of minerals over long distances is a limiting factor. Coal is bulky and heavy, and natural gas requires expensive equipment to prevent loss in transfer. Only the transportation of oil is feasible from a cost standpoint. In common practice, minerals move for processing to the country that possesses plentiful supplies of fuels (*Fig. 3-5*).

Coal. Coal, an indispensable mineral in the production of iron and steel, is the top supplier of energy for industrial purposes. It is by far the greatest reserve of energy, except possibly nuclear energy, and it is the backbone of industrial expansion in national emergencies. Because of its importance as a source of energy and as a raw material, coal reaches directly or indirectly into almost every phase of daily life and national well-being. It has been a significant factor in the development of the great iron and steel and electric power industries. The

employment, health, and prosperity of many millions of people rest upon its production, distribution, and utilization.

The distribution of coal and lignite fields in the United States and Canada is extensive, with many fields still unexplored, but the largest production is concentrated in the Allegheny Plateau fields (*Fig. 3-6*). In Canada, particularly, many coal deposits are remote from populated places where the coal can be used most efficiently, and coal is a commodity too expensive to transport long distances except in emergencies.

Thus, in the long run it is the amount of coal produced, rather than the potential supply, that counts in developing an intensified industrial economy. Our actual production of coal plus our potential supplies are the most important present-day factors in maintaining our leading position in manufactured goods for both peace and war. In addition to uses for

FIGURE 3-5. *Changes in Anglo-America's energy source patterns, 1940, 1960, and projections for 1980 and 2000.*

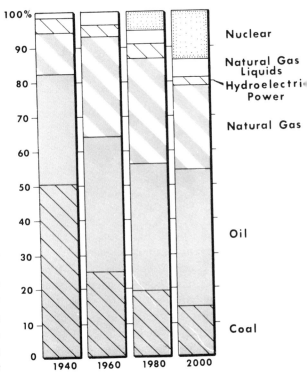

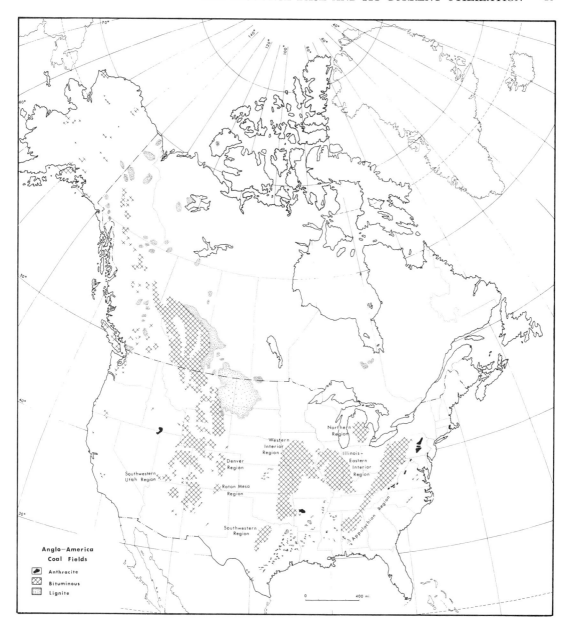

FIGURE 3-6.

power, coal is a most important mineral from which refrigerants, explosives, and resins can be obtained. These products are of inestimable usefulness in an advanced economy such as ours, and we would continue to need coal to produce them even though better sources of fuel might eventually be found.

The United States, with about 1.8 trillion tons of coal in the ground, has one-third of the earth's known reserves. On the basis of heating value per pound, nearly 80 per cent of the reserve is bituminous and subbituminous. These ranks of coal are distributed over all the United States—about one-third east of the Mississippi River, one-third in the interior, and one-third in the northern Great Plains, Rocky Mountains, and Gulf and Pacific areas. Much of this coal is of good coking quality and can be mined easily by machine methods. Coal is mined in more than half the 50 states.

The bituminous and lignite coal industry, widely dispersed over the nation, reached its peak production of over 630 million tons in 1947. Between that time and the present, annual production has dropped to about 410 million tons; the number of mines has decreased from 9,400 to 8,200; and the number of men employed has dropped from more than 440,000 in 1948, to fewer than 200,000. This decline in production has resulted primarily from the competition of oil and natural gas in the energy market.

Canada has 1.9 per cent of the world's coal reserves, of which more than 90 per cent are to be found in the west, chiefly in Alberta, Saskatchewan, and British Columbia (see Fig. 3-6). Smaller amounts also occur in the Maritime Provinces, particularly in Nova Scotia and New Brunswick. The geographic distribution of Canadian coal is unfortunate, however, since the population and major markets are in the industrial centers of southern Ontario and the St. Lawrence Valley. Thus, transportation costs are necessarily high because of the great distances involved in shipping western coal to the eastern markets. Freezing of the St. Lawrence River prevents year-round shipments to the same markets from Nova Scotia. Consequently, Canada imports considerable coal from the United States.

Although coal production has dropped seriously in recent years, and coal's share of the total energy market has declined markedly, coal is still the major supplier of industrial energy, largely because of the increased use of coal for steam generation by electric power utilities.

Anglo-America's energy requirements are expanding so rapidly that coal's future appears secure. New uses for coal will be found in hydrogenation, gasification, gas synthesis, and carbonization processes, and in the production of nuclear fuels. In view of these and other factors, some experts predict that the demand for energy will be so greatly expanded that the annual coal output may reach 770 million tons within the next 20 years.

Petroleum. Anglo-America has ten major petroleum fields: Appalachian, Northeast Indiana-Ohio, Michigan, Illinois-southwest Indiana, Midcontinent, Gulf Coast, Central Plains, Rocky Mountain, California, and the Northern Plains Province in Canada (Fig. 3-7). Thirty-three of the 50 states are oil or oil and gas producers, with the highest production coming from Texas, California, Louisiana, Oklahoma, Kansas, and Wyoming, in the order named. Some of the best areas, based on present knowledge, are offshore in California and Louisiana. Their development is a matter of economics, because operation costs run two to ten times those on land.

With about 12 per cent of the proved oil reserves of the world, the United States produces roughly 40 per cent of its oil. Ultimate reserves are placed at 460 billion barrels of liquid hydrocarbon (crude plus natural gas liquids),[2] of which perhaps some 400 billion barrels are crude alone. Excluding past production of roughly 60 billion barrels, some 340 billion would be available in the future. Assuming that even a 50 per cent recovery may not be possible, a more realistic future availability of 250 billion barrels can be predicted.

Some 500,000 oil and gas wells have been drilled in the United States to date, and about 46,000 more are drilled each year. The production, refining, and marketing of such petroleum products as gasoline, lubricating oil, fuel oil, and kerosene make up one of the largest American industries, employing well over one million people.

Canada's petroleum reserves are estimated at nearly 3,700 million barrels, a supply large enough to provide for the needs of the country for several decades. Although oil was discovered in 1913 in the Turner Valley field near Calgary, Alberta, the major impetus to production came in 1947 with the opening of the Leduc field near Edmonton. Spectacular exploration and development of the sedimentary basin of the Prairies followed. In Saskatchewan, commercial production, which had started

[2] Lewis G. Weeks, "Where Will Energy Come from in 2059?" *The Petroleum Engineer* (August, 1959), pp. 29–31.

during World War II, passed the one million barrel mark in 1950. Production commenced in Manitoba in 1951, and by 1954 had passed the million barrel mark. British Columbia fields, opened in 1955, had attained an annual capacity of over one million barrels by 1961. Now, Alberta accounts for roughly 70 per cent of the total output, and Saskatchewan for 25 per cent. Manitoba, British Columbia, the Northwest Territories, and New Brunswick share the remaining 5 per cent.

Canada faces the same problems with petroleum that it faces with coal. The petroleum fields are located so far from the major population and market centers of southeastern Canada that oil cannot be transported there as cheaply as foreign oil can be imported, even though the nation operates more than 6,000 miles of

FIGURE 3-7.

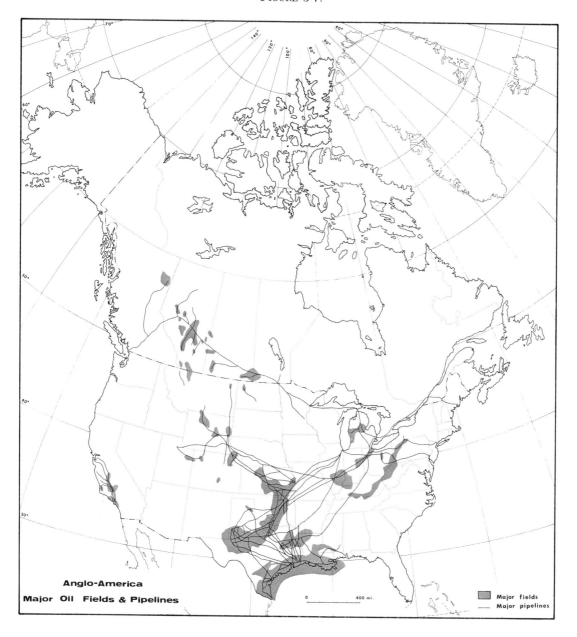

Anglo-America

Major Oil Fields & Pipelines

0 _____ 400 mi.

Major fields
Major pipelines

pipelines. Although Canada produces only about three per cent of the world's oil, geologists are highly optimistic regarding the country's future.

About fifteen years ago, the world's oil industry was dominated by American interests. The United States had the major share of known oil reserves and produced more than half the oil consumed and most of the natural gas utilized. Refining capacity was entirely adequate for both domestic markets and export demands. This country also supplied the bulk of the money, management, organization, and technical staff for the industry.

Recently, however, great changes have occurred in all aspects of the industry, and further changes are anticipated. Of particular significance has been the rapid shift in location of the world's major oil reserves from the United States to the Middle East. The United States has become a net importer of oil, although its petroleum resources have continued to grow. The Persian Gulf area, because of exploration and discoveries made primarily since World War II, now has a proved oil reserve about twice that of the rest of the world. More discoveries are expected in both the Near East and North Africa because of favorable geology in these areas. Most of the operators are American oil companies, but an increasing number of European and Asian companies, some government owned, are participating. The ever-growing Middle Eastern and Venezuelan oil resources now supply one-sixth of our needs and most of the liquid fuel needs of the rest of the noncommunist world. These abundant low-priced oils have altered fuel-use patterns in the United States and Europe, so that residual and distillate petroleum fuels are replacing solid fuels in both industrial and domestic uses.

The demand for motor gasoline is expected to continue its steady upward rise, unless, of course, the battery-driven experimental car is sufficiently successful in the future to replace the combustion engine. Reciprocating engine gasoline will decline in relative use as demands for jet fuels increase. There will be a decided upturn in the use of liquefied petroleum gases as fuel and as raw material for petrochemicals.

Natural gas. Closely allied to, and often associated with petroleum, are the gaseous hydrocarbons (mainly methane), or natural gas. Because of its sootless and essentially odorless qualities, low cost, ease of transmission, and high heat value (100 cubic feet equals 8 to 13 pounds of coal), natural gas is the most rapidly growing of all energy sources in the United States. A system of pipelines totaling more than 165,000 miles distributes natural gas to all parts of the country, supplying almost 30 per cent of the total fuel energy needs of the nation. Two states, Texas and Louisiana, have roughly 67 per cent of the proved reserves and account for about 68 per cent of the nation's natural gas production. Other large producers are Oklahoma, Kansas, New Mexico, and California. Estimated proved reserves total 260 trillion cubic feet, more than adequate to meet our needs for many decades.

Canada's estimated proved reserves of natural gas total over 33.5 trillion cubic feet, with 85 per cent in Alberta, 11 per cent in British Columbia, 3 per cent in Saskatchewan, and the remaining 1 per cent in Ontario, New Brunswick, and the Northwest Territories. Although natural gas is by far the cheapest source of energy in Canada, it currently supplies only about 7 per cent of that nation's energy market. Nearly one-third of the natural gas produced in Canada is marketed in the United States, being transmitted by pipeline as far as California (*Fig. 3-8*).

Water. Although less generally used than coal or petroleum, water power is of great industrial importance when it can be converted into its most convenient form—hydroelectric power. It should be noted, however, that hydroelectricity alone is of little value as a resource. It must be combined with raw materials and labor and must be produced in steady flow and volume if it is to function properly as a force. It should also be noted that hydroelectric power cannot be stored; it must be used as it is produced.

The United States leads all nations in the total amount of water power developed. The Federal Power Commission estimates the potential hydroelectric capacity of the conter-

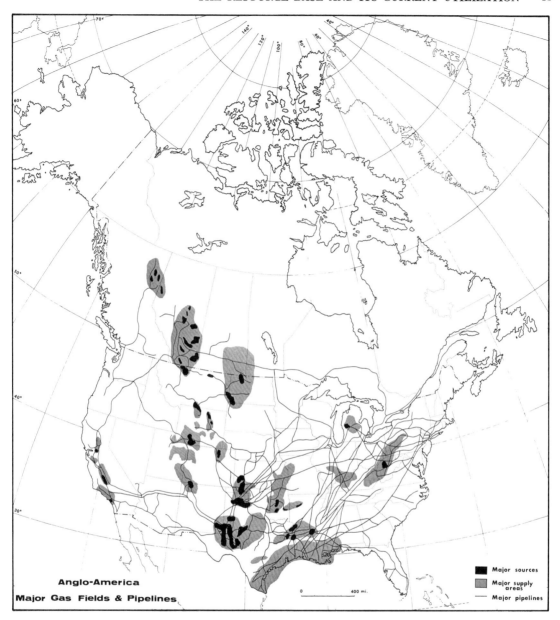

FIGURE 3-8.

minous United States at around 127 million kilowatts, the component parts of which would operate for various fractions of the year.[3] Installed capacity, including non-utility, is 31.9 million kilowatts (*see Fig. 3-2*).

Even if it were feasible by the year 2000 to

exploit the entire 127 million kilowatt potential, which would produce some 530 billion kilowatt-hours, only a little over 10 per cent of the projected electricity demand would be met by falling water. Thus, although hydroelectricity may continue to play a dominating role in regions with unusually favorable sites, it is bound to be of decreasing significance in the nation's power economy. Water presently supplies only 4 per cent of the total energy of the United

[3] *Hydroelectric Power Resources of the United States, Developed and Undeveloped, 1960* (Washington, D.C.: United States Federal Power Commission, undated).

States on a BTU basis, compared with 50 per cent for petroleum, 24 per cent for coal, and 27 per cent for dry natural gas.

Potential water power resources of the United States are greatest in the Pacific Northwest—about one-fifth is in Washington and Oregon. The Tennessee Valley Authority, consisting of the Tennessee River and its tributaries, is also a very important producer of hydroelectric power. Embracing more than 40,000 square miles and lying in seven states, TVA's water power capacity is about four million kilowatts.

Canada, a land of many large lakes and fast-flowing rivers, is richly endowed with immense water power resources. With the exception of the midwestern prairies, these resources are found in considerable magnitude in almost every part of the country. British Columbia and the Great Lakes-St. Lawrence area of Quebec and Ontario are the most highly developed water power sites (see Fig. 3-2).

Canada ranks fifth among the countries of the world in potential water power development and ranks second only to the United States in total installed capacity. Table I shows available and developed water power.

Nuclear Power. Although there has been much publicity about the use of nuclear fuels as an

TABLE I

WATER POWER RESOURCES, BY PROVINCE, AS OF JANUARY 1, 1965[a]

PROVINCE OR TERRITORY	UNDEVELOPED WATER POWER			DEVELOPED WATER POWER
	Available Continuous Power at 88 Per Cent Efficiency			Installed Generating Capacity
	at Q95[b] (kw.)	at Q50[c] (kw.)	at Qm[d] (kw.)	(kw.)
Newfoundland	1,240,000	3,635,000	4,871,000	453,000
Prince Edward Island	....	1,000	2,000	....
Nova Scotia	21,000	112,000	165,000	143,000
New Brunswick	62,000	222,000	499,000	229,000
Quebec	9,000,000	27,200,000	34,200,000	9,553,000
Ontario	493,000	1,148,000	1,747,000	5,937,000
Manitoba	2,990,000	5,583,000	5,997,000	747,000
Saskatchewan	387,000	812,000	1,089,000	320,000
Alberta	806,000	2,289,000	3,604,000	291,000
British Columbia	6,039,000	17,436,000	32,442,000	2,613,000
Yukon Territory	841,000	3,932,000	6,625,000	28,000
Northwest Territories	525,000	1,153,000	1,826,000	17,000
Canada	22,404,000	63,523,000	93,067,000	20,331,000

[a]Roger Duhamel, Canada Yearbook (Ottawa: Queen's Printer, 1966), p. 645.
[b]Power equivalent of flow available 95 percent of the time.
[c]Power equivalent of flow available 50 percent of the time.
[d]Power equivalent of arithmetical mean flow.

important source of energy, conventional fuels appear to be more practical for at least a generation. Most of the trillion kilowatt-hours of electricity generated in Anglo-America last year were produced by central station power plants burning fossil fuels—coal, oil, and gas. Coal alone supplies half of the electrical energy, and electric utilities are the bituminous coal industry's best customers (*see Fig. 3-5*).

After much atom smashing, it was discovered that when a neutron "bullet" strikes the nucleus, or heart, of an atom of uranium (the heaviest of natural elements), it splits into two lighter atoms and other fission fragments. Curiously, the combined weight of the pieces is less than that of the original atom. The explanation is that the missing mass has been converted into energy, according to Einstein's formula for the equivalence of mass and energy. Since additional neutrons are also released in the process, a chain reaction can be achieved and a continuous flow of energy in the form of heat is produced. The heat is then utilized to produce electricity, as in a conventional power plant.

A nuclear power plant does not pollute the atmosphere with fly ash and sulfurous fumes. This is a compelling argument in favor of nuclear power, since the majority of Anglo-America's population lives in great metropolitan centers where most of the industrial and commercial pursuits are carried on.

Now that the latest nuclear plants can compete on a cost basis with coal-burning stations, some nuclear power enthusiasts are ready to order a tombstone for coal. It is a bit premature, however, to write coal's obituary, because it continues to support the heaviest power load. It is true, however, that in contrast to coal, a bright future is anticipated for nuclear fuels because of the rapidly changing technology.

OTHER MINERALS

Anglo-America either leads the world in the production of numerous other mineral resources, or at least has adequate amounts to insure normal domestic supplies. It holds first rank in the production of copper, zinc, and lead. In fertilizer minerals, Anglo-America is well supplied with phosphate and sulfur and can produce the nitrogen and potash it needs.

Anglo-America has serious limitations in other minerals, however. Although it has ample deposits of molybdenum, it lacks many other alloys that are essential in the steel industry. These include vanadium, tungsten, and antimony, which are all used in small quantities, and manganese and chromium, which are demanded in large amounts. Of the minerals that Anglo-America must import, those that cause most concern are manganese, tin, bauxite, chromium, and mica. In peacetime these can be obtained from other countries without much difficulty, but in wartime, acquisition of these minerals becomes a problem of paramount importance. Thousands of miles separate Anglo-America from the deposits of Malayan tin; Indian and Russian manganese; Russian, Turkish and Rhodesian chromium; and Indian and Malagasan mica. Since the lack of these essential minerals during war periods inevitably proves to be a serious handicap, they rank high on Anglo-America's list of strategic materials.

Water Resources

Water is indestructible. Presumably there is exactly as much water on earth today as there was at the time of creation. The water required for daily living in the United States weighs more than 100 times as much as all other materials consumed, including food, fuel, metals, plastics, lumber, sand, gravel, and stone. At present, industry and agriculture together account for more than 90 per cent of the total withdrawal use of water, excluding that used for hydroelectric power. Municipal and rural use accounts for the remainder (*Fig. 3-10*).

The average daily precipitation on the land surface of the conterminous United States is almost five billion acre-feet, or about 4,300 billion gallons. Deducting estimates of loss by evaporation and transpiration, and minima for stream flow, the amount of beneficial use is estimated at 650 billion gallons per day.

MAJOR REGIONS OF WATER SUPPLY AND DEMAND
IN THE U.S.

FIGURE 3-9.

Estimated consumption is now 350 billion gallons daily, a figure that will rise to 650 billion gallons per day by 1980. By the turn of the century our water requirements are projected at a trillion gallons per day (*see Fig. 3-10*). It is not the total amount of water that concerns mankind, however; it is the quality of the water and its availability for human use.

The crux of the U.S. water problem is twofold: (1) The available supply of good water is so limited that within 35 years demand will outstrip supply by 350 billion gallons daily. (2) The water in the nation's major river basins is being polluted by municipal, industrial, and agricultural wastes. The work of improving the water quality of just 17 of these streams has cost nearly $3.1 billion since the program began in 1957 (*Fig. 3-11*).

SUPPLY

Water is the key to the future of the entire West. In all that vast area, only the Pacific

FIGURE 3-10.

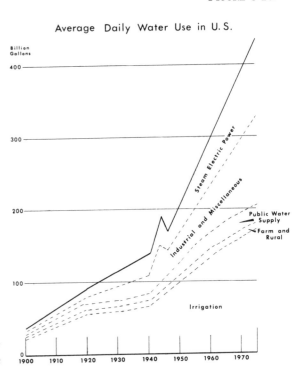

Average Daily Water Use in U.S.

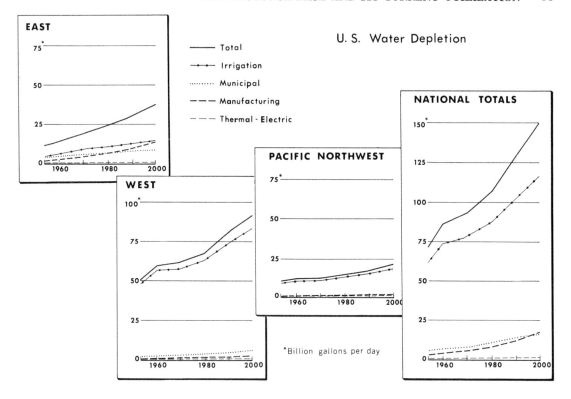

FIGURE 3-11.

Northwest has an adequate supply to maintain population and economic growth. The other regions of the West must face important decisions soon. They cannot continue both to support irrigation agriculture and to encourage urban-industrial expansion. The chronic water shortage in many arid regions would be greatly relieved if these regions would cut back sharply on irrigation agriculture and encourage industrial development.

Industry depletes comparatively little water, because recycling, which permits the same water to be used over and over again, is quite generally practiced. However, industrial saturation of the West could threaten the *quality* of water supplies unless rigid controls were applied to check industrial pollution.

In some arid parts of the West, population growth in recent decades has acutely depleted fresh water supplies that were limited long before those areas became migrant meccas. Water supplies now are being "mined" in certain areas: California's Sacramento and San Joaquin

Valleys, south-central Arizona, the high plains country of northwestern Texas (where water "mining" since 1935 has practically exhausted reserves), eastern New Mexico, and a small area of eastern Arkansas are already near the point of no return.

The rest of the country is not without its water problems. Ground water supplies are now very limited in parts of Kentucky, West Virginia, Illinois, Indiana, Ohio, Pennsylvania, Tennessee, Georgia, Missouri, Oklahoma, Arkansas, and Kansas. And, where local supplies are plentiful, the water is very hard. Surprisingly, some of the vast urban-industrial complexes in the Great Lakes region could feel the pressure of increasing demand on supplies before 1970 unless water reserves are more extensively developed.

The Midwest's most acute, immediate problem, drought, and its customary companion, the grasshopper, have ruined crops in the Great Plains "dust bowl" area and the eastern parts of some western states. The Plains stretch across 386 million acres from Canada to Texas. The "dust bowl" consists of some 14 million acres of sandy soil suitable only as grassland. Only grass can hold the soil against the 55- to 90-mile-an-hour wind that frequently whips across the Plains. For many years now, however, the land has been plowed, replowed, and planted, mainly with wheat. Its loose-lying, parched, sandy topsoil is being carried away by the wind, so that the stage is set for a tragic recurrence of the disaster of 1934-1935, which extracted a heavy toll in land and livestock.

POLLUTION

The fact that the nation's waters are being polluted is probably no surprise to anyone, especially anyone who has tried to swim in the waters off Milwaukee, Cleveland, or New York City. Pollution is a variable, however, and its definition depends upon the intended use of the water.

For domestic use, water must be clear and free of disease organisms, bad taste, and odor. It must not have a dissolved mineral content higher than 500 parts per million, according to U.S. Public Health Service standards. Hard water, for example, will not form a lather with soap, because of the presence in solution of calcium, magnesium, and iron compounds.

Water for fish propagation must be relatively free of industrial and municipal wastes and be able to sustain a flora for the small organisms that serve as fish foods. It must also have a minimum dissolved oxygen content of at least four per cent. Throughout the populous East today and in the congested industrial areas of the Middle West and West, pollution has already reduced the *quality* of municipal water supplies. When population was sparse, conventional filtering systems and chlorine were adequate. Now, as cities are becoming more and more congested, one city draws its water supply chiefly from another city's wastes, thereby endangering the health of all who live in the area.

As population, urbanization, and industrialization increase, environmental pollutants of all kinds will also increase. Unless an aroused public insists that measures be taken to control them, these pollutants will threaten the quality of the water people drink, the food they eat, and the air they breathe.

Control is possible today. However, like the water supply problem, the pollution problem has social, economic, and political overtones, and these could delay the decisions that must be made within the next few decades. Pollution control will come when the public insists upon necessary remedial action, and not before.

OUTLOOK

In 1960, the United States used 60 per cent of its water supply, compared with only 8 per cent in 1900. It has been estimated that by 1975, the country will be using 88 per cent of its total supply. Underground water supplies all across the country could be fully developed and utilized by the year 2000.

In spite of the tremendous quantities of water used daily and the prospect of greatly increased consumption with future expansion of population and industry, there are many reasons why the nation as a whole need not run out of water. Unlike most mineral commodities, water is a renewable resource. It circulates unendingly in its various forms from the seas, to the atmosphere, to the land, and back to the sea again. This has been called the hydrologic cycle.

Greater reuse of water may be expected as demands increase. It is true that some lowering in quality normally occurs with each reuse. But there are technological processes available that will offset the lowering of water quality. The control of waterborne wastes, which is an important factor in an extensive program of water reuse, will assume much greater importance in industry.

In most areas only a fraction of the supply potential that can be developed at a reasonable cost is being used. Increasing water demands may be expected to result in more adequate flood control measures to save large quantities of potable waters that now rush to the sea.

Although water supply potential for the country as a whole is tremendous, there is a limit to the supply that may be developed at presently acceptable costs. On the other hand, increasing population and expansion of industry have caused the demand for water to grow. As the demand for water approaches the potential supply for a given area, the cost of developing increased supplies may be expected to result in higher prices for water.

Water-short areas of the West are much closer to this situation now than eastern areas having more plentiful rainfall. Even in areas of more abundant rainfall, however, the large demands of heavily populated and industrialized areas are taxing the limit of supplies.

The development of new sources of supply through cloud-seeding techniques to induce rainfall and through conversion of saline water to fresh water is still in the development stage. The effectiveness of cloud-seeding is controversial, and, in any event, seeding is not expected to affect the overall water supply greatly. The myth that there will be enough water for everyone now that the nation's first desalination plant is in production, with others to follow, could be a dangerous opiate. Even if the present high production and distribution costs are drastically reduced, desalination cannot be a magic solution to the water problem.

Land As a Resource

Land is the resource base not only of food, clothing, lumber, and other direct or indirect products of farms, grasslands, and forests, but also of the space required for towns and cities, highways, railroads, airports, recreation, wildlife habitats, reservoirs, and other aspects of daily living.

The land and water area of the United States exceeds 3.6 million square miles. About five-sixths is in the 48 contiguous states. All but two per cent is land. What and where it is, how it has been used since it was settled, who owns it, and how it is related to the growth of population and production, bear on the country's social and economic development and future.

About 60 per cent of the total land of the 50 states is used directly to produce crops and food for livestock. Twenty per cent is used for forests. Less than 3 per cent is devoted to urban and related intensive uses. Land designated as primarily for recreational or wildlife uses and that devoted to public installations and facilities accounts for about 5 per cent. The remaining 12 per cent is mainly desert, bare rock, swamp, and other land of limited economic use (*Fig. 3-12*).

FOREST RESOURCES

Forest products and forest industries play an important role in the economy of the United States and Canada. The extent of forest land in relation to total land area, the proportion of forest land that is available for commercial timber production, the location of such land geographically, its ownership, its condition, the forest types represented, the degree to which it is stocked with growing trees, and the condition of the timber, are all significant facts essential to an understanding of the current timber situation and its future potentialities.

The United States. The total forest area is considerably larger than the area devoted to

FIGURE 3-12. *Usage of land area, United States.*

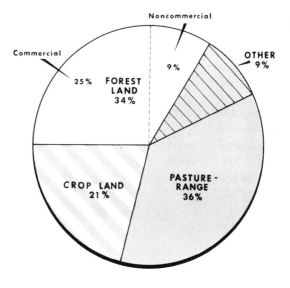

cropland, but slightly smaller than the pasture and range area. Of the 664 million acres of forest land in the conterminous United States and coastal Alaska, 489 million acres, or about one-fourth of the total land area of the United States, is classed as commercial forest land.

It is significant that three-fourths of the commercial forest land is in the East, West Gulf, and Great Lakes regions (*Fig. 3-13*). Such heavily industrialized and densely populated regions as the Middle Atlantic, South Atlantic, and Central states have about as much commercial forest land as does the Pacific Northwest—the region with the greatest commercial forest area in the West (*Fig. 3-14*).

The forests of the United States fall about equally into hardwood and softwood types. The West, including coastal Alaska, is almost exclusively a softwood area; the South, despite extensive pine (softwood) forests is 58 per cent hardwood; and the East is largely hardwood.

The original forest stand (virgin forest) was composed of more than 1,100 species of trees, of which more than 100 have been of economic value. Twenty-nine types are widely used in the production of lumber, plywood, and wood pulp. In order of importance, these include: Southern pine, Douglas fir, oak, hemlock, gum, maple, spruce, cypress, and redwood.

The two leading lumbering regions are the South and the Pacific Coast, although 31 of the 50 states produce important commercial tree crops. Oregon leads all other states in lumbering.

The future need for timber to supply demands of a growing population will be strikingly greater than today or at any time in the past. If per capita use of timber products increases only 4 per cent by the year 2000, as indicated by medium projections of demand, total wood consumption will be 83 per cent greater than at present, primarily because of an estimated 75 per cent increase in population. There is the potential to meet that need if forestry knowledge and skills are applied promptly and with utmost vigor and determination.

Canada. Canada is richly endowed with forest resources, estimated at 1,710,788 square miles,

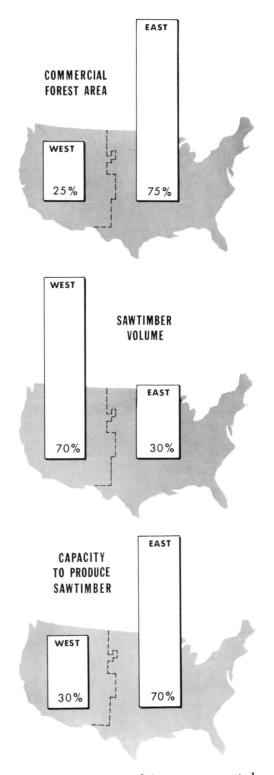

FIGURE 3-13. *Commercial forest area, sawtimber volume, and capacity to produce sawtimber in the conterminous United States.*

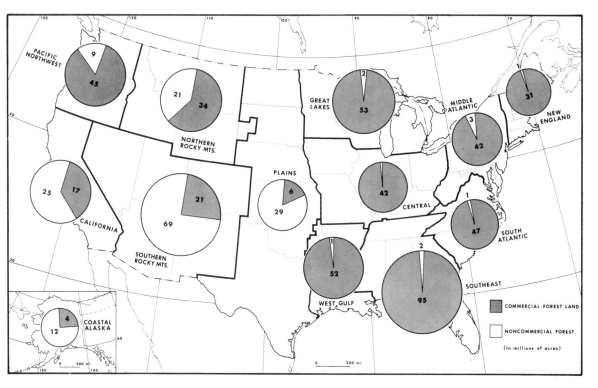

FIGURE 3-14. *Acreage of commercial and noncommercial forest land by region, as classified by the U.S. Department of Agriculture.*

of which roughly 57 per cent is capable of producing marketable timber (*Table II*). There are more than 150 tree species in Canada, of which 31 are conifers, commonly called softwoods. About two-thirds of these softwoods and 10 per cent of the deciduous, or hardwood species are of commercial importance. Approximately 81 per cent of the volume of merchantable timber is made up of softwood species.

Canadian-United States trade relations in forest products are important to both countries. For example, about 91 per cent of all lumber imported by the United States comes from Canada, as does 82 per cent of the wood pulp. A high proportion of United States' imports of other timber products likewise comes from Canada.

OUTLOOK

One needs to review the potential of the land to see how well it will meet future needs for food, forest products, urban uses, and recreation, and how effectively it can be shifted from one use to another. Nations, as they become more urban, find new ways to meet their needs for land or to adjust their demands to available supplies. Space requirements may be met by increasing the height of apartments and office buildings, for example. Food can be imported. Outdoor recreation needs can be met by more intensive use of available recreation land.

The United States has abundant land to supply most of its wants. With rapidly improving technology, our cropland can furnish more farm products than we can profitably use. From 1950 through 1960, for example, when the population increased by only 18 per cent, farm output rose 20 per cent. Per capita demands for farm products changed very little over this period, however. Production in recent years has outrun effective demand by about 8 per cent per year. Except when there was drought or a war emergency, the United States has had surpluses every year since 1930.

TABLE II

Productive and Nonproductive Forest Land, by Province, 1963*

Province or Territory	Productive Forest Land (sq. miles)	Nonproductive Forest Land (sq. miles)	Total (sq. miles)
Newfoundland	33,862	53,930	87,792
Prince Edward Island	813	121	934
Nova Scotia	15,080	1,194	16,274
New Brunswick	23,887	442	24,329
Quebec	220,625	157,500	378,125
Ontario	164,568	97,174	261,742
Manitoba	58,189	64,632	122,821
Saskatchewan	50,239	67,499	117,738
Alberta	116,572	41,023	157,595
British Columbia	208,411	59,227	267,638
Totals, Provinces	892,246	542,742	1,434,988
Yukon Territory	42,100	39,100	81,200
Northwest Territories	33,600	161,000	194,600
Canada	967,946	742,842	1,710,788

*Mitchell Sharp, *Canada Yearbook* (Ottawa: Queen's Printer, 1965), p. 507.

Output per man-hour almost doubled from 1940 to 1950, and almost doubled again from 1950 to 1960, largely because of mechanization. Crop yield per acre rose only 15 per cent from 1940 to 1950, but it went up by 40 per cent from 1950 to 1960, in large part due to a fourfold increase in the use of fertilizer from 1950 to 1960.

Technological progress will continue, and the Department of Agriculture estimates that by 1980 the United States can meet its food needs and exports, with 326 million acres actually used in crop production, including harvested cropland, crop failure, and fallow.

The greatest change in land use since 1920 has been the doubling of the area used for special purposes. This includes intensive uses, such as for urban and built-up areas, and extensive uses, such as for recreation, wildlife, and for public installations and facilities. Over the next two decades, special purpose uses are expected to increase by almost 50 million acres, or about 33 per cent. Urban and built-up areas are expected to increase by almost 40 per cent, and the less intensive, non-agricultural areas by almost 30 per cent.

Selected References

BARACH, ARNOLD B., and MODLEY, RUDOLPH, *U. S. A. and Its Economic Future, a Twentieth Century Fund Survey*, New York: The Macmillan Co., 1964.

BARNETT, HAROLD J., "The Changing Relation of Natural Resources to National Security," *Economic Geography*, Vol. 34, July, 1958, pp. 189–201.

CLAWSON, MARION, *Land for Americans, Trends, Prospects, and Problems*, Chicago: Rand McNally and Co., 1963.

DEUTSCH, J. J., KEIRSTEAD, B. S., LEVITT, K., and WILL, R. M., *The Canadian Economy, Selected Readings*, Toronto: Macmillan of Canada, 1961.

EKIRCH, ARTHUR A., JR., *Man and Nature in America*, New York: Columbia University Press, 1963.

GOLDFIELD, EDWIN D. (ed.), *Statistical Abstract of the United States*, Washington, D. C.: United States Bureau of the Census, 1966.

GOLDSMITH, RAYMOND W., *The National Wealth of the United States in the Postwar Period*, Princeton, N. J.: Princeton University Press, 1962.

HIGBEE, EDWARD C., *Farms and Farmers in an Urban Age*, New York: The Twentieth Century Press, 1962.

HIGHSMITH, RICHARD M., and JENSEN, J. GRANVILLE, *Geography of Commodity Production*, Philadelphia: J. B. Lippincott Co., 1963.

HIGHSMITH, RICHARD M., JENSEN, J. GRANVILLE, and RUDD, ROBERT D., *Conservation in the United States*, Chicago: Rand McNally & Co., 1962.

HUNKER, HENRY L. (ed.), *Erich W. Zimmerman's Introduction to World Resources*, New York: Harper & Row, 1964.

JOHNSON, H. G., *Canada in a Changing World Economy*, Toronto: University of Toronto Press, 1962.

LANDSBERG, HANS H., FISCHMAN, LEONARD L., and FISHER, JOSEPH L., *Resources in America's Future*, Baltimore: The Johns Hopkins Press, 1963.

LEESTON, ALFRED M., CRICHTON, JOHN A., and JACOBS, JOHN C., *The Dynamic Natural Gas Industry*, Norman, Okla.: University of Oklahoma Press, 1963.

MAUZON, OLIN T., *Resources and Industries of the United States*, New York: Appleton-Century-Crofts, 1966.

Minerals Yearbook, Washington, D.C.: U.S. Bureau of Mines, Government Printing Office, annual.

OTTOSON, HOWARD W., *Land Use Policy and Problems in the United States*, Lincoln, Neb.: University of Nebraska Press, 1963.

SELL, GEORGE, *The Petroleum Industry*, New York: Oxford University Press, 1963.

SEWELL, W. R. DERRICK, "The Role of Regional Interties in Postwar Energy Resource Development," *Annals of the Association of American Geographers*, Vol. 54, December, 1964, pp. 566–581.

SMITH, GUY HAROLD (ed.), *Conservation of Natural Resources* (3rd ed.), New York: John Wiley & Sons, Inc., 1965.

UDALL, STEWART L., *The Quiet Crisis*, New York: Holt, Rhinehart and Winston, Inc., 1963.

UNITED STATES BUREAU OF MINES, *Minerals Yearbook*, Washington, D. C.: Government Printing Office, Annual.

WAHL., E., *This Land, a Geography of Canada*, Toronto: Oxford University Press, 1961.

WATKINS, M. H., *Economics: Canada, Recent Readings*, New York: McGraw-Hill Book Co., Inc., 1963.

WHITE, C. LANGDON, GRIFFIN, PAUL F., and McKNIGHT, THOMAS L., *World Economic Geography*, Belmont, Calif.: Wadsworth Publishing Co., 1964.

WOYTINSKY, EMMA, *Profile of the U. S. Economy: A Survey of Growth and Change*, New York: Frederick A. Praeger, Inc., 1967.

4 *The Industrial Pattern*

Anglo-America is the world's leading industrial area. Its most highly developed manufacturing belt extends inland from the Atlantic seaboard for more than a third of the distance across the continent. Specifically, the area is encircled by a line running from Minneapolis south to Kansas City, then east to Norfolk, north to the St. Lawrence Valley and the Canadian shores of Lake Erie and Lake Ontario, and west to the starting point in Minneapolis. Most of the remaining industry is concentrated in the piedmont area of North Carolina, South Carolina, and Georgia; around Birmingham, Alabama; around the Dallas-Fort Worth area in Texas; along the Gulf Coast; and in the Far West, especially in the San Diego, Los Angeles, and San Francisco metropolitan districts in California, and to a lesser degree in the Puget Sound (Seattle, Washington) and Willamette Valley (Portland, Oregon) areas (*Fig. 4-1*).

Anglo-America holds a unique position in manufacturing in that it dominates the world completely in most of the heavy manufacturing industries that require enormous amounts of power, raw materials, and capital, as well as large numbers of scientists, entrepreneurs, and skilled laborers. These heavy manufacturing industries, which include iron and steel, industrial machines, railroad cars and locomotives, ships, electrical machinery, agricultural implements, machine tools, tractors, automobiles, aircraft, and electronic equipment, are the backbone of any great industrial power.

The United States: Industrial Giant

The growth of American production is the wonder of the world. With only about six per cent of the world's population and roughly six per cent of the world's area, the United States produces from one-third to one-half of the world's industrial goods.

Starting as a collection of struggling colonies in the early part of the seventeenth century, the United States has become the world's foremost economic power. This economic growth has no parallel in the output of goods and services, the increase of leisure time, per capita income, and consumer purchases of goods and services. The standard of living of most Americans is considerably above that of most other peoples, and there are far more medical, educational, and recreational facilities available to the population.

From 1750 to the present, the growth of the United States' economy has far outstripped that of the rest of the world. One needs to think only of life in the United States in 1750 compared with that of today to realize what great changes have taken place. The amount of goods and services available per capita in

1750 was less than 40 per cent of those available today. Many of the material items Americans now regard as necessities were either nonexistent, or of an inferior quality, or available only to the wealthy—such things as central heating, automobiles, radios, television sets, electrical appliances, and frozen foods.

In 1750, the average American family lived on a small farm. The house was constructed from hand-sawn boards and hand-hewn timbers and was roofed with hand-split shingles, all derived from the nearby forest. From the same source came fuel for heating and cooking and the material for building fences. Aided by his sons, the head of the household raised fields of corn and wheat or barley for the family's bread. A garden supplied vegetables through the warm months and an orchard

FIGURE 4-1.

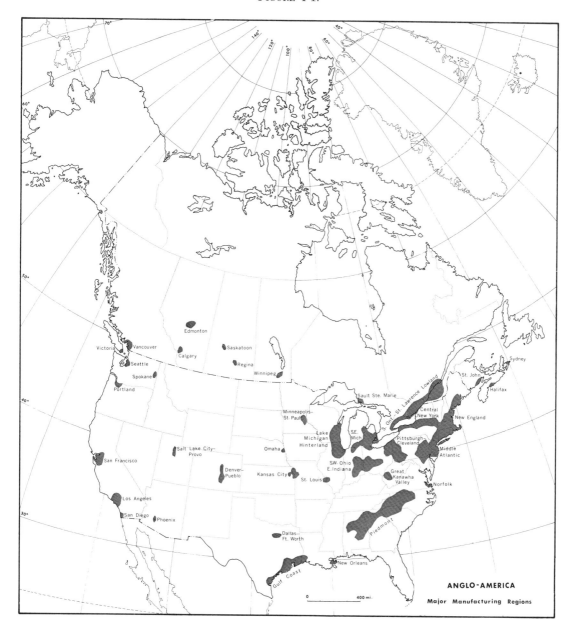

ANGLO-AMERICA

Major Manufacturing Regions

furnished apples and other fruits. Some of the fruits and vegetables were stored for winter use in cellars or in pits filled with straw, and as many varieties of fruit as possible were dried for later use.

Chickens, pigs, a few cattle and sheep, and an occasional bit of wild game furnished the family's meat. Sugar was supplied from a bee tree, a patch of sorghum, or a maple grove. Patches of flax and hemp, together with wool sheared from local sheep, furnished materials that were spun and woven into cloth. The cloth was then dyed with walnut, sassafras, or some other local dye before it was fashioned into garments. Cattle hides were tanned with chestnut or hemlock bark and made into shoes in the family workshop. Furniture and most of the family's tools and utensils were also made in the farmer's workshop. Soap was produced from animal fats and from lye that was derived from wood ashes. Shoes were polished with bear grease or mutton tallow.

Virtually all that the average American family of 1750 needed to buy was salt, shot made of lead, and gun powder. The salt probably came from an evaporator located at a not-too-distant salt well; the shot, from a small, nearby galena mine and shot tower; and the gunpowder, from a small powder mill. The total cash expenditures by the average family probably did not exceed $10.00 to $15.00 annually. This money was supplied by the sale of a few cattle, a little tobacco or wheat, or other products.

The family of 1750 had to be largely self-sustaining, because the community in which it lived was generally self-contained and economically self-sufficient. Trade was small, slow, and confined to traffic in a few essentials and luxuries that could not be produced locally. Thus, if a district did not have food, clothing, shelter, and fuel immediately available, it remained unpopulated.

Speaking in cultural and economic terms, we can say that the average American family of today lives in an entirely different world. The man of today devotes his working hours to one activity, and earns from its sufficient income to provide himself and his family with all the goods and services they need or can afford. This changeover from a self-suffi-

cient way of life to a high degree of specialization has occurred through the development of a wonderfully productive technology. It has resulted in increased benefits for man, but has also created many social problems, such as slums, technological unemployment, and mass stereotypes of human behavior.

A nation achieves power in proportion to the quality of the natural resources available to it, the energy and ability of its inhabitants, and the effectiveness of its resource utilization. The United States was fortunate in its original abundance of fertile soils, minerals, forests, fish, game, water, grasslands, and other natural resources. In addition, the early Americans were nonconformists—descended largely from religious, economic, and social dissenters—and they didn't follow the traditional patterns of the Old World. Moreover, America's population was expanding just at the time when new forms of business organization and a new industrial technology were being invented. Before the population had become too large, Americans developed an enormous economic production. This gave them a huge exportable surplus and resulted in the accumulation of great reserves of capital in the form of goods, money, and credits. This has pyramided so rapidly that, so far, it has kept ahead of a steadily increasing population.

Other factors that were especially important in the emergence of the United States as the world's industrial leader are:

1. Business was given a free hand to develop. The government helped to finance improvement of transportation and communication. Liberal immigration policies helped provide a labor force. Tariffs protected home industries so that domestic trade flourished.

2. The profit system provided incentives for entering business. United States' laws encouraged the holding of property and the accumulation of capital necessary to the operation of a business.

3. The political system was democratic, encouraging individual initiative. United States' institutions emphasized equality of opportunity and extensive and tax-supported public education, although

until fairly recent times this "equality" did not usually apply to minority racial groups.

4. Because labor was scarce in the early years, Americans were forced to use more machines to produce goods. Population increase and immigration soon provided a rapidly growing labor force, however, and it became necessary to increase the workers' productivity by more training and education. These workers did not resist the introduction of machinery, and thus did not seriously interfere with the general mechanization of industry.

5. A large number of businessmen were willing to mechanize, to undertake research, and to take risks if there were a prospect of profits. They showed an amazing ability to obtain money with which to acquire the necessary capital goods. This was possible through the exploitation of resources and through borrowing. The absence of high taxes and an unequal distribution of income were other factors that made ready capital available to businessmen.

6. Another important factor in the United States' growth has been the existence of a large home market. Relatively high profits have resulted in an emphasis on mass distribution, which, in turn, has led to standardization of goods, specialization of manufacturing plants, the use of more and more machinery, and industrial plants of maximum size.

7. Economic growth was further increased by certain developments or inventions that led to new investment. During the 1830's, the Erie Canal brought growth. Then, during the 1850's, the 1860's, and the 1880's, railroads opened up new lands. In the 1920's, the growing utilization of the automobile required huge investments in manufacturing plants, roads, service stations, and garages. In the 1950's and 1960's, the airplane has revolutionized travel and the means of shipping goods and conducting business.

8. Communication was always emphasized —from the time of the first post offices to the telephone systems, newspapers, magazines, and radio and television networks of the present. As a result, communication of needs, ideas, and desires has always been rapid. Advertising alone has contributed much to the demand for new and better products and services and their rapid distribution.

Some of the preceding factors important to economic growth are unique to the United States; others are not. Some are natural, while others are man-made and available to any country that would adopt them. Some are of declining importance.

MANUFACTURING

The term "manufacturing" includes those activities by which man changes the form or nature of raw materials, converting them into more useful products. These transforming operations are conducted in factories, to which are brought raw materials from various resource regions, and from which go finished products to diverse markets.

Importance. Manufacturing is the leading economic activity in the United States. No other country in the world employs so many tools per capita or tries so hard to substitute the machine for man's brain and muscles. The tools and machines at each worker's disposal may be valued at $100,000 or more, and a single company may employ thousands of workers (*Fig. 4-2*).

The United States annually exports more than $20 billion worth of goods and imports more than $15 billion worth. Total export trade is almost twice as much as that of Great Britain or West Germany, the nearest competitors, and about five times more than that of Japan. No other nation approaches the volume of United States exports.

The single most important factor in United States' manufacturing is its high production per man-hour. This enables American industry to compete even though hourly labor costs are lower in other nations (*Fig. 4-3*).

The American people have always been noted for their mechanical ingenuity. They have invented or discovered many things that

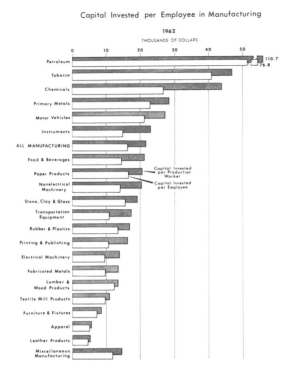

FIGURE 4-2.

have greatly influenced and, in some cases, revolutionized the world. Chief among these are the cotton gin, sewing machine, steamboat, reaper, telegraph, telephone, airplane, and the discovery of how to harness nuclear energy. Above all, the system of interchangeable parts, introduced by Eli Whitney in 1798, has enabled American manufacturers to make machines that can be repaired and made more serviceable. Mass production by assembly-line methods, standardization of parts, and streamlined business management also have contributed to American leadership in manufacturing.

Advantages. The extent and variety of agricultural products assure an abundance of food supplies for the American people. The machine methods of agriculture are such that a very small proportion of the employable population (less than seven per cent) can produce a surplus for export. This leaves large numbers of workers free to engage in other, nonagricultural occupations. The abundance of coal, iron ore, and other useful natural resources makes the manufacture of many items convenient and

relatively inexpensive. This is particularly true of iron and steel and their products. The presence of clay and various forms of building stone is advantageous in the construction of factories and other establishments connected directly or indirectly with manufacturing industries. The great forest areas provide an abundance of lumber and timber for a variety of finished goods.

No other country has such extensive and numerous transportation lines, by rail, water, and highway. The United States, with roughly 6 per cent of the world's population and land surface, has about 30 per cent of its railway mileage. The nation owes much to its railroads; industrial development would have been impossible without them. Some 23,170 miles of navigable waterways service the nation. There are nearly 3 million miles of roads and highways, of which 2.4 million miles are paved. These combined facilities make the carrying of goods from one region to another comparatively easy and inexpensive.

The freedom of commerce between the states is one of the greatest advantages enjoyed by American businessmen. In few, if any, other regions of the world, is there such an extensive market area entirely free from tariff barriers. In addition, the country embraces localities with widely different needs, giving

FIGURE 4-3.

rise to considerable interstate and intrastate movement of goods.

The Industrial Economy

INDUSTRIAL LOCATION

The location of industrial activities is rather firmly determined by economic considerations. Industries in which the cost of transporting raw materials looms large, such as cement plants or paper mills, locate near their source of supply; processes in which the product gains rather than loses weight, and in which distribution to the consumer is a major cost factor (bottling plants, for example), are located near their markets. For many industries, the point of minimum transport costs is by no means evident in advance, and has to be calculated from a careful consideration of alternate places of supply and alternate transport routes. A steel works, for example, will locate at a point where the total cost of shipping its ore, its coal, and its finished product will be at a minimum (*Fig. 4-4*). The cost of transporting energy is in many cases an important factor; aluminum smelters, chemical plants using electrolytic processes, or atomic energy installations will locate near sources of cheap electric power. Since high losses occur in the transmission of electric power, thermal power plants serving cities will locate as close to their consumer as possible, at a place where they have an ample supply of water for cooling purposes, and, preferably, coal or oil deliveries by barge.

Labor costs are also an important locational factor. In some highly automated industries, such as oil refining, labor costs can be negligible; but in other industries, such as textiles, costs may be high. Both the cost of labor and the quality of the labor force are important. For example, the producers of precision instruments seek areas with a tradition of high skill; whereas apparel manufacturers need pools of cheap female labor. Differences in tax, insurance, and interest rates, or in climate, topography, or social environment also enter into the location decision.

FIGURE 4-4. *Aerial view of Sparrows Point, a tidewater steel plant near Baltimore. Sparrows Point is well situated for supplying the large urban industrial market of the Atlantic seaboard. The plant depends largely on iron ore from Venezuela. Coal and limestone are secured in West Virginia and Pennsylvania. (Bethlehem Steel Corp.)*

The economics of agglomeration is a third important factor in industrial location. For example, an isolated oil refinery may waste some of its by-products that could be utilized as raw materials by subsidiary chemical plants if these were located next door. Small industries producing a nonstandardized product, such as the fashion-oriented ladies' garment industry, are highly dependent on urbanized economies. Research-oriented industries prefer to locate near centers of learning with which they can share reference facilities and highly trained personnel (*Fig. 4-5*).

FIGURE 4-5. *The building of research-oriented Applied Technology, Inc., in the Stanford University Industrial Park. (Stanford University)*

INDUSTRIAL TRENDS

Between 1920 and 1960, American industry passed through three distinct phases. The first, the decade of the twenties, was a time of great prosperity, marked by the flourishing of the automobile industry and the rise of the radio, motion picture, and chemical manufacturing businesses to major rank. The second phase was the great depression of the 1930's—years of stagnation, when new investment fell to as little as half a billion a year. At the low point in 1932, steel production was down to 13.5 million tons from 56 million in 1929, and automobile sales suffered a proportionate decline. Then, with the outbreak of World War II, industry embarked upon the third phase, an expansive spurt that actually accelerated when the war ended. By 1960, the index of manufacturing production had risen 63 per cent over the 1949 level, which, in turn, was nearly double the 1939 level.

Electronics, aircraft production, and a new defense industry, combined with an acute shortage of consumer goods during World War II, triggered the postwar boom. Although these industries were scattered all over the country, from Florida to Washington and from California to New England, their greatest concentration was in the Far West. The virtual monopoly of the Northeast as the most important manufacturing section was fast disappearing. The newer industries reflected trends that were transforming all manufacturing: use of automatic machinery, emphasis on skilled labor and scientific research, and an increasing participation by the federal government both as a designer and a purchaser of manufactured products.

INDUSTRIAL EMPLOYMENT

Roughly 300,000 factories in the United States employ more than 17 million employees, of whom about four-fifths are production workers (see Table III).

Approximately one fourth of the gainfully-occupied population of the United States is engaged in manufacturing, and this group accounts for about one fourth of the national income. That the large urban concentrations have played a monumental role in American expansion is underscored by the fact that in 1961, 37.5 per cent of the nation's value added by manufacture was accounted for by ten metropolises containing 27 per cent of the total 1960 population. Thus, manufacturing represents an intensive use of relatively small areas of land in contrast to farming, grazing, and forestry.

Ever since the industrial revolution it has been rumored that "some day machines will replace man." Where this has become a reality through automation and technology, it has been found that men's minds are needed elsewhere in greater numbers to help the American economic system continue to prosper.

Since 1950, the number of employed people has grown by 14 million—with women representing 8.6 million of that increase, and men, 5.4 million. Today 62 per cent of married females are employed, compared with 52 per cent in 1950. As a result, dual-income families have risen from approximately 9 million in 1950 to 16 million. In many households several family members are often gainfully employed. The resulting increase in family income has been a great factor in the rise in consumer spending.

Gross average weekly earnings for production workers in manufacturing industries have almost doubled since 1950. Since living costs for most of this time have not risen nearly as rapidly, the average American worker has been able to stay well ahead of inflation. In addition to his basic wages, the American worker enjoys a goodly number of fringe benefits that have further improved his standard of living and his security.

CORPORATION PROFITS

The graphic story of corporate profits (Fig. 4-6) clearly shows that corporations have enjoyed a good return on their investments in the past few years, particularly in 1966. After

TABLE III

Manufactures and Minerals
General Statistics for Major Industry Groups, 1963[*]

INDUSTRY	PLANTS WITH OVER 19 EMPLOYEES	ALL EMPLOYEES		PRODUCTION WORKERS			VALUE ADDED BY MANUFACTURE, ADJUSTED (Millions of Dollars)
		Number (Thousands)	Payroll (Millions of Dollars)	Number (Thousands)	Man Hours (Millions)	Wages (Millions of Dollars)	
Food and kindred products	14,162	1,642	8,602	1,094	2,230	5,124	21,364
Tobacco manufactures	233	76	328	67	130	269	1,678
Textile mill products	4,435	865	3,388	776	1,567	2,766	6,150
Apparel and related products	13,129	1,300	4,480	1,151	2,084	3,532	7,792
Lumber and wood products	6,259	602	2,367	528	1,054	1,957	4,205
Furniture and fixtures	3,368	381	1,743	318	647	1,302	3,093
Paper and allied products	3,550	589	3,508	470	992	2,552	7,295
Printing and publishing	7,251	919	5,542	565	1,090	3,227	10,494
Chemicals and allied products	4,052	747	5,022	480	978	2,805	17,501
Petroleum and coal products	702	153	1,133	109	217	742	3,568
Rubber and plastic products	2,480	417	2,363	330	661	1,670	4,590
Leather and leather products	2,119	337	1,263	301	556	1,008	2,119
Stone, clay, and glass products	4,766	585	3,248	465	956	2,375	7,223
Primary metal industries	3,563	1,119	7,669	917	1,877	5,885	14,949
Fabricated metal products	9,321	1,096	6,447	854	1,756	4,510	11,865
Machinery, except electrical	8,395	1,463	9,581	1,046	2,164	6,184	16,897
Electrical machinery	4,729	1,472	8,850	1,034	2,051	5,253	16,333
Transportation equipment	2,881	1,618	12,009	1,149	2,447	7,712	22,720
Instruments and related products	1,389	367	2,367	239	482	1,295	4,681
Miscellaneous manufacturing	3,766	604	3,444	432	848	1,994	5,878
Administrative and auxiliary	(NA)	713	6,371	.....	.....	.....	.....
All Industries Total	(NA)	17,065	99,725	12,325	24,787	62,162	190,395

[*]Source: U.S. Bureau of Census. The estimates for 1963 in the following table are based upon reports from a representative sample of about 60,000 manufacturing establishments. This table includes data for privately-owned or operated establishments. Government-owned and operated establishments are excluded. In addition to the employment and payroll for operating manufacturing establishments, manufacturing concerns ordinarily reported separately for central administrative offices or auxiliary units (e.g., research laboratories, storage warehouses, power plants, garages, repair shops, etc.) that service the manufacturing establishments of a company.

U. S.   Economic   Trends

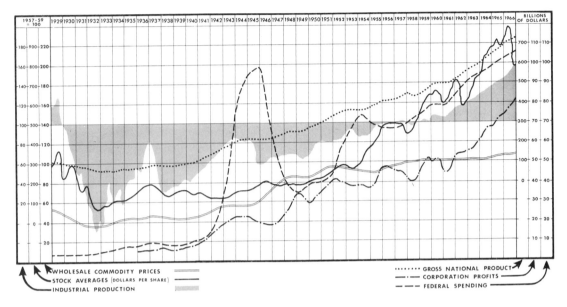

FIGURE 4-6.

lagging behind the general pace of the economy in the latter 1950's and early 1960's, profits have risen normally in the cyclical expansion since 1961. In 1965 and 1966, profit margins and rates of return on invested capital finally recovered to the levels of 1955-57, the last previous period of sustained full employment and high-capacity utilization.

Higher production costs have been more than offset by rising volume and greater efficiency, yielding wider profit margins. Within this climate of good profits, corporations have invested heavily in new plants and equipment to insure even greater efficiency and productivity for the future. In addition, American corporations have shared their increased profits with millions of shareholders through higher dividends and extra payments.

FEDERAL SPENDING

The graphic line of federal spending (*see Fig. 4-6*) clearly shows that in the fiscal year 1965, the federal government surpassed the previous all-time spending record, which had occurred during the peak of World War II.

There was a further increase in the fiscal year 1966. Of the estimated $106 billion expenditures, $56 billion was expended for national defense. Interest on the national debt accounted for $12 billion; and health, labor, and welfare payments, more than $8 billion. The estimated deficit between receipts of $102 billion (including $51 billion in individual income taxes, $29 billion in corporate income taxes, plus excise and other taxes) and federal expenditures of $106 billion was $4 billion.

THE STOCK MARKET

The trends of the stock market are charted in Figure 4-6, using the monthly averages of the Dow-Jones 30 Industrials. It is obvious that the gigantic American news communication industry, including newspapers, magazines, television, and radio, has helped the stock market investor to keep abreast of the great economic growth. He is also knowledgeable about such factors as tight money, higher interest rates, possible tax increases, budget controls, and international defense problems. As a result, the stock market is particularly vulnerable to the daily newscasts.

THE KEY INDICATORS

Of the hundreds of thousands of statistics that are gathered, two of the most quoted indicators are the Gross National Product and the Index of Industrial Production. Both of these indicators are charted in Figure 4-6.

Gross National Product (the market value of the output of goods and services produced by the nation's economy) continued its move upward in 1966. A $700 billion annual rate was reached in the final quarter of 1965, and the rate continued upward to the $750 billion point in 1966. Part of this rise was due to an increase in prices, but the greater share was attributed to the buoyancy of the economy. If brakes are applied to spending by consumers, business, and government, the fast growth pace of the Gross National Product is certain to slow down. The vast diversification of the American economy, however, may provide the impetus that will push the GNP to the $800 billion mark in the near future.

The industrial arm of the United States is depicted by the Federal Reserve Board's Index of Industrial Production. Although the nation's capacity to produce was enlarged considerably in 1966, the rise in industrial output was even greater. The gap between potential and actual output was lower than at any other time in the current economic rise. Orders on record for future deliveries indicate that industrial production will remain strong.

Selected Major Industries

IRON AND STEEL — THE BASIC INDUSTRY

This is the steel age—the atomic bomb notwithstanding. The United States' citizen uses more steel than any other commodity except water—some 1,400 pounds of it per year. Without steel the American economy would suffer greatly. The airplane, automobile, and am-

munition industries would close their doors; international, even local, trade would be at a standstill; most of us would be without light, heat, and power; and many of us would go hungry. This is because our present economy is (1) a machine economy and (2) an exchange economy.

A *machine economy* means production of goods by mechanical rather than manual means. Production of goods by machinery calls for metal. Although machines could be made of wood, they would be crude, costly to construct, and short-lived. Therefore, they are made of metal; and, significantly, they are made of cheap metal. Of the six so-called useful metals, none can compete with iron and steel if quality is considered in relationship to price.

An *exchange economy* means a mode of life characterized by trade. This rests on subdivision of labor, or specialization of task. Individuals, communities, and entire nations make only a limited variety of goods and exchange their surpluses to mutual advantage. As Adam Smith observed, subdivision of labor is limited by the "extent of the market."

The extent of the market, in turn, is limited largely by legal barriers and the cost of transporting goods. Ships, trucks, railroad trains, airplanes, and pipelines are made principally of iron and steel. Without these cheap and efficient metals, transportation would be curtailed, standards of living would fall, and we would revert to the days of self-sufficiency.

Anglo-America produces about 26 per cent of the pig iron and nearly 30 per cent of the steel in the world. Almost all is made in the United States, where there is enough plant capacity to produce 150 million tons; but the present demand, despite the use of great quantities in armaments, is still not sufficient to engage all this capacity (*Fig. 4-7*).

Nine-tenths of the steel made in Anglo-America comes from the main manufacturing belt, which enjoys low-cost water transport for its raw materials: coal from the Appalachia, iron ore from the Lake Superior district and Labrador, local limestone, and imported ferroalloys (*Fig. 4-8*). The Chicago area, including

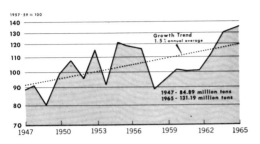

FIGURE 4-7. *United States steel ingot production.*

Indiana Harbor, Calumet, and East Chicago, leads all others in output. The Pittsburgh district, with many plants on the Ohio, Monongahela, and Allegheny Rivers, is second in importance. The Lake Erie district, which extends from North Tonawanda to Detroit, has nearly a dozen centers with integrated iron and steel plants, and nearly three times that many centers with rolling mills.

FIGURE 4-8.

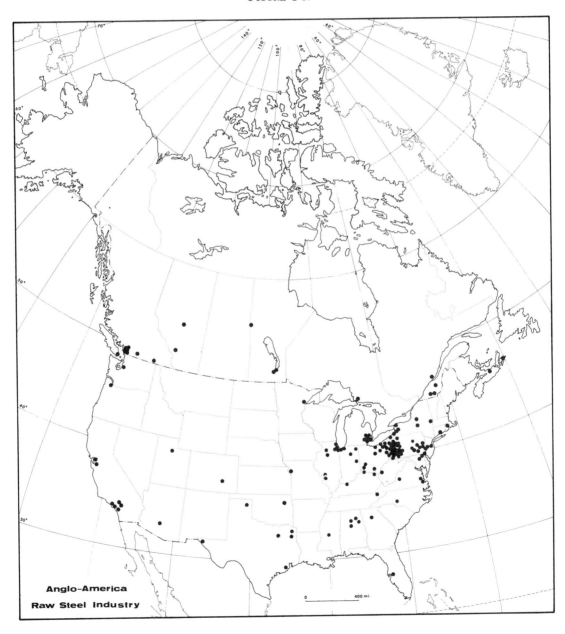

Anglo-America
Raw Steel Industry

Other, less important steel districts are: (1) the southern New England, east-central New York, and New Jersey district, which operates plants that are not fully integrated establishments, but which convert pig iron, steel scrap, and alloy metal into special steels; (2)the fully integrated mills in eastern Pennsylvania (Morrisville) and Maryland (Sparrows Point), which are based on local coal and imported high grade iron ore from Venezuela and Chile; (3) the Birmingham, Alabama, district, which has most of the necessary raw materials for making steel within a 20-mile radius; (4) the Houston and Daingerfield (northeastern Texas) integrated plants; and (5) the western iron and steel districts at Pueblo (Colorado), Provo (Utah), Fontana, South San Francisco, Pittsburg, and Torrance (California) and Seattle (Washington). Of the far western mills, only two—Provo and Fontana—are fully integrated.

Table IV shows the interactions among the steel industry and selected other industries. Columns 1 and 2 present the sale of steel from the standpoints of both the steel and the named industries. Columns 3 and 4 look at the purchases by the steel industry on the same bases. Column 5 examines the total requirements needed from other industries per unit of production of steel, and Column 6 shows the contribution of the steel industry to the total requirements of the named industries.

Imports and exports.[1] Since 1954, imports of iron and steel have been growing at four times the rate of total merchandise imports. Nationwide steel strikes in the U.S. and favorable prices of imported steel have been the principal reasons for this increase.

Growth of imports of steel mill products has come in sharp spurts. Although occasioned by temporary conditions, these spurts were followed by only moderate declines, leaving a substantial net rise. For example, in 1956 (a year that included a 36-day strike in the steel industry), imports of steel products jumped to

[1] Comparison of the rates of change for both imports and exports has been limited to 1954-64. As a result of World War II, the 1947-54 period was marked by heavy exports from the U.S., but few to the U.S.

$201 million, up from $127 million in 1955; volume then eased a little to $197 million in 1957. Again, in 1959 (a year that included a 116-day strike), steel imports climbed to $521 million. The following year, steel imports receded to $442 million but were still twice as high as in the year preceding the long strike. The trend continues; for example, imports of steel mill products in the first quarter of 1965 were 33 per cent higher than in the same period in 1964.

Having once become accustomed to buying foreign steel when domestic steel was not available, steel users in the U.S. have tended to continue buying steel mill products of foreign countries when they find no difference in quality and when there is a distinct price advantage. In the past, wire and wire products, as well as welded pipe and tubing, have been the major steel imports. During the current inventory building, imports have also included sheet steel in relatively large amounts. If buyers are sufficiently satisfied with both the price and quality of foreign sheet steel, they may continue to buy that item abroad after the present tight supply situation has eased.

At the same time that steel imports have been growing vigorously, exports of steel mill products from the United States have been declining. Between 1954 and 1964, exports of iron and steel declined at an average annual rate of 0.7 per cent; in contrast, total merchandise exports (less military materials) *increased* at an average annual rate of 5.5 per cent. Moreover, the decline in exports of iron and steel probably would have been even greater in recent years except for increased tie-ins between U.S. foreign aid and foreign purchases of American goods.

Both the increase in imports and the decline in exports of American steel mill products since 1954 have reflected the expansion of the iron and steel industry in other countries, chiefly in Japan and the Common Market nations. During the 1950's, continued growth in capacity and advancement in technology of the steel industry in these nations made it possible for them to fulfill domestic requirements for steel and to seek markets outside their own

TABLE IV

STEEL AND SELECTED OTHER INDUSTRIES[a]

	Steel Sales as % of Total Output of Steel Industry	Purchases of Steel as % of Total Output of Named Industries	Purchases by Steel Industry as % of Total Inputs of Steel Industry	Purchases by Steel Industry as % of Total Output of Named Industries	Requirements from Other Industries per Dollar of Steel Production	Steel Costs per Dollar of Sales of Named Industries
Primary iron & steel manufacturing	20.9%[b]	22.7%[b]	22.7%	22.7%	$1.32	$1.32
New construction	11.5	4.2	0	0	0	0.11
Motor vehicles & equipment	10.3	8.5	0.2	0	0.01	0.20
Heating, plumbing, & structural metal products	9.4	23.8	0.2	0	0.01	0.36
Metal containers	4.7	43.9	0	0	c	0.60
Other fabricated metal products	4.2	19.3	1.7	4.6	0.03	0.29
Stampings, screw machine products, & bolts	3.4	19.9	0.6	3.1	0.01	0.30
Construction, mining, & oil field machinery	2.4	15.4	0.1	0	0.01	0.26
Other transportation equipment	2.2	11.7	0.1	0	c	0.22
Aircraft & parts	2.1	3.2	c	0	c	0.09
Farm machinery & equipment	1.9	14.3	0.1	0	c	0.25
General industrial machinery & equipment	1.9	10.6	0.3	1.3	0.01	0.20
Electrical industrial equipment & apparatus	1.5	5.7	0.4	1.6	0.01	0.11
Household appliances	1.4	7.6	c	0	c	0.16
Metalworking machinery & equipment	1.3	7.5	0.7	3.1	0.01	0.15
Engines & turbines	1.2	10.1	c	0	c	0.20
Machine shop products	0.6	7.9	0.7	8.8	0.01	0.14
Chemicals & selected chemical products	0.5	0.6	1.0	1.4	0.03	0.03
Nonferrous metal ores mining	0.3	3.9	c	0.5	0.01	0.07
Stone & clay products	0.2	0.2	1.5	3.9	0.03	0.02
Iron & ferroalloy ores mining	0.1	1.5	5.4	84.0	0.08	0.03
Coal mining	0.1	0.8	2.6	18.4	0.04	0.04
Primary nonferrous metal manufacturing	0.1	1.2	1.6	2.7	0.04	0.05
Petroleum refining & related industries	c	c	0.8	0.9	0.02	0.01

[a]Source: "The Interindustry Structure of the United States, a Report on the 1958 Input-Output Study," *Survey of Current Business* (November, 1964), U.S. Department of Commerce, Office of Business Economics.

[b]Conceptually, the direct purchases by an industry of its own output should equal the industry's direct sales to itself. However, the figures vary slightly because of computational procedures.

[c]Negligible.

borders as well. In addition, relatively lower wages, newer and more efficient equipment, and more flexible export pricing policies have frequently enabled foreign mills to sell steel at lower prices than those quoted by U.S. steel companies. In short, expansion of the iron and steel industry abroad has allowed the steel industries to supply their domestic needs, compete against U.S. steel exporters for other foreign markets, and take an increasingly larger share of the U.S. steel market.

Corporate profits. The iron and steel industry exhibited some growth in profits during the 1947-64 period, but much less than was achieved by all manufacturing industries as a group. In dollar amount of corporate profits after taxes, the average annual rate of increase achieved by iron and steel firms was 1.6 per cent for the 17-year period, as compared with 4.1 per cent of all manufacturing. Similarly, the trend of profits expressed as a per cent of assets has been less favorable for iron and steel companies than for all manufacturing firms. For both groups the ratio of profits to assets has declined, but the rate of decline has been steeper for iron and steel than for all manufacturing.

Using either of these measurements of profits, the average annual rate of change for iron and steel in the 1949-54 period matched the rate of change for all manufacturing, whereas divergent rates of change showed up in the 1954-64 period. The profit trend in iron and steel began to deviate from that of all manufacturing in 1959, and its altered course became more noticeable in succeeding years.

In seeking a reason for this, we must consider the level of production, depreciation costs, prices, and wages—all of which have had a strong influence on profits. In recent years all manufacturing has had an advantage over iron and steel in at least two of these key factors. Production in all manufacturing has reached a new high every year since 1958, whereas the increases in iron and steel production during that period only represent a recovery of lost ground. Depreciation costs as a per cent of sales have risen faster in the iron

and steel industry than they have in all manufacturing. Proportionately greater investment in new plants and equipment in the iron and steel industry and changes in rules governing depreciation allowances have accounted for part of the greater increases in iron and steel depreciation costs. Relatively less growth in the iron and steel industry has accounted for the remainder of the increase. Some indication of the relative role of depreciation costs in the steel industry is provided in *Table V*.

Summary. It is not necessarily surprising when an industry, particularly one as old as iron and steel, accounts for a smaller proportion of total manufacturing activity over a period of years. New products (e.g., plastics, television sets, detergents) that either substitute for old ones or are a net addition to total production are constantly being introduced. Usually greater growth rates occur in newer products. An older industry need not necessarily decline in relative importance, however, if new uses are found for its products, and if, at the same time, it retains its old markets. The steel industry has lost the overwhelming position it once enjoyed, and, consequently, has assumed a decreasingly important role in the economy since 1947. Not only have there been indications of a lack of innovation in finding new uses for steel, but materials such as aluminum, concrete, plastics, and glass have made inroads into markets for steel products.

The rapid rise in steel prices from 1947 to 1958 undoubtedly was an important factor in the poor showing of steel in the import and export sectors of the economy. It is certain that some substitutions for steel resulted from the sharp price increases.

During the earlier postwar years, both prices and costs rose faster in steel than in all manufacturing. With the leveling off of prices and the continuing rise in costs since 1959, profits at first declined. Gains in production in 1963 and 1964 were enough to reverse the downward plunge of profits and bring about a recovery of some of the ground lost since 1957.

During the 1947-64 period, four recessions, four strikes, and numerous possibilities of

TABLE V

RELATIVE ROLE OF DEPRECIATION COSTS IN THE STEEL INDUSTRY*

Year	Steel Ingot Production (Millions of Tons)	Depreciation Costs (Millions of Dollars)	Depreciation Costs (per Ton)
1949...............	78	$ 329	$ 4.22
1950...............	97	380	3.92
1951...............	105	445	4.23
1952...............	93	519	5.57
1953...............	112	699	6.26
1954...............	88	773	8.75
1955...............	117	832	7.11
1956...............	115	844	7.33
1957...............	113	875	7.76
1958...............	85	806	9.45
1959...............	93	799	8.55
1960...............	99	825	8.31
1961...............	98	863	8.80
1962...............	98	1,069	10.87
1963...............	109	1,144	10.47
1964...............	127	1,224	9.64

*Steel ingot production figures are those published by the American Iron and Steel Institute; depreciation costs are from the Federal Trade Commission and the Securities and Exchange Commission.

strikes perpetuated the feast and famine pattern of demand for steel that has always characterized the industry. If a semblance of production stability could be achieved, the showing of the steel industry would improve. During periods of inventory building by steel consumers, old and inefficient steelmaking equipment is brought back into use. Later, while these high-cost steel stocks are being liquidated, the newer and more efficient equipment sits idle.

The possibility of the iron and steel industry improving its relative position in the economy appears to rest on success in making costs and prices competitive, and success in finding new applications for steel.

THE PETROLEUM INDUSTRY

Petroleum, more than any other manufacturing industry of the United States, has not only a national but an international outlook. American refineries account for more than half the total output of refined petroleum products. Although all but a few states have refineries, about 90 per cent of the total capacity is in ten states: Texas, California, Pennsylvania, New Jersey, Illinois, Indiana, Oklahoma, Massachusetts, Kansas, and Ohio (Fig. 4-9).

Petrochemicals. Of the many dramatic changes in technology, few can be more significant than the ever-widening application of chemical science to petroleum. Chemical derivatives of oil and gas are becoming increasingly important in meeting not only our transportation requirements, but also the basic physical needs of food, clothing, and shelter.

At first, refiners gave little thought to changing the chemical structure of crude oil. For the most part, their refining was simple distillation to separate the different fractions—the main commercial fraction then being kerosene for lamp oil. Much later, when gasoline was suddenly in great demand, pressure cracking and thermal cracking techniques were developed,

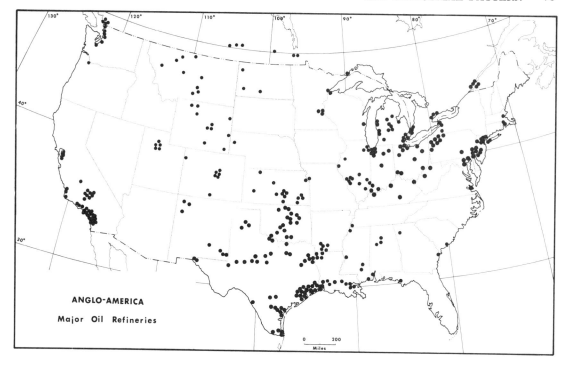

FIGURE 4-9.

the latter employing the principle of continuous flow. Then came the revolutionary process of catalytic cracking, along with other basic chemical processes, such as polymerization, hydrogenation, and alkylation. All of these techniques were developed to meet the insistent, growing demand for high-performance fuels required for vehicles and aircraft.

In the highest-quality motor gasoline today, only about 20 per cent of the molecules are distilled from crude oil without changing. The other 80 per cent are synthetic. In addition, this gasoline contains many chemical additives, none of which occurs naturally in petroleum. Today's jet engine lubricating oils, although derived from petroleum, are 100 per cent synthetic. Indeed, it would not be much of an exaggeration to describe modern oil refining as a specialized chemical industry—one that happens to concentrate on making fuels, and for this purpose, puts petroleum hydrocarbons through various chemical reactions at a rate of several hundred million tons a year.

Oil companies now have chemical sales in the United States approaching $3 billion a year. Still bigger petrochemical sales are being made by chemical companies that buy the raw materials they need from the oil industry. Over 200 American firms now use petroleum and its derivatives to make chemicals.

The petrochemical business has inherited vitally important features from the oil industry, among them the processes used. Without these large-scale processes and the economics they make possible, the oil companies would scarcely have been able to enter the chemicals field in any substantial way. The chemical industry itself, including petrochemicals, would not be the fourth largest industry in the noncommunist world. It certainly would not have spread, as it has begun to in recent years, beyond the highly industrialized countries into less developed areas. There, in many cases, the first chemical manufacturing facilities of any kind are those associated with oil refineries.

THE FOOD PROCESSING INDUSTRIES

Food is by far the largest single item in the American family budget, taking over a fifth of all consumer expenditures after taxes. In 1967 the nation's retail food bill came to more than $100 billion. In one way or another, the task of keeping people fed involves about 15 per cent of the productive activity of the whole economy. Based on value of products shipped and number of establishments, the food industry outranks all others (*Fig. 4-10*). On the basis of aggregate value added, it is near the top, and the number of workers employed represents almost 10 per cent of the workers engaged in all manufacturing.

Food processing has many purposes. Perishable foods are converted into stabilized products that can be stored for extended periods of time. Examples of the basic preserving processes are canning, freezing, dehydrating, and ionizing radiation. Processing can also change foods into new or more usable forms. Examples include wine making, flour milling, olive brining, oil extracting, and butter churning.

Flour milling. Of the 1,538 pounds of food consumed annually per capita in the United States, 159 pounds, or slightly more than 10 per cent, are represented by flour and grain products. Flour milled from wheat is the most important component and accounts for 127 pounds.

The conversion of wheat into flour is one of the simplest manufacturing operations and is almost wholly mechanical. The simplicity of the task results in a low value added. Only 31,000 employees work in the industry, and their wages total $121 million. The value of products shipped amounts to about $2 billion, of which only 18 per cent represents value added. The three traditional flour-milling centers—Minneapolis, Buffalo, and Kansas City—are still the leaders (*Fig. 4-11*).

Meat and poultry. The U.S. meat and poultry industries are the world's largest, with a yearly output of over 31 billion pounds of meat and 10 billion pounds of poultry. Americans eat an average of more than 174 pounds of meat and more than 38 pounds of poultry per capita a year. About 40 per cent of American food dollars go for meat and poultry, the leading items in family food budgets.

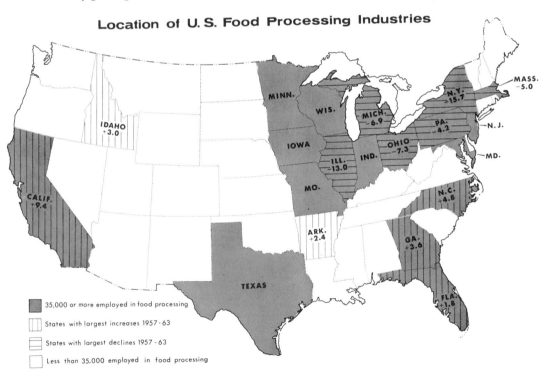

Location of U. S. Food Processing Industries

35,000 or more employed in food processing

States with largest increases 1957-63

States with largest declines 1957-63

Less than 35,000 employed in food processing

FIGURE 4-10.

The meat-packing industry includes more than 2,000 plants dispersed over the entire country. The large national packers—Swift, Armour, Wilson, and Cudahy—at one time did more than half of the total business, but as a result of the entry of new firms and the expansion of existing firms during World War II, the "Big Four's" share of the market has declined. Cudahy now ranks eighth among U.S. meat-packing companies in terms of total sales. Swift is the largest unit in the industry, operating about 50 meat-packing plants, 275 distributing houses, over 100 dairy and poultry plants, and a number of oil mills.

In addition to national packers, there are also regional and local packing houses. Some of the better known regional packers include Morrell, Rath, Hormel, and Hygrade (*Fig. 4-12*).

In spite of the importance of its products in the national diet, the industry is in a precarious position. Its livestock supply comes from millions of producers; the flow is beyond its control, and the costs are subject to wide fluctuations. Moreover, most of its products are perishable and must be sold quickly.

The price paid for livestock is determined by supply-and-demand conditions. Meat packers must compete not only with other packers in the same area, but also with packers in other areas. Seasonal competition is increasing as the industry decentralizes and more packing houses are established nearer the source of supply.

Eggs, poultry, dairy products, and the fats and oils provided by other industries—notably cottonseed and soybean oil products—all offer stiff competition to the meat packers. Price and personal income are the principal factors that determine the position of the meat industry's products against these substitutes, although supply does play a part. The packing industry must maintain a greater supply of its products in the stores, or its share of the market will shrink.

Vegetable and fruit canning. Production of canned foods has increased 20 times since the turn of the century, a gain matched by few U.S. industries. Canning today is a multi-

million dollar industry, widely distributed throughout the U.S. and its territories, and producing a wide variety of canned fruits, vegetables, juices, soups, and specialty products, in both cans and glass containers.

Geographically, the U.S. canning industry has plants in every state but Nevada (*Fig. 4-13*). A considerable degree of localization exists, of course, according to product; for as

ANGLO-AMERICA
Major Flour-milling Centers

FIGURE 4-11.

FIGURE 4-12.

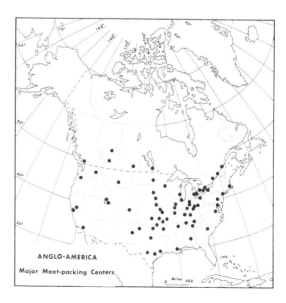

ANGLO-AMERICA
Major Meat-packing Centers

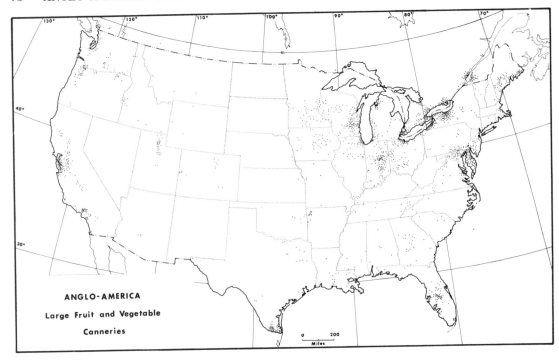

ANGLO-AMERICA

Large Fruit and Vegetable

Canneries

FIGURE 4-13.

the industry grew, its various branches tended to concentrate in regions where soil and climatic conditions were most favorable for the production of a particular product or group of products. As a result, the canning of an item may be confined to certain localities. On the other hand, some products are canned in many areas. Corn, for example, is canned in 30 states, and peas in 27. Even in this case, however, over half of the peas and corn grown and canned in the U.S. come from one general region—a rectangular area that includes southeastern Minnesota and the bottom half of Wisconsin.

California is the leading canning state, with about 250 canneries being supplied by 700 square miles of land devoted to fruits and vegetables. It accounts for about half of the total national tonnage of processed fruits and about 36 per cent of the nation's processed vegetables. The San Francisco Bay area leads, with 75 canneries that process chiefly apricots, peaches, pears, asparagus, tomatoes, spinach, and both green and wax beans.

The Atlantic Coastal Plain, including New York City and Baltimore, is one of the world's leading vegetable canning areas. Tomatoes, sweet corn, and peas that are grown in Delaware, Maryland, and New Jersey are processed in some 400 canneries in the area.

Canning is a highly seasonal industry; therefore, unlike most industries, it has a small permanent work force. In most areas, women make up the largest portion of the labor force, accounting for 50 to 68 per cent of the total number of workers. Casual laborers, part-time workers, and those employed in other seasonal occupations, such as farm workers, comprise the rest of the labor force.

In addition to the regular and seasonal employees, a warehouse force works throughout the year in almost all canneries to take care of labeling the cans and shipping them to local distributors, and, in the case of large plants, to destinations all over the world.

Frozen foods. Like the canning industry, the frozen food industry is predominantly small-scale. As in canning, California leads in volume of frozen food production, contributing more than 60 per cent of the total U.S. frozen pack of vegetables and deciduous fruits. The greatest concentration of freezer plants in California is in the Santa Clara, Pajaro, and Salinas Valleys. Other important areas in California are Los Angeles, Anaheim, and Santa Barbara in the southern coastal area, and Fresno, Modesto, and Sacramento in the Central Valley.

The Pacific Northwest nurtured the frozen food industry almost from its birth, beginning with some experimental packs in 1917. For many years the area produced over half the national supply of frozen food. Today the region accounts for about two-fifths of the national total. It is a leading processing region for strawberries, red raspberries, blackberries, peas, green beans, and corn. The greatest concentration of plants is to be found along Puget Sound and the irrigated areas around Ellensburg, Grandview, Prosser, and Walla Walla in Washington, and Oregon's Willamette Valley.

METAL FABRICATING INDUSTRIES

The process by which iron, steel, copper, aluminum, and other metals are converted into finished products is known as metal fabrication. The first step is to shape raw materials as they come from refining furnaces. This is done by rolling, casting, and hammering. But these processes give only crudely-shaped castings or forgings, or rolled stock such as sheets, plates, rods, and bars. For most purposes, metal parts must be accurately and precisely shaped. This requires machine tools to do drilling, boring, planing, grinding, turning, milling, and shearing or pressing.

There are more than 200 major types of machine tools, and the industry is unique in that it makes not only the machine tools used in all the metal fabricating industries, but also the machine tools that make the machine tools. The industry consists of some 500 manufacturers, heavily concentrated in Ohio, Michigan, Illinois, and southern New England. The Lower Great Lakes area dominates, with about 60 per cent of the national output. Many of the firms are small, and companies with less than 1,000 workers account for almost 75 per cent of the total United States machine tool output (*Fig. 4-14*).

FIGURE 4-14.

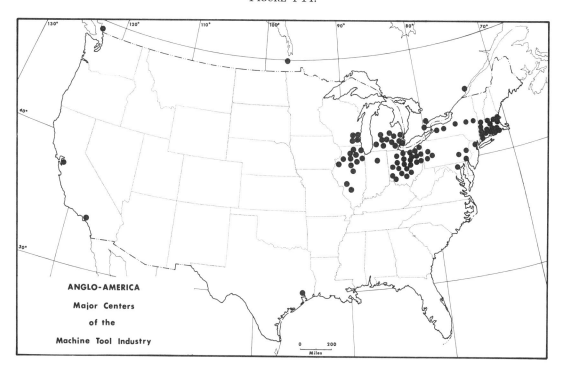

ANGLO-AMERICA

Major Centers

of the

Machine Tool Industry

The final step in the fabrication of metal products is the assembly. An outstanding example of an assembly industry is the automotive industry, which is also the classic example of mass production. It converts a vast stream of diversified raw materials into highly standardized products for sale at prices that yield high wages to employees, big dividends to stockholders, and, apparently, satisfactory value to its customers. The industry is concentrated primarily in the Lower Great Lakes area, with Detroit as its center. Outstanding automotive centers besides Detroit are Flint, Lansing, and Pontiac, Michigan; Kenosha, Wisconsin; and Toledo, Ohio (*Fig. 4-15*).

Other important assembly industries include agricultural implements and farm tractors, concentrated in the Lower Great Lakes area and in California; aircraft assembly—military, commercial, and private planes—mostly located west of the Mississippi River, with California, Texas, and Washington the leading states; and shipbuilding on the Great Lakes and the Atlantic, Gulf, and Pacific Coasts, with the chief centers on New York Harbor, the Delaware River, and Chesapeake Bay. (In Part II, individual manufacturing industries are treated in greater detail along with the regions they dominate.)

Manufacturing in Canada

Canada is one of the world's leading industrial nations. About 30 per cent of Canada's national income is derived from manufacturing. The pulp and paper, nonferrous metal smelting and refining, petroleum products, food processing, and sawmilling industries all use domestic raw materials; but the machinery, motor vehicles, aircraft, rubber, textiles and clothing, and electrical apparatus industries depend chiefly on imported raw or semi-manufactured materials. All but 6 per cent of the manufactured goods are for home consumption. Although manufacturing has spread rapidly in the postwar period into the Prairie Provinces and British Columbia, Quebec and Ontario are still the prime industrial areas. Quebec predominates in the pulp and paper, aluminum, textile and

FIGURE 4-15.

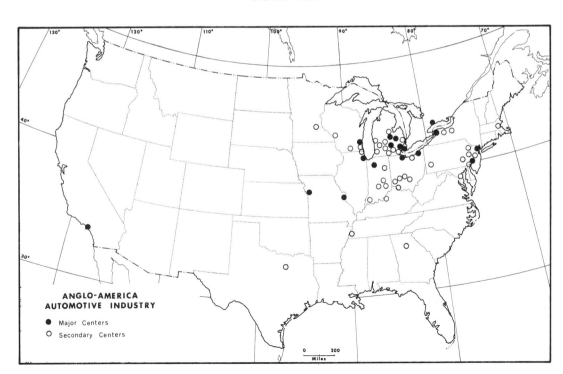

ANGLO-AMERICA
AUTOMOTIVE INDUSTRY

● Major Centers
○ Secondary Centers

TABLE VI

Indexes of Volume of Manufacturing Production for Major Canadian Industry Groups, 1946-64

(Ranked according to 1964 percentage increase over 1949; 1949 = 100)

Industry Group	1946	1954	1959	1960	1961	1962	1963	1964
Products of petroleum and coal	74.3	165.0	241.5	250.6	258.8	272.8	296.0	304.2
Chemical products	87.0	152.1	208.4	219.7	222.1	233.2	249.1	279.0
Nonmetallic mineral products	72.0	146.1	223.2	210.9	220.2	240.9	243.0	277.6
Miscellaneous manufacturing industries	80.2	134.3	183.2	191.6	213.0	237.2	246.2	261.9
Electrical apparatus and supplies	67.7	151.7	184.8	180.2	182.6	212.9	223.5	239.2
Tobacco products	90.6	124.7	179.9	182.0	193.6	203.7	207.7	214.0
Rubber products	89.5	119.2	161.1	143.3	145.7	167.6	190.5	213.8
Transportation equipment[a]	80.6	137.3	131.5	130.0	129.8	156.7	181.4	198.5
Iron and steel products	80.8	106.2	147.2	137.3	139.4	152.1	161.8	182.4
Paper products	81.0	124.1	144.7	148.4	153.4	159.1	164.3	179.0
Food and beverage products	98.0	120.6	147.6	150.2	154.2	158.9	162.1	174.1
Textile products	88.7	94.3	124.4	122.5	134.6	146.6	159.5	172.2
Wood products	86.8	124.2	136.6	136.0	139.6	151.5	159.0	165.1
Printing, publishing, and allied industries	76.9	121.6	143.2	146.5	148.2	154.0	156.7	164.6
Nonferrous metal products[a]	81.8	117.0	134.7	148.3	147.6	148.9	148.8	162.0
Clothing products	95.3	108.9	113.1	107.9	107.1	111.0	137.0[b]	135.8[b]
Leather products	124.0	100.2	120.3	111.8	123.8	126.7	127.0	130.9
Nondurable manufactures	89.8	121.2	150.1	151.8	157.0	164.8	172.2	184.5
Durable manufactures	79.9	124.8	149.5	146.4	148.4	165.0	175.9	192.7
All Manufactures	85.2	122.9	149.8	149.3	153.0	164.9	173.9	188.2

[a]Durable manufactures; other groups are nondurable.
[b]Not comparable with earlier years.

clothing, and railroad rolling stock industries. Montreal is the top industrial center, with Toronto a close second (*see Fig. 4-1*).

Ontario, a treasure-house of natural resources, is the most industrialized province, producing annually about half of the manufactured goods. All of the major industries are represented here, including automobiles, agricultural implements, tobacco processing, and iron and steel.

The primary iron and steel industry of Canada is concentrated largely in three districts: (1) the western end of Lake Ontario (Hamilton, Port Colborne, and Welland); (2) Sault Ste. Marie, Ontario; and (3) Sydney, Nova Scotia. These three centers have all the by-product coke ovens operated by the iron and steel companies, all the blast furnaces, and all the open-hearth, Bessemer, and oxygen steel converters (*see Fig. 4-8*).

VOLUME OF PRODUCTION

Since manufacturers' selling prices change, and since production from other industries (and countries) is embodied in Canadian factory shipments, a measure of fluctuations and long-term growth in the physical volume of production within the Canadian manufacturing industry itself is desirable. Such a measure of volume, or "real" domestic production, is provided by the index of manufacturing production. This index differs from current statistics on the gross value of factory output in two important ways besides the exclusion of price change: it uses the 1948 rather than the 1960 standard industrial classification, and it is designed to represent net production. Although a revision is under way, because of their central importance to the study of Canadian manufacturing, the unrevised indexes are shown for selected years in *Table VI*.

plants went up 49 per cent between 1960 and 1966, an average annual gain of almost 7 per cent. In sharp contrast, the growth rate in the preceding six years, 1954-1960, averaged 4 per cent a year, about in line with the long-term trend. In short, the nation's industrial output has been growing one and one-half times faster between 1960 and 1966 than previously.

Industrial prospects for the next decade or two are difficult to grasp in terms of past experience, for science and technology are in the midst of a great transition. For the moment, at least, no big individual developments like the computer or television appear to be on the horizon. Instead, the emphasis of invention seems to be on ideas, techniques, and systems rather than on patented devices.

As yet, this dramatic onrush of accumulating technology has barely touched many older industries, and these remain yawning areas for redevelopment. A good deal of technology is already at hand to do the job; the problem is to overcome social, political, and economic obstructions to change.

Industry is changing through systems management—putting all the individual developments, new devices, and techniques together. Lockheed is an outstanding example of the new commitment. In 1964 it made the decision that its strongest capabilities led through systems analysis, computers, electronics, and mathematics to the design of information storage and retrieval systems.

Technically feasible in the forseeable future is a variety of great central-computer utilities, each available to home or office consoles by simply dialing. These would encompass such things as banking and credit, theater and plane reservations, mail order and shopping services, library and reference services, and possibly even books, magazines, and the daily newspaper.

Outlook for Anglo-America

The rise of U.S. industrial production between 1960 and 1966 was little short of phenomenal. The total output of the nation's factories, mines, gas and oil refineries, and power

Selected References

ADAMS, WALTER, *The Structure of American Industry*, New York: The Macmillan Company, 1950.

Airov, Joseph, *The Location of the Synthetic Fiber Industry*, New York: John Wiley & Sons, Inc., 1959.

Alexandersson, Gunnar, "Changes in the Location Pattern of the Anglo-American Steel Industry: 1948-1959," *Economic Geography*, Vol. 37, April, 1961, pp. 95–114.

Boas, Charles W., "Locational Patterns of American Automobile Assembly Plants," *Economic Geography*, Vol. 37, July, 1961, pp. 218–230.

Edwards, Courtnay, "The Battle of the Baby Cars," *Steel Review*, Vol. 17, January, 1960, pp. 34–39.

Fowler, B. B., *Men, Meat and Miracles*, New York: Julian Messner, 1952.

Fuchs, Victor, *Changes in the Location of American Industry, 1929-1956*, Cambridge, Mass.: Harvard University Press, 1962.

Glover, J. G., and Cornell, W. B., *The Development of American Industries* (3rd ed.), Englewood Cliffs, N. J.: Prentice-Hall, Inc., 1951.

Harris, Chauncy D., "The Market as a Factor in the Localization of Industry in the United States," *Annals of the Association of American Geographers*, Vol. 44, December, 1954, pp. 315–348.

Hess, Katherine P., *Textile Fibers and Their Use*, Philadelphia: J. B. Lippincott Co., 1958.

Holmes, Charles H., "Factors Affecting Development of the Steel Industry in Intermountain America," *The Journal of Geography*, Vol. 58, January, 1959, pp. 20–31.

Kerr, Donald, "The Geography of the Canadian Iron and Steel Industry," *Economic Geography*, Vol. 35, April, 1959, pp. 151–163.

Lougheed, W. F., *Secondary Manufacturing Industry in the Canadian Economy*, Toronto: Baxter Publishing Co., 1961.

Pollock, Eric, "Prospects for the Motor Industry," *Steel Review*, Vol. 26, April, 1962, pp. 16–25.

Pred, Allan, "The Concentration of High-value-added Manufacturing," *Economic Geography*, Vol. 41, April, 1965, pp. 108–132.

———, "The Intrametropolitan Location of American Manufacturing," *Annals of the Association of American Geographers*, Vol. 54, June, 1964, pp. 165–180.

———, "Manufacturing in the American Mercantile City: 1800-1840," *ibid.*, Vol. 56, June, 1966, pp. 307–338.

———, "Toward a Typology of Manufacturing Flows," *The Geographical Review*, Vol. 44, January, 1964, pp. 65–84.

Rae, John B., *American Automobile Manufacturers: The First Forty Years*, Philadelphia: Chilton Book Co., 1959.

Reinemann, Martin W., "The Pattern and Distribution of Manufacturing in the Chicago Area," *Economic Geography*, Vol. 36, April, 1960, pp. 139–144.

Robinson, N. M., *New Industrial Towns in Canada's Resource Frontier*, Chicago: University of Chicago Press, 1962.

Rodgers, Allan, "Some Aspects of Industrial Diversification in the United States," *Economic Geography*, Vol. 33, January, 1957, pp. 16–30.

Taylor, F. Sherwood, *A History of Industrial Chemistry*, New York: Abelard-Schuman, Ltd., 1957.

Wallace, William H., "Merrimack Valley Manufacturing: Past and Present," *Economic Geography*, Vol. 37, October, 1961, pp. 283–308.

Zelinsky, Wilbur, "Has American Industry Been Decentralizing?" *Economic Geography*, Vol. 38, July, 1962, pp. 251–269.

5 *The Urban Pattern*

Man by nature is gregarious. His dependence on his fellows for mutual defense and companionship leads to settlement. People, however, are unevenly distributed, with some living on widely dispersed farms and others clustering together in rural settlements. These settlements eventually become hamlets, and, in turn, may evolve into villages, towns and cities. It is possible to live under conditions of dispersed habitation only when there is no threat of danger too great to be overcome by the individual or his family.

Origins

The origin of the urban agglomeration as a form of human settlement is not precisely known. The name "city" is derived from a Greek root that signified *state* more than *city*. The modern meaning of the term has risen from the fact that the ancient states were very similar in territory and character to the present concept of a city.

In medieval times, Europeans united for defense purposes in settlement agglomerations. They owed allegiance to professional warriors who defended the settlement against aggression. When the threat of war was removed, individuals would establish farms, often located at some distance from towns and forti-

fied points. This is now a common practice on newly settled lands of the world.

Often the establishment of a farm or two in a favorable location attracts other farmers or ranchers, and a settlement node begins to form. Sometimes the beginnings of settlement are vague, perhaps consisting of loosely related farms belonging to members of the same family. It is possible to find settlement names attached to a hamlet made up of only two or three farmhouses. From these beginnings an agglomeration occurs. Soon village functions may be noted, such as fire protection, legal authority, and a voting precinct. Later, when population has increased, health protection, sewage disposal, village officials, community recreation, public libraries, hospitals, post offices, and other necessary components of settled life will be found.

Early American hamlet and village settlements were frequently haphazard in their growth. Narrow streets or alleys, winding roads, and relatively small property holdings were common. Often, the village streets evolved along unplanned and unsurveyed roads, providing different physical characteristics for the towns (*Fig. 5-1*).

Crossroads or road junctions were typical places where a village might form. A village that was situated at a road fork became y-shaped in its major pattern. Other villages took on a circular pattern; the principal feature was a street encircling the whole settlement. Another common type was the simple "string town." It consisted of two long rows of houses facing each other on either side of a main street. Still another pattern was circular in nature and centered upon a village square, or "common." Towns established by the colonists in New England were often in this pattern. Another, less-used pattern was the radial town. These towns represent a concentration of routes of travel and are found occasionally among older American settlements.

Urbanization

The United States Bureau of Census defines the term "urban" as comprising all persons living in:

1. Places of 2,500 inhabitants or more that are incorporated as cities, boroughs, villages, and towns (except towns in New England, New York, and Wisconsin).
2. The densely settled urban fringe, whether incorporated or unincorporated, of urbanized areas.

3. Towns in New England and townships in New Jersey and Pennsylvania that contain no incorporated municipalities as subdivisions and have either 25,000 inhabitants or more, or a population of 2,500 to 25,000 and a density of 1,500 persons or more per square mile.
4. Counties in states other than New England, New Jersey, and Pennsylvania that have no incorporated municipalities within their boundaries and have a density of 1,500 persons or more per square mile.
5. Unincorporated places of 2,500 inhabitants or more.

Urbanized areas are divided into the central city, or cities, and contiguous areas constituting the urban fringe. All persons residing in this urbanized area are included in the urban population.

FORM

The form of any urban organism depends upon a number of factors, of which the following are significant: (1) The character of the site, e.g., hilly, level, waterfront, etc.; (2) the

FIGURE 5-1. *Settlement patterns of early American communities.*

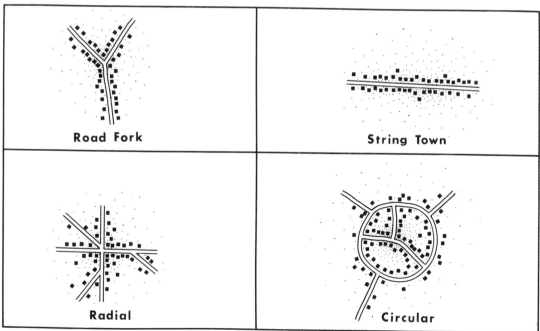

character of the functions carried on, e.g., industrial, commercial, residential, recreational, political, institutional, etc.; (3) the type of transportation available, e.g., rapid transit, expressway, public carrier, private carrier; (4) the stage of the ecological cycle; (5) the nature of the population, e.g., density, level of cultural attainment, mores, social institutions; (6) the type of government; (7) the climate; and (8) the technology of building and the materials used.

Some characteristic urban forms have emerged over the years. Washington, D.C. is a good example of a simple *radial*, or *stelliform*, pattern (*Fig. 5-2*). Chicago, Cleveland, and Buffalo are *crescentic*, or *arcuate*, in design (*Fig. 5-3*). Seattle is an *isthmian* city (*Fig. 5-4*). New York and Los Angeles are *clustered* (*Fig. 5-5*), while Minneapolis-St. Paul and St. Louis-East St. Louis are *twin cities* (*Fig. 5-6*). The San Francisco Bay Area is a notable example of a *perithalassic* urban complex—one built around a body of water (*Fig. 5-7*).

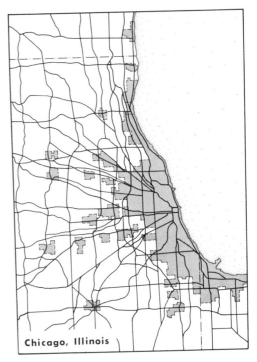

Chicago, Illinois

FIGURE 5-3.

TRENDS IN URBAN GROWTH

When the first census of the United States was taken in 1790, 95 per cent of the population lived in rural places of fewer than 2,500 persons. There were only 24 urban places in the nation, only 2 of which had populations in excess of 25,000. Only 1 in 20 inhabitants was classified as urban; in 1960, 7 out of 10 persons were so classified.

It was not until the nineteenth century that mankind achieved the level of technological development and social organization that permitted the relatively widespread appearance of very large cities. In the year 1800, for example, only six cities in Europe—London, Paris, Vienna, Moscow, St. Petersburg (Leningrad), and Constantinople (Istanbul)—had populations exceeding 200,000 inhabitants. During this period there were no cities in the United States anywhere near that size. Philadelphia, the largest city, had 69,000 people; New York, 60,000; Baltimore, 26,000; Boston, 25,000; Charleston, South Carolina, 20,000; Richmond, Virginia, 10,000. Even in 1840, New York City had less than 500,000 people. The city procured its water supply from town pumps. Pigs were reared in Central Park and goats were pastured in the vicinity of present-day Grant's tomb and Columbia University.

FIGURE 5-2.

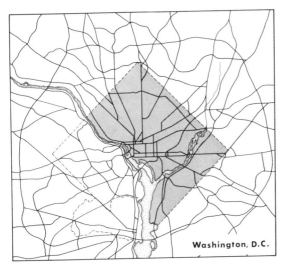

Washington, D.C.

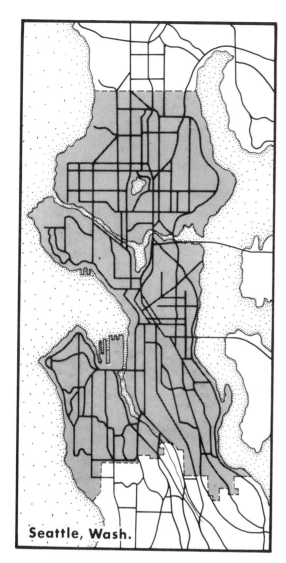

Seattle, Wash.

FIGURE 5-4.

FIGURE 5-6.

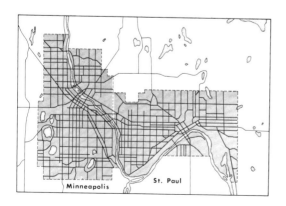

Minneapolis   St. Paul

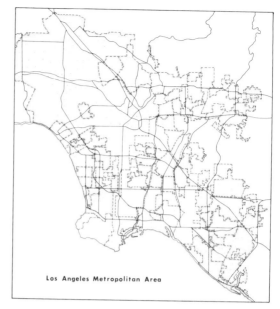

Los Angeles Metropolitan Area

FIGURE 5-5.

FIGURE 5-7.

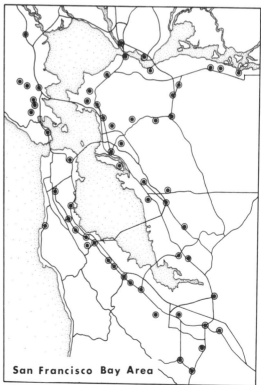

San Francisco Bay Area

◉ Cities of 5,000 or more population

In 1900 there were only five metropolitan areas in the United States having a million or more persons. These areas contained about 16 per cent of the total population. By 1960 there were 24 such areas in which 34 per cent of the nation's population resided. Over the first 60 years of the century, then, total population increased about two and a half times, urban population increased almost fourfold, and large metropolitan area population increased fivefold.

During this period, the United States changed from a predominantly rural to a predominantly urban nation. At the turn of the century, about 40 per cent of the population was urban; by 1920, 51.2 per cent; and in 1960, 70 per cent (*Fig. 5-8*). It will not be until the end of this decade, 1970, that the United States will have completed its first half century as an urban nation. All signs point to a continued growth of cities and larger urban proportions of a larger total population. By 1980, urban population may represent 75 per cent of the total; by 2000, 80 per cent.

Standard Metropolitan Statistical Areas

It has long been recognized that for many types of analysis it is necessary to consider the entire population in and around a city as a unit, because it forms an integrated economic and social system. To permit all federal statistical agencies to utilize the same areas for the publication of general-purpose statistics, the Bureau of the Budget has established "standard metropolitan statistical areas" (SMSA's). Every city of 50,000 inhabitants or more according to the 1960 Census of Population is included in an SMSA (*Fig. 5-9*).

An individual standard metropolitan statistical area has two requirements: first, a city or cities of specified population to constitute the central city and to identify the county in which it is located as the central county; and, second, economic and social relationships with contiguous counties that are metropolitan in character, so that the periphery of the specific metropolitan area may be determined.[1]

Each standard metropolitan statistical area must include at least one city with 50,000 inhabitants or more, or two cities having contiguous boundaries and constituting, for general economic and social purposes, a single community with a combined population of at least 50,000, the smaller of which must have a population of at least 15,000. If two or more adjacent counties each have a city of 50,000 inhabitants or more and the cities are within 20 miles of each other (city limits to city

Trends in U.S. Population

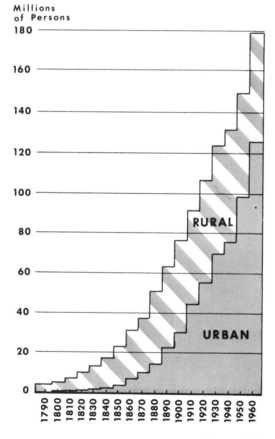

Millions
of Persons

RURAL

URBAN

1790 1800 1810 1820 1830 1840 1850 1860 1870 1880 1890 1900 1910 1920 1930 1940 1950 1960

FIGURE 5-8.

[1] Central cities are those appearing in the standard metropolitan statistical area title. A contiguous county either adjoins the county or counties containing the largest city in the area, or adjoins an intermediate county integrated with the central county. There is no limit to the number of tiers of outlying metropolitan counties so long as all other criteria are met.

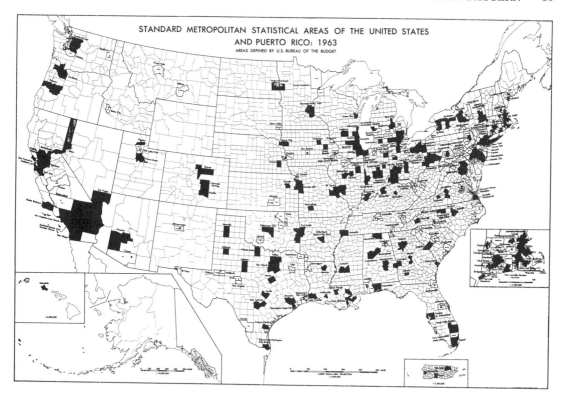

STANDARD METROPOLITAN STATISTICAL AREAS OF THE UNITED STATES
AND PUERTO RICO: 1963
AREAS DEFINED BY U.S. BUREAU OF THE BUDGET

FIGURE 5-9.

limits), they are included in the same area unless there is definite evidence that the two cities are not economically and socially integrated. Standard metropolitan statistical areas may cross state lines.

"Standard consolidated areas" are contiguous standard metropolitan statistical areas. Only two were delineated in the 1960 Census, one for New York-northwestern New Jersey and the other for Chicago-northwestern Indiana.

Growth of Cities

Anglo-America today is a land of many great cities. This persistent trend toward urbanization is a result of many factors, including: (1) a favorable environmental setting, (2) a highly developed technology, (3) a social organization conducive to urban-industrial life, and (4) a superabundance of natural wealth favorably located with respect to international trade. As mentioned in Chapter 3, no other area in the world, save perhaps the Soviet Union, rests on such a firm foundation of natural resources—iron, coal, petroleum, forests, water, fertile soil, vegetation, wildlife, and favorable climate. When the American people began to exploit the natural wealth, the result was an expansion of agriculture, industry, transportation, and trade, together with the universal concomitant of such expansion—the growth of cities.

Cities have grown in relative importance because there has been a shift in demand from agriculture to services, because the relative importance of raw material locations has decreased, because the manufacturing role of establishments has tended to become more specialized and interrelated, and because larger urban areas generate their own internal forces of growth by providing a wide array of intermediate "inputs" and markets big enough to support more local plants.

Historically, the importance of being close to transportation centers was critical for industry and commerce, and large cities developed at the nodes of the transportation system—where ships put in from sea, where trails crossed a stream, where paths converged upon a mountain pass, where rivers and railroads had their junction points. The truck and the automobile have loosened the bonds of manufacturing plants to these transportation nodes and allowed them to consider locations more distant from the center of urban complexes. In this sense, the tie of manufacturing plants to metropolitan areas has been weakened.

PLANNING

Since the bulk of the American people now live in cities, one would expect the greatest attention to be paid to their planning and development. One would expect them to be constructed, regulated, and designed so as to provide the best possible social environment; but this is not the case. The American city is in a state of chaos, a monument to man's failure to organize for the social good.

Many cities grew up without a plan and, as a result, are wasteful in their incessant change. Residences are built, then torn down to provide space for shopping centers. Districts in many cities have been replaced wholesale by factories. Often the factories are crowded together in an industrial district, which results in bad lighting, air pollution, traffic congestion, fire hazards, high insurance, high rents, and exorbitant taxes. Under such conditions the only way to expand is to build upward or to move out of the city at greater expense.

Congestion makes necessary the construction of parks, wider streets, and boulevards. Then, too, many buildings must be torn down because they are condemned. The end result of the construction is higher taxes. Often a factory or a warehouse springs up in the midst of a residential district. The residence value declines; eventually the area becomes a slum, and social problems result.

The railroad, the streetcar, and the automobile permitted people to live in the suburbs away from the noise and congestion. Since 1920, the downtown districts of most cities have actually lost population. Sometimes even the things for which a city is noted are located in the suburbs, because of cheaper building sites and lower taxes. Many of the automobiles accredited to Detroit are actually made in two suburbs, Highland Park and Hamtramck, for example. Even in an urban setting such as San Francisco more than one-half of the population of the metropolitan area resides on the East Bay shores. In the eastern U.S., several million people live on the New Jersey shore, a part of the metropolitan area of New York City (*Fig. 5-10*).

CENTRAL CORE

The character of its central core still defines the personality of a great city, but it is no longer the exclusive determinant. The cores are not expanding. Each amenity they offer has to be shared by more people. Many so-called city dwellers never visit the cores, and in a few cities, such as Los Angeles, the cores are difficult to find. Nevertheless, if these centers disappear or deteriorate, there will be no true cities at all.

PERIPHERY

A typical contemporary metropolis has three parts. The central core is surrounded by a gray ring of dreary blight, of second-class industry, commerce, and housing. It is growing faster than other areas are being reclaimed, but apparently no practical proposals for making it better have been advanced. Outside this is the area of hope, the limitless and ever-expanding periphery. Except for a few suburbs associated with older cities, the periphery is neither city nor country, and grows without plan. Its residents are lucky when their stores and their houses are merely banal and boring and not downright ugly.

Most urban peripheries may never become orderly. The political, economic, and social elements are too small and too lightly rooted. Many people who live there are transients; many of those who build the establishments are absentees. Thus, public opinion rarely comes to

FIGURE 5-10. *Aerial view of a portion of New York City, Anglo-America's largest metropolis. Over eight million people live in the city proper, with another seven million residing in the rest of the metropolitan area of New York-northeastern New Jersey. (The Port of New York Authority)*

a focus. Most entrepreneurs of the periphery have no personal desire for beauty and no conviction that it will reap profits. The public, in turn, displays no resentment and applies no pressure against the ugly and the vulgar; it takes what it gets.

The periphery has not learned how to organize itself in the communal self-interest, nor even how to achieve economic stability and political influence, adequate schools, hospitals, transportation, and a sense of neighborhood and cooperation. It is difficult to organize or to achieve basics; it is almost impossible to deal with the subtle and "impractical" questions of grace and beauty. People everywhere seem to have lost much of the collective and intuitive good taste of earlier societies, like those of European or New England towns, whose communal standards developed slowly. There the power of any individual to mar the general quality of the community was limited, though less by law than by public opinion. Only a little of this hidden restraint remains in a few old suburbs and a few special city streets or neighborhoods.

But on the periphery there are no such restraints. Here design is swayed by each new meretricious gimmick. No conviction prevails that harmony may be more important than novelty. The desire for unity has to come first, and this raises prodigious problems. We must face the fact that all the world's great urban unities have been achieved under some form of autocracy. Our quandary is how to achieve unity by democratic procedures.

At best, it seems that the periphery may offer a bland, neutral, decent way of life. Its occupants will still crave an occasional larger, more exciting experience. For this, they will have to turn to the central city. So, we need fine urban cores even if we achieve decent peripheries, and still more if we do not. Exciting urban centers are not a substitute for decent housing, but they can bring light to an otherwise drab life.

FUTURE TRENDS

Marketing, transportation, and service industries have formed the nuclei for an increasing number of population concentrations. In the fields of trade and service, there has been a 34 per cent rise in employment during the past 80 years. The service industries in particular can be located anywhere in the city, and are clean, neat, and adaptable to either vertical or horizontal buildings.

The annual GNP is expected to reach three-quarters of a trillion dollars by 1975, nearly double its present size. This increase is reflected in city growth statistics. City payrolls more than doubled in the last decade and are continuing to grow in size. They now amount to more than $450,000,000 a month.

Urban land values have increased from three to six times in the same period, giving rise to slum situations. Many of the central business districts are composed of decrepit buildings standing on the nation's highest-priced land. The buildings themselves house great numbers of people who are literally jammed into every conceivable space far beyond all health and safety standards. Because of the high land values, rents are correspondingly high, and the cost to the individual family is well out of line for what is received in terms of services and space.

Government-financed housing is increasing at a pace more than equal to that of private city housing, although it will still remain only a small percentage of the total residential living space in the future. In New York, for instance, although the roughly 100,000 public housing apartments built by the government are only 4 per cent of total housing, such government housing has constituted 25 per cent of all residential building since World War II.

Two decades hence this government housing is expected to have changed in at least three ways:

1. More responsible middle-income families displaced by renewal projects will be allowed to reside in public housing.
2. In many cases, units will be less institutionalized. Officials are now experimenting with scattered-site, prefabricated housing in Cedartown, Georgia, and with city-bought private row houses in Philadelphia.

3. Public housing may become more private if federally financed; privately-bought co-operative apartments are one of the expected vogues in downtown areas.

A San Francisco planner states that the two-house family will become fairly common in the coming decades. He bases his assessment on the growing number of families who have a town house or apartment and a simple country or summer house as well.

The automobile population of the country is expected to grow about twice as fast as the human population in the next 20 years, so traffic engineers rather wistfully conclude that the three-car family may be common in another generation's time.

These may be promises and the assessments for the American city in 1975, but a careful look at today's urban scene discloses many problems to be surmounted before the future will fall cozily into this pattern.

PROBLEMS TO BE OVERCOME

The most basic problems concern popular attitudes. There are several crucial areas in which the sum total of millions of individual decisions will affect the future of the city.

Population increase. More people means more markets and perhaps more prosperity. But if the capital required for schools, housing, hospitals, sewers, and retail stores rises sharply, capital may be diverted from more productive sections of the economy (*Fig. 5-11*).

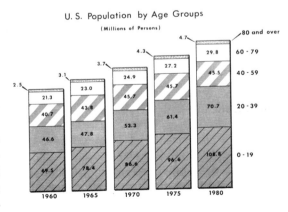

FIGURE 5-11.

The crucial question for planners of the city, as for planners of the national economy, is: If national wealth increases, how will the gain be divided between additional goods and services and additional leisure?

Taxes. Will citizens persist in their present reluctance to allocate personal income to local taxes for personal services? Cities everywhere are crouched uncomfortably beneath the iron bars of debt ceilings that have failed to keep pace with expanded growth. These cities wouldn't have to expand their debts if they could get more tax revenues. But their citizens, already paying heavy taxes to nation and state, often draw the line on paying a cent more for local taxes.

Immigrants and race. Will the disadvantaged racial and ethnic minority groups and other low-income Americans be integrated into full, urban citizenship at a fast enough pace to prevent urban deterioration through suspicion, violence, and neglect?

In Denver a planner reports that concentration of urban renewal efforts on physical construction has caused cities to overlook the human elements. Many newly arrived Mexicans do not feel that they belong to the Denver community enough to use the park and recreation facilities so proudly provided by the city.

Technological change. The same process of technical improvement that will bring atomic power and greater mechanization to cities may also make it possible for changes to take place with less regard to the human element. The insurance company, for instance, that is now reluctant to move to the suburbs because its office girls like the city may find computers more tractable.

Motormania—enemy to urban beauty. The automobile has seriously marred the beauty and serenity of American cities. Boston's ugly elevated freeway system has deprived pedestrians of easy access to the handsome Charles River embankment and has separated the harbor from the city as brutally as the railroads carved up Cleveland and Chicago in the nineteenth century. Expressways have appropriated the river banks of Manhattan and much of Chicago's downtown lakefront. Yet the automobile can be controlled. If anybody has to move through the city in tunnels, it should be the motorist and not the pedestrian. The river banks and malls belong to people who sit and walk, not to people who whiz by. They can be restored if the public will give up the notion that every citizen has the inalienable right to drive his car wherever he wants to go and to leave it there until he is ready to depart.

Americans face a crucial decision. If freeways and parking lots are to have the highest priority, the new cities will not be beautiful, and the old ones will lose even the limited beauty that they still have (*Fig. 5-12*).

CITY VERSUS SUBURB — THE ARTIFICIAL WAR

The U.S. Census Bureau condenses the nation's cities (1967) into a total of only 231 metropolitan areas. But within those 231 areas there are more than 16,000 separate governmental units with powers to tax and spend. For the very real benefits of community independence, urban citizens are often sacrificing other

FIGURE 5-12. *A freeway section in Los Angeles. (California State Div. of Highways)*

important benefits—efficient financing, logical transportation development, and coordinated water and sewage systems.

The problem is to strike some sort of balance. The attractive communities surrounding a big city have no desire to be swallowed up in a morass of decay and indebtedness. Yet, by remaining aloof from their neighbors, they are multiplying both their own problems and costs and those of the central city to which they are attached.

Denver, Colorado, makes an illuminating example. There, according to regional planning authorities, subdivisions spilling over the city's boundaries are a source of confusion. Speculating developers, they say, tend to feel that if they can get two basic services—sewage and water—they have it made. Officials in the neighboring areas are under strong pressure to say "yes" to the big developers; yet they cannot provide the approximately 20 services needed where houses are going to be crowded in at densities of four or more per acre. To provide these additional services, the county governments resort to a system of special districts, each with its own board, engineers, and maintenance staff. As a result, there are 46 sanitation districts in the Denver metropolitan area and some 130 smaller governmental units in the five-county Greater Denver area.

Actually many of the larger cities in the nation have done something about halting this duplication of effort. Seattle, Miami, Detroit, Kansas City (in Missouri and Kansas), Peoria, and Minneapolis-St. Paul have all made notable strides toward conquering common problems on an area-wide basis. Chicago is the core city for a huge six-county regional planning effort. St. Louis, Cleveland, Sacramento, Indianapolis, Nashville, and even Denver, are in various stages of progress toward metropolitan government. Toronto, Canada has led the way in this field, having had a solid metropolitan government for more than five years.

Although there is widespread feeling that the advent of this so-called "fourth layer" government (the other three layers are local, state, national) will be accompanied by a more natural development of neighborhood communities throughout the city and its suburbs, most of the growth to date has been in the field of planning rather than administering. One of the chief reasons for this paradox is that the American citizen-voter-consumer has been bombarded with journalistic accounts of the battle between city and suburbs until he has built up an almost irreversible conviction that such conflict is necessary. Thus, city and suburb have come to be fixed in the public mind as being engaged in a kind of gigantic tug-of-war. Urban specialists are concerned lest it take years to overcome the effects of this popular image and to establish cooperation between what are essentially the interdependent communities of each metropolitan area.

Political boundaries. Essentially, the battle between the city and the suburb is an artificial war fought along battle lines that are often arbitrary, outdated, political boundaries. If the central cores of American cities are to be rebuilt, there is going to have to be a major shifting of people—voters—across these boundaries. In Cincinnati this has already meant the shifting of some residents out of the slums of the lower city into surrounding suburbs. In Pittsburgh, progress generated by the great downtown Golden Triangle rebirth hit a snag when redevelopers ran head-on into the problem of where to resettle lower income families.

City finance. The classical theory of city finance —if an idea only a few decades old can be called classic—was that the central city automatically carries much of the financial weight of the suburbs, and that free-riding outer towns could steer clear of entangling city alliances, while at the same time reaping the benefits of proximity.

There are far too many variables to generalize correctly about whether the taxpayer of city or suburb is getting the short end of the financial stick. But it should be apparent that leaders in communities outside the core city cannot afford to ignore chances to work with their neighbors. Too much money and too much urban beauty are at stake.

Transportation. Because the car has created suburbs by making it possible to go twice as far to work by the simple expedient of going twice as fast, transportation comes in for an inordinate amount of scrutiny in any examination of the city-suburb equation. One of the greatest unsolved problems in American urban life is that of mass public transit systems.

Some traffic engineers have even suggested that downtown subways and buses be free in order to keep auto traffic away from the city center and to save money on expressways. The pacesetting new mass transit center strips now being built into Chicago's expressways cost less than one-third the highways themselves; yet they are expected to carry two to three times more passengers during the rush hour.

Solutions. Although frequently this new spirit of metropolitan cooperation has resulted in more talk than action, definite progress in the solution of problems of transportation and municipal finance can be seen in cities across the country. All that is lacking to give this new movement full momentum are time and greater public awareness. Then the artificial war can be brought to some sort of truce under which neighboring communities can preserve their treasured independence while reaping the financial benefits of interdependent planning.

Some communities are already arriving at solutions. Detroit has an organization of mayors and labor, industrial, and civic leaders convening regularly to discuss metropolitan needs. Seattle is mapping projects on a metropolitan basis. San Francisco will soon achieve a bay area transit system. Metropolitan Miami has created a reverse pattern in which suburban dominance shows up—a new civic center built in the suburbs.

Los Angeles planners are attempting to revise that city's whole growth pattern in the future by seeking methods of compartmenting land uses to localize and control growth rings of decay that start with industrial slums. By more strictly segregating industry and residences throughout the community, they hope to eliminate the classic pattern in which decay at the center forces each successive ring of suburbs to be stepped down a notch in value. Under this system, industry would be redeveloped in its own area, thereby causing less decay in adjoining residential areas and making evacuation of homeowners while redevelopment takes place

unnecessary. Hopefully, this type of planning would break Los Angeles away from the system established when land speculators of the 1920's operated buses from downtown and offered free lunches to prospective buyers of oat-field lots outside the city.

Another solution to the basic problem of duplicating units of government in the same city area has been the strengthening of county governments. Some 91 of the 231 metropolitan areas in the United States now are defined as extending to the same boundary lines as those of the surrounding county. The International City Managers Association reports that this geographical fact is being turned to advantage by many metropolitan areas where the county government has taken over administration of water supply, waste disposal, airport operation, hospitals, election registration, property-tax assessment, parks, recreation, and civil defense. Yolo County, California, and Davidson County, Tennessee, have even taken over direction of federal urban renewal programs from local municipalities.

AIR POLLUTION—A MAJOR PROBLEM

Dirty air can kill you, and Americans are pouring 130 million tons of pollution into the sky every year. The nation's cities, say the experts, are ripe for disaster; yet control is costly, inefficient, and slow. The auto and the smoke-stack are the major villians, but curbs are coming.

In Chicago alone, a million automobiles and 50,000 troublesome smokestacks manufacture pollution, puff by noxious puff. In Los Angeles, 3.5 million cars burn seven million gallons of gasoline a day, and dump more than 10,000 tons of exhaust gases into the air, despite stringent controls.

But air pollution could potentially extend over every town in America. It is already in some most unlikely places. Where once the gaseous wastes were small enough to be imperceptible, excessive concentrations are now ubiquitous. Places such as Denver, Phoenix, and Albuquerque, as well as cities in Montana, Oregon, and Washington, all traditionally associated with fresh, clean air, now have recurrent smog.

Smog. A thick yellowish radiation fog over a city, where large quantities of soot act as nuclei for condensation and sulfur dioxide adds to the acrid flavor, smog is not just a tenant of Los Angeles and a few other big cities. The U.S. Public Health Service reports that no less than 7,300 communities are afflicted with air pollution in varying degrees. In some of these communities, the mildness or infrequency of smog has lulled people into thinking it will go away. They are mistaken—if not dealt with, smog gets worse.

Air pollution has overtaken the nation suddenly, just as water pollution did. People think of air as an unlimited resource, just as they once thought of water. But air is stringently limited. The air enveloping the earth extends up only about 12 miles before it becomes thin and useless for man. Into the air above the United States is now going, every day, more than 360,000 tons of gaseous wastes. In sheer weight of emitted gases, automobiles account for nearly two-thirds of the national atmospheric waste load, mostly in carbon monoxide gas. But industry (including power generation) produces nearly three times as much as automobiles in more noxious affluents.

The California Institute of Technology has calculated that in Los Angeles County, which has more than six million inhabitants, gaseous wastes average 9,850 metric tons a day. This amounts to 1,470 grams (about three pounds) per person per day on a dry-weight basis—twice as much as solid refuse disposal, and six times as much as the contaminants in waste water.

Evenly distributed, this load of waste would be innocuous. But it isn't evenly distributed. Half the nation's population is concentrated on only 1 per cent of its land area, and weather conditions more or less regularly trap concentrations of pollutants there. An historic example is Donora, Pennsylvania, where a spell of smog killed 20 people and sickened thousands in 1948.

City dwellers typically have higher rates of respiratory ailments—lung cancer, emphysema, chronic bronchitis—than rural residents. Several spells of smog have caused thousands of statistically "excess" deaths in New York and other cities.

The more obvious smog damage, such as damage to materials and crops, has been estimated nationally at $65 per person a year—$11 billion in all, or about 10 per cent of the national budget. Still, most experts consider this figure illusory in its understatement. And how does one put a price tag on the 23 atmospheric "blackouts" on the New Jersey Turnpike in 1965? Or on the aviation operations that increasingly are hampered and endangered by man-made muck?

Air pollution programs. Most air pollution enforcement activities to date have scarcely made a dent in the problem. The latest survey of the Public Health Service showed that only $14,250,000 were spent for 130 city, county, and regional air pollution programs in the country, and a quarter of that total was in Los Angeles alone. Los Angeles County headed the list with its outlay of $3,663,000—60.8 cents per person.

New York City, with one of the nation's more severe pollution situations and about one million more people than Los Angeles County, ranked 65th in per capita expenditure with a rate of only 15.7 cents. San Francisco and Chicago generally are rated near Los Angeles in the scope of their programs. Detroit, Pittsburgh, St. Louis, Boston, and a few other cities have achieved results. But after that, the list peters out.

In 1963, Congress passed the Clean Air Act, which covers the current federal activities authorizing the Public Health Service to impose limits for automobile emissions. The first such regulation, based on a California law, requires manufacturers to put "smog control devices" on car engines. This regulation, however, is denounced by the auto industry as "a billion-dollar hoax" for two reasons. They say that it discriminates against smog-free localities, and that it will produce little immediate improvement since it will take ten years to retire the 90 million unequipped cars already in use. Moreover, health experts predict that even though such devices might reduce automobile-caused pollution by 50 per cent today, in a decade or two the numbers of cars will more than double the present count, so the problem will not be solved.

Megalopolis

Jean Gottman was the first to apply the term "megalopolis"—used originally by the ancient Greeks and meaning "very large city"—specifically to the United States' eastern seaboard. The megalopolis stretches from southern New Hampshire to northern Virginia and from the Atlantic shore to the Appalachian foothills. This geographical region, which runs through ten states, is the most active crossroads on earth for people, ideas, and goods. Its principal cities are as follows: Lawrence-Haverhill in Massachusetts, but extending into southern New Hampshire; Boston, Brockton, Fall River, Lowell, New Bedford, Springfield-Chicopee-Holyoke, and Worcester, Massachusetts; Providence-Pawtucket, Rhode Island; Bridgeport, Hartford, Meriden, New Britain, New Haven, Norwalk, Stamford, and Waterbury, Connecticut; New York; Atlantic City, Jersey City, Newark, Paterson-Clifton-Passaic, and Trenton, New Jersey; Allentown-Bethlehem-Easton, Harrisburg, Lancaster, Reading, York, and Philadelphia, Pennsylvania; Wilmington, Delaware; Baltimore, Maryland; and Washington, D.C. (*Fig. 5-13*).

These cities and their suburbs have 21.5 per cent of the nation's population, do more than 19 per cent of the nation's retail store business, and account for almost 23 per cent of total manufacturing. This is the largest, wealthiest, and most productive urbanized region on earth, and it exerts an influence on the economic, political, and cultural life of the United States out of all proportion to its size. Within this strip are located the seat of federal govern-

FIGURE 5-13. *Megalopolis, U.S.A.*

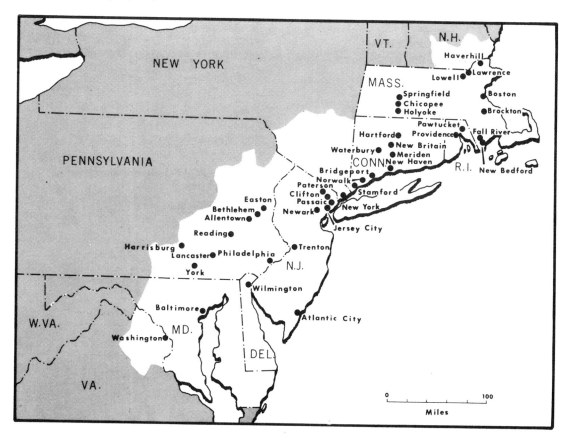

ment and the nation's money market. Mass communications, publishing, advertising, theater, and music are dominated by the institutions in megalopolis. Its combined libraries contain one-third of the nation's library books.

The more than 37 million people, about 700 per square mile compared to a national average of 51, earn their living on 1.8 per cent of the country's land area. Along with the highest number of well-educated adults, the urban centers have, with few exceptions, the largest percentage of poorly educated people. The urban slums are dismal; yet children living there have greater opportunity for a good job and a good education than those in rural slums.

The megalopolis originally developed as a great manufacturing and trading area, but now, with the increasing employment in service jobs, the relative importance of manufacturing is decreasing. The demand for services, in turn, creates new jobs and is a reflection of the steady rise in personal income and the general standard of living. This job revolution, although most evident in the megalopolis, is becoming a national trend and can be compared in scope and importance to the industrial revolution.

All is not beauty and comfort in the megalopolis, however. Traffic conditions are worsening. The "downtown" center is threatened by physical and social decay. If this continues, the service industry will migrate and decentralize as manufacturing did, taking its jobs with it. In many cities within the region, the air is contaminated, the noise deafening, and the water polluted. Slums and "gray areas" continue to spread.

Despite the many problems in the megalopolis, the crowded people are extremely fortunate. They form, on the average, the richest, best-educated, best-housed, and best-serviced of any similar-sized group in the world. If the people of the megalopolis follow the American tradition of liberty and concern for the general welfare, they will build not only the largest and most prosperous region, but also the most livable and brightest city region ever to inspire the world (*Fig. 5-14*).

Metropolitan Regions and Functions

In its structural and spatial aspects, the metropolitan region consists of the metropolis and its surrounding settlements. Functionally, the region is a complex web of economic, cultural, and political relationships that bind these settlements into a unit with a dominant center and subordinate parts. Although topographic or climatic factors certainly affect, or at least limit, regional developments, the metropolitan region as here conceived is essentially a cultural phenomenon. It is a product, to a great extent, of new methods of transportation and communication—the automobile, truck, transport and rapid transit systems, and the newspaper, television, radio, telegraph, and telephone. By means of these technological facilities, the subordinate settlements have become integrated with each other and with larger nuclear centers.

CLASSIFICATION OF METROPOLISES

Metropolises may be classified according to both metropolitan functions and regional relationships.

National metropolis. These are the five largest metropolitan areas—New York, Chicago, Los Angeles, Philadelphia, and Detroit. They are pre-eminent in financial-commercial activities,

FIGURE 5-14. *Typical of the new professionally-planned downtown areas is Charles Center, in Baltimore. (Charles Center Information Service)*

although several have heavy manufacturing concentrations. The national metropolis has a vast local hinterland, but exerts strong national, and even international influence.

Regional metropolis. The areas in this category—San Francisco, Minneapolis-St. Paul, and Kansas City, among others—specialize in finance and trade and in industries whose inputs come from contiguous areas. In sum, they are metropolises without the national scope of those in the class above.

Regional capital, submetropolitan. Houston, New Orleans, and Louisville are included in this category. These areas are smaller in size than regional metropolises, and their metropolitan functions of finance and trade serve a smaller territory.

Diversified manufacturing, with metropolitan functions. This category includes, among others, Boston, Pittsburgh, and St. Louis. Cities in this class combine large size and moderate-to-heavy emphasis on manufacturing with a considerable range of financial and commercial functions. These metropolises show evidence of dominating moderately large contiguous hinterlands, but have strong competition from nearby national centers.

Diversified manufacturing, with few metropolitan functions. Baltimore, Milwaukee, and Albany-Schenectady-Troy, examples of this class, all have high-to-very-high specialization in manufacturing, but little banking, wholesaling, and the like. They do not dominate a large contiguous hinterland.

Diversified manufacturing centers. Providence with textiles, Youngstown with heavy metals, Rochester with photographic equipment, and Akron with rubber are examples of this class. Wholesaling, trade, and finance are little developed. These metropolises do not dominate a large adjacent hinterland.

Special cases. These are metropolises with distinct and unusual functions: Washington, D.C. (government); San Diego, San Antonio, Norfolk (major military installations); Miami, Atlantic City (tourism); and several others.

Outlook

Many factors have helped to fuel both public and official interest in city problems in the last few years. Among them were President Johnson's Great Society program and the candor of young mayors, such as New York's John V. Lindsay and Detroit's Jerome Cavanagh, who declared that the problems of the cities were more important than missiles, rockets, space, or reaching the moon.

From the vantage point of the federal government, three main indicators of the interest in urban affairs stand out: first, the elevation of the Housing and Home Finance Agency to cabinet status as the Department of Housing and Urban Development, and the subsequent recruitment of new and often brilliant personnel to man departmental posts; second, the introduction and enactment of two new programs; and third, the recent Senate hearings on city problems, further illuminating urban troubles.

These three developments did more than merely dramatize city problems. They also made possible a reassessment of the federal approach to urban America and set the stage for what many officials hope will be a sustained, better-coordinated, and large-scale attack on the ills of urban life.

The Department of Housing and Urban Development (HUD), armed with new powers, has rearranged the old housing programs in more rational groupings and endowed old programs with new philosophies. Urban renewal, for example, had long been criticized for destroying neighborhoods at the expense of the poor. The Department began stressing rehabilitation instead of total clearance.

In 1966, the Model Cities and Metropolitan Development Bill was passed, authorizing $900 million in fiscal 1968 and 1969 to help selected cities redevelop blighted neighborhoods, and $12 million a year in fiscal 1967 and 1968 to help cities plan redevelopment programs. It also encourages metropolitan cooperation through several new approaches.

The bill goes well beyond urban renewal legislation by seeking to tie together the social and welfare programs of the government and the rehabilitation of blighted dwellings, thereby combining human and physical renewal in slum areas.

The bill's key mechanism is its financing provision. It does not initiate any new programs as such; it merely gives cities supplemental funds to carry out demonstrations. However, the amount of a grant is directly tied to the number and size of existing programs a city decides to concentrate in a demonstration neighborhood. In effect, then, a bonus is given to cities willing to mesh their physical and social programs in a concentrated fashion.

Selected References

BOLLENS, JOHN C., and SCHMANDT, HENRY J., *The Metropolis: Its People, Politics, and Economic Life*, New York: Harper & Row, Publishers, 1965.

CHAPIN, F. STUART, JR., *Urban Land Use Planning* (2nd ed.), Urbana, Ill.: University of Illinois Press, 1965.

DACEY, MICHAEL F., "A County-seat Model for the Areal Pattern of an Urban System," *The Geographical Review*, Vol. 46, October, 1966, pp. 527–542.

DAVIS, J. TAIT, "Middle Class Housing in the Central City," *Economic Geography*, Vol. 41, July, 1965, pp. 238–251.

GIST, NOEL P., and FAVA, SYLVIA, *Urban Society* (5th ed.), New York: Thomas Y. Crowell Co., Inc., 1964.

GOODWIN, WILLIAM, "The Management Center in the United States," *The Geographical Review*, Vol. 45, January, 1965, pp. 1–16.

GOTTMAN, JEAN, "Why the Skyscraper," *The Geographical Review*, Vol. 46, April, 1966, pp. 190–212.

HAUSER, PHILIP M., and SCHNORE, LEO F., *The Study of Urbanization*, New York: John Wiley & Sons, Inc., 1965.

HIGBEE, EDWARD C., *The Squeeze, Cities Without Space*, New York: William Morrow & Co., 1960.

KASPERSON, ROGER E., "Toward a Geography of Urban Politics," *Economic Geography*, Vol. 41, April, 1965, pp. 95–107.

KING, LESLIE J., "A Multivariate Analysis of the Spacing of Urban Settlements in the United States," *Annals of the Association of American Geographers*, Vol. 51, June, 1961, pp. 222–233.

LEIGHTON, PHILIP A., "Geographical Aspects of Air Pollution," *The Geographical Review*, Vol. 56, April, 1966, pp. 151–174.

MAYER, HAROLD M., and KOHN, CLYDE F., *Readings in Urban Geography*, Chicago: The University of Chicago Press, 1959.

MURPHY, RAYMOND E., *The American City, an Urban Geography*, New York: McGraw-Hill Book Company, Inc., 1966.

NEWLING, BRUCE E., "Urban Growth and Spatial Structure: Mathematical Models and Empirical Evidence," *The Geographical Review*, Vol. 46, April, 1966, pp. 213–225.

NORTHAM, RAY M., "Declining Urban Centers in the United States: 1940–1960," *Annals of the Association of American Geographers*, Vol. 53, March, 1963, pp. 50–59.

PERLOFF, HARVEY S. (ed.), *Planning and the Urban Community*, Pittsburgh, Pa.: University of Pittsburgh Press, 1961.

PRESTON, RICHARD, "The Zone in Transition: A Study of Urban Land Use Patterns," *Economic Geography*, Vol. 42, July, 1966, pp. 236–260.

SMITH, P. J., "Calgary: A Study in Urban Pattern," *Economic Geography*, Vol. 38, October, 1962, pp. 315–329.

TAAFFE, EDWARD J., "The Urban Hierarchy: An Air Passenger Definition," *Economic Geography*, Vol. 38, January, 1962, pp. 1–14.

THOMAS, EDWIN N., "Areal Associations Between Population Growth and Selected Factors in the Chicago Area," *Economic Geography*, Vol. 36, April, 1960, pp. 158–170.

VANCE, JAMES E., JR., "Housing the Worker: The Employment Linkage as a Force in Urban Structure," *Economic Geography*, Vol. 42, October, 1966, pp. 294–325.

———, "Labor-shed, Employment Field, and Dynamic Analysis in Urban Geography," *ibid.*, Vol. 36, July, 1960, pp. 189–220.

VERNON, RAYMOND, *Metropolis 1985*, Cambridge, Mass.: Harvard University Press, 1960.

WEBB, JOHN W., "Basic Concepts in the Analysis of Small Urban Centers of Minnesota," *Annals of the Association of American Geographers*, Vol. 49, March, 1959, pp. 55–72.

6 *The Agricultural Pattern*

The United States has shifted in the past century from a predominantly agricultural economy to an industrial and commercial economy: The industrial sector is now beginning to give way, at least relatively, to a growing variety of personal services. The shift has been possible primarily because Americans have been able to specialize in the production and processing of food and fiber by the use of science and technology, which, in turn, has increased output per worker in farming and agribusiness.[1]

The impact of labor-saving equipment on agriculture is already clear. In 1880 it took a farmer 46 man-hours to plant, cultivate, and harvest an acre of corn. In 1960 it took 7 hours, and by 1965 progressive farmers were doing the job in 2 hours. In addition to taking less time, today the entire job is done with much less manpower than formerly (*Fig. 6-1*).

Likewise, the impact of technological and management advances on yields is dramatic. The farmer of 1950 harvested an average of 38 bushels of corn per acre. By 1965, corn yields had nearly doubled, and nearly 10 per cent of American farmers were achieving yields of 150 bushels an acre (*Fig. 6-2*).

[1] The art or science of cultivating the ground is but one link in the long chain of feeding and clothing people. For this whole complex of agricultural production and distribution functions, some persons use the term "agribusiness."

In the not-too-distant future, highly automated systems may help make it possible to produce close to 500 bushels of corn an acre in less than two hours. A distinguishing feature of rural America in the year 2,000, suggests L. S. Fife, agricultural economist for International Harvester Company, will be towers containing television scanners to keep an eye on robot tractors.

World Outlook

The United States has an abundance of foods available, and a wide variety as well. A wondrous assortment of quality, size, brand, and type of package is ours to command. So highly efficient and productive are the American farms that every day of the year each of us can have well-balanced, delicious meals from a variety of foods for a relatively low price.

For most of the rest of the world, however, the food outlook isn't so bright. It is estimated that 300 million to 500 million persons currently live on the brink of starvation in Asia, Africa, Latin America, and the Middle East. Another 1.5 billion of the world's total population of more than 3 billion people are malnourished, prey to disease, and often too listless to struggle effectively against poverty (*Fig. 6-3*).

Distressing as this picture is, the future will be darker unless great strides are made in food

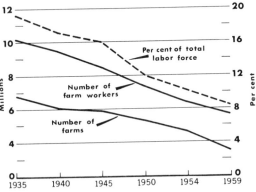

FIGURE 6-1.

production. By the end of this century, the population of the underdeveloped regions of the globe is expected to reach 5 billion. According to the United Nations, to feed these masses and improve their diet modestly over the present unsatisfactory standards, food supplies would have to increase 306 per cent in the Far East, 207 per cent in the Middle East, 238 per cent in Latin America, and 159 per cent in Africa. By contrast, food production in these areas as a whole rose 54 per cent during the past 25 years.

Even more alarming, per capita food production in these regions has actually been declining between one and two per cent a year since the 1958-1960 period. U.S. food shipments have filled the gap in many countries, but American surpluses no longer exist in substantial quantities. Secretary of Agriculture Orville L. Freeman warns that by 1985 the annual food deficit in the underdeveloped countries may widen to the equivalent of 88 million tons of food grain—more than three times the weight of annual food shipments from the developed to the underdeveloped lands in the 1960's.

Most observers refuse to forecast a truly catastrophic famine in underdeveloped areas of the world between now and the end of the century, but the squeeze between population and food production nevertheless has chilling implications. Indeed, food already is a major force in world power politics.

The world food situation is of immense significance to U.S. taxpayers. In addition to shipments abroad by the U.S. government, which are expected to rise from the present annual rate of $1.6 billion to a level of $2 billion to $3 billion in coming years, it is estimated that agricultural capital investments totaling at least $80 billion will be needed over the next 14 years if the underdeveloped nations are to reach minimum self-sufficiency. On the basis of America's past role in agricultural investment overseas, the U.S. share of this outlay would amount to about $1.5 billion annually.

The pressure of food shortages abroad, coupled with the anticipated jump in the U.S. population from the present 200 million to almost 340 million by the year 2000, is expected to provide the impetus for great strides ahead in the science of farming, just as the exigencies of war force breakthroughs in the science of weapons. Already, there are no less than 48,000 agricultural research projects underway.

Agricultural Revolutions

Agriculture is now in its third great revolution. The first came in the middle of the nine-

FIGURE 6-2. *A corn harvester in operation in northern Illinois. Corn is picked, husked, and shelled in one operation. (Deere and Co.)*

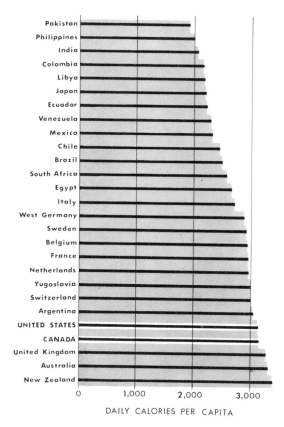

FIGURE 6-3. *Food consumption, selected countries.*

teenth century, when man began to substitute animal energy for human energy. The invention of the reaper is the best-known event associated with this period. This and other developments increased output per worker on farms and started the United States on the path of feeding its growing citizenry with a constantly shrinking proportion of its total population living on farms. Agriculture began to take on some characteristics of a commercial enterprise, although sometimes the change was almost imperceptible.

The second great revolution began in the 1920's, with the substitution of mechanical energy for animal energy. It likewise increased the commercialization of agriculture, shifted a number of production functions off the farm, substantially increased output per worker, and further reduced the proportion of the total working population on farms.

Farm output expanded rapidly during World War II and the immediate postwar years, when favorable price relationships encouraged farmers to adopt improved production practices rapidly. Use of purchased farm supplies increased at a record annual rate from 1940 to 1950, and their substitution for farm labor and farm land was accelerated. Average crop yields rose about 10 per cent during the 1940's. Production efficiency—farm output per unit of production resources—rose at a much faster rate from 1940 to 1950 than in any previous decade.

Although many observers at the time viewed the changes in U.S. farming during the 1940's as a "technological revolution," this term more aptly describes the period after 1950, when the nation's growing investment in research and education paid off greatly as agricultural production increased through the application of science, technology, and business management.

From 1950 to the mid-1960's the following changes occurred: 35 per cent more farm output, with 11 per cent fewer acres of crop land used; 45 per cent less farm labor; 48 per cent more purchased farm supplies; and little change in total production resources used. Three features of the technological revolution stand out: (1) over-all production efficiency increased at a record rate; (2) the rate of decline in use of farm labor far exceeded the large annual reduction from 1940 to 1950; and (3) a sharp upsurge in per acre yields of crops occurred.

The Agriculture Industry

It is incorrect to think of agriculture as a declining industry. American agriculture is an expanding business in every important respect except one—the number of people required to run the nation's farms. Each year, the country's agricultural plant uses more capital, more science and technology, more managerial capacity, more purchased production inputs, more specialized marketing facilities, and more research than the year before.

The assets of agriculture are roughly $216 billion, equal to nearly half of the market value of all corporation stocks on the New York Stock Exchange. The investment in agriculture's production assets represents $25,000 for each farm worker.

Farmers have invested about $16 billion in cars, trucks, tractors, and other farm machinery. Production expenses have quadrupled in 40 years, going from $7 billion in 1923 to $29 billion in 1963. Gross farm income has more than tripled, from $12 billion in 1923 to $42 billion in 1963, plus $7 billion earned off the farm. Production assets used for 1963 farm output were worth $170 billion, up from $94 billion in 1950 and $38 billion in 1940. The average per farm value of assets used in farm production has increased 50 per cent since 1958.

These national totals and averages are significant to industrial producers. It is important to realize that, although the number of farms and farm workers has steadily decreased, farmers' total expenditures continue to increase (*Fig. 6-4*).

SCOPE

The agricultural industry is big, broad, and basic. Of the 70 million persons employed in America in 1965, about 28 million worked somewhere in agriculture—6.5 million worked on farms, 8.5 million produced goods and services purchased by farmers, and 13 million processed and distributed farm products. Hence, almost two-fifths of all gainfully employed people were engaged in work related to agriculture.

The declining trend in farm population is itself a sign of a strong agriculture. Brainpower has replaced horsepower as the essential ingredient on American farms. The total U.S. agricultural output increased by two-thirds in the past two decades, while the number of farm workers declined some 3 million. This means that production per worker on American farms has doubled in the past 20 years. This remarkable increase in production efficiency can be matched by no other major sector of the U.S. economy.

INTERDEPENDENCE

Industry depends on agriculture as a customer to a greater extent than most persons realize. A generation ago, farmers were producing most of their own fuel, power, and fertilizer. Today industry is furnishing farmers: over 7 million tons of steel each year—more than is used for a year's output of passenger cars; 45 million tons of chemical materials—about five times the amount farmers used in 1935; 18 billion gallons of crude petroleum—more than is used by any other industry; 285 million pounds of raw rubber—enough to make tires for 6 million automobiles; and 28 kilowatt hours of electricity—more than enough to serve the cities of Chicago, Detroit, Baltimore, and Houston for a year.

The agricultural world and the industrial world are not two separate communities with merely a buyer-seller relationship. They are so bound together and so interrelated that one must think of them jointly in order to reach sound conclusions about either one.

Agricultural Land Resources

The land area of the 50 states totals 2.3 billion acres. Forest land accounts for a third of this. More than a fourth is grassland pasture and range. About a fifth is classified as cropland. The remaining fifth includes urban areas and serves other purposes.

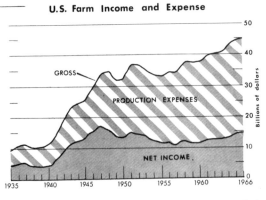

U.S. Farm Income and Expense

GROSS

PRODUCTION EXPENSES

Billions of dollars

NET INCOME

1935   1940   1945   1950   1955   1960   1966

FIGURE 6-4.

Figure 6-5 shows the division of land in the United States by ownership. Private agricultural land provides most of the nation's food, fiber, timber, water, wildlife, and much of its outdoor recreation.

LAND CAPABILITY

Eight *land capability classes* express the wide range of suitability for cultivation. The limitations in use increase as the class number increases; for example, Class I has few or no limitations, whereas Class VIII has a great many (*Fig. 6-6*).

USES

Agricultural land of the conterminous United States is about equally divided among three major uses: (1) cultivated cropland, 31 per cent; (2) pasture and range, 33 per cent; and (3) forest and woodland, 31 per cent. The remaining 5 per cent, used as farm roads, farmsteads, wildlife areas, and for other, miscellaneous purposes, is classified as "other land."

Cultivated cropland. This includes all land that has been harvested, is fallow, is being prepared, or is used for soil-improvement crops, rotation pasture, tame hay, wild hay, vegetables, fruits, and nuts, and land where crops have failed.

FIGURE 6-5. *Ownership of land in the conterminous United States.*

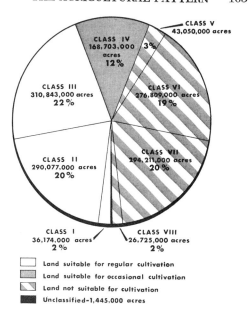

FIGURE 6-6. *Land in the United States by classification.*

Pasture and rangeland. This classification includes grassland, nonforested pasture, wild hay harvested (except some irrigated) west of the Mississippi, and other grazing land except pasture in a crop rotation. It may have shade trees or scattered timber trees making a canopy of not more than 10 per cent.

Forest and woodland. This includes land at least 10 per cent stocked by trees capable of producing timber or other wood products, or exerting an influence on the water regime, as well as undeveloped land from which such trees have been removed, afforested land, and chaparral areas.

CONSERVATION NEEDS

Sixty-two per cent of the present cropland needs conservation treatment. The dominant conservation problems are erosion, excess water, unfavorable soil, and adverse climate (*Fig. 6-7*).

Almost three-quarters of private pasture and rangeland needs conservation treatment, with the major requirements being improvement of existing cover, establishment of new cover, and

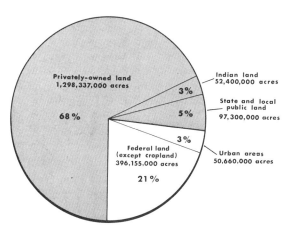

protection from overgrazing, fire, erosion, rodents, brush, and weeds (*Fig. 6-8*).

More than half of private forest and woodland (241 million acres) needs conservation treatment—the establishment of new stands, improvement on existing stands, and erosion control. More protection also is needed to stop losses from fire, insects, diseases, and animals that damage trees.

FUTURE USE

Estimated changes in land use indicate that more than 20 million acres can be expected to go out of private agriculture by 1975. In addition, the U.S. Department of Agriculture indicates that some 101 million acres will be shifted to new agricultural uses by 1975, with the most extensive contemplated shift from cropland to pasture and range.

Most of the land withdrawn from agriculture will be from cropland. It will be for industrial plants, shopping centers, and homes, and for the airports, schools, hospitals, and highways demanded by the expanding mobile American population. In addition, much land remaining in private ownership will shift from "production" uses to outdoor recreational uses.

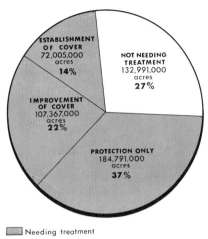

Needing treatment

FIGURE 6-8. *Condition of private pasture and rangeland in the United States.*

Farming

There are more than 70,000 kinds of soil in the United States. On that basis alone, one could almost say that there are 70,000 kinds of farms. In general, however, the kind of farming that goes on in a region is determined by natural resources, transportation, the nearness of cities, and the size of markets.

MAJOR SPECIALIZATIONS

Corn belt. Perhaps the leading agricultural area in the United States is the so-called "Corn Belt," a midwestern region of feed grains and livestock, where the land is generally level, with deep, rich, fertile soils that are well adapted to mechanization and the production of corn. A monthly rainfall of three to six inches during June, July, and August, with hot days (70° to 80° F.) and warm nights (above 58° F.), are optimum conditions for high corn yields. The Corn Belt covers parts of Ohio, Indiana, Illinois, Wisconsin, Minnesota, Kansas, Nebraska, Missouri, and South Dakota, and all of Iowa (*Fig. 6-9*).

Corn Belt farmers generally have cropping systems that may include corn, oats, wheat, soybeans, and hay and pasture crops (*Fig. 6-10*). When a farmer in the region doesn't

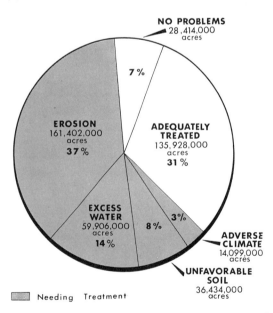

FIGURE 6-7. *Condition of United States cropland.*

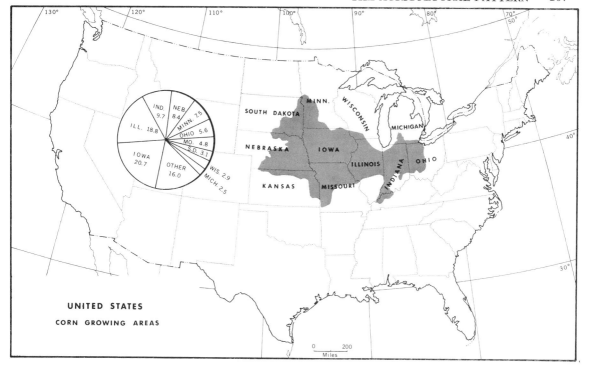

FIGURE 6-9.

FIGURE 6-10. *Aerial view of farm land in Clayton County, Iowa. Strip cropping (the practice of growing crops in a systematic arrangement of strips) is carried on to protect the soil against wind and water erosion. (U.S. Dept. of Agriculture)*

feed all the grain he grows to animals on his farm, he sells it for cash.

Most farm families own the land they till. Their work is heaviest from early spring to mid-fall; for, during this period, they must plant, cultivate, and harvest their many field crops. They use machines to prepare the ground for planting, put in the seed, harvest the crop, carry it, and even feed it to animals. Most of the farms are of moderate size—100 to 400 acres—and thus are small enough to be operated by a farm family with the aid of these machines.

Cotton. The most important field crop of South Carolina, Alabama, Georgia, Mississippi, Arkansas, Louisiana, Tennessee, and Texas, cotton is less important in other states—even in California, one of the main cotton producing states (*Fig. 6-11*).

The southeastern cotton region has a long, warm growing season and ample rainfall, usually. Cotton can be picked about six months after it is planted. On the smaller farms (5 to 50 acres) the farmer and his family plant and

harvest the cotton by hand; but on the many large farms in the region, sharecroppers or hired laborers do this work. A sharecropper receives a share of the crop in return for his effort, but he does not own the land; the hired laborer, on the other hand, receives a wage.

On many small subsistence farms in the cotton region, horses or mules are still used for heavy tasks like pulling the plow. A common sight on these farms is the owner or tenant guiding a plow that is pulled by one or two mules. Most of the large farms and many of the smaller ones, however, are equipped with machinery to plow, seed, harvest, and bale the cotton.

The cotton region is changing rapidly as the emphasis is switching from cotton. Southern farmers have always grown other crops—vegetables, tobacco, fruit, corn, nuts—and raised animals for their own use or sale in the neighboring cities. Peaches have long been an important crop in Georgia and South Carolina; and rice, in Louisiana, Arkansas, and Texas. But in recent years, many farmers in the South have begun to grow more hay and livestock feed to fatten cattle for market or to feed dairy cows

FIGURE 6-11.

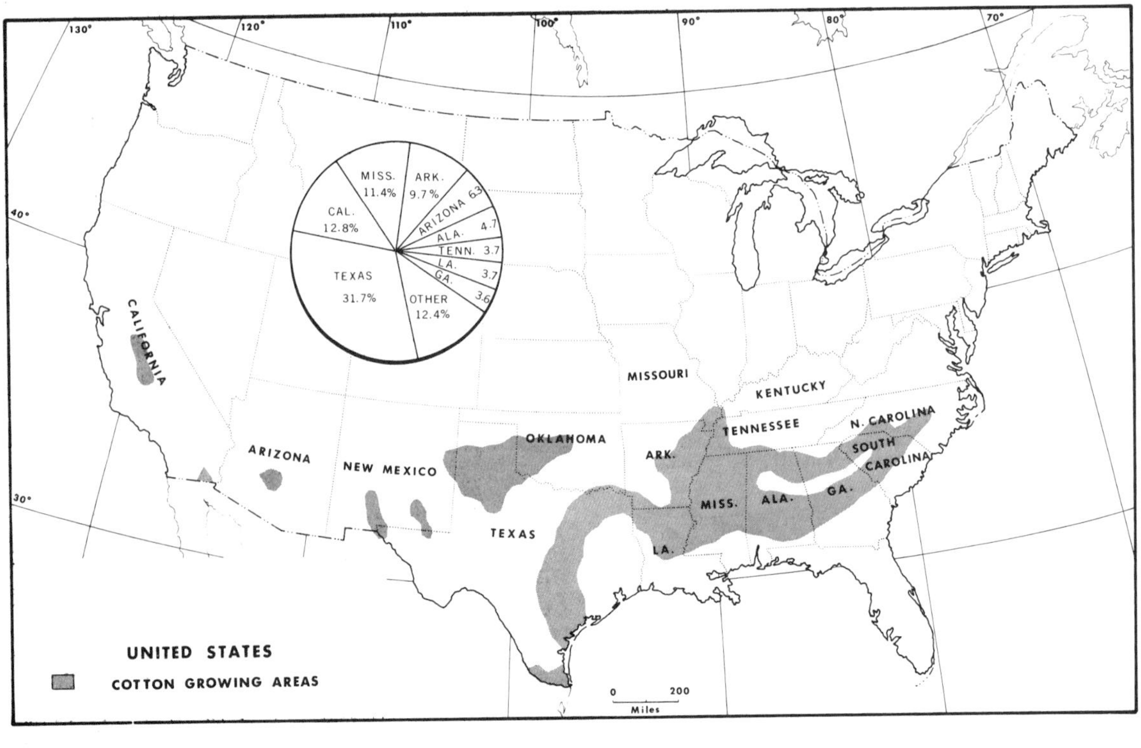

UNITED STATES
COTTON GROWING AREAS

or flocks of chickens. The broiler-fryer industry in Georgia, for example, ranks ahead of cotton in cash income.

Tobacco. The main crop in North Carolina and Kentucky, and in parts of South Carolina, Virginia, and Maryland, tobacco is grown also in Georgia, Florida, Pennsylvania, Ohio, Connecticut, Massachusetts, and Wisconsin (*Fig. 6-12*).

A demanding crop, tobacco requires close attention. The fields are usually fertilized very carefully, and then much hand labor is needed to transplant, weed, and cultivate the plants. Because growing tobacco is so time-consuming, one man and his family can work only a small amount of land, usually less than four acres. The larger farms employ several tenant farmers.

Curing tobacco is an important part of the farmer's work. After the leaves of the plants are picked or the whole plants are cut, they are dried out by air or fired in heated barns. The fields are dotted with these curing barns in which the tobacco hangs to dry.

Some tobacco farmers plant other cash crops, such as melons or peanuts. Most of them grow vegetables and raise a few meat animals for their own tables, and they feed draft animals with hay grown on their own places. Some farmers in the tobacco-growing states get income from other sources. In Kentucky, for example, which is known all over the world for its burley tobacco, dairying and cattle raising bring farmers almost as much income (*Fig. 6-13*).

Upland farming. The areas of upland farming include parts of Pennsylvania, Maryland, West Virginia, Virginia, North Carolina, Tennessee, Kentucky, Missouri, and Arkansas (*Fig. 6-14*). Many farms in these areas are not only small in size, but also are located at a considerable distance from large urban markets. These factors give rise to agricultural self-sufficiency practices, the farmer and his family working the land mainly for their own needs and without benefit of hired labor. Vegetables and feed grains, dairy cattle, beef cattle, poultry, and hogs constitute the major types of farm pro-

FIGURE 6-12.

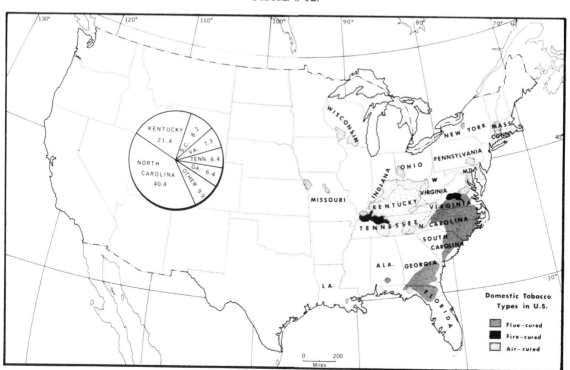

FIGURE 6-13. *Broadleaf burley tobacco growing on terraced and contour-planted fields near Georgetown, Kentucky. (U.S. Dept. of Agriculture)*

FIGURE 6-14.

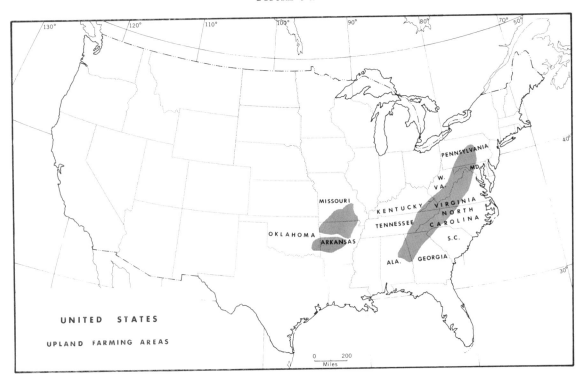

duce. Woodlands are often an important part of such agricultural enterprises.

Dairying. The Northeast, the Great Lakes states, and parts of the Far West make up the dairy regions. These regions include most of Wisconsin, large areas of Pennsylvania, Maryland, New York, Connecticut, Massachusetts, Rhode Island, Vermont, Michigan, and Minnesota, and smaller areas of Virginia, Maine, Ohio, Illinois, Washington, Oregon, and California (*Fig. 6-15*).

Dairying is the main form of agriculture for two reasons: (1) In parts of these areas, the summers are too short and the land is not suited to growing crops other than hay and pasture grasses. (2) These regions contain or are adjacent to many large cities, such as New York, Chicago, Boston, and Los Angeles, which provide good markets for fluid milk and other dairy products.

The average dairy farm is owned and operated by one family, with the help, sometimes, of one or two hired men. Usually, the family has invested almost all of its resources in dairy herds and very expensive equipment and buildings needed for successful dairy farming. Unfortunately, return on the investment is quite small, especially when one considers the seven-day-a-week routine necessary, the high cost of feed and irrigated pasture, and other such related items, plus the precarious market and price structure.

The dairy regions, of course, are not the only places with dairy cows. Much milk, butter, and cheese are produced in other areas. Farmers in Texas, for example, receive more than $130 million annually from the sale of dairy products.

Wheat. Although wheat grows in many states, one region to the west of the Corn Belt is particularly noted for the amount of wheat produced there. It includes North Dakota, parts of South Dakota, Montana, Nebraska, Kansas, Oklahoma, Texas, Washington, Oregon, Colorado, and Idaho (*Fig. 6-16*). This wheat region has two sections: the spring wheat area in the north, and the winter wheat area in the south. In the first, wheat is planted in the spring and harvested in late summer and early fall;

FIGURE 6-15.

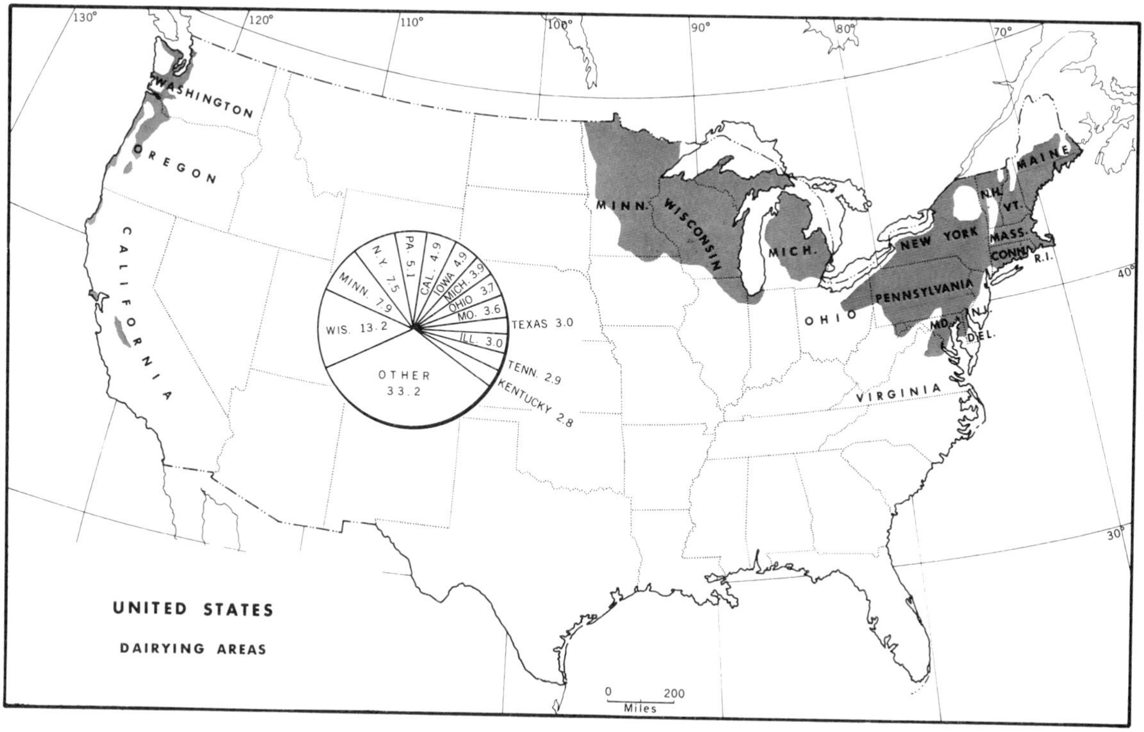

UNITED STATES

DAIRYING AREAS

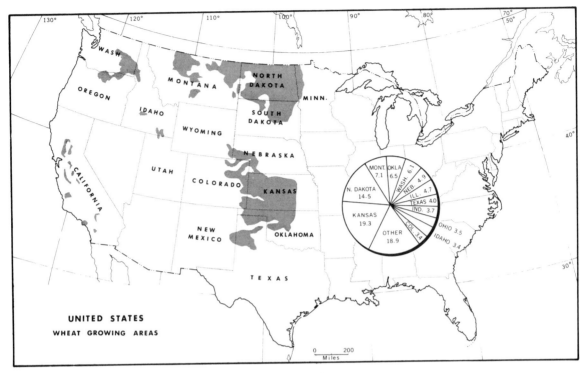

FIGURE 6-16.

in the second, it is planted in the fall and harvested in early summer.

The driest parts of the region go through long periods with no rain at all. Strong winds often erode the unprotected, dry soil, limiting the land use to a few drought-resistant crops, such as wheat and sorghum. Elsewhere in the region, barley and oats grow well. In addition, farmers in both the spring and winter wheat belts feed livestock as a supplement to wheat culture. For example, in Kansas, the heart of the winter wheat belt, farmers often receive more money from the sale of livestock and its products than from the sale of wheat.

Wheat farms are large, varying in size from 250 acres or more in Kansas to a thousand acres or more in North Dakota. The fairly level to rolling, stoneless wheat land is conducive to the use of large-scale machinery for plowing, planting, cultivating, harvesting, storing, and marketing of the wheat crop.

Livestock. Rangeland in the western states covers more than 700,000,000 acres. From the Dakotas and the sandhills of Nebraska, it extends westward and south over much of south-western Texas, the mountain and intermountain states (Arizona, Colorado, Idaho, Montana, New Mexico, Nevada, Utah, and Wyoming), and the Pacific Coast states (California, Oregon, and Washington). Soils, elevation, topography, and climate make the production of range livestock more profitable than crops over the greater portion of this area (*Fig. 6-17*).

Fruit. The United States is the world's largest producer of apples and apricots. Apple production is concentrated on the West Coast, particularly in Washington, although apples are also grown in New York, New England, the Appalachian subregion, and Michigan. In apricot production, California is dominant, as it is for clingstone peaches, grapes, plums, and prunes, among others (*Fig. 6-18*).

Although the United States is the only major pear producer outside Europe, it is a relatively modest exporter. California accounts for about half the nation's pear output; Oregon, Washington, and Utah each contribute a third to a fourth as much as California. East of the Rocky Mountains, Michigan is the only important producer.

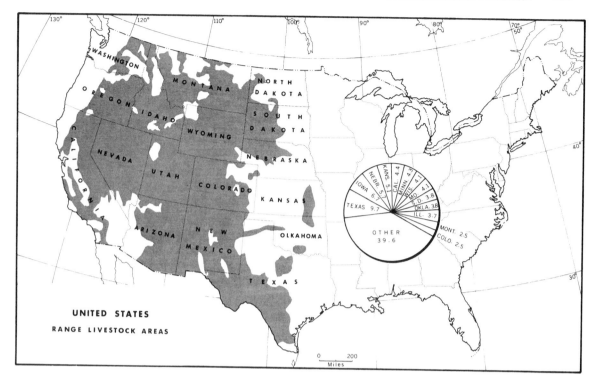

FIGURE 6-17.

FIGURE 6-18.

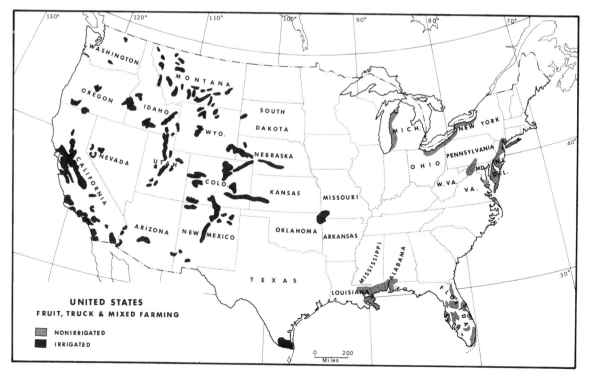

Citrus and truck crop areas are located on the central California coast, in southern California, southwestern Arizona, the lower Rio Grande Valley, and central Florida.

As a producer of oranges, California has yielded first place to Florida, since many groves in California have been subdivided for housing. In lemon production, however, California and Arizona together grow more than half of the world's lemons, with the frost-sensitive tree finding its best clime in the coastal areas of southern California. Florida formerly was a lemon producer, but output has become negligible because the frost hazard has proved to be too formidable.

Grapefruit is an American monopoly. The United States produces nearly nine-tenths of the world crop, consumes about five-sixths of it, and accounts for nearly half of the world's exports. Florida is the major producer, with Texas a close second. Production in the latter area (lower Rio Grande Valley) has been marked by violent ups and downs, however, because this northerly limit for citrus cultivation has been harassed by both freezes and droughts.

Arizona and California grow 70 per cent of the cantaloupes, while Florida, Texas, and Georgia produce more than half of the watermelons.

Vegetables. The United States produces more than twenty million tons of vegetables for *fresh consumption*. In tonnage, the leaders are potatoes, lettuce, onions, tomatoes, and cabbage. Vegetables for *processing* amount to another ten million tons a year; tomatoes, sweet corn, peas, green beans, and cucumbers for pickles are the five leaders.

Vegetable production is concentrated in a few relatively small areas in the United States. Five states—California, Florida, Texas, Arizona, and New York—produce 67 per cent of the tonnage of vegetables for fresh market, with 32 per cent of that total coming from California (*Fig. 6-18*). California, Wisconsin, New York, Ohio, and Illinois grow 61 per cent of all vegetables for processing, with California contributing 37 per cent of that total. Idaho, Maine, California, New

York, and North Dakota grow 55 per cent of the potatoes.

California, New Jersey, Ohio, and Indiana account for 80 per cent of the tomatoes for processing. California, New Jersey, and Washington grow 90 per cent of the asparagus for fresh and processed use.

The vegetable season begins with the harvesting of fall, winter, and early spring vegetables in Florida, the lower Rio Grande Valley of Texas, southern California, and Arizona. Production moves northward and ends with late harvest in fall (*Fig. 6-19*).

Yields per acre have trended sharply upward since 1940—some 100 to 300 per cent—because of better cultivating practices, improved varieties or hybrids, and a concentration of acreage in districts where yields are well above the average. In addition, high costs and shortages of labor have caused United States growers to increase the mechanization of vegetable production.

IRRIGATED AGRICULTURE

Dry lands become highly productive when irrigated, and it is estimated that one acre of irrigated land is equivalent to four acres of nonirrigated, tillable (dry-farmed) land. The area presently under irrigation—roughly 30 million acres—is reported to be about half the total possible irrigable land. The remaining

FIGURE 6-19. *Winter harvest of tomatoes near Homestead, Florida. (Florida News Bureau)*

portion undoubtedly will be reclaimed, but this will require a huge financial outlay, since the largest reservoirs, the longest canals, and the costliest tunnels and inverted siphons are yet to be constructed.

In addition to the handicap of expensive water and improvements, irrigated farms must market their products mainly in the humid Middle West and East, where the same products are grown without irrigation and much closer to market. The irrigated areas in the subtropical part of the nation are an exception, because they grow mostly noncompetitive crops.

Farmers who work irrigated land grow many kinds of crops—sugar beets, fruits, vegetables, alfalfa, nuts, grasses, wheat, cotton, and seeds for use in other regions. Much of this irrigated land is farmed as a modern factory is operated. A manager supervises a large force of technicians and laborers who maintain complicated irrigation systems, prepare the ground for planting, apply fertilizer, fight weeds, insects, and plant diseases with chemicals, and harvest the crops.

East of the Mississippi River, where ample rain usually falls, irrigation farming is practiced more and more. Some farmers have found that irrigation not only increases the production of their farms, but is also a source of water for crops if drought hits the region. Most states west of the Mississippi River are heavily dependent upon irrigation. Of these, California leads all others, with more than seven million acres devoted to it. Some 68.5 per cent of all California farms (about 84,500) are irrigated, and they require approximately 21 million acre-feet of water per annum.

SHIFTING FARMLANDS

In recent years there have been steady shifts in the geography of American farming. According to the U.S. Department of Agriculture, for instance, Texas harvests more acres of cotton than the combined total acreage in the traditional cotton region of North Carolina, South Carolina, Georgia, Tennessee, and Alabama. And, in yield per acre, California and Arizona rank far ahead of every other cotton producing state. Florida, in spite of its high percentage of swamp and marshland, is an important cattle raising state; sugar beets, traditionally grown in Colorado, Utah, California, and the Red River Valley, may shortly move east to become a major crop in such untraditional locations as Maine and New York.

Several factors have influenced this shift, including government controls and programs, consumer demand, improved irrigation, automation, and the pressures of real estate developers, whose bulldozers and carpenters precede the movement of urban dwellers into farm lands surrounding metropolitan areas. In addition, much of this shifting grows from farmer ingenuity. As government allocations took cotton lands out of production, for example, the farmers in the South moved quickly to shift to other high-income crops. Much former cotton land is now used for cattle, and even more has been put into soybeans, once thought of as a crop that would grow only in the flat lands of Illinois and Iowa.

New patterns. In addition to its new importance as a beef-cattle center, Florida has become a big dairy state. This is caused, in part, by the great demand of the rapidly growing population for milk and milk products. Also, bulk milk prices are about twice as high in Florida as in the Great Lakes states.

Many midwestern cattle growers consider the newly developed hybrid cattle that are raised in Florida to be scrubby and inferior in appearance. But once they are "finished off" by concentrated high protein feeding, their meat is just as good as that from cattle raised in any other state. Georgia, Alabama, and Mississippi beef, too, is taking its place in restaurants that once got most of their choice beef from the Middle West.

California, Arizona, and other western states are also challenging the Middle West for cattle production supremacy, primarily because of the use of the *feed lot technique*. The owners of feed lots grow no crops and raise no cattle. Rather, they buy large herds that can be moved economically by truck or train, feed them concentrated diets through highly automated machinery, and bring them rapidly up from poor to choice grades. One feed lot can turn over 2,000 to 30,000 head of cattle annually, whereas a midwestern farm produces only a few hundred that the farmer raises from birth to market age.

Despite this new competition, because of the steadily growing demand for meat and meat products, the Midwest is not declining as a cattle raising area. Instead, cattle raising is spreading throughout the South and Southeast and expanding in the Far West to keep up with the demand. There are more cattle ranches in more places now than ever before.

Poultry raising, a highly specialized commercial operation, used to be centered in New Jersey, Delaware, and Maryland. These three states were the leading sources of broiler-fryers, although most major metropolitan areas were, and still are, supplied by a number of nearby chicken farms producing eggs and chickens. Now, however, there has been a big movement to the South, with Georgia becoming one of the big chicken and egg producers.

Production of sugar beets has grown steadily in spite of efforts by the sugarcane industry to prevent it. Since many big users of sugar would prefer to buy home-grown sugar rather than continue to import it or transport it from cane producing areas, a movement to develop sugar beet farming in New York and Maine has begun. It will take at least $20,000,000 to construct adequate processing plants in each of these states, however, and there is some question about whether the money will be available in Maine, traditionally a potato and lobster state. A major soft drink company has plans to finance such a plant in New York. This would make sugar beets a major crop in a state better known for other vegetables, apples, and grapes.

Canadian Agriculture

Despite the pre-eminence of industry in Canada's economy, agriculture remains an important economic activity, employing about one-seventh of the total working population and accounting for nearly a third of all exports.

In the last 20 years the volume of farm production has increased by more than 50 per cent, though the area of improved land has increased by only 11 million acres, from 86 million to 97 million. This increase has been achieved mainly by a great rise in productivity per acre as a result of a mechanical revolution, abandonment of land of poor quality, development of disease-resistant grain crops, and expansion of irrigation and of acreage devoted to high-value specialty crops, such as sugar beets and tobacco.

Before World War II, each farm worker in Canada produced enough food to feed 10 people; now the figure has risen to 32. Much of this increased efficiency may be attributed to research. The Canadian Department of Agriculture carries out about 70 per cent of the agricultural research in Canada, the remainder being done by universities, provincial governments, and private industry.

LOCATION AND DISTRIBUTION

The occupied agricultural land of Canada covers only about 7.5 per cent of the total land area, including the Yukon and the Northwest Territories. Climate, geology, and topography have combined to concentrate agriculture in the southern third of the country, largely within 200 miles of the U.S. border. In the northern pioneer fringe, agriculture is not a dominant economic activity, and it tends to be associated with, or replaced by, mining, forestry, fishing, and trapping.

Among the provinces, Prince Edward Island has the greatest proportion of its land area in farms—two-thirds of the total. Saskatchewan follows with 46 per cent in farms. In contrast, farm land constitutes a very small proportion of the total land area in Newfoundland, and amounts to less than 5 per cent in both British Columbia and Quebec. The average size of Canadian farms is 359 acres. As may be expected, the farms in the grain-growing prairies are the largest, averaging over 600 acres, and those in the mixed farming region of central Canada (Ontario and Quebec) are the smallest, averaging 151 acres.

In general, Canada may be divided into four main agricultural areas—the Maritime Provinces (excluding Newfoundland), central Canada, the Prairie Provinces, and British Columbia. Although local differences in agricultural production exist within these areas, one or two major crops predominate.

The regional differences in Canadian farm production are indicated by the distribution of cash income from farm product sales.

Tables VII and *VIII* show cash receipts by item and province from the sale of farm products, 1961-64.

Wheat still reigns supreme among Canadian grains. In fact, in recent years the carry-over of wheat has run into the hundreds of millions of bushels at the beginning of the crop year. Elevators have also been jammed to capacity with additional hundreds of millions of bushels of oats, barley, rye, and flaxseed. The surplus problem was slightly alleviated in 1961 and again in 1964, with the sale of large quantities of wheat to China and the U.S.S.R. respectively. Moreover, the specialized wheat economy of the Prairie Provinces is slowly being replaced by a more diversified cultivation and by the raising of livestock. Dairy production has expanded rapidly there; and, in addition, the Prairie Provinces are now Canada's main source of beef.

In the east, livestock has become by far the largest source of income to the farmers. A federal freight assistance program has aided this trend by increasing consumption of feed grain shipped from the west, for livestock depends more on fodder crops here than on pasture. The other striking development in the east is an increasing diversification resulting from the exploitation of special soil and climatic conditions, such as tobacco in Norfolk County (Ontario) and Joliette County (Quebec), potatoes on Prince Edward Island, fruit (especially apples and peaches) in the Niagara and St. Lawrence Lowlands, and truck farming in southern Ontario and around Montreal.

Outlook

In the year 2000 the Anglo-American farmer will be a sophisticated executive with a computer for a foreman. The fisherman will be a farmer methodically harvesting the oceans. The rancher will ride herd on nothing more ornery than huge livestock hotels where every aspect of the environment is precisely controlled.

As a result, Anglo-Americans will eat better than ever, despite a population far larger than today's. Food pills, though they are under development for possible use in the space program, will remain the gourmet's nightmare of a more distant future. At the very worst, a budget-minded housewife might serve up tasty dishes that look like meat but have been created from the protein of soybeans or algae at half the cost and twice the convenience.

In general, according to agricultural scientists and food technologists, the outlook in Anglo-America is for more of the same foods we eat today; but they will be better and, quite possibly, cheaper.

COMPUTER AGRICULTURE

Farming has become a highly complex business, with the level of profit governed by how well a farmer chooses among variables, such as types of crops and seed, and quantity and type of fertilizer. Agricultural experts contend that computers could prove invaluable in guiding farmers to the best decision. They cite the following example of a Prairie City, Illinois, farmer who, in 1965, competed against an International Minerals and Chemical computer to see whether man or machine could come up with the most profitable plan for a farm.

With both the computer and the farmer using the same anticipated operating costs and market prices, the farmer chose to plant 98 acres in corn, 16 acres in oats, 20 acres in alfalfa, 20 acres in soybeans, and 8 acres in wheat. Based on this planting scheme and his choice of fertilizers, the farmer arrived at an estimated gross profit of $6,789.

The computer came up with a different plan, however. It calculated that by planting 134 acres in corn, 20 acres in alfalfa, and 8 acres in wheat, and by using different intensities of fertilizer, profit would zoom to $8,829, an increase of 30 per cent.

TABLE VII

CASH RECEIPTS FROM THE SALE OF CANADIAN FARM PRODUCTS, 1961-64*

Item	1961 (Thousands of Dollars)	1962 (Thousands of Dollars)	1963 (Thousands of Dollars)	1964 (Thousands of Dollars)
Grains, seeds, and hay..........	794,765	916,566	960,591	1,208,148
Wheat	487,320	526,527	598,102	741,004
Wheat participation payments..	122,330	152,523	123,968	199,744
Oats	23,900	33,531	45,745	33,011
Oats participation payments	8,928	4,301	......	10,673
Barley	63,813	52,385	67,744	71,972
Barley participation payments ..	2,022	24,244	......	14,092
Canadian Wheat Board net cash advance payments	−34,538	5,916	11,203	−12,123
Rye	4,946	8,647	7,763	8,059
Flaxseed	49,770	47,617	36,367	59,754
Rapeseed	17,047	10,127	11,715	17,957
Soybeans	12,649	14,906	13,463	15,709
Corn	21,866	24,331	29,004	35,873
Clover and grass seed	11,541	10,367	15,056	11,970
Hay and clover	3,171	1,144	461	453
Vegetables and other field crops...	227,380	227,256	262,178	257,764
Potatoes	38,101	37,025	41,945	55,114
Vegetables	74,002	80,016	79,891	86,036
Sugar beets	12,525	13,706	26,138	19,891
Tobacco	102,752	96,509	114,204	96,723
Livestock and poultry	1,102,423	1,174,355	1,134,873	1,153,605
Cattle and calves	628,842	680,055	638,122	645,487
Sheep and lambs	11,678	10,681	9,715	9,437
Hogs	317,745	330,301	318,174	325,526
Poultry	144,158	153,318	168,862	173,155
Dairy products	533,978	499,576	509,812	530,983
Fruits	53,722	58,355	66,431	71,131
Other principal farm products	157,634	156,995	166,203	147,028
Eggs	141,970	141,601	148,381	132,566
Wool	3,003	2,784	2,652	2,520
Honey	5,605	5,204	7,444	6,855
Maple products	7,056	7,406	7,726	5,087
Miscellaneous farm products	35,954	34,655	35,029	37,236
Forest products	27,841	26,580	26,475	26,820
Fur farming	18,117	19,351	21,623	22,000
Deficiency payments	48	2,267	1,311	867
Eggs	15	577	59	867
Sugar beets	......	733	1,251	......
Potatoes	33	957	1	......
Cash receipts from farm products Total	2,951,862	3,115,956	3,184,526	3,455,582
Supplementary payments	35,766	70,313	14,769	8,477
Total, cash receipts	2,987,628	3,186,269	3,199,295	3,464,059

*Roger Duhamel, *Canada Yearbook* (Ottawa: Queen's Printer, 1966).

TABLE VIII

CASH RECEIPTS FROM THE SALE OF CANADIAN FARM PRODUCTS, BY PROVINCE, 1961-64°

Province	1961 (Thousands of Dollars)	1962 (Thousands of Dollars)	1963 (Thousands of Dollars)	1964 (Thousands of Dollars)
Prince Edward Island	23,913	24,929	25,764	32,723
Nova Scotia	45,498	46,028	46,251	43,910
New Brunswick	42,311	42,477	42,754	49,070
Quebec	437,309	449,632	459,515	456,635
Ontario	890,880	925,810	986,370	996,596
Manitoba	242,678	248,111	264,784	293,956
Saskatchewan	600,964	675,848	690,835	836,711
Alberta	531,510	552,624	519,642	596,058
British Columbia	136,799	150,497	148,611	149,923
Total	2,951,862	3,115,956	3,184,526	3,455,582

°Roger Duhamel, *Canada Yearbook* (Ottawa: Queen's Printer, 1966).

It is true that computers are quite expensive for a small farmer to lease or own, but farms are rapidly becoming both fewer and larger. There are now 3.2 million farms in the United States, 42 per cent less than in 1950; and it is estimated that 140,000 of these produce 42 per cent of the nation's foodstuffs. By 1975, it is estimated, there will be only 2 million farms; and, according to researchers, the use of computers will be widespread.

AUTOMATION

Farm machinery will be automated in the future, too, as planting and tilling become more precise and harvesting comes to include more processing and packaging operations. According to the experts, tape-controlled programs will direct unmanned machines over fields in predetermined patterns. Sensing devices similar to those of space telemetry systems will relay information on field and crop conditions to a computer that will be able to send back orders instantaneously to speed up or slow down operations, alter the depth at which seeds are being planted, and regulate the intensities with which fertilizer is being applied.

Hopefully, geneticists will breed plants so they mature at the same time. Giant harvesters could then not only pick food crops like peas, but could shell, grade, package, and freeze them. When finished, the harvesters could roar down the highway at the speed of trucks to deliver the produce to transportation depots for direct dispatch to retail warehouses, while it was still in a fresh-from-the-farm state.

CONTROLLED-ENVIRONMENT AGRICULTURE

High land values may eventually make it worthwhile for some farmers and ranchers to move their operations into multi-level structures. Besides utilizing land more fully, indoor farming would raise production by permitting the raising of crops year-round.

Crops. One Chicago engineering consultant sees the possibility of huge skyscraper "factories" located in major cities for the production of tomatoes, lettuce, and other truck produce. The plants might be grown in trays of chemical solutions or synthetic "soils." Carefully controlled doses of carbon dioxide and artificial light would speed growth and insure uniformity. Proximity to market would enhance the flavor of products grown in such an environment.

Livestock. Controlled-environment breeding and raising of livestock is almost a certainty. A Kansas City agricultural equipment concern recently began marketing the "bacon bin," a fully mechanized facility for raising hogs. The two-story circular structure contains wedge-shaped pens for 46 sows and 450 hogs. Feed and water are deposited in the pens by a rotating augur, and waste disposal systems under the slatted floors permit farmers to liquidize and store manure for possible use on fields. Temperature controls allow the hogs, whose weight-gaining ability is impaired by heat, to gain more weight on less feed.

The farmer of the future may need to spend only ten minutes or so a day looking after his hogs. Hog production may be limited to a few-score producers, each of whom will raise up to a million swine at a time in neatly arranged rows of "bacon bins."

Selected References

BRAIDWOOD, ROBERT J., "The Agricultural Revolution," *Scientific American*, Vol. 203, September, 1960, pp. 131–148.

CAMU, PIERRE, WEEKS, E. P., and SAMETZ, Z. W., *Economic Geography of Canada*, Toronto: Macmillan of Canada, 1964.

CANADALE, G. S., *Animals and Man*, New York: Frederick A. Praeger, 1953.

CLAWSON, MARION, *Land for Americans, Trends, Prospects, and Problems*, Chicago: Rand McNally & Co., 1963.

GREGOR, HOWARD F., "Industrialized Drylot Dairying: An Overview," *Economic Geography*, Vol. 39, October, 1963, pp. 298–318.

HARRIS, CHAUNCY D., "Agricultural Production in the United States the Past Fifty Years and in the Next," *Geographical Review*, Vol. 47, April, 1957, pp. 175–193.

HAYSTEAD, LADD, and FITE, GILBERT C., *The Agricultural Regions of the United States*, Norman: University of Oklahoma Press, 1955.

HIDORE, JOHN J., "The Relation Between Cash-Grain Farming and Landforms," *Economic Geography*, Vol. 39, January, 1963.

HIGBEE, EDWARD C., *American Agriculture: Geography, Resources, Conservation*, New York: John Wiley & Sons, Inc., 1958.

————, *Farms and Farmers in an Urban Age*, New York: The Twentieth Century Fund, 1963.

KELLOG, CHARLES E., *The Soils That Support Us*, New York: The Macmillan Co., 1941.

LYON, T. LYTTLETON, BUCKMAN, HARRY O., and BRADY, C. NYLE, *The Nature and Property of Soils*, New York: The Macmillan Co., 1952.

MELLOR, JOHN W., *The Economics of Agricultural Development*, Ithaca, N. Y.: Cornell University Press, 1966.

PARKER, W. H., *Anglo-America, a Systematic Regional Geography*, London: University of London Press, 1962.

PATERSON, J. H., *North America: A Regional Geography* (3rd ed.), London: Oxford University Press, 1965.

PUTNAM, D. F. (ed.), *Canadian Regions: A Geography of Canada*, New York: Thomas Y. Crowell Co., 1952.

ROBINSON, J. L., and ROBINSON, M. J., *The Geography of Canada*, Toronto: Longman's 1950.

STEELE, J. G., *The Measure of Our Land*, Washington, D.C.: Soil Conservation Service, Government Printing Office, 1951.

WAHL., E., *This Land, a Geography of Canada*, Toronto: Oxford University Press, 1961.

WOOTEN, HUGH H., and ANDERSON, JAMES R., *Agricultural Land Resources in the United States* (Agricultural Information Bulletin No. 140) Washington, D.C.: Government Printing Office, 1955.

WOYTINSKY, EMMA S., *Profile of the U.S. Economy: A Survey of Growth and Change*, New York: Frederick A. Praeger, 1967.

Yearbook of Agriculture, Washington, D.C.: U.S. Department of Agriculture, Government Printing Office, 1958, 1959, 1960, 1964, 1966.

7 The Transportation Pattern

Transportation is inseparable from human progress and has shaped much of the history of civilization. It has caused the values of natural resources to be realized, the products of labor to be interchanged, natural site advantages to be exploited, workers and production to become specialized, and over-all productivity to increase. It is a truism that the world's most advanced and prosperous nations are the ones with the greatest facilities for the movement of people and goods, and that the world's most backward nations are those with a paucity of transport.

The United States

The transportation system of the United States is more complete and better integrated than that of any other large country. All types of modern transport facilities—railroads, roads, waterways, airways, and pipelines—are extensively used throughout the country.

WATERWAYS

Until the development of the railroads in the mid-nineteenth century, the majority of goods transported in the United States were moved by water. Although railroads and, later, trucks and airplanes, have dominated the shipment of most kinds of goods, water transportation has remained important, especially for bulky products of low value in relation to weight, such as coal and iron ore (*see Fig. 1-21*).

With the exception of the Great Lakes and the coastal waters, improvement of the waterways of the United States has failed to keep pace with that for land transport. The only modern river and canal transport routes that carry appreciable amounts of traffic are the Ohio, the lower Mississippi, the Illinois, the Black Warrior-Tombigbee, and the Tennessee (*Fig. 7-1*). On the Pacific Coast, the Columbia and Sacramento-San Joaquin are major waterways, although they generally carry only bulky commodities of low value.

Today there are some 23,170 miles of navigable waterways in the nation. In some respects, they have played a less significant role in the country's national life than have the rivers of most countries. Perhaps one explanation is that the major streams generally flow from north to south, whereas most traffic flows east-west. Moreover, when the country was expanding and developing, railroads experienced a tremendous building surge; during the same period relatively little development of river and canal transport took place.

The one waterway in the country that has retained its early importance is the Great Lakes-Mohawk-Hudson system. Not only does this continuous chain of navigable waters offer favorable east-west orientation, but it also taps the exceedingly rich iron ore deposits and the great grain harvests of the north-central part of the country (*Fig. 7-2*).

Although the Mohawk-Hudson portion has declined in significance because of both highway and railroad competition, the Great Lakes are today more valuable than ever, especially since the completion of the St. Lawrence Seaway in 1959. The Seaway Project, a joint enterprise of Canada and the United States, took five

years to complete and cost some $500 million, but it opened the entire St. Lawrence Basin to ocean-going vessels that were capable of carrying up to 25,000 tons of cargo. This made it possible for midwestern producers of grain, lumber, automobiles, and many other types of goods, to ship directly to European markets without the expense of transshipment, and for steel manufacturers to tap the rich iron ore deposits of Labrador at the very time when the high-grade Lake Superior deposits were beginning to be exhausted. (*Fig. 7-3*).

RAILROADS

The United States has roughly 6 per cent of the world's population and land surface, but about 30 per cent of its railway mileage. The trackage operated by American railroads grew from 9,000 miles in 1850 to 226,000 in 1945. After World War II, there was a slight but clear drop in the total amount of railroad trackage used in the U.S., as well as a change in the kind of power used. The coal-burning locomotive almost completely disappeared, and its place was taken by the oil-consuming diesel engine.

National, political, and economic unity probably would not have been possible in the United States had the nation not been knit together by an elaborate pattern of integrated railroad systems. Until the middle of the nineteenth century, the inland waterways had shaped the main avenues of trade in a north-south direction. The railroads changed the face of the nation by developing east-west routes across mountains and rivers, thus contributing to the rise of many new cities. Today, all of the important cities of the country, including the major ports of the Atlantic and the Pacific coasts, are connected by railroads (*Fig. 7-4*).

The density of the railroad lines conforms rather closely to the distribution of the population and, therefore, to the needs of the country. Seven transcontinental lines pass through the sparsely populated mountain, desert, and semi-arid lands of the West to connect the eastern part of the country with the metropolitan areas and the productive valleys of the Pacific Coast states. Although the railroads are owned by

FIGURE 7-1. *An aerial view of the steelmaking and rolling facilities of Wheeling Steel Corp. at Steubenville, Ohio. Shipping by barge on the Ohio River provides low transportation costs.*

FIGURE 7-2. *The Mohawk Valley has been a travel route since the earliest days. New York's Barge Canal uses the Mohawk River as part of a crossstate route from Albany to Buffalo.*

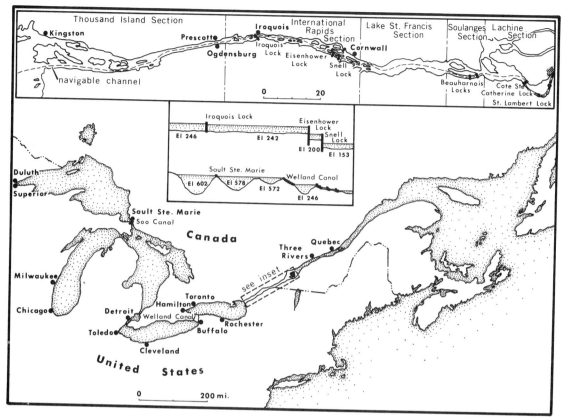

FIGURE 7-3. *The St. Lawrence Seaway.*

more than 150 large companies as well as by innumerable small ones, uniformity of gauge makes it possible to run any trains on any tracks, and the various companies freely interchange rolling stock to avoid transfer of merchandise in transit.

Freight. During World War II, railroads carried the largest share of intercity freight traffic, and it was their chief source of revenue. As late as 1955 they still carried half of it, but by the start of the 1960's the share had dropped to below 45 per cent, although it still yielded approximately 85 per cent of all rail operating revenue. Railroads are rapidly losing their passenger trade to the automobile, which, by 1960, accounted for almost 90 per cent of intercity passenger traffic.

In the early years of this century, coal accounted for perhaps one out of every three tons of materials transported between cities. It has

been the number one commodity carried by the railroads in terms of both freight and revenue, and it has been responsible for a relatively constant proportion of rail traffic. In absolute tonnage, the amount of coal consumed in the United States now and the amount moved by rail is not too different from what it was before World War I. In relative terms, however, coal has declined from supplying about two-thirds of U.S. energy needs at the end of World War I to supplying about one-fourth now; thus the relative fuel-carrying importance of the railways has also declined. Gas moves by pipeline, and petroleum and its products chiefly by pipeline, tank ship, and barge.

In the second largest segment of intercity carriage, manufactured products, rail's absolute tonnage position has changed little from World War II, although output of manufactured products has increased. Trucking has captured most of this increase. Except for

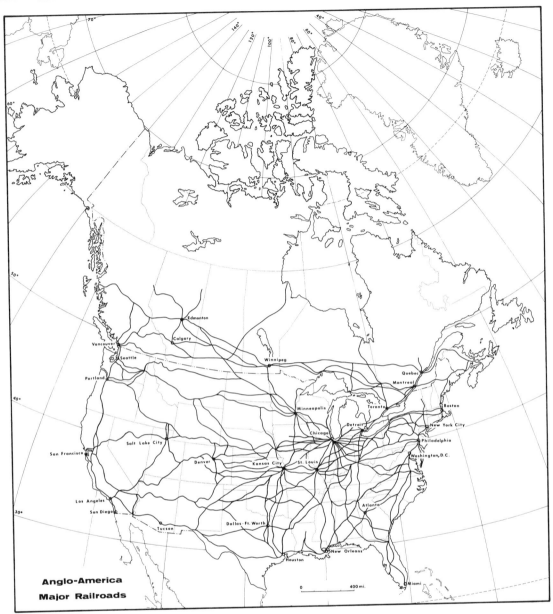

Anglo-America

Major Railroads

FIGURE 7-4.

grains, railroads have also lost out to trucking in the carriage of most agricultural commodities.

Movements of bulk commodities over long distances will no doubt continue to be shared by the low-cost agencies—rail, waterway, and pipeline. Although both trucks and railroads will participate in transporting the growing volume of carload shipments, it is anticipated that trucks will probably take the greater share (*Fig. 7-5*).

For smaller shipments, trucks have the advantage, although air shipments promise to become increasingly important. Regionally, trucks are the means by which increasingly large urban agglomerations can be welded into economic units. Long-distance trucking may be expected to continue its expansion.

TABLE IX

RAILWAY STATISTICS FOR THE UNITED STATES*

	1945	1950	1955	1960	1962	1963
Trackage Owned (Miles)	226,696	223,779	220,670	217,552	215,090	214,387
Trackage Built (Miles)	40	33	105	21	41	23
Locomotives in Use (Number)	46,253	42,951	33,533	31,178	30,701	30,506
Freight Cars in Use (Number)	1,787,073	1,745,778	1,723,747	1,690,396	1,581,213	1,542,456
Passenger Cars in Use (Number)	38,633	37,359	32,118	25,746	23,430	22,616
Passengers Carried (Number)	897,384,000	488,019,000	433,307,627	327,171,745	313,083,814	310,999,221
Freight Carried (Tons)	2,961,789,000	2,710,919,000	2,745,378,713	2,409,039,608	2,400,211,182	2,492,971,683
Employees (Number)	1,439,000	1,237,000	1,071,393	793,071	711,000	690,585
Employees' Wages (Dollars)	3,900,928,000	4,644,890,000	5,044,278,278	4,956,902,360	4,721,895,326	4,690,052,576

*Source: Interstate Commerce Commission.

Outlook. Since World War II, U.S. railroads have poured some $16 billion into such improvements as more powerful locomotives, specialized freight cars, and elaborate traffic control systems that greatly speed the distribution of goods. Profit statistics are gloomy, but despite them, there is currently much optimism within the industry. The Association of American Railroads is pressing hard for legislation that will improve the competitive position of members. It is asking more freedom in rate-making, the end of "subsidies for competitors," reduced taxes, and the right to diversify by offering airline, barge, and truck service.

There has been more hopeful, aggressive thinking in the railroads in the last few years than there had been in the previous twenty.

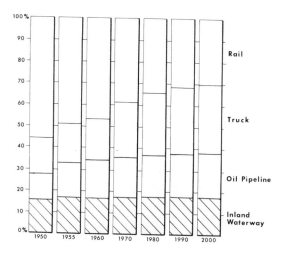

FIGURE 7-5. *Intercity freight transportation in the United States, with projections for 1970-2000.*

The most spectacular gains have been in freight handling methods, such as piggybacking, the hauling of loaded truck trailers on flatcars; in containerization, essentially piggybacking without wheels; in development of cars that carry specific products more efficiently; and in faster schedules.

PIPELINES

When all methods of transportation are considered, there is still nothing cheaper than the ocean tanker or freighter. Considering transportation just on land, however, pipelines are more economical than railroads. It costs roughly 20 cents to transport a barrel of oil 100 miles by rail; by pipeline the cost can be as low at 3 cents.

There are other advantages: no empty vehicles or cartons to be returned, fewer problems with dust or contamination, smaller losses in transport, less maintenance of equipment, and a saving in labor through less handling.

There are also drawbacks: the initial cost of construction is high; the pipe may be eroded if it is used to transport such materials as sand or coal; the materials themselves may "wear" during shipment; there must be a long-term source of supply and a market large enough to make the investment worth while; large volumes of fluid (usually water) in which to "float" the piped material may be required at the dispatching end; and, in some cases (as for fine coal), the cost of separating the product from the water at the receiving end is high.

Cargoes. Although natural gas and petroleum are still their primary cargoes, pipelines are growing more versatile and sophisticated as their share of Anglo-America's freight business multiplies. As recently as World War II, the United States had only 395,093 miles of pipeline. Now more than 886,719 miles of pipeline criss-cross the nation. Pipelines recently upped their share of the cargo market threefold, as they now haul about 18 per cent of the nation's freight (see Figs. 3-7 and 3-8).

A key feature of this expansion has been the myriad new uses that are constantly cropping up. For example, one pipeline in Portland, Oregon, transports sardines from fishing dock to cannery. And in Knoxville, Tennessee, coffee beans travel underground from one building to another across town. These pipelines vary from 1 to 16 inches in diameter, and travel anywhere from a few hundred feet to 50 miles or more. Such pipelines, of course, can hardly be classed in size and weight with the giant tubes carrying petroleum or natural gas. Nevertheless, they are bona fide pipelines in that they transport material over considerable distances on a regular basis.

Acids, hydrocarbon-base chemicals, hydroxides, and various other chemicals in liquid and gaseous forms move via pipelines. And many solid materials, such as iron and copper ores, sand, gravel, coal, borax, limestone, and gilsonite (a form of asphalt) in lump or pulverized form, move through pipelines in liquid suspensions. These slurry pipelines generally extend less than 100 miles, but longer ones are in the offing.

In many cases there is actually no need to build additional pipelines to haul extra freight. A whole range of commodities can simply hitch a ride in sealed containers in existing pipelines carrying crude oil and gas. If the container is designed just slightly smaller than the inside diameter of the pipe, it can be propelled by the pressure of the liquid or gas. If made substantially smaller than the inside diameter, the capsule can simply float along with the stream. In fact, the Research Council of Alberta, Canada, has already floated wheat, heavy chemicals, and minerals in sealed cylindrical and spherical plastic capsules through pipelines carrying crude oil.

The use of pipelines can sometimes bring down manufacturing and processing expenses as well as transportation costs. One company already floats up to 200 tons of sulphite pulp a day through pipelines from its pulp facility to a newsprint mill, thus saving a half million dollars a year. If the company used overland transportation, it would mean dehydrating the heavy pulp, hauling the sheets by rail, and finally remixing them with water to turn them back into pulp.

Actually, the pipelines could serve as processing equipment as well as conveyors. The chips in a long pipeline would soak up enough water as they floated along to speed up their conversion into pulp. This could eliminate the soaking ponds that some pulp mills use to prepare wood chips for processing. Furthermore, chemicals can be added to a large variety of items carried in water to help process them as they move.

Versatility. Homeowners, as well as industry, are benefiting from the versatility of pipelines. For years, direct underground connections between crude oil producing fields, refineries, and central storage facilities have cut transportation costs while raising the operating efficiency of oil companies. Soon some of these pipelines may be extended right into the home. In fact, a first step in this direction has already been taken in Ledyard, Connecticut, when some 350 residents recently were able to use fuel oil from pipelines running directly into their homes. This direct service saved each household an average of $12 through the winter over the cost of truck delivery to their home tanks. It also eliminated the need for individual basement storage tanks and, most important, guaranteed the consumer a round-the-clock fuel supply for his furnace.

Outlook. Many industry officials believe that the expansion of pipeline systems is bound to continue, even though rising costs may slow construction of some lines. Tomorrow's pipelines will make use of new coatings, new and lighter installation equipment, automatic controls, and currently experimental automatic welding techniques to join sections of pipe. Automation will become more prevalent too.

Whatever the developments in pipelining, the biggest users of pipes in the next 20 to 70 years will probably still be the oil and natural gas companies. Here the big changes will be in engineering and in new materials for pipes. Already some plastic pipelines exist, although production is limited because plastic pipe is comparatively expensive and lacking in strength.

HIGHWAYS

In a land abounding in gadgets, probably none has had more impact on American living habits than the automobile. Automobiles, however, do not run on gasoline alone. Decisions to purchase automobiles imply decisions to build highways (*Fig. 7-6*). Providing for highways traditionally has been a state and local government concern. This is still true, but the federal government has, in the past dozen years, considerably expanded its role in highway finance.

Federal-aid highway systems. There are really a number of highway systems in this country, such as federal-aid, state, county, and township. The federal-aid system has two major components: (1) the primary system, approximately 256,000 miles of roads connecting all principal cities, county seats, ports, manufacturing regions, and other traffic generating areas; and (2) the secondary system, some 590,000 miles, including important feeder roads that connect farms, factories, distribution out-

FIGURE 7-6. *A freeway extension under construction in San Francisco. Freeway construction in urban areas involves fantastic expenditures of money. (California State Division of Highways)*

lets, and smaller communities of the nation with the primary system.

The primary network generally comprises the main state trunkline roads, while the secondary system is commonly known as the "farm to market" roads. Federal aid for these two systems (often referred to as the ABC program) amounts to approximately 50 per cent of the cost of engineering, construction, and right-of-way acquisition. Maintenance and policing are, however, supported entirely by state and local governments. An apportionment formula, based on land use, road mileage, and population, is used to determine the amount of aid given to each state. Adjustments are made for those states, mainly in the West, that contain large areas of federally-owned land. The federal government, primarily through the Bureau of Public Roads in the Department of Commerce, maintains some control over standards.

Interstate Highway System. In 1944 Congress authorized the selection, primarily out of the federal-aid primary system routes, of a special network of roads not to exceed 40,000 miles in length. These roads would be located so as "to connect by routes, as direct as practicable, the principal metropolitan areas, cities, and industrial centers, to serve the national defense, and to connect at suitable border points with routes of continental importance in the Dominion of Canada and the Republic of Mexico." The result was the National System of Interstate Highways, later renamed the National System of Defense and Interstate Highways. The authorized length was extended to 42,000 miles in 1956.

Figure 7-7 shows the designated routes of the system. Most of the mileage is concentrated in areas of high population density, where traffic volume is heaviest. The system has been designed to carry the kinds and volume of traffic predicted for 1975, and it is expected to handle an estimated 25 per cent of all highway traffic.

Not until 1952 were funds authorized specifically for the Interstate System, and then it was the rather small amount of $25 million annually. In 1954 the authorization was increased to $175 million per annum, and the federal con-

tribution to the system increased from 50 to 60 per cent.

A marked enlargement of the program came with the Federal-aid Highway Act of 1956. In important respects, this law made a distinct break with the traditional federal approach:

1. Grants were to be made to the states over a 13-year period for the Interstate System, with the federal contribution covering 90 per cent of the total cost of planning and placement.
2. The funds for the program were to be obtained by earmarking highway-user taxes, and were to be placed in a special trust fund. Through a requirement that the funds remain solvent at all times, the project was put on a build-as-you-pay basis.
3. Allocation of funds after 1958 was to be made on the basis of amounts needed to complete the system.

The total cost of this network of high-speed super roads is currently estimated at $51 billion, of which the federal government will pay 90 per cent and the states 10 per cent. To appreciate the magnitude of this expenditure, it might be recalled that the economic assistance to Europe under the Marshall Plan amounted to $10.7 billion.

The impetus for extensive federal support in highway expenditures had its roots in two pressures: (1) the depression periods and World War II were times of subnormal replacement and repair, and (2) the postwar increase in traffic volume required concomitant highway expenditures at a time when pressures for state and local services were especially strong. The postwar toll road movement was in large part a response to the demands for the extension of roads that carried a heavy volume of traffic, and for more safety on these roads.

Some of the reasons given to justify the cost of the system deserve enumeration:

1. Even apart from the demands resulting from an expanding economy, highway passenger and freight travel have generally increased more than other means of conveyance.

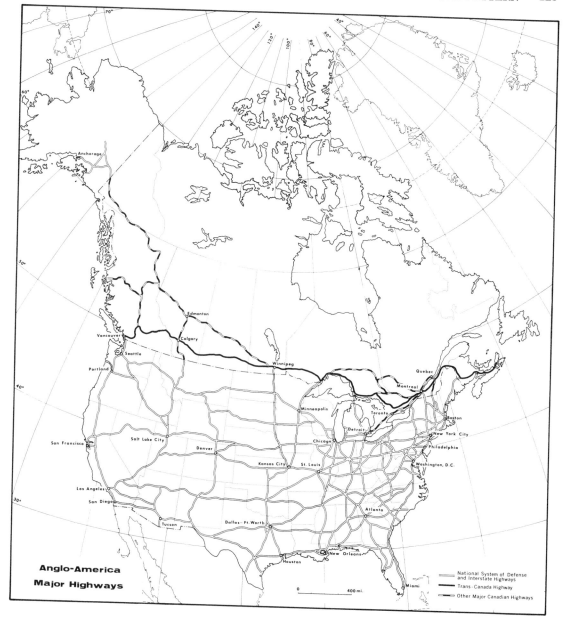

Anglo-America
Major Highways

National System of Defense
and Interstate Highways
Trans-Canada Highway
Other Major Canadian Highways

0   400 mi.

FIGURE 7-7.

2. Highways are important both f   ˄ses   highways for passenger cars that are in good
of national defense and civil d(

3. The cost of operating vehic'   ıtage is the reduc-
cient highways is substan   ɔs that must be made.
monetary and human terms   ɔ; for estimates of cost

Road-user costs will be reduc   ˍ speed of 60 miles per hour
replacement of many two-lane   ınat each stop costs 2.03 cents for fuel,
multiple-lane divided highwɛ   tires, brakes, and other items.
this reduction, *Table X* prese
estimates on two-lane and ˌᴜᴜᴜ   ᴊt   This example illustrates the important fact
ꞁed   that the reduction in operating costs on newer

TABLE X[a]

Road-user Costs for Passenger Cars in Rural Areas[b]

	Cents Per Vehicle Mile at 60 Miles Per Hour	
Cost Elements	Four-lane Divided Highways	Two-lane Highways
Fuel	2.73	3.65
Tires	0.56	0.84
Oil	0.52	0.52
Maintenance & repairs	1.20	1.20
Depreciation	1.50	1.50
Total	6.51	7.71

[a]Source: American Association of State Highway Officials.
[b]0-3% gradient class.

highway systems is substantial. There are other savings that cannot be measured in dollars and cents, however: travel time, convenience, and the spectacular reduction in the number of fatalities and injuries. The latter is in large part due to limited access onto the highways, a development cited as "the most important single factor in accident reduction ever developed." The effects of access control are illustrated in Figure 7-8.

Vehicle growth rate. In 1920, there were about 9 million motor vehicles in operation in the United States, or 87 per thousand population. They rolled up an estimated 45 billion vehicle miles a year, or about 5,000 miles per vehicle. The nation had developed 369,000 miles of hard-paved highway.

Forty-four years later, in 1964, national motor vehicle registrations had grown to about 72 million. Some 720 billion miles were driven annually, or more than 9,000 miles per vehicle (*Fig.* 7-9). An additional 180 billion miles were driven annually by the nearly 15 million trucks and buses. Paved highways approached 3 million miles, and cities, counties, states, and the federal government were hard put to provide for the steadily increasing highway demand.

The annual growth rate of motor vehicle registrations in the past few years has been more than twice the prewar rate, and every indicator of motor vehicle usage displays this acceleration—automobile production, fuel consumption, and traffic volume.

Outlook. Projections of automobile ownership and usage foresee a 20 per cent increase in the ratio of private cars to people by 1980. It is estimated that, by then, there will be, as a national total, about one passenger car registered for every 2.4 people. Approximately 120 million vehicles would be registered in 1980, and 70 per cent of them would be owned in urban areas.

The decline in usage of mass transportation facilities and the rise in the use of the automobile, it appears, are parallel phenomena resulting largely from a common cause—the changes in form and structure of the metropolis. Public transportation principally serves those travel components that are characterized by high concentrations of time and travel path. Its greatest use is in rush-hour travel into the central business district in the morning and out of it at the close of the business day. Conversely, private transportation is relied upon mostly by those components of urban travel that are characterized by either time spread or route dispersal, or that involve family travel. Thus, the automobile dominates week-end and holiday travel, off-peak travel, reverse commuting, and inter-suburban travel. Travel relating to these ele-

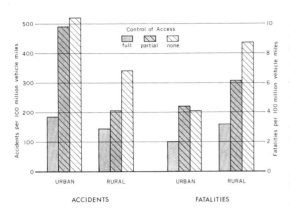

FIGURE 7-8. *Effects of access control on accidents and fatalities on urban and rural highways.*

ments is growing at a faster rate than the travel generated by downtown employment. This growth will present serious problems in the future—problems of highway capacity, route selection, traffic control, adequacy of parking facilities at outlying points, and the levels of public expenditure.

FIGURE 7-9.

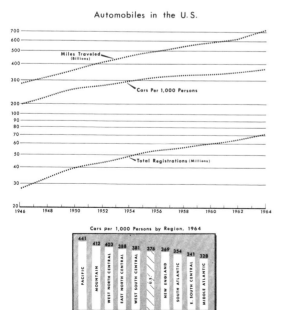

AIR TRANSPORTATION

In less than forty years, air transportation has changed from an experimental novelty to an accepted, routine way of travel. From its early role at the county fair, it has grown into a major industry (*Fig. 7-10*). Equipment has changed from open-cockpit, slow-flying planes to high-speed jet aircraft. Not only has the air transport business itself changed, but it has brought about changes in travel patterns, in business organizations, and in recreational preferences. Air transportation has helped the United States become a single market, for now buyers and sellers from distant points can meet at common points and on brief notice to conduct face-to-face negotiations. It has also made the world "smaller" by greatly facilitating travel between countries and continents.

Three major airlines (TWA, United, and American) and numerous smaller ones were operating regularly in the U.S. by the early 1930's. But domestic commercial aviation truly came of age in 1936 with the introduction of the Douglas DC-3, which combined speed, safety, and operational economy. After World War II, domestic air traffic boomed. Airports expanded again and again, new routes crisscrossed the nation, and a succession of such new planes as the Constellation, the DC-7, and the jets, were introduced to handle the increasing traffic. By 1965 there were 49 certified airlines in the U.S., carrying 85 million passengers and more than one billion ton-miles of freight per year.

Outlook. The age of jet flight is actually just beginning. Each generation of planes is larger and flies faster than the previous one. Within ten years, planes capable of carrying 350 passengers and traveling 2,000 miles an hour between New York and Los Angeles will be a common phenomenon.

Under a government-sponsored program administered by the Federal Aviation Agency, one airplane manufacturer (Boeing) and one engine builder (General Electric) are constructing the prototype of a supersonic airliner. It is scheduled to be completed in 1969, and the

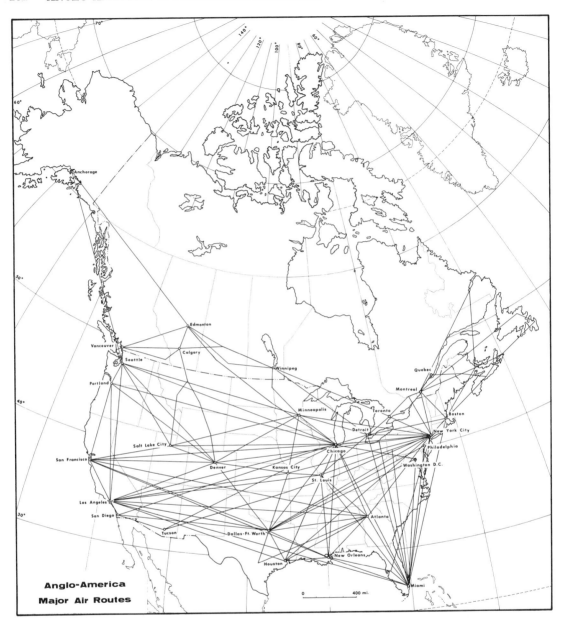

FIGURE 7-10.

first American-built supersonic transport is expected to carry paying passengers through the sound barrier by 1974 (*Fig. 7-11*).

Inevitably, the supersonic transport has been a subject of discussion and controversy. Is it worth investing billions of dollars, people ask, to cross the ocean in three hours instead of six or seven? Who needs to fly faster than sound?

The answers are not simple, but to leaders of the air transportation industry they are convincing. Since commercial flight began, airplanes have grown steadily larger and speedier. This has been the result of both passenger preference and the fact that bigger, faster, planes can—up to a still undetermined point—move more people at lower cost than smaller, slower ones. For example, when the first jet transports were introduced in 1958, they almost doubled the speed of propeller planes then in use. Today they carry more than 90 per cent of all passenger traffic. It is expected that, at least on long-range flights of 2,500 miles or more, the SST will eventually win the bulk of the business.

Nor do the experts see the SST as the end of the line when looking into the future of transportation. They already talk of an orbital transport capable of carrying passengers from any terminal on earth to any other in less than an hour. When asked who is in such a hurry, they say, in effect, "Time is the one irreplaceable resource man has. As long as it is possible to move faster, man will avail himself of the opportunity."

Commercial aviation may be about ready to burst through the sound barrier, but the feat won't mean much if it can't lick the "ground barrier" first.

Already the baggage handling, ticketing, parking, and internal transport system of many major U.S. airports are strained to the point of breakdown. According to experts, they will be hopelessly swamped once the high performance, bigger capacity planes of tomorrow begin flying. So aviation planners now are feverishly working on designs for new airports.

Some of these plans are of the more-and-bigger variety, envisioning major expansions of conventional facilities but no great breakthroughs in design. Others, however, are as radically innovative as the aircraft of tomor-

row. Samples of the latter include: (1) a terminal building two miles long, its interior threaded with roads on various levels; (2) a robot baggage handling system; and (3) a subterranean airport complex with only bubble domes up above an ocean of asphalt.

Planners say such striking departures from present designs will be necessary at many airports if they are to handle the crush of travelers expected in the 1970's when the "jumbo jets" and the supersonic transports take to the skies. The result, say aviation traffic forecasters, will be another boom in air travel. In 1965 some 50 million passenger trips over domestic routes were logged; by 1970 it is expected this figure will be 75 million, and by 1975, a whopping 150 million.

Canada

The physiographic and population characteristics of Canada present unusual difficulties from the standpoint of transportation. The country extends 4,000 miles from east to west, and its main topographic barriers run in a north-south direction. Thus, sections of the country are cut off from one another by such water barriers as Cabot Strait and the Strait of Belle Isle, which separate the island of Newfoundland from the mainland, and by rough, rocky forest terrain, such as the New Brunswick-Quebec border region and the areas north of Lakes Huron and Superior, which divide the industrial region of Ontario and Quebec from the prairies and the Pacific Coast. Unevenly distributed along a narrow southern strip of Canada's vast area is its relatively small population of less than 20 million. To such a country, with its dispersed population and its production for consumption as well as for export in distant parts of the country, efficient and economical transportation facilities are necessities for existence.

INLAND WATERWAYS

The canals and canalized waters of Canada comprise a series of waterways providing navigation for 1,875 miles inland from salt water.

FIGURE 7-11. *Drawing of the Boeing variable-sweep-wing supersonic airliner. This craft will be capable of transporting up to 350 passengers at 2½ times the speed of sound. (The Boeing Co.)*

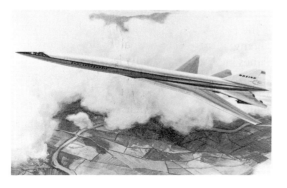

Bounded by water on all sides (except the long land boundaries with the United States), and with many inland lakes and rivers that serve as traffic arteries, Canada makes much use of water transport in domestic and foreign commerce. Two-thirds of the freight traffic with the United States is handled by Canadian ports on the Great Lakes (see Fig. 1-21).

The St. Lawrence Seaway and the many canals provide a 27-foot navigation channel from Montreal to Lake Superior (see Fig. 7-3). The Athabasca River, the Slave River, and the MacKenzie River provide seasonal inland water transportation from the end of the railway in Alberta to the Arctic Ocean. The Yukon River is usually open from the middle of May to the middle of October.

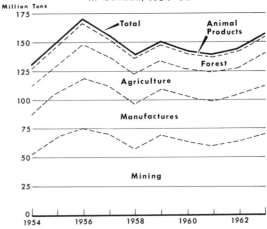

FIGURE 7-12.

RAILWAYS

Since confederation, the railways of Canada have been the principal transport facility throughout the nation (Fig. 7-12). The two great transcontinental systems, the Canadian Pacific (17,000 miles) and the Canadian National (23,000 miles), serve this large country, for the most part avoiding duplication of service. They are supplemented by a major north-south line in the west and a number of regional independent railways (see Fig. 7-4). The CNR and CPR, in addition to operating almost 90 per cent of the railway facilities, maintain steamships and ferries, nationwide telegraph services, highway transport services, hotel chains, and domestic and international air services.

The government-owned Canadian National Railway System is the country's largest public utility and operates the greatest length of trackage in Canada. It is the only railway serving all ten provinces and is currently completing a branch line to serve the Great Slave Lake area of the Northwest Territories.

PIPELINES

Oil and gas pipelines are a major element in Canada's transportation network. Since 1950, when pipelines were a negligible factor in intercity freight traffic, growth has been so rapid

that oil and gas pipelines now account for about one-fifth of the ton-mile freight traffic.

Until 1950 Canada's large potential reserves of oil and gas were landlocked in the center of a vast continent. The nation was dependent upon imports of coal and oil for the populous areas of the Pacific Coast and the lower Great Lakes-St. Lawrence River system. Since then, two of the world's longest oil and gas pipelines, nearly 2,000 miles in length, have been built to link the western Canadian oil fields of Alberta and Saskatchewan to major cities as far east as Montreal. In addition, three major pipelines, several hundred miles in length, cross the Rocky Mountains and supply the lower mainland of British Columbia and the northwestern United States (see Figs. 3-7 and 3-8).

In 1961 a new 1,100-mile pipeline was completed from Alberta to California, 400 miles of which are in Alberta and British Columbia. An additional 483 miles of intraprovincial pipeline have since been built to facilitate the gathering of crude oil within the provinces of Alberta, British Columbia, and Saskatchewan.

The oil pipeline transport industry moves almost 700,000 barrels of crude oil per day from the oil fields of Alberta, British Columbia, Saskatchewan, and Manitoba to the major refineries located across Canada from Vancouver to Toronto.

The gas pipeline transport industry encompasses those pipelines that are engaged in the transportation of gas from gas fields or processing plants to local distribution systems. The movement of 550 billion cubic feet of gas an average distance of 888 miles illustrates the tremendous distances involved in this industry.

HIGHWAYS

Because of its large land area and the unusual distribution of its relatively small population, no other country is more dependent on its transportation facilities than Canada. At one time rail and water were the primary modes of transportation. However, economic, technological, and demographic changes over the past fifty years have increased the importance of road transportation to such an extent that Canada can rightly be considered a nation on wheels.

There are more than 6 million motor vehicles registered in the country. Of these, 79 per cent are passenger automobiles; 18 per cent are trucks and road tractors; 1 per cent consists of buses of all types; and 2 per cent comprise other vehicles, such as motorcycles and farm tractors. On a total Canadian registration basis, there is one motor vehicle for every 3.1 persons, compared with the United States ratio of one motor vehicle for every 2.3 persons.

The Trans-Canada Highway was officially opened for traffic in September, 1962. Although not necessarily the most important highway economically, it is certainly the most spectacular (*Fig. 7-13*). It provides a continuous east-west thoroughfare from St. John's, Newfoundland, to Victoria, British Columbia, a distance of 5,000 miles (*see Fig. 7-7*). The highway is "unbroken" only in the technical sense, however. There are no plans to build bridges between Newfoundland and Nova Scotia, between Nova Scotia and Prince Edward Island, or across the Strait of Georgia from Vancouver to Nanaimo and Victoria; and it is necessary to traverse those parts by ferry.

The coast-to-coast route is not a superhighway in today's sense of the word. For the most part, it is two lanes, with a maximum width of 24 feet and 10-foot shoulders on both sides. It has been paved throughout with asphalt (except for some sections in Newfoundland).

Besides the Trans-Canada, other new highways are being built and existing ones improved in all the provinces. The Alcan, or Alaskan-Canadian Highway connects the conterminous United States with Alaska via Canada. It starts at Dawson Creek, British Columbia, and ends via Richardson Highway in Fairbanks, Alaska, a distance of 1,523 miles.

To meet the problem of increasing traffic congestion, many urban areas in Canada have embarked upon the construction of limited-access throughways designed to speed traffic flows between suburban and central districts during peak traffic periods, and to permit through traffic to bypass the congested central areas where traffic densities are already too high. The Metropolitan Boulevard in Montreal, the Ottawa Queensway, the Route 401 Bypass and the Gardiner Expressway in Toronto, and the Deas Island Road and Tunnel in Vancouver are examples of such highway development.

The trucking industry is one of the more important providers of freight transportation, especially of packaged goods over short distances. Roughly 975,000 trucks and road tractors operate on Canada's roads and streets. Although freight-carrying trucks account for only 6.2 per cent of the total number of trucks,

FIGURE 7-13. *The Trans-Canada Highway, as it winds through Glacier National Park, British Columbia. (Canadian Government Travel Bureau)*

they are by far the most important class in providing transportation services.

AIRWAYS

Vast distances, rugged terrain, and extreme variations in weather have contributed to the growth and development of civil aviation in Canada. Air Canada (formerly Trans-Canada Air Lines) and Canadian Pacific Air Lines Limited link five continents as well as major cities in Canada and the United States. In addition to the two major Canadian air carriers, there are four domestic air carriers licensed to operate scheduled commercial air services in Canada (*see Fig. 7-10*).

Outlook

The advances made in transportation in Anglo-America since World War II far exceed those of any period in our history. Even more revolutionary developments may be anticipated during the next decade. Greater speed and more comfort, safety, and economy are the engineering objectives of the future. Tomorrow's trains and other vehicles will no doubt operate without wheels, using the air-cushion principle. A dream that may one day be realized is a hypersonic plane capable of traveling five times or more the speed of sound.

Moving sidewalks, monorails, and tubes may one day eliminate the traffic problems of urban Anglo-America. The circular airport, which requires less than a third as much space as is needed by today's airports with their long runways, may solve the problem of ground space near cities.

Pipelines on or under the ground may also solve the problem of providing high-speed passenger travel for a world in which traffic often comes to a standstill. Passengers would be carried in cigar-shaped, air-cushioned vehicles that would skim through pipelines at speeds as high as 2,000 miles per hour.

The successful orbiting of the earth in manned spacecraft and the landing of satellites on the moon point to the fact that man has virtually an unlimited horizon. He has accomplished tasks that a decade ago were little more than wild dreams. The world of tomorrow will enable him to accomplish even greater feats in the realm of transportation.

Selected References

BROWN, ANDREW H., "New St. Lawrence Seaway Opens the Great Lakes to the World," *The National Geographic Magazine*, Vol. 115, March, 1959, pp. 299–339.

CARLSON, FRED A., "Traffic on the Ohio River System," *The Journal of Geography*, Vol. 59, November, 1960, pp. 357–360.

CARTER, RICHARD E., "A Comparative Analysis of United States Ports and Their Traffic Characteristics," *Economic Geography*, Vol. 38, April, 1962, pp. 162–175.

CURRIE, A. W., *Economics of Canadian Transportation* (2nd ed.), Toronto: University of Toronto Press, 1959.

FAIR, MARVIN L., and WILLIAMS, ERNEST W., JR., *Economics of Transportation*, New York: Harper & Row, Publishers, 1950.

GRIFFIN, PAUL F., "Blueprint for Autobahn, U.S.A.," *The Scientific Monthly*, Vol. 78, June, 1954, pp. 380–387.

———, "Transportation and Communication," *Global Geography*, New York: Thomas Y. Crowell Company, 1957, pp. 313–323.

HALL, J. W., "Pipeline Construction in the Past, Present, and Future," *Proceedings, American Society of Civil Engineers*, Vol. 85, January, 1959, pp. 9–25.

HASTINGS, D. C., "Impact of the Federal Highway Program on the Nation and the Eighth District," *Monthly Review*, Federal Reserve Bank of St. Louis, Vol. 39, March, 1957, pp. 34–43.

HILLS, T. L., "The St. Lawrence Seaway," *Focus*, Vol. 11, December, 1960, pp. 1–6.

LANCASTER, JANE, "A Railroad to Great Slave Lake," *The Professional Geographer*, September, 1961, pp. 31–35.

LESSARD, J. C., *Transportation in Canada*, Ottawa: Royal Commission on Canada's Economic Prospects, 1957.

MANNERS, G., "The Pipeline Revolution," *Geography*, Vol. 47, April, 1962, pp. 154–163.

MAYER, HAROLD M., "Great Lakes-Overseas: An Expanding Trade Route," *Economic Geography*, Vol. 30, April, 1954, pp. 117–143.

PATTON, DONALD, "The Traffic Pattern on American Inland Waterways," *Economic Geography*, Vol. 32, January, 1956, pp. 29–37.

PEARCY, G. E., and ALEXANDER, L. M., "Pattern of Commercial Air Service Availability in the Western Hemisphere," *Economic Geography*, Vol. 27, October, 1951, pp. 316–320.

SINGER, S. R., "Transmission of Natural Gas," *Business Review*, Federal Reserve Bank of Dallas, Vol. 46, May, 1961, pp. 1–8.

TAAFEE, EDWARD J., "Trends in Airline Passenger Traffic: A Geographic Case Study," *Annals of the Association of American Geographers*, Vol. 49, December, 1959, pp. 393–408.

ULLMAN, EDWARD L., "Rivers as Regional Bonds: The Columbia-Snake Example," *The Geographical Review*, Vol. 41, April, 1951, pp. 310–325.

————, "The Railroad Pattern of the United States," *ibid.*, Vol. 39, April, 1949, pp. 242–256.

VANCE, JAMES E., JR., "The Oregon Trail and Union Pacific Railroad," *Annals of the Association of American Geographers*, Vol. 51, December, 1961, pp. 357–379.

WALLACE, WILLIAM H., "Freight Traffic Functions of Anglo-American Railroads," *Annals of the Association of American Geographers*, Vol. 53, September, 1963, pp. 312–331.

————, "The Bridge Line: A Distinctive Type of Anglo-American Railroad," *Economic Geography*, Vol. 41, January, 1965, pp. 1–38.

WILLIAMS, G. B., "The Trans-Canada Highway," *Canadian Geographical Journal*, Vol. 54, February, 1957, pp. 42–67.

WILSON, G. M., *Oil Across the World, the American Saga of Pipelines*, New York: Longmans, Green, & Co., 1946.

WOLFE, ROY I., "Transportation and Politics: The Example of Canada," *Annals of the Association of American Geographers*, Vol. 52, June, 1962, pp. 176–190.

8 *The Political Pattern*

The United States

GOVERNMENTAL FRAMEWORK

The United States of America is a federal union of 50 states or commonwealths. Its basic law is the Constitution, which prescribes the form and method of national government, specifically lists its rights and fields of authority, and reserves other rights and activities to the individual states.

Each state contains smaller subdivisions, such as counties, townships, cities, and villages, that have their own governments; and the powers of each unit of government are generally set forth in the state constitutions and in the state laws.

All government in the United States is government by elected representatives functioning only with the consent of the governed. The people retain full sovereignty. The federal Congress and the president, state legislatures and governors, and county and city legislative bodies and officials are elected by popular vote. Other government officials and judges in all courts are either elected directly by the people or appointed by elected officials.

The secret ballot is the foundation of self-government. By use of the ballot, the voters may elect officials, return them to office, or put others in their places. Officials, regardless of position, can also be ousted through recall or impeachment.

The Constitution. Drafted in 1787, the Constitution guarantees individual rights and freedoms to all the people of the country. These rights include freedom of speech, freedom of the press, freedom of worship, the right to peaceful assembly, the right to be secure in one's home against unreasonable searches and seizures, and the right of an accused person to a speedy and public trial by an impartial jury.

Under the Constitution, the powers of the national government are divided among three branches: the executive branch, headed by the president; the legislative (or lawmaking) branch, which includes both houses of Congress, the Senate and the House of Representatives; and the judicial branch, headed by the Supreme Court (*Figs. 8-1* and *8-2*).

Like the national government, the state governments have three independent branches: legislative, executive (with a governor as chief executive), and judicial. The same pattern of separate branches is found in county, township, and city governments.

The framers of the federal Constitution foresaw that the future would bring changes and development and thus provided for amending the Constitution. Twenty-three amendments since its ratification have kept it modern and effective. It is somewhat remarkable that the

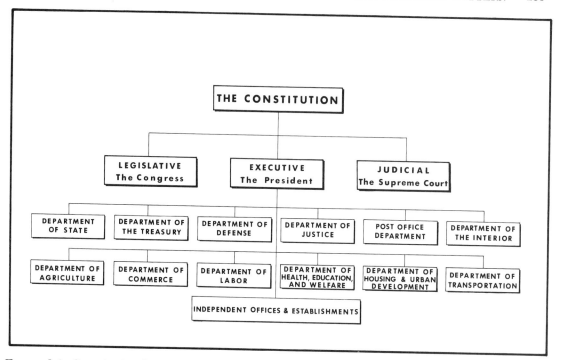

```
                          ┌──────────────────────┐
                          │   THE CONSTITUTION   │
                          └──────────────────────┘
```

| LEGISLATIVE The Congress | EXECUTIVE The President | JUDICIAL The Supreme Court |

| DEPARTMENT OF STATE | DEPARTMENT OF THE TREASURY | DEPARTMENT OF DEFENSE | DEPARTMENT OF JUSTICE | POST OFFICE DEPARTMENT | DEPARTMENT OF THE INTERIOR |

| DEPARTMENT OF AGRICULTURE | DEPARTMENT OF COMMERCE | DEPARTMENT OF LABOR | DEPARTMENT OF HEALTH, EDUCATION, AND WELFARE | DEPARTMENT OF HOUSING & URBAN DEVELOPMENT | DEPARTMENT OF TRANSPORTATION |

INDEPENDENT OFFICES & ESTABLISHMENTS

FIGURE 8-1. *Organizational structure of the United States government.*

pattern of government laid down in the Constitution for the thirteen original states nearly two hundred years ago still meets the need of a nation with roughly 200 million people in fifty states, including some 3,000 county administrations and many thousands of local governmental units, all with elected officials.

State constitutions have also been amended as required to keep pace with changing conditions, and local governments have been established by vote of the people to suit the different needs of city and rural communities.

Behind the whole system of government lie traditional American political principles. Division of power between executive, legislative, and judicial branches helps to prevent any man or small group of men from establishing a dictatorship. Government is decentralized as far as possible; local governments deal with local problems, state governments deal with those problems that concern a number of communities within the state borders, and the national government deals with problems that concern more than a single state. There is no national police force. State police forces are

FIGURE 8-2. *The Capitol in Washington, D. C., the capital of the United States of America. (Washington Convention and Visitors Bureau)*

usually small, and the locally controlled police of cities and towns handle most law enforcement duties.

The Constitution contains a specific list of subjects on which Congress may pass laws. As the nation has developed, this list has been interpreted to embrace a broad range of subjects, including provisions for social welfare and public works, economic controls, and protection of the rights of labor. There is a continuous safeguard against undue extension of federal power, however. The Constitution defines and limits the powers of each branch of the federal government, providing a system of "checks and balances" to prevent any one branch from acquiring undue power. The Supreme Court, for example, has the power to nullify legislation approved by the Congress and by the president if a majority of the Court's members find the legislation conflicts with the Constitution. Another check specifically written into the Constitution provides that Congress alone may declare war, even though the president is commander-in-chief of the nation's armed forces.

A WORLD POWER

When due allowance is made for its favorable geographic position, natural resources, manpower, financial means, military strength, political organization, and diplomatic influence, the United States of America may be regarded as the world's leading power. It has maintained such a status, however, for but a very short period of time. In fact, it was not until 60 to 70 years ago that the United States emerged as one of the major powers of the world.

As yet, the United States is a relatively young power. During the first century of its existence, the nation was busily engaged in creating, preserving, and consolidating the American Union. In its march across the continent from the Appalachians to the Pacific Ocean, it increased its size by more than threefold.

For the most part, these acquired lands were sparsely settled. When the growth of population coming from the older sections warranted it, the land was carved into states that were ad-

mitted to the Union with all of the rights and privileges of the original 13 members. Expansion of this type was not imperialism in the strictest sense; imperialism began only when American sovereignty was extended over thickly settled lands whose peoples were so different from Americans that their assimilation into the American state system was either impossible or impractical.

Overseas expansion. The first acquisition of noncontiguous territory was the purchase of Alaska from Russia in 1867. At that time, too, interest developed in what may be regarded as the beginnings of an overseas empire; the Midway Islands, for instance, were annexed in that year.

The event that first marked the emergence of the United States as a world power was the Spanish-American War (1898). The cause of the war, generally speaking, was that Spain's mismanagement of its Cuban colony became intolerable to American sentiment. As a result of the war, the United States acquired Puerto Rico in the Caribbean area, and Guam and the Philippine Islands in the Pacific. Later, it assumed a protectorate over Cuba. In 1898, too, consummating a move that had been in the minds of some for a good many years, the United States annexed the Hawaiian Islands. The following year it took over Wake Island and part of the Samoan Islands, including Tutuila, with the harbor of Pago Pago. Now, the United States had, in truth, become a world power with an overseas empire.

Foreign policy. Two closely related American foreign policies that originated during the early days of the republic definitely affected both the rise of the United States to the position of one of the leading powers and the history of its subsequent relations with the rest of the world. The first was set forth by George Washington in the Neutrality Proclamation, which announced that the United States was not required to take sides in European wars nor to enter conflicts not of its own choosing. The second and more fundamental principle was the Monroe Doctrine, which was likewise a policy of restraint: Europe was to stay out of the affairs of the western continents, and the United States would, in turn, stay out of European internal affairs. Though modified and subject at intervals to varying interpretations, for a long time the Monroe Doctrine has remained one of the basic tenets of American foreign policy. In later years, there has been a connection between it and the movement known as Pan-Americanism.

THE WESTERN HEMISPHERE

Throughout the nineteenth century, the need for a canal across the Isthmus of Panama grew more acute. With commerce and defense fleets in the Atlantic and Pacific involved, control of the canal was essential to the United States.

After a route had been chosen across Panama (then a part of Colombia), Colombia refused to ratify the treaty granting the United States a lease for the six-mile-wide strip of land. Thereupon, Panama seceded from Colombia; the United States intervened to protect it and immediately recognized its independent status. The new state then accepted a treaty that gave the United States a perpetual lease of the Canal Zone, a ten-mile strip across the isthmus (*Fig. 8-3*). In return, the United States agreed to maintain the independence of Panama. Thus it became not only a protectorate, but also a virtual military outpost of the United States. To guard the eastern approaches to the Panama Canal, the United States devised a system of protectorates to keep much of the Caribbean area in its sphere of influence. Cuba, the Dominican Republic, and Haiti made agreements with the United States similar to Panama's. The treaties mainly provided that in return for United States protection of their independence: (1) the weaker powers would remain intact and independent, not ceding any territory to a third party; (2) the United States could intervene, if necessary, to maintain order or independence; (3) the United States was to supervise financial policies of these states; and (4) the United States was to have use of naval bases in these "protected" states.

During the early twentieth century, the United States intervened in the affairs of these countries and established a varying degree of

FIGURE 8-3. *The Panama Canal, one of the strategic economic and military waterways of the world. (Panama Canal Co.)*

imperialistic control within strategic range of the Panama Canal. During World War I, the Danish West Indies (renamed the Virgin Islands) were purchased as additional insurance (*Fig. 8-4*).

The policy of the United States was to assume the responsibility of protecting the rights of European nationals in Western Hemisphere countries, thus making it unnecessary for European states to intervene in this hemisphere.

THE FAR EAST

The acquisition of island possessions in the Pacific during the period of the Spanish-American War marked a definite turning point in American foreign policy in the Far East. Throughout the greater part of the nineteenth century, the United States had preferred to play the role of spectator of the Far Eastern scene, generally content with the so-called "most-favored nation" policy relative to the rights of its citizens in China. Thereby it had secured for them all the privileges of residence, travel, navigation, and trade that imperialistic powers of Europe had won for their nationals only after numerous wars. In taking the Philippines from Spain (not to mention other areas

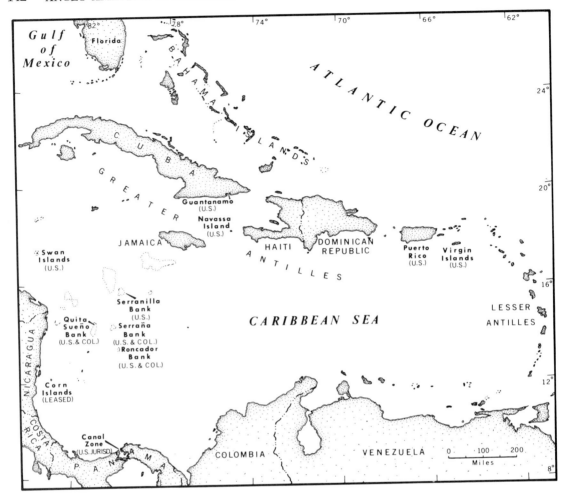

FIGURE 8-4. *United States extraterritorial possessions and military bases in the Western Hemisphere.*

in the Pacific), however, the United States acquired more fundamental Far Eastern interests that had to be protected (*Fig. 8-5*). Thus, it became involved directly in Far Eastern politics. This led to a policy of cooperation with European powers with respect to the Orient, in contrast to its policy of nonintervention in European affairs.

Secretary of State John Hay announced the new policy in his well-known "Open Door Notes" of 1899. Therein he proposed to Great Britain, Germany, France, Italy, Japan, and Russia that those powers holding leased territory of interest in China should not discriminate against the commerce of other powers with respect to harbor fees, railroad charges,

and tariff dues. Then came the Chinese Boxer Revolt in 1900, after which a Hay circular insisted upon the territorial and administrative entity of the Chinese Empire. A series of diplomatic notes between that date and the outbreak of World War I enhanced and elaborated both the policy of the Open Door and the administrative integrity of China, resulting for the time in a precarious balance of power in the Far East.

Japan, having won wars against China and Russia, began to emerge as a world power around the turn of the century, and naturally was destined for considerable expansion in Asia. The interests of the United States and Japan in the Far East, therefore, came increas-

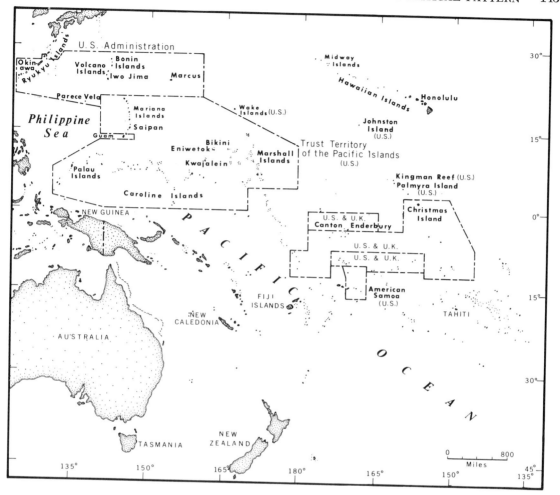

FIGURE 8-5. *United States extraterritorial possessions and military bases in the Pacific Ocean.*

ingly into conflict. This engendered a spirit of unfriendliness between the two powers that was not minimized by the United States' immigration policy of discrimination against Far Eastern peoples. Japanese ambitions in Asia undoubtedly would have been blocked by a strict compliance with the principles of the Open Door Policy, but the United States was unwilling to maintain the armed strength necessary to uphold the policy. In the ensuing diplomatic maneuvers, the vulnerable Philippine Islands became Japan's hostage. In return for repeated pledges not to molest this Far Eastern possession, the United States made several agreements giving Japan more and more of a free hand in Korea and in Manchuria

and contiguous portions of China during the early years of the century. Probably the most significant of these understandings was the Lansing-Ishii Agreement of 1917 reiterating the principle of the Open Door in China.

WORLD WAR I

The United States was the only one of the great powers completely disassociated from the controversies that led, in 1914, to the outbreak of World War I. The initial reaction of the American people was a strong desire to avoid that conflict. In the end, however, that proved to be impossible. Although Wilson proclaimed neutrality for the U.S., our cultural background, commerce, finances, sympathies, and vital interests soon were enmeshed completely with the cause of Great Britain and her allies. Though we helped win World War I, we did not use victory as a basis for acquiring power either in the Old World or in Asia; indeed, we withdrew far too hastily from our obligations and allowed the League of Nations to sicken and decay. The United States not only rejected the League, but repeatedly refused to join the Permanent Court of International Justice.

BETWEEN THE TWO WORLD WARS

Within the two decades following World War I, the foreign policy of the United States was characterized by a spirit of anti-imperialism. Probably the most important evidence of that trend was the Act of 1934 that provided for complete independence of the Philippine Islands after an intermediate period of ten years. Although joining the League of Nations in fruitless pronouncements against the use of force, the United States took no action whatever when Japan conquered Manchuria in 1931, then moved into North China, and finally began an all-out conquest of that hapless country in 1937. The American people apparently were altogether unwilling to use force to maintain the Open Door Policy and the integrity of China. These developments indicated also an unmistakable disposition to withdraw from active diplomacy in the Far East as well as in Europe.

The wave of anti-imperialism spreading over the United States was demonstrated in a liquidation of the protectorates in Central America and the Caribbean area. These protectorates had been the occasion for numerous interventions in an earlier period. It should be noted that, in its 1930 Clark Memorandum, the Department of State repudiated Theodore Roosevelt's "corollary" to the Monroe Doctrine, the theory on which those earlier interventions had been based. The memorandum stated, in substance, that the Monroe Doctrine had been erroneously credited with giving the United States a right to interfere in the internal affairs of other nations; instead, it was a declaration of the United States against Europe, and not

of the United States against Latin America. President Franklin Roosevelt perfected this noninterference policy and happily called it the Good Neighbor Policy. Pursuing the policy, the United States concluded a number of multilateral treaties with other American states, pacts that elaborated a system of peace through arbitration, conciliation, and good will, without resort to force. The Good Neighbor Policy, or the Inter-American System as it has been called, clearly indicated a doctrine of nonintervention.

WORLD WAR II AND ITS AFTERMATH

On the instant of Pearl Harbor, the United States had to think in global terms, but it was quite unprepared for such thinking. Perhaps 95 per cent of the population "finished" geography in the seventh grade of elementary school. The United States was "parochial" in thought, to use Lord Morley's term for British thinking in 1910. Distant countries were words and pictures in a book, not land, culture systems, and irreducible human diversities. They were strange and far away except as sources of trade or as fields of Christian missionary endeavor.

Once victory had been achieved in World War II, the U.S. contented itself with trying to put the broken fragments of the war-torn world together again. It hosted the world conference of 46 nations in San Francisco that adopted the charter of the United Nations in 1945 (*Fig. 8-6*). It launched the Marshall Plan in 1947. The latter was credited with restoring economic health and halting the march of Communism in those countries cooperating in the plan. The United States was instrumental in setting up the Charter of the Organization of American States, signed April 30, 1948, at the Ninth International Conference of American States in Bogotá, Colombia.

The formation and development of the North Atlantic Treaty Organization, the first treaty of alliance the United States had ever concluded in peacetime, was further evidence of the leading role played by the United States in world affairs in the postwar period. NATO was created April 4, 1949, in a treaty signed in Washington. The member states—Belgium, Canada, Denmark, France, Iceland, Italy, Luxembourg, the Netherlands, Norway, Portugal, the United Kingdom, the United States, Greece, Turkey, and West Germany—agreed to settle disputes by peaceful means, to develop their individual and collective capacity to resist armed attack, to regard an attack on one as an attack on all, and to take necessary action to repel such an attack under Article 51 of the United Nations Charter.

Four years after coming to the aid of South Korea at the request of the United Nations Security Council, the United States joined Australia, France, New Zealand, Pakistan, the Philippines, Thailand, and the United Kingdom to provide for collective defense in Southeast Asia (SEATO) in a pact signed September 8, 1954. With the signing of this pact, the United States, in effect, had committed itself to the same responsibility for Asia that it has for Western Europe.

Whatever the cause, after almost thirty years of active involvement in world affairs, the United States finds itself with a variety of international commitments. The commitments, whether originally wise or unwise, are real. They cannot be simply ignored or wiped out (*Fig. 8-7*).

Canada

NATIONAL GOVERNMENT

Canada's democratic parliamentary system of government reflects both its ties to the Old World and the influences of the New. Although the British North America Act of 1867 provides Canada with a written constitution, many of the country's legal and parliamentary practices are based on established unwritten custom, as is the case in Great Britain. On the other hand, the federal structure of the state—the uniting of ten provinces in a federal government—bears somewhat of a resemblance to that of the United States (*Fig. 8-8*).

While the British North America Act is not as detailed as the U.S. Constitution, it provides for a central government having 29 specific powers, including those relating to defense, trade and commerce, banking and currency, criminal law, postal services, and certain taxes, as well as all powers not expressly granted to the provinces. To the provinces goes authority to administer and legislate on such matters as education, property laws, health, and local affairs generally.

Queen Elizabeth II is queen of Canada and the head of the Canadian states. She serves as

FIGURE 8-6. *The General Assembly of the United Nations in session. (United Nations)*

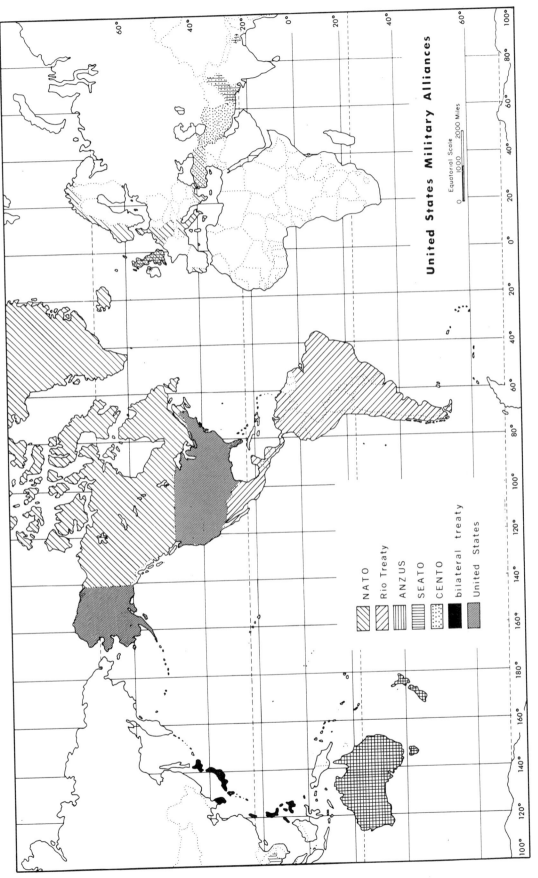

United States Military Alliances

NATO
Rio Treaty
ANZUS
SEATO
CENTO
bilateral treaty
United States

Equatorial Scale
0 1000 2000 Miles

FIGURE 8-7.

FIGURE 8-8. *Parliament Buildings in Ottawa, the capital of Canada. (Canadian Government Travel Bureau)*

a symbol of the free association and unity of the equal and sovereign nations of the Commonwealth. Her personal representative in Canada is the governor general, who is appointed by the queen entirely on the advice of the Canadian prime minister, usually for a five-year term.

Parliament consists of the governor general, the Senate, and the House of Commons. The Senate has 102 members, appointed on a regional basis by the governor general on the advice of the prime minister, and holding office until they reach the retirement age of 75. The 265 members of the House of Commons are elected by the people of Canada for a nominal term of five years. At any time, however, the prime minister may advise the governor general to dissolve Commons and call a new election. If the government loses the support of the majority in the House of Commons, it is obliged either to resign or to call another election.

After an election, the party with a majority in the House of Commons forms the government. If no party commands a majority, a government can be formed by the coalition of two or more parties, although this has seldom happened in Canada. The leader of the party that has most elected members normally becomes prime minister and chooses a cabinet from among his supporters in the House. He and his cabinet colleagues are responsible individually to the electors of their constituencies, and collectively to the Commons. Cabinet members head the various government departments, which are staffed by civil servants who retain their positions no matter what party is in power (*Fig. 8-9*).

The franchise, or right to vote, is conferred upon all Canadian citizens or British subjects, male or female, 21 or over, who have been residing in Canada for 12 months prior to polling day. There are certain exceptions, such as persons confined in penal institutions or mental hospitals, federally-appointed judges, and returning officers for electoral districts. Seats in the House are distributed by provinces and territories as follows:

Newfoundland	7
Prince Edward Island	4
Nova Scotia	12
New Brunswick	10
Quebec	75
Ontario	85
Manitoba	14
Saskatchewan	17
Alberta	17
British Columbia	22
Yukon Territory	1
Northwest Territories	1
Total	265

Representation in the Senate is as follows:

Ontario	24
Quebec	24
Nova Scotia	10
New Brunswick	10
Prince Edward Island	4
Newfoundland	6
Manitoba	6
British Columbia	6
Alberta	6
Saskatchewan	6
Total	102

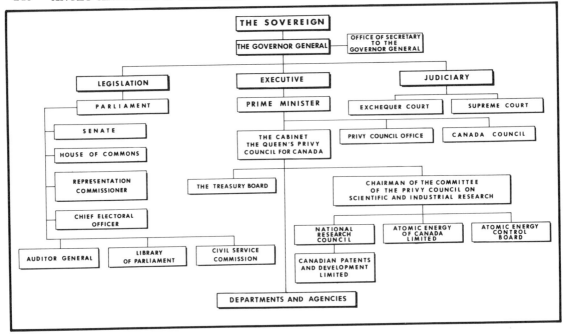

FIGURE 8-9. *Organizational structure of the Canadian government.*

Legislation may be introduced in either chamber, with an important exception that no bill involving public expenditure, which is controlled by the House of Commons, may be initiated by the Senate. Although the Senate possesses the power to reject any but a money bill, it rarely does so. Before a bill can become law, it must be signed by the governor general. It would, however, be contrary to long established constitutional practice (based on the unwritten custom already mentioned) for the governor general to withhold his signature from any measure adopted by the two chambers of Parliament.

PROVINCIAL AND TERRITORIAL GOVERNMENTS

Political institutions and constitutional usages in the government of the ten provinces are similar to national ones. Each province has a legislature, and the queen is represented by a lieutenant governor appointed by the governor general for a term of five years. The lieutenant governor is an officer of the federal government, but his powers in the provincial sphere are essentially the same as those of the governor general in the federal sphere.

The vast and sparsely populated regions of northern Canada lying outside the ten provinces, and comprising the Yukon Territory and the Northwest Territories, have attained both elected representation in the House of Commons and a measure of local self-government. The local government of the Yukon Territory is composed of a resident commissioner, appointed by the federal government, and a locally-elected Legislative Council of seven members, meeting at Whitehorse. The government of the Northwest Territories is vested in a full-time commissioner, who resides in Ottawa, assisted by a Legislative Council of twelve elected and appointed members.

LOCAL GOVERNMENT

Since local government at the municipal level falls under the jurisdiction of the provinces, there are ten distinct systems of municipal government in Canada and many variations within each system. These variations can be attributed to differences in historical development, in area, and in population density of the 4,470 incorporated municipalities. Possessing the power exclusively to make laws respecting municipal institutions, each provincial legislature has divided its territory into varying geographical areas known generally as municipalities, and more particularly as counties, cities, towns, villages, townships, rural municipalities, or municipal districts. In addition, metropolitan government corporations in Montreal, Toronto, and Winnipeg are organized to provide certain services to a number of area municipalities.

CANADA AND THE COMMONWEALTH

The Commonwealth, originally called the British Commonwealth of Nations, is an association of nations loosely joined by a common interest based on having been parts of the old British Empire (*Fig. 8-10*).

Canada, like the other members of the Commonwealth, makes its own laws, decides its own policies, negotiates and signs its own treaties, has its own diplomatic service, and decides for itself whether or not it shall declare war. The governments of the Commonwealth nations are entirely separate and function independently; no member country can be taxed by any government but its own.

The nations of the Commonwealth have widely different interests and responsibilities. It is recognized that, in all matters, each government must decide its policy for itself and that this need not be the same as the policy of another government. They do, however, consult together in all matters of common concern and try to coordinate their policies whenever this appears useful. The bond among the members of the Commonwealth is maintained by their common ideals, their memories of association in the past, and their conviction that that association has been, and will continue to be, for the benefit of their people.

INTERNATIONAL RELATIONS

Since Canada achieved its status as a sovereign government, there has been a gradual growth of its stature on the international scene, paralleling an equally evolutionary assumption by Canada for its own foreign relations. In Canada's early days as a nation, its foreign affairs were conducted by the United Kingdom. Canadian participation increased steadily in the ensuing years, and by 1909 it was considered necessary to create a Department of External Affairs, the counterpart of the United States' Department of State. After World War I, Canadian representatives signed the Treaty of Versailles; the country's first bilateral treaty was signed in 1923 with the United States. Yet, by the outbreak of World War II, Canada's diplomatic and consular service consisted of only 32 officers serving at Ottawa and at seven posts abroad.

World War II gave considerable impetus to Canadian participation in world affairs. As it had done in World War I, Canada mustered a huge proportion of its manpower and material resources to fight for the Allied cause. At the war's conclusion, Canada took an active part in the creation of the United Nations, which it has since strongly supported. Canada has been a member of the Security Council, served three terms on the Economic and Social Council, and belongs to all the U.N. specialized agencies. It has been in the forefront of U.N. efforts to preserve the peace and has taken a prominent part in disarmament negotiations.

Along with other nations, Canada has exercised its right under the U.N. Charter to participate in regional collective security arrangements. A member of NATO since its inception, Canada has assumed important responsibility for the protection of the North Atlantic Treaty area.

Canada is one of the original members of the Commonwealth-inspired Colombo Plan, which provides economic aid to less developed countries in Asia. Canada also participates in the Canada-West Indies Aid Program and the Special Commonwealth Africa Aid Program (SCAAP). Other forms of mutual assistance, such as military training and academic fellowships and scholarships, are likewise provided by Canada on the basis of Commonwealth relationships.

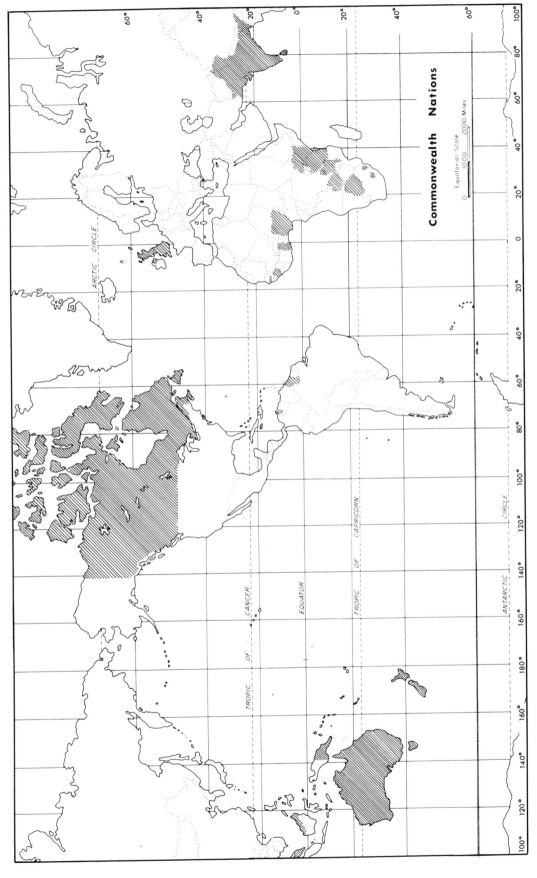

Commonwealth Nations

Equatorial Scale

0   1000   2000 Miles

ARCTIC CIRCLE

TROPIC OF CANCER

EQUATOR

TROPIC OF CAPRICORN

ANTARCTIC CIRCLE

FIGURE 8-10.

Canada and the United States

Obviously, relations between the United States and Canada constitute a very important element in the external affairs of both countries. Reflected in the day-to-day relations between the two countries are not only cooperation and mutual respect based on each country's recognition of the other's sovereignty, but also the interdependence of their common futures. Geography and easy communication have encouraged close and friendly relations, and Canada and the United States have chosen to develop and maintain a close partnership in their common defense of democratic governments and individual liberties; in economic, trade, and cultural relations; in scientific research; and in the resolution of problems concerning the waters that they share along their boundaries.

DEFENSE

U.S. joint defense arrangements with Canada are more extensive than with any other country in the world; fully a third of U.S. major agreements with Canada relate to defense. This cooperation began during World War II with the establishment in 1940 of a Permanent Joint Board of Defense. The subsequent Hyde Park Agreement concerning defense procurement was entered into on April 20, 1941, by President Roosevelt and Prime Minister Mackenzie King.

Geography is the key to the mutual need of Canada and the United States to assure their joint security. In the event of a general war, an aggressor would probably first seek to breach the contiguous northern frontier of the two countries. This frontier, however, constitutes a vast and largely unsettled region that enemy aircraft or missiles would have to traverse before reaching strategic targets in the settled portion, and it consequently provides valuable time to put defensive measures into effect. To this end, three radar chains have been constructed across Canada.

Cooperation in the joint employment of these defense facilities is extremely close. An integrated Canada-U.S. North American Air De-fense Command, known as NORAD, has been in operation since 1957 at Colorado Springs, Colorado. NORAD exercises operational control over all combat units of the national forces made available for the air defense of the two countries. It is headed by a U.S. general whose deputy is a Canadian air marshal.

Matters relating to continental defense are subject to civilian guidance through a cabinet committee known as the Canadian-U.S. Ministerial Committee on Joint Defense. The committee, which meets alternately in Washington and Ottawa, consults on matters bearing upon the joint defense of Canada and the United States.

Regarding the use of atomic energy for mutual defense purposes, Canadian-U.S. cooperation was strengthened by an agreement signed in May, 1959. This accord authorizes exchange of classified information on defense plans, military reactors, and use of and defense against nuclear weapons. It also provides for the transfer to Canada of nonnuclear parts of atomic weapons systems. Previous agreements for the exchange of information on the use of atomic energy for both mutual defense and civil purposes were signed June 15, 1955.

The warm friendship that has long existed between the United States and Canada, and their parallel interests, enable them to speak to each other with a forthrightness that is possible for very few countries. This candor strengthens their mutual trust and helps them to avoid the pitfalls of misunderstanding ⁅ ⁆ have bedeviled relations of so many other countries in the world.

Selected References

ALEXANDER, LEWIS M., *World Political Patterns*, Chicago: Rand McNally & Co., 1957.

BAILEY, THOMAS A., *A Diplomatic History of the American People*, New York: Appleton-Century-Crofts, Inc., 1950.

BLOOMFIELD, LINCOLN P., *The U.N. and U.S. Foreign Policy*, Boston: Little, Brown & Co., 1960.

BROGAN, D. W., *The American Character*, New York: Vintage Books, 1956.

CARLSON, LUCILLE, *Geography and World Politics*, Englewood Cliffs, N. J.: Prentice-Hall, Inc., 1958, pp. 246–283.

CARR, EDWARD HALLETT, *Nationalism and After*, New York: The Macmillan Co., 1945.

COHEN, SAUL B., *Geography and Politics in a Divided World*, New York: Random House, Inc., 1963, pp. 91–139.

EAST, W. G., and MOODIE, A. E. (eds.), *The Changing World*, New York: World Book Co., 1956, pp. 239–311.

MAYER, HAROLD M., "Politics and Land Use: The Indiana Shoreline of Lake Michigan," *Annals of the Association of American Geographers*, Vol. 54, December, 1954, pp. 508–523.

OSGOOD, ROBERT E., *Limited War: The Challenge to American Strategy*, Chicago: University of Chicago Press, 1957.

POUNDS, NORMAN J. G., *Political Geography*, New York: McGraw-Hill Book Company, Inc., 1963, pp. 67–78.

PRESCOTT, J. R. V., *The Geography of Frontiers and Boundaries*, Chicago: Aldine Publishing Co., 1965.

ROBINSON, J. LEWIS, and ROBINSON, M. JOSEPHINE, *The Geography of Canada*, New York: Longmans, Green & Co., 1950.

ROCK, VINCENT P., *A Strategy of Interdependence*, New York: Charles Scribner's Sons, 1964.

SMITH, DAVID A., "Interaction Within a Fragmented State: The Example of Hawaii," *Economic Geography*, Vol. 39, July, 1963, pp. 234–244.

SPYKMAN, NICHOLAS, *America's Strategy in World Politics: The United States and the Balance of Power*, New York: Harcourt, Brace & Co., 1942.

TEAL, JOHN J., JR., "Alaska, Fulcrum of Power," *Foreign Affairs*, Vol. 27, October, 1948, pp. 86–96.

VAN ZANDT, FRANKLIN K., "Boundaries of the United States and the Several States," *Geological Survey Bulletin 1212*, Washington: U.S. Government Printing Office, 1966.

WEIGERT, HANS W., STEFANSSON, VILHJALMUR, and HARRISON, RICHARD EDES (eds.), *New Compass of the World*, New York: The Macmillan Co., 1953, pp. 25–60.

Part II *Anglo-America: A Regional Appraisal*

Regional geography is the geographical study of a unit-area that reveals some degree of identity. Whereas systematic geography, as illustrated in Part I, depends on analysis, regional geography is the product of synthesis, of integration. The regional device enables the geographer to divide the earth into units within which there are unique interpretations of social and physical phenomena.

Each region has some kind of internal homogeneity that distinguishes it from surrounding areas. Its distinct character may be the uniformity of its landscape features or its mode of life, or it may be the way all parts work together in a functional system. A region is an areal generalization. It is always defined in terms of specific criteria.

The really keen observer perceives that things do not occur separately upon the surface of the earth, but that they everywhere fall into natural groupings. The objects that exist together in the landscape exist in interrelation. We assert that they form a whole, an area that is not expressed by the constituent parts separately, that area has form, structure, and function in a system, and is subject to development, change, and completion.

Anglo-America is actually a mosaic of several unlike regions (as indeed is the world itself on a much more extensive scale). Within the entire realm of geography, therefore, there are few valid generalizations that can be made for Anglo-America as a whole; a statement made regarding one region has almost no validity when applied to other regions. In view of this, regionalism and the regional concept afford a valid method of social analysis.

In Part II of *Anglo-America, a Systematic and Regional Geography*, a major effort is made to delineate boundaries that separate areas with major topographical or geological differences. An examination of many publications in the field of geography reveals surprising flexibility in the criteria used to establish regions. (All criteria are perfectly valid, for no one system of dividing the earth into homogeneous areas is inherently better than any other.) There are climatic regions, natural vegetation regions, soil regions, economic regions, sociological regions, and the like. To our way of thinking, *landform regions* offer a valid method of dividing Anglo-America into regions for further study, and we have delineated ten such regions. The existence of mountains, hills, plateaus, and plains cannot be questioned. Their influence upon climate, distribution of natural vegetation, soils, and man himself is significant. It must always be kept in mind that each region is only a small part of a larger whole, and that important relationships exist within and among regions.

Boundaries between regions are drawn where transitions in landform characteristics are relatively rapid. Such differences in surface configuration from region to region are often sufficiently conspicuous to make even a casual observer aware of them. These differences do not vary from season to season or from year to year. This does not imply, however, that landform features totally dominate the character of regions. Within any region it is the combination of physical, cultural, and human elements that provides the total regional character.

The transition from region to region may be sharp, even spectacular, as it is around the edges of California's Central Valley or along the western boundary of the Great Plains. But there are places where changes occur so gradually that no two people could agree on the location of a boundary. Such is the case at many points between the Interior Lowlands and the Great Plains. Here the difference is primarily one of elevation, and the definitions of "low plains" and "high plains" are arbitrary.

Any region is, therefore, no more than an intellectual concept, an entity for purposes of a more thorough comprehension of the order of earth-space. A region then, as here defined, is a portion of earth-space possessing homogeneity in terms of criteria used.

9 *Northeastern Lowlands and Uplands Region*

The Northeastern Lowlands and Uplands Region (*Fig. 9-1*) is, topographically, dominantly an upland surface, submaturely dissected, some valleys being several hundred feet deep (*Fig. 9-2*). This upland level is analagous to the older peneplain in the Appalachian Subregion and, in part, has the same age. A few wide valleys are cut down to a younger peneplain, e.g., the very important Connecticut Valley and the long limestone valley on the east side of the Taconic Mountains. Some other low areas near the coast are peneplains younger than the central upland (*Fig. 9-3*).

The whole area was glaciated, leaving many lakes and swamps. Superimposed drainage occasions numerous falls and rapids. There are some terminal moraines, occasional kames and eskers, and a small area of drumlins in eastern Massachusetts. The topsoil is generally stony, owing to glacial drift.

The shoreline was made by the submergence of a rugged surface. On account of repeated small uplifts, erosion has cut to lower levels, giving rise to many harbors as the sea flowed back into the valleys. The shore has a few features of glacial origin, such as Cape Cod and some morainic islands.

Its geological and climatical complexity makes this region one of the most difficult in all of Anglo-America to describe. Differences in accessibility, climate, soil types, stages of development, and the like cause great variations in population density and distribution between uplands and lowlands. Because of these variations in land use, we have divided the region into two subregions, the New England-Canadian Lowlands and the Northeastern Uplands.

Surface Features

NEW ENGLAND-CANADIAN LOWLANDS

From New York City northeast along the Atlantic shore stretches a land whose history is long. Splendid forests once stood by the sea almost everywhere. Today, except for occasional stands, those forests have disappeared, leaving rolling hills mantled with smaller trees, shrubs, summer houses, villages, towns, and huge urban centers. The farms of note tend to be concentrated within a few fertile valleys.

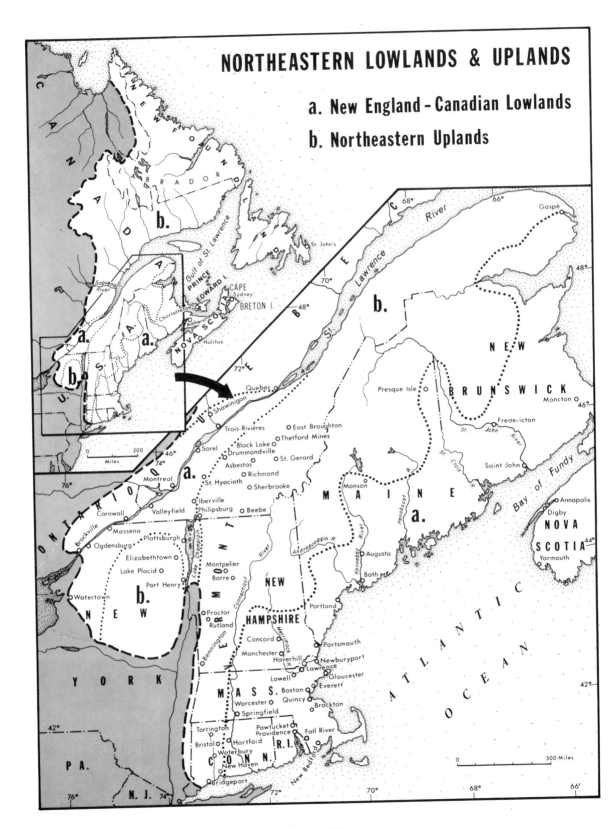

FIGURE 9-1.

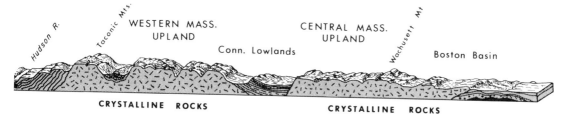

FIGURE 9-2. *Generalized cross-section of New England.*

From New York's Westchester County to Quebec's Gaspé Peninsula this land looks to the sea. Away from the sea there is still ample water—the fresh water of a multitude of lakes and swamps, remnants of an age when glaciers sculptured the interior highlands and parts of the coastal area, scouring basins and blocking the courses of streams with debris. By and large, this is not a rugged land, but in places it seems rugged. In the north, especially, winters are long and cold, and the soil, if any, is thin.

Elevation differences are not great along the New England coast and the Maritime Provinces. The local variation in relief—the extreme difference in elevation—is less than 1,000 feet. Connecticut, except for the northeast corner and a small section northeast of Hartford, is in a region of rolling hills and valleys. Near New Haven the rougher interior Berkshire Hills approach Long Island Sound to offer southern New England its greatest variation in topography.

Lakes and swamps dot the rolling country of coastal Connecticut, and continue northeastward through Rhode Island, Massachusetts, New Hampshire, and Maine, into the three Maritime Provinces of Canada—New Brunswick, Prince Edward Island, and Nova Scotia. Rhode Island's southern mainland is particularly swampy. This smallest state contains no hills of note. Nearly everywhere there are readily visible evidences of glaciation in addition to the numerous lakes and poorly drained flat areas. Near Kingston, for instance, there are irregular deposits that were laid down at an edge of the ancient ice sheet. Off the coast, Block Island is pitted with depressions left when solid chunks of ice melted and caused the

sand and soil covering them to slip into what otherwise would have been a cavity.

Southern Massachusetts is much like Rhode Island, but more gently rolling. Lakes and swamps occupy numerous swales. Much of the topography is hummocky, particularly Barnstable County (Cape Cod) and the islands—Nantucket and Martha's Vineyard. Similar landscape is also found to a lesser extent farther north. In and around Boston Bay are a multitude of small drumlins, formed under a relatively thin waning glacier. Along parts of Cape

FIGURE 9-3. *The Northeastern Lowlands and Uplands Region, physical relief.*

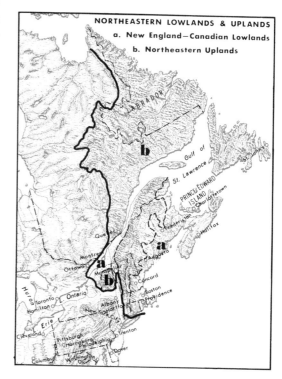

Cod's east coastline a bluff 100 feet high overlooks the Atlantic. Offshore bars exist in various places, Newburyport, for example; sometimes the bars are backed by coastal marshes.

Relief is slight, ranging from 200 to 300 feet throughout most of this portion of Massachusetts. Inland local elevation differences increase to 500 or even 700 feet, but steep slopes are rare. In New Hampshire, relief near the coast is greater than that to the south, but the general aspect remains the same. The only large areas of nearly flat land are scattered along the Merrimack River and near the Atlantic shoreline.

Northward the region is more rugged. Along Maine's island-studded coast are many bold headlands, some of them at the ocean end of long peninsulas that are nearly surrounded by bays, inlets, and tidal river mouths. The Androscoggin, Kennebec, and Penobscot Rivers, each a major stream, drain most of Maine. Spacious, gently rolling lands suitable for farming are not uncommon. Only in the southwest near Portland and in the Aroostook country in the northeast are there large blocks of agriculturally productive soils.

The very irregular North Atlantic coastline extends northeastward from Portland, mixing land and sea to such an extent that land travel parallel to the shore and near the ocean is virtually impossible. A 25-mile auto trip is likely to be the only land means of reaching a neighbor who lives only a mile away by boat.

The summits of such prominent peaks as Mt. Desert and Mt. Megunticook attain elevations of over 1,000 feet within two or three miles of salt water. Much of the shoreline is rocky, with many small sandy beaches in small coves (Fig. 9-4). Inland the topography is more subdued and less spectacular, but there are steep hills scattered in many places in the rolling terrain and among the lakes and swamps. Even in the well-known Aroostook Valley, gently sloping land is at a premium. Near Presque Isle, Hedgehog Mountain and several other steep hills serve notice that this is not the rolling plain of southern New England.

New Brunswick is sparsely settled. Homesteads are scattered, a response to the long winters and the rocky soils that make farming difficult. Only along the St. John River is there a nearly continuous string of settlements, and they occupy the flatter lands near the stream. In many places, however, the steepest slopes are to be found near rivers, with the upland surfaces more gently rolling. By and large, this area is very similar to its counterpart across the border in Maine.

Prince Edward Island, on the other hand, exhibits very little local relief (Fig. 9-5). In fact, all places on the island are less than 500 feet above sea level. Mudflats prevail along some of the coast, which is indented by many bays and inlets. Charlottetown Harbor, where three rivers, the Hillsborough, Yorke, and Eliot, join, is perhaps the best-known bay.

Nova Scotia is more varied. Separated from New Brunswick by a low isthmus, so flat that ships used to be hauled across it by rail, most of mainland Nova Scotia is rolling country, with some very high concentrations of lakes. Many of the landforms trend northeast-southwest, especially near the Bay of Fundy. Here a single ridge slopes gently toward the bay, with a steep bluff (in some places over 500 feet high) overlooking the Annapolis-Cornwallis Valley, which also trends northeast-southwest.

Southern Nova Scotia is unusually rich in lakes, and the coastline is highly indented along the Bay of Fundy. This is a fascinating peninsula, culturally as well as topographically, where such place names as New Glasgow, Denmark, Lunenburg, and Yarmouth indicate a cultural diversity.

FIGURE 9-4. *A beach on the rocky coast of Maine. (Maine Dept. of Economic Development)*

Cape Breton Island, with its Inverness, Margeree, Ingonish, Judique, and Sydney, is equally rich in place names. The magnificent Cape Breton Highlands National Park, with its highest point 1,750 feet above sea level, offers a striking example of scenic grandeur. The Cabot Trail, now an improved road, skirts the base of this wilderness area, but actually, one must walk through the area to appreciate fully the rolling, tundra-like upland, which is almost entirely surrounded by steep, seaward-facing slopes unpierced by highway. Where streams leave the upland, which is nearly everywhere over 1,200 feet in elevation, narrow canyons cut into its edges. In the west these streams have removed parts of the upland, leaving "islands" of steep-sided, rolling highlands separated from the main mass.

The St. Lawrence Lowlands begin at the northeastern end of Lake Ontario. On the north, they are separated from the extensive lowlands that border Lake Ontario by a spur of hard granitic rocks from the Canadian Shield. On the south, they are bounded by the Adirondacks and the mountains of upper New England and lower Quebec. The soft sandstones and shales of this district weathered away faster than neighboring hard rocks, to form a valley about 70 miles wide at Montreal and 20 miles wide at Quebec. On the south, the district widens out to include the Lake Champlain Lowlands, which connect with the Hudson Valley.

NORTHEASTERN UPLANDS

In general, the land of the Northeastern Uplands is steeper, with longer slopes and more local relief than in the surrounding Lowlands. In most places local differences in elevation exceed 1,000 feet. In New York's Adirondack Mountains, for instance, this relief may be more than 4,000 feet, as near Lake Placid, Elizabethtown, or Mt. Marcy. Here many lakes and swamps are nestled between steep hills and mountains as high as Whiteface (4,867 feet) or Marcy (5,344 feet). The heart of the Adirondacks is not, perhaps, spectacular. Near Raquette Lake, for instance, the topography is best described as knobby. There

FIGURE 9-5. *The landscape near Mayfield, Prince Edward Island. (National Film Board of Canada)*

are a few steep hills and the area abounds in lakes and swamps.

The unique surface configuration within the Adirondacks is partially attributable to the ancient granites and other extremely hard rocks making up these mountains (*Fig. 9-6*). During the geologic era when the Appalachians were upraised, the Adirondack area was uplifted like a dome, then eroded by streams for thousands of years. Subsequently, huge masses of ice moved over the entire area, removing all vestiges of soil and loose rock from the mountain summits and leaving smoothed and bare granite behind. Much of the material eroded by the glaciers from the mountain tops and sides was deposited later in the numerous valleys, filling them to great depths. Many glacially formed depressions in these valleys are now the sites of the lakes for which the Adirondacks are famous. Because of the hardness of the rocks, the Uplands have retained many of their glacial-scoured characteristics.

To the south, the rather low but fairly steep Taconic Mountains straddle the boundary between New York and her three neighboring states to the east—Vermont, Massachusetts, and Connecticut. Near Bennington, Vermont, for instance, the land is rough to rolling, with a local relief of 2,300 feet. Mt. Greylock (3,505 feet), in the northwest corner of Massachusetts, has the highest elevation and greatest relief (2,900 feet) in the Taconics. To the

FIGURE 9-6. *Whiteface Mountain in the Adirondacks. (New York State Dept. of Commerce)*

south, local relief is progressively less and the slopes, in general, less steep. This terrain continues southward almost to New York City.

East of the Taconics lie the Berkshire Hills of Connecticut and Massachusetts. These rise to the north to become the Green Mountains of Vermont. Although not a rugged range, these mountains are cut by some very steep-sided canyons. Mt. Mansfield (4,393 feet), in northern Vermont, is the culminating peak. As is the case in most parts of the Northeastern Uplands, lakes and swamps are much in evidence in certain places.

The surface of eastern Vermont is not as high and steep as that of the Green Mountains. Local relief tends to be slightly more than 2,000 feet, and much of the terrain varies from undulating to rugged relief. In western New Hampshire the topography is even more subdued, with local elevation differences of about 1,500 feet. In the north, however, the White Mountains, topped by Mt. Washington (6,288 feet), have a maximum local relief of 5,200 feet, and are very rough, with many steep slopes (*Fig. 9-7*).

The White Mountains continue into Maine and might be thought of as being connected to Mt. Katahdin (5,257 feet). This is an unusual peak, for near its summit is a large area of tableland. Much of the upland surface in this vicinity appears to be rather subdued. The mountain's south and east slopes are long and steep, however.

Upland Maine has a variety of landform features in addition to its many lakes and swamps. In places the terrain is knobby or rolling, but it may be rough, with short, steep slopes. In a few areas the local relief is less than 500 feet, but it tends to be over 1,500 feet in most places. The least known part of the state is in the northwest—north and east of the Boundary Mountains. This is truly a land of lakes and swamps. Poorly drained areas are found away from and above streams as well as near them. These and other evidence of glaciation abound. Rocks and stones of a variety of shapes and sizes cover the surface for miles and miles, except where farmers have attempted to clear land for plowing. Many of these rocks are too large to have been carried by streams or currents. The fact that they were glacially deposited is further proved by the fact that a small percentage of them are types not found within a hundred miles of their final resting places. The same glaciers removed most of what little soil might have existed in the Uplands before the Ice Age, so that now the soils, if any, are thin and infertile.

The Northeastern Uplands continue northward across the international boundary into southeastern Quebec and northwestern New Brunswick until they are interrupted by the St. Lawrence Lowland. This area includes most of eastern Quebec and all of Newfoundland-Labrador.

FIGURE 9-7. *Mt. Washington (6,288 feet) and the Presidential Range from Intervale. (New Hampshire Development Commission)*

North of Vermont, the Sutton Mountains form a short extension of the Green Mountains. The relief here, about 3,000 feet, is unusually high for Quebec, although there are several other ridges and summits of considerable relief. Several other smaller isolated masses are scattered between New England and the St. Lawrence, but in general, as one proceeds toward the river, slopes become gentler and there is less relief.

A core of upland connects southern Quebec to Gaspé, where the steep north slopes of the Shickshock Mountains look down upon the mouth of the St. Lawrence. Towards the south, the upland surface, still strongly rolling, grades down to Chaleur Bay.

Northern New Brunswick, which is inadequately mapped, is much like adjacent portions of Maine and Quebec. As in most of the Northeastern Uplands, lakes and swamps are common and the general surface configuration is strongly rolling. Steep slopes tend to be near the many streams that have eroded rather deep, narrow valleys through much of this area.

Two hundred and fifty miles east of Gaspé, across the Gulf of St. Lawrence, lies the island of Newfoundland. This is, except for northern Labrador, the most rugged part of the Uplands, for not only is the surface rough, but the climate is severe, the soils thin, and the vegetation sparse. More than half the island is barren, covered only by mosses, bogs, and lakes.

The Long Range comprises the western and roughest portion of Newfoundland. South of the Strait of Belle Isle, the coast of the Gulf of St. Lawrence is particularly steep and rugged, with a rolling upland surface dotted with lakes and swamps, abruptly sloping down 1,500 to 2,500 feet to the sea. A steep bluff overlooks the Atlantic side of northwestern Newfoundland, too. To the east this land is less rugged, but still rough, with a much-indented coastline. Lakes, bogs, swamps, and streams are everywhere. Steep slopes near the coast are not as common as in the northwest (*Fig. 9-8*).

Nearly half of Newfoundland's population lives on the edges of Avalon Peninsula, at the island's southeastern extremity. Here, too, are lakes and swamps and poor soils. Local relief is generally less than 1,000 feet, while it is over 2,500 feet in many places in the northwest. Rocky and inhospitable, this peninsula offers little in the way of making a living from the land. People here look to the sea.

Labrador, a mainland peninsula to the north of the Strait of Belle Isle, belongs to Quebec and Newfoundland. Its northern portion is the roughest area in provincial Canada east of the Rockies. The rugged and Alp-like Torngat Mountains, with at least one summit 5,500 feet above sea level, are near the boundary of Quebec, just south of Hudson Strait. Elevations become lower southward, and much of the southern half of Labrador is rolling upland country with many lakes and swamps. Certain areas are somewhat rougher than others, such as in the Laurentides, where local relief is over 1,000 feet and steep slopes are common.

FIGURE 9-8.

CROSS–SECTION OF
NEWFOUNDLAND

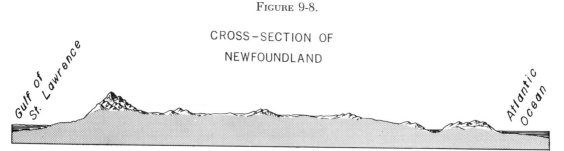

GULF OF ST. LAWRENCE — Atlantic Ocean

LONG MOUNTAINS   CENTRAL PLATEAU   AVALON PENINSULA

The interior upland of eastern Quebec, which has not been mapped adequately, is best described as having a rolling surface broken here and there by steeper sloping summits and rich in lakes and bogs.

Climate

NEW ENGLAND-CANADIAN LOWLANDS

The varied topography of this region at first leads one to believe that its climates are equally diverse. Such is not the case. Throughout the region summers are cool and winters cold. The length of summer decreases to the north. Winter, the longest season, dominates the northern Maritime Provinces (*Fig. 9-9*).

The only weather stations in the entire region having average January temperatures above freezing are on the small islands east of Long Island. Even Provincetown at the tip of the Cape Cod Peninsula has a January average below 32° F. Sometimes during winters the thermometer drops to −15° along the Rhode Island or Connecticut coasts and to −50° in the Aroostook Valley and the Maritimes.

With these winter temperatures and the sea's proximity, heavy snow might be expected. The southern portion of the region receives an average of 25 to 30 inches, but northern New Brunswick and Cape Breton Island have over 100 inches. The total annual precipitation varies from about 35 to 55 inches (100 inches of snow

equals 10 inches of rain), and is well distributed throughout the year, although less falls in the winter.

Winter, with its "nor'easters" and fishermen far from home in small boats, is the season that never seems to end for many of those who live in the region. Such winters may be a factor in producing the hardy souls of conservative stock for which the area is noted.

The St. Lawrence-Champlain Lowlands lie in the path of the major storms that cross the northeastern section of the continent. The interaction of the air masses along the polar front produces cyclonic storms that tend to move toward the Great Lakes and the St. Lawrence Lowlands under the influence of the middle latitudes' general westerly circulation. Polar air from the Arctic, most common in the winter season, often brings very low temperatures, high winds, and heavy precipitation. The St. Lawrence River and Gulf are icebound from December to April. Summers are warm and often quite humid. Montreal, for example, has a July mean of 70° F.

NORTHEASTERN UPLANDS

The Northeastern Uplands are lands of great climatic extremes (*Fig. 9-10*). Lying in middle latitudes, it comes within the influence of constant conflicts between cold, dry air masses flowing out of the great subpolar region to the northwest and the warmer, moisture-bearing, tropical marine air from the south. The ten-

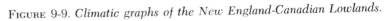

FIGURE 9-9. *Climatic graphs of the New England-Canadian Lowlands.*

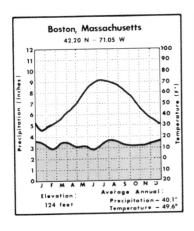
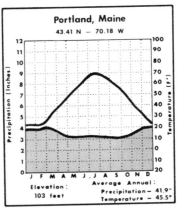
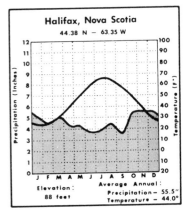

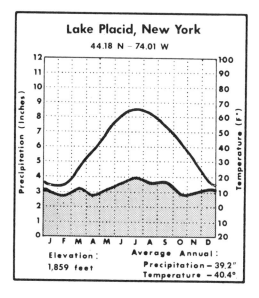

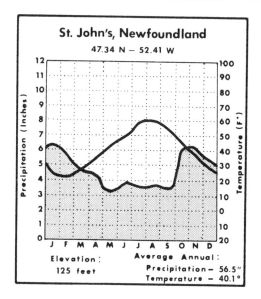

FIGURE 9-10. *Climatic graphs of the Northeastern Uplands.*

dency of most of the general cyclonic disturbances to skirt the polar front puts their paths of movement through this subregion. This results in a more or less regular succession (twice a week) of snowstorms or rainstorms alternating with two- or three-day periods of fair weather, typically with intervening warm west or southwest winds in summer and cold northwesterly winds in winter.

Continental influences prevail because the general movement of air masses in these latitudes is from west to east. By the time winter air has moved eastward across snow-covered interior Anglo-America, it is bound to be cold. Therefore winter temperatures here are far colder than those on the continent's west coast at the same latitude where maritime influences are at work. By the same token, summers in the Uplands are warmer than one might expect.

In the Taconic Mountains of Connecticut, January temperatures average about 25° F., which is about the same as the south coast of Newfoundland, many miles to the north. In Newfoundland, the influence of the sea provides a warmer climate than might be predicted on the basis of latitude. In the high mountains, such as on Mt. Washington in New Hampshire, temperatures average well below

0°, with −50° F. readings on the coldest days.

Summers are very short in northern Quebec and Labrador, although some days are quite warm. In the Uplands south of the St. Lawrence, summers are longer, but nowhere is summer the dominant season. In the far south, average July temperatures are about 72° F.; in the north they are below 50° F. and frosts are to be expected even in July. With the exception of a few coastal locations in Newfoundland, summer is the season of maximum precipitation. Summer rains are supplemented significantly by winter snows, however, and these usually pile up to depths of 100 inches or more in the southern half of the subregion. The deep winter snows of the more accessible parts of the Northeastern Uplands attract thousands of skiers and other winter sports enthusiasts each season.

Total annual precipitation is high in the south and east. St. John's, Newfoundland, receives about 56 inches a year and southeastern Connecticut only 5 to 10 inches less. The total gradually decreases towards the north until it may be as little as 15 to 20 inches in northern Quebec. The higher elevations, such as in the Laurentides, receive substantially more precipitation than the surrounding rolling uplands.

No climatic discussion of this region would

be complete without mention of the frequent winter storms, with their high winds and biting cold. The area is visited by most of the storms that cross the continent and by others that form in the eastern half of Anglo-America. Fog, too, plagues fishermen, especially over the Grand Banks, a shallow area in the Atlantic off the southeast coast of Newfoundland.

Natural Vegetation and Soils

NEW ENGLAND-CANADIAN LOWLANDS

The New England-Canadian Lowlands is a region of forests, cleared in places, cut over at least once almost everywhere, so that very little virgin timber remains. In southern New England, most of the forest cover is gone and the land is occupied by man. Deciduous varieties predominate, dropping their broad leaves during the long winters. In Maine, the "Pine Tree State," needleleaf evergreens prevail, although deciduous trees are still common in areas of suitable soils.

The Maritimes, too, are dominated by needleleafs, especially red spruce, balsam fir, white pine, hemlock, and white spruce. In swampy areas cedars, tamarack, and black spruce are found. In the valleys and richer areas there are several varieties of ash, birch, maple, elm, and beech. The upland of northern Cape Breton Island is covered by a barren of bog and heath. An unusual vegetation consisting of salt-tolerant grasses and plants grows on the tidal flats along the shores of Nova Scotia and Prince Edward Island, and especially along the Bay of Fundy, with its 50-foot tidal range.

Glacial till, lake or marine sands, outwash sands and gravels, and alluvial soils occur in the St. Lawrence-Champlain Lowlands. Much of the district is floored by lake silts and fine alluvium and is very fertile. Peat bogs prevail where remnants of the much larger Champlain Sea persisted. Reddish-brown clay soils are found in the Quebec area. The natural vegetation is that of a mixed deciduous-coniferous forest. Sugar maple, hemlock, white pine and yellow birch, scattered white spruce, and balsam fir dominate.

The soils of the northern Lowlands came from parent material that varied from hard crystalline rocks to sands and clays. When the area was glaciated, it resulted in the mixture of older soils with various kinds of rocks, such as sandstones, shales, limestones, and clays. The gray-brown podzolic soils are the most important agricultural group in the Lowlands.

NORTHEASTERN UPLANDS

This subregion is of such wide latitudinal extent that vegetative types tend to be belted according to distance from the southern boundary at New York City. There are significant differences caused by elevation changes, too, and in parts of the region exposure to prevailing winds or the sun is important in conditioning the type of vegetation to be found. In the far north and along the coast of Labrador the so-called tundra prevails. This moss- and lichen-covered barren is similar to vegetation above timberline on high mountains in western Anglo-America. Protected locations sometimes support dwarfed trees, and wild flowers flourish during the short spring. Much of insular Newfoundland also has tundra-like plant life.

South of the tundra belt are thin, stunted conifers, particularly balsam fir and black spruce. These trees grow taller and become more numerous as one moves southward, and other varieties, such as jack pine and white pine, become important. Deciduous trees mixed with needleleaf are to be found near the St. Lawrence, and this mixed forest type continues to the subregion's southern limits. Typical varieties are maple, birch, and aspen, and these often are associated with white pine (the best timber tree in the region) as well as hemlock and other conifers.

The Northeastern Uplands have old granitic rocks that are very hard, high in coarse crystals of quartz, and very low in lime. The soil material that comes from them is stony, sandy, and low in fertility; therefore, the agriculture of the Uplands is poor. Timber and scenery are the most valuable resources, and the cool climate and annual precipitation make forest cover the natural vegetation of the region. Good soils exist only in pockets, like those found near Lake St. John, or along streams.

Forestry

Lumber is a bulky commodity, unprofitable to ship. But the Northeastern Uplands have an advantage over many other parts of the country because of their proximity to the biggest wood pulp market in the United States and to a heavily populated region needing lumber for housing. On the other hand, the fact that much of the timber grows in inaccessible places, so sparsely populated as to be lacking in roads and railroads, poses a problem.

Much of the more accessible forest has been cut or burned. Some has regrown in assorted less desirable hardwoods instead of the conifers that once covered it. Some has been farmed or close cut and then abandoned. Considerable acreage is in small lots, unprofitable to cut.

The greatest forest wealth lies within the Laurentian Plateau (Quebec), which forms part of northern Canada's extensive softwood belt. White pine once reigned supreme, but it was so extensively exploited during the past century that it has been virtually eliminated in many areas. In the openings created by cuttings, mixed stands of spruce and balsam fir have sprung up (although there are some pure stands of spruce) to cover the immense Laurentian territory. Hardwood stands of white birch and aspen occasionally occur between the softwood forests, adding variety to the landscape. The many rivers flowing south from the Laurentian Plateau into the St. Lawrence River have made accessible much of this vast forest land whose products are the basis of Quebec's pulp and paper industry.

FOREST PRODUCTS

Pulp and paper. Companies engaged in the manufacture of pulp and paper lead all other types of forestry enterprises in the Uplands. They control the largest area of land, employ the most foresters, and have the greatest financial stake in sustained-yield forestry. Their programs date from the turn of the century.

Quebec produces more than one-third of all Canada's pulp and paper products (*Fig. 9-11*). About half of Canada's coniferous trees lie within its boundaries. In addition to this supply of raw material, Quebec has an unparalleled waterways system to carry logs to the mills and to supply the mills with the hydroelectric power that runs the paper-making machines. Deep, swift rivers wind through the forests; the winter's cut of pulp logs is thrown into streams to ride with the spring freshets down to the pulp and paper mills on the St. Lawrence, the Saguenay, and other rivers. Manufactured pulp, paper, and by-products from the mills are loaded directly into the holds of ocean-going freighters and carried via the St. Lawrence to the sea and the markets of the world.

Several paper companies operate large-scale enterprises in the Northeastern Uplands. The most notable are Great Northern in Maine;

FIGURE 9-11. *Logs being watered to minimize fire hazard at a Quebec mill. (National Film Board of Canada)*

Eastern Pulpwood in Maine and New Brunswick; International Paper in New York, Vermont, New Hampshire, and Maine; and Finch-Pruyn in the Adirondacks.

Ownership of large forest properties in the Uplands has changed appreciably during the past two decades. Pulp and paper companies are the strongest and most stable owners. The large investments in pulp and paper mills can be liquidated only over long periods of time; such investments make necessary a continuous supply of timber. Many of the companies are enlarging their holdings. Others are attempting to stimulate good forest practices on the part of private owners who control land tributary to their mills.

In spite of the large proportion of forest in the New England Uplands, the area is presently producing less than half of the 2.5 billion board feet of lumber annually consumed in the adjoining Lowlands. One-fourth of the 2.3 million cords of pulpwood used must also be imported. Paper consumption per capita has increased drastically in the United States in the last century until it is now over 400 pounds per capita. With coniferous forest running short and the size of trees diminishing, the pulp users in New England are filling the gaps by importing from the South, the Great Lakes states, and Canada.

The one hopeful note for the Uplands, which produce most of the pulp, is the expansion into the use of hardwoods. Since coniferous forests tend to be replaced by hardwoods after cutting or burning, this new use would make profitable the growth of hardwoods, which are unsuitable for saw logs. Hardwoods may be utilized in the manufacture of opaque paper and in the making of corrugating medium, the middle ply of cardboard used in containers.

Christmas trees. Balsam fir and spruce Christmas trees traditionally have been shipped from New England to all major Eastern cities. Most of the trees have been cut on abandoned farm land in New Hampshire, Vermont, and Maine, and in the higher elevations in Massachusetts. Such trees, growing in the most favorable locations, receive sunlight from all sides and are generally balanced, compact, and free of dead limbs.

Maple syrup and sugar. The maple syrup and sugar industry, once an important enterprise, has shown considerable decline since the early part of the century. This decline has not been regular, for some rises occurred during periods of strong prosperity. The drop in the amount produced is caused by increasing use of a combination of cheap substitutes and by rising labor costs. Maple syrup, often mixed with corn and cane syrups, usually shows steadier prices than maple sugar. Retailing for as much as 80 cents a pound in some areas, maple sugar has become a luxury most people rarely enjoy. Vermont is the leader in the industry.

Agriculture

THE CONNECTICUT VALLEY

From its origin in northern New Hampshire, the Connecticut River flows 400 miles southward to Long Island Sound through fertile farm land, wooded hillsides, and thriving industrial cities. It is a land rich in agriculture, industry, and tradition.

The valley's principal sources of farm income are dairy products, tobacco, potatoes, truck crops, and poultry. In general, the more fertile and higher-priced land is located near the river. Crops having a high dollar value per acre are raised in the valley, while those of lower value are grown in the foothills. Tobacco is the predominant crop (*Fig. 9-12*). Farther from the river, potatoes, dairy products, and poultry are emphasized.

CAPE COD CRANBERRIES

Cranberries, a native North American fruit, were brought by Indians to the first Thanksgiving in Plymouth, and Cape Cod sea captains used them to prevent dreaded scurvy.

Cranberries are harvested from early September through late October. Since the harvesting period is relatively short, especially if the season is late, many growers have to begin picking when the fruit is only partly colored.

FIGURE 9-12. *Tents of cheesecloth are spread over tobacco in the Connecticut River Valley to create an even temperature, high humidity, and shade similar to that found naturally in Sumatra. The use of tents greatly increases production costs. It takes 5,000 yards of cloth to tent each acre, and most of it must be replaced annually. (Standard Oil Co. of New Jersey)*

The longer the berries are allowed to remain on the vines, the deeper red and larger they become and the higher their sugar content.

New England produces approximately two-thirds of the nation's cranberries. Income from the first family bogs was used primarily as a means of raising the yearly taxes. Cape Cod and southeastern Massachusetts lead the nation in production.

AROOSTOOK POTATOES

Northeastern Maine's Aroostook County is second to Idaho as a potato producer. The county's cool, moist growing season and easily-cultivated silty loam soil favor both high quality and high quantity yields.

The first potatoes were planted in the county for conversion into starch for the New England textile industry. After rail transportation was available, the emphasis shifted to producing for urban dinner tables. The starch industry, however, is still an important user of potatoes, consuming an average 5,000 tons per month.

Aroostook is pre-eminent as a certified potato seed producing area. The cooler climate enables the grower to control vine diseases better than can be done in warmer parts of the country. Aroostook Valley produces about 12 per cent of the nation's total potato crop. Average yields per acre are 480 bushels (*Fig. 9-13*).

THE MARITIMES

The chief agricultural products of the Maritime Provinces are hay, clover, potatoes, dairy products, oats, turnips, and apples. Agriculture is the main industry of Prince Edward Island and New Brunswick. These two areas produce 85 per cent of Canada's seed potato crop and export abroad about one-third of their output. The Annapolis Valley of Nova Scotia produces apples in quantity.

ST. LAWRENCE-CHAMPLAIN LOWLANDS

The portion of the St. Lawrence-Champlain Lowlands lying in the states of New York and Vermont is primarily a dairy land. Poor soils,

FIGURE 9-13. *A government inspector checks potatoes during harvest in Aroostook County, Maine. Note the large size of the potatoes, their uniformity, and the number of potatoes in the row. (Agricultural Extension Service, University of Maine)*

short growing seasons, and considerable distance from markets, combined with little available flat land, preclude most other agricultural enterprises. St. Lawrence is the leading dairy county in New York State, ranking first in the number of cows milked and in milk and hay produced. It is fourth nationally in the number of cows milked, fifth in milk production and value of dairy products sold, and third in hay production.

Most of the milk from this area is shipped into the New York City market in fluid form. The surplus is processed locally into cheese, ice cream, and other dairy products. Other notable farm products include McIntosh apples from the Lake Champlain Valley, seed potatoes grown in New York's three northernmost counties—St. Lawrence, Franklin, and Clinton—and maple syrup and sugar from St. Lawrence County.

Until 1870, nearly 80 per cent of the population of Quebec lived in rural areas. During the great industrial development of the last 50 years, the rural population has fallen to 35 per cent. The fast-growing and numerous industrial towns have provided excellent markets for farm products.

Mixed farming combined with dairy farming is widely practiced, because this system is best adapted to climatic and economic conditions. The improved quality of livestock, particularly of dairy cattle and bacon hogs, is the dominant feature of animal husbandry today.

Dairy products rank high in the economy. Quebec has nearly 950 butter and cheese factories, over 50 plants for processing milk, and many city dairies. Altogether, these industries employ more than 5,000 people. Quebec is Canada's leading butter producer and ranks second to Ontario in cheese manufacturing.

Next in value are cereal products. Besides large mills (supplied by Western grain), Quebec has many small mills for preparing feeds.

Meat products, too, are important. Packing plants in Montreal and Quebec turn out products grossing around $90 million each year. Mention also should be made of the more than 140 hatcheries and numerous candling stations serving the poultry industry.

During the past 40 years, great advances have occurred in vegetable culture, a response to urban growth and needs resulting from industrialization. In the 1920's, only 7,457 acres were cultivated on a commercial basis, compared with about 50,000 acres today. Canning factories, almost unknown in the 1920's, now produce goods valued at over $27 million.

Fruit growing, too, has developed appreciably. Quebec apples and strawberries are famed for their quality and flavor. The apple crop is sizable—two million bushels a year on the average. The strawberry harvest yields about six million quarts. Other fruit crops include raspberries, currants, and cranberries.

NORTHEASTERN UPLANDS

Uplands agriculture is, at best, likely to be a marginal enterprise. Commercial crops may be grown only where market orientation offers sufficient advantage to cover the cost of overcoming climatic and soil discrepancies between regions. As soon as transportation voids this advantage the crops cease to be grown except for local markets.

The two main commodities of the area are dairy and poultry products. Both of these do better on the Lowlands, but high prices and great demand encourage their existence on a commercial level throughout the subregion. Pastures are planned, seeded, and rotated as well as possible to avoid the purchase of feed. Grain is imported from the Midwest and supplements local hay and silage corn. Grass silage is also used. Along with various grasses, oats, barley, and rye are grown for hay. Most of the milk moves to the Boston milkshed in fresh form for daily consumption.

The raising of beef cattle, sheep, swine, and horses is a supplementary enterprise. Beef cattle raising is increasing, with the establishment of select purebred herds. Climate and topography are ideal for sheep; labor requirements are small and extensive equipment is not necessary. Sheep produce two sources of income, wool and lambs, and nearby markets for these are among the best in the world.

Small fruits are grown commercially. Most berries and small fruits, however, have fallen to levels that barely can supply local needs, including roadside stands selling to tourists. Only blueberry production has risen considerably above home market demands. Blueberries constitute a rather important industry; they are grown on cut-over forest land. Production varies with the stand, the age of the plant, the season, and many other factors; it can range from almost nothing to nearly 1,000 quarts per acre.

Blackberries and grapes are grown commercially to a limited extent. The acre yield of these fruits is low, however, compared to that in the more favorable sections of the country.

Fishing

Fishing has always occupied an important place in the economic and industrial growth of the New England-Canadian Lowlands, although it has suffered a serious decline in the past decade. Indeed, New England now imports some fish products from Canada and Japan. The several thousand square miles of fishing grounds that parallel the Atlantic coastline contain over 80 species of edible fish that flourish in the food-rich, cool waters on the continental shelf. Haddock, redfish, flounder, cod, whiting, pollock, cusk, and hake are the principal demersal varieties (bottom feeders). Herring and mackerel are pelagic (surface feeders); they are migratory fish, and their abundance is subject to great fluctuations. Deep-sea fishing operations take place in Atlantic waters covering the upland portions of the ocean bed between the outer edge of the shore fisheries and the extremely deep waters of the ocean. These "banks" cover an extensive area, ranging from Georges Bank, off Cape Cod, northeastward along the coasts of New England and eastern Canada to Newfoundland and into the Gulf of St. Lawrence. The Grand Banks, the tops of an old submerged mountain range about 300 miles long and 80 to 100 fathoms deep, are the most famous of these prized fishing areas.

The shellfish industry, mainly scallops, lobsters, and clams, provides a substantial portion of income and employment. Lobstering provides full- or part-time employment for about 5,000 fishermen. Canada's lobster industry leads the world in production. Clamming also is important, both as full- and as a part-time occupation. Manufactured fishery products provide more revenue than the part of the catch that is marketed for fresh consumption. Processing includes packaging, freezing, canning, and curing by salting, drying, pickling, and smoking. Important by-products are fish oil, fish meal, and buttons.

Of the New England states, Maine and Massachusetts are foremost in fishing activities. Chief fishing ports are Boston, Gloucester, New Bedford, and Provincetown, Massachusetts (Fig. 9-14). These ports land about two-thirds of the weight and five-sixths of the value of New England fish.

The small coastal villages are tuned to the ocean more than they are to the land. Village life reflects the season's fishing just as surely as life in an inland village relates to the work on the surrounding farms.

Electronic equipment and other technical innovations are causing great changes in the fishing industry. Methods of catching, processing, and marketing fish are improving considerably—echo sounders, filleting machines, precooked and breaded fish are examples.

FIGURE 9-14. *The fishing fleet docked at Gloucester, Massachusetts. (Massachusetts Dept. of Commerce)*

Despite a continual decline in the industry for over a decade, the emergence of technological developments promises even richer rewards. Nature has been niggardly in giving the region metals, minerals, and oil, but she has endowed it generously with an extensive coastline, good harbors, and relatively short distances to rich fishing grounds.

Mining and Quarrying

ADIRONDACKS AND NEW ENGLAND

The Adirondack Mountains of New York and the New England Uplands are poor in minerals. With the exceptions of iron and titanium, most of the minerals are in such small quantity and are produced with such difficulty that if they occurred anywhere else in the country, they would probably not be worked commercially. Even though many of these minerals are relatively close to market points and refineries, the difficulty of transportation alone has kept some of them from being used. Subzero winter temperatures inhibit year-round operations in some areas; in others, no one is willing to invest the necessary capital for transportation of ores to market.

Iron ore is found chiefly on the slopes of the Adirondack Mountains in New York. As mines in the Great Lakes area are forced to use lower-grade ores, these deposits are coming into more favorable competition since they are closer to Pittsburgh. Now being worked are: Republic Steel Corporation's properties at Lyon Mountain, near Plattsburgh, and Mineville, near Port Henry; the deposits of the Jones and Laughlin Steel Corporation at Benson Mines; and the titanium-iron mines of the National Lead Company at Tahawus. Containing from 25 to 35 per cent iron, these ores are beneficiated at the mines into concentrates of 68 per cent iron and then sintered.

Granite is the principal stone quarried in the Uplands. Vermont's "Rock of Ages" quarry at East Barre yields a famous type of granite with a superior color and texture that makes it popular for use in monuments (*Fig. 9-15*).

FIGURE 9-15. *Rock of Ages Quarry, East Barre, Vermont. This 350-foot, 20-acre granite quarry has been called one of the man-made wonders of the world. More than a hundred granite manufacturing plants are located in the Barre-Montpelier area. (Rock of Ages Corp.)*

New Hampshire's quarries are around Concord, on the slopes of the White Mountains, and in the southwest section of the state near the borders of Vermont and Massachusetts. Production is small, accounting for slightly more than four per cent of New England's total.

Vermont usually leads the nation in the production of marble. Quarries near Rutland and Proctor on the west flank of the Green Mountains are without rival in the United States. Marble from this area varies in color from pure white to gray, pink, and even green, and is used extensively for construction and interior decoration.

Two of the more important slate producing areas are those near Monson, Maine, and along the Vermont-New York border. The Monson area produces a black variety of high quality that is in demand for electrical panels and blackboards. Vermont slate occurs in several colors and is used primarily for roofing.

QUEBEC AND THE MARITIMES

The highlands of southern Quebec produce an immense variety of minerals that have given rise to large mining operations in several localities. Copper, lead, zinc, gold, and chromite are all mined in this area. Copper ore occurrences have been reported from many places. What may become an important producer of medium-grade copper ore has, in recent years, been prospected at the headwaters of the York River, in Gaspé. Latest report by Noranda Mines, Ltd., a large Canadian company that holds an option on Gaspé copper, is that at least 70 million tons of copper ore can be mined profitably during the next 43 years. This is an extraordinary life expectancy for a copper mine. The vast Arizona copper field in the United States, geologically similar to the Gaspé find, has a life expectancy of only 23 years.

Lead and zinc also are known to exist in this eastern peninsula, and small quantities of these metal ores are being produced southeast of Ste. Anne des Monts. Chromite, a substance with many industrial uses and from which chromium is obtained, has been mined sporadically at several localities in the vicinity of Richmond.

Nonmetals include limestone, marble, talc and soapstone, granite, roofing slate, marl, peat, petroleum, and asbestos.

Of all the mineral substances contributing to the wealth of Quebec, asbestos is the most important. Discovered in 1876, the deposits, until a few years ago, were mined by open-pit methods; today the larger producers have gone underground, using mining methods initiated in the large copper mines of the southwestern United States. East Broughton, Thetford Mines, Black Lake, Coleraine, Asbestos, and Norbestos are fiber-producing centers from which over nine million tons of asbestos-bearing rock are mined each year and sent to defibering plants.

Interior Quebec and Labrador are made up of hard crystalline rocks extending from the St. Lawrence River northward over the rest of the province to its limit at Hudson Strait. The area has already yielded such metals as gold, silver, copper, zinc, lead, iron, molybdenum, tungsten, and titanium, as well as several commercially important industrial minerals, such as apatite, asbestos, fluorspar, garnet, graphite, silica, magnesite, mica, and pyrite.

The most publicized mineral area at the moment is that section of Ungava and Labrador called the Labrador Trough. This covers a northwest-trending stretch of country, about 40 miles wide and 350 miles long, extending from the headwaters of the Hamilton River to beyond the Koksoak River. Geologically, the area is similar to the famed Mesabi iron district of Minnesota. Its sedimentary formations hold thick beds of high-grade iron ore, the total dimensions of which are not as yet known. The iron ore is moved by rail to Sept Isles on the St. Lawrence River, where it is then loaded into ore boats for shipment to interior and seaboard steel mills in the United States and Canada.

The province of Newfoundland has other extensive mineral deposits. Iron ore is mined from the huge Wabana deposits on Bell Island. Approximately one-third of the output goes to Sydney, Nova Scotia; the remainder to West Germany and the United Kingdom.

The remainder of the province's metal production—zinc, lead, copper, silver, and gold—comes from the operations of the Buchans Mining Company, Ltd., near Red Indian Lake in central Newfoundland.

Nova Scotia has long been famous for its extensive coal deposits. There are four fields with thick seams of bituminous coal, the most important of which is the Sydney field in Cape Breton, which produces three-quarters or more of the annual output of the region.

Settlement

NEW ENGLAND

The south. Successive occupancy by Indians, European agriculturists, and manufacturers has left distinctive landscape impressions in southern New England, a land with a long history of settlement. New land in the colonies beckoned to people of all classes in Britain. To the poor it was an escape from unemployment; to the artisan it was independence; to the small landowner it meant cheap, large estates without the crushing burdens of taxation; to the merchant, a chance to sell English surpluses; to the aristocrat, the opportunity for investment of profits.

The new homeland offered advantages the colonists soon learned to use. Here were great tracts of virgin forest to furnish wood for shelter, for protective stockades, and for fuel. The forests yielded edible nuts and berries and offered an abundant supply of game—deer, bear, squirrel, rabbit, quail, and pigeon—as a meat supply for the colonists. Fur-bearing animals were plentiful, and the skins of beaver, mink, otter, fox, and muskrat gave the settlers desirable articles for trade. Numerous streams flowing to the sea furnished fresh drinking water, a means of transportation and communication, and fish—chiefly salmon, shad, and trout. Along the seaward margins were oysters, scallops, clams, crabs, and an endless variety of fish.

Friendly Indians taught the colonists how to raise native corn and how to fertilize their fields. With the enormous task of clearing off the virgin forest before them, and with an excess of wood on every side, the colonists frequently resorted to fire as the cheapest and quickest method of preparing the area for the raising of crops or the pasturing of animals.

Corn, pumpkins, squash, and beans were planted in small earth mounds and fertilized by dropping fish and seaweed in among the seeds.

With remarkable rapidity, the landscape was radically transformed. No longer was it forbidding. Man in his infinite ingenuity had made the change. From a virgin forest with scattered natural and Indian-made clearings appeared open fields of corn and grain and pastures supporting cattle and sheep. Even the areas of poorer soils were transformed; only the rougher slopes remained unaltered.

During the colonizing period the amount of agricultural labor expended was enormous.

Forests had to be cut down or burned and the stumps of trees removed. The boulders and stones that seemed to be everywhere were piled laboriously into the long stone walls characteristic of New England. Today these stone walls —as much a part of the Yankee heritage as Lexington and Concord—are going the way of many things from our rural past. With current farming methods demanding unimpeded acreage for strip-cropping, diversion terraces, and other conservation practices, as well as the efficient use of mechanized equipment to boost production, the barricades that for so long have been a part of the New England landscape are being torn down at an accelerated rate.

The great era of wall building was between 1700 and 1875. Innumerable farmers worked themselves into early graves in their endless bout with boulders. And even after the surface rocks were subdued, others had a way of rearing up out of the ground with the spring thaws, encouraging folk tales about rocks that "grew."

New England's thin, stony, and infertile soils and its short growing season (120-150 days) have limited its agriculture severely. Even the favored coastal lowlands and stream valleys could not compete with the more productive plains west of the Appalachians, and the old New England rural economy gradually crumbled. Emigration, first to the new areas of the West, and later to nearby cities, took from each New England generation its most ambitious sons. Gradually the fields that had been reclaimed from the wilderness at so great a cost in human labor and in so short a time reverted to brush. Old farms, the ancestral homes of the present generation of city dwellers, were abandoned and slowly fell into picturesque ruin.

The north. Although northern New England today is sparsely inhabited compared to the industrial sections of Massachusetts, Connecticut, and Rhode Island, its history predates that of perhaps any other portion of the continental United States. Historians dispute the date Maine's history began. If the accounts of explorations by Norsemen are considered, it is possible that Maine was first sighted by these hardy seamen and explorers about A.D. 1000, when Leif Ericson supposedly discovered Vinland. The French settled at St. Croix Island in 1604; Popham colonists settled at the mouth of the Kennebec River in 1607—13 years before the Pilgrims landed at Plymouth Rock. The settlement was abandoned the following year. In 1620 the Council of New England, the successor of the Plymouth Company, obtained a grant of the country between 40° and 48° N., extending from sea to sea, and a grant of the territory between the Merrimack and Kennebec Rivers for 60 miles inland under the name of the "Province of Maine." Many grants in this vicinity followed within a few years.

Puritan Massachusetts interpreted its charter to make its northern boundary run east and west from a point three miles north of the source of the Merrimack River. On this basis it claimed almost all the settled portion of Maine. This area remained a part of Massachusetts until 1820, whereupon it was admitted to the Union as a separate state.

Population. In 1809, New England accounted for 20.4 per cent of the nation's population— one in every five Americans lived in New England. By 1960, the percentage was only 5.9 per cent, about one out of every sixteen.

Of the 10,427,000 people dwelling in New England in 1960, approximately 90 per cent,

or 9,384,300, were lowland inhabitants, largely concentrated in the three industrial states— Massachusetts, Connecticut, and Rhode Island.

Prior to 1800, New Englanders were predominantly British, mostly of Puritan stock. Between 1800 and 1850, Irish and French Canadian immigration was conspicuous. Since 1850, every wave of European immigration has washed over New England—Austrians, Poles, Italians, Russians, Swedes, Finns, Lithuanians, and Portuguese, to name a few.

Immigrants have flocked to the urban centers and come into conflict with the older population. In many cities, the foreign born exceed the native born. This is especially true in the mill towns—Lowell and Fall River—and in Boston, the metropolitan hub.

Seventy-seven per cent of all New Englanders live in cities and villages. Yet there are very few large cities and there is no huge industrial metropolis. In 1960, only a dozen cities exceeded 100,000 inhabitants; sixteen had populations ranging between 50,000 and 100,000. Even Boston, the trade hub, ranked thirteenth nationally with less than one million people (682,303). The Boston metropolitan area, however, ranked sixth, with 2,566,732 (*Fig. 9-16*).

The Boston Basin, a low plain surrounding the city, is thickly populated. Three million

FIGURE 9-16. *Located on Boston Bay at the mouths of the Charles and Mystic Rivers, Boston is an important port as well as a major financial and manufacturing center. (American Airlines)*

people live within a radius of 30 miles of Boston. Very few major markets have the size, services, and facilities of the Greater Boston area. Rail and truck service enables the industrialist to obtain delivery to 18 major cities in the eastern United States and Canada within three days.

Table XI lists the population of the 14 largest New England metropolitan areas and their growth or decline in population from 1960 to 1965, with an analysis of the components of change.

Table XII lists the population of the New England states and their growth from 1950.

CANADA

The Maritimes. The Maritime Provinces are historic parts of Canada. It was in this area,

known as Acadia to the early French settlers (later as Nova Scotia to the English), that the first attempt at colonization was made in 1604 when Samuel de Champlain founded Port Royal (Annapolis, Nova Scotia). The first commerce of sparsely populated Acadia was a royal monopoly based on furs and fish.

During the long struggle between France and England for control of North America, Acadia changed hands several times. In 1713, the Treaty of Utrecht ceded the peninsular portion (the mainland of Nova Scotia) to the English. During the next half century, English settlements centered on Halifax (founded by the English as a naval base in 1749) and gradually supplanted most of the French Atlantic settlements. By 1758, the bulk of the territory was in English hands. After 1776, the population was increased by 30,000 Loyalist refugees from the

TABLE XI

POPULATION AND COMPONENTS OF POPULATION CHANGE FOR NEW ENGLAND METROPOLITAN AREAS, 1960 AND 1965*

(In thousands, except as indicated)

NEW ENGLAND METROPOLITAN STATE ECONOMIC AREAS	POPULATION		PER CENT CHANGE	COMPONENTS OF CHANGE, 1960–1965	
	April 1, 1960	*July 1, 1965*	*1960 to 1965*	*Natural Increase*	*Net Migration*
Boston, Lawrence-Haverhill, Lowell, Mass. ...	3,110	3,205	3.1	178	−82
Bridgeport, Stamford, Norwalk, Conn.	654	746	14.2	39	53
Brockton, Mass.	248	296	19.1	17	30
Fall River, New Bedford, Mass.	398	411	3.1	18	−6
Hartford, New Britain, Conn.	690	765	11.0	49	27
Lewiston-Auburn, Maine	86	91	5.3	5	−1
Manchester, N. H.	178	205	15.3	12	15
New Haven, Waterbury, Meriden, Conn.	660	704	6.6	38	5
New London-Groton-Norwich, Conn.	186	216	16.1	17	13
Pittsfield, Mass.	142	144	1.5	8	−6
Portland, Maine	183	197	7.7	11	3
Providence-Pawtucket-Warwick, R. I.	719	739	2.8	35	−15
Springfield-Chicopee-Holyoke, Mass.	533	550	3.3	31	−13
Worcester, Fitchburg-Leominster, Mass.	583	608	4.2	32	−8

*Source: Statistical Abstract of the U.S. (Washington, D.C.: U.S. Department of Commerce, Bureau of the Census, 1967), p. 21.

TABLE XII

Population of the New England States*

	1970 (projected)	1966	1960	1950
New England	11,708,000	11,224,000	10,427,109	9,314,453
Connecticut	3,080,000	2,875,000	2,514,897	2,007,280
Maine	1,002,000	983,000	964,623	913,774
Massachusetts	5,556,000	5,383,000	5,114,558	4,690,514
New Hampshire	729,000	681,000	599,533	533,242
Rhode Island	922,000	898,000	846,207	791,896
Vermont	419,000	405,000	387,291	377,747

*Source: U.S. Department of Commerce, Bureau of the Census, preliminary figures.

United States. Prince Edward Island became a separate province in 1769, and New Brunswick in 1784.

The Maritimes have a largely rural population of approximately 1,492,000 (1965), or slightly under 8 per cent of Canada's total of over 20 million. The great majority of the people are of British stock; in New Brunswick 38.3 per cent of the people are of French origin. The proportion of Canadian-born is high—95.9 per cent. The largest city is Halifax, capital of Nova Scotia, with 93,301 people (183,946 including its suburbs). Next is St. John, New Brunswick, with 77,500 (greater St. John, 95,563). Fredericton, capital of New Brunswick, has a population of 22,158, and Charlottetown, capital of Prince Edward Island, 18,499.

St. Lawrence-Champlain Lowlands. Jacques Cartier discovered the mouth of the St. Lawrence River in 1535, and spent the winter on the site of Quebec. The first permanent settlement in Canada was made at Quebec in 1608 by Samuel de Champlain; a few years later, a temporary settlement was made at Montreal.

Colonization was slow to develop, largely because fur traders resisted settlement. Today, this district is one of the most densely settled parts of Canada. Montreal is Canada's largest city, with a metropolitan area population of more than 2,250,000, and is the largest French-speaking city in the world after Paris (*Fig. 9-17*). Greater Quebec City's population is some 400,000; Ottawa, the capital of Canada,

has a metropolitan area population of about 500,000.

New England Manufacturing

HISTORICAL DEVELOPMENT

The industrial period began with handicraft on the farm. Whole families participated during the long, inactive winters. Surpluses accumulated. Wool cloth was exported to England in the early 1600's. English merchants, sensing

FIGURE 9-17. *The most inland major ocean port in the world, Montreal has increased in importance since the St. Lawrence Seaway was completed into the heart of North America. (Canadian Government Travel Bureau)*

competition, stifled such trade by law. Therefore the New Englander, in order to get rid of his surplus, became a peddler during the winter months. Soon professional peddlers emerged. Traveling on foot with packs, and later on horseback or by sleigh or wagon, the peddlers ranged over a wide area and sold the common necessities of life. Metals imported from England gave great impetus to smithing. As New England grew, the smith became a manufacturer. This led to the growth of artisanship that served an established market in many parts of the Atlantic seaboard. Shortly thereafter, sea peddlers began to transport these "Yankee" goods in American ships to be sold in foreign markets.

Ships brought hides back to Boston, and then skilled labor turned the hides into shoes. All these activities provided capital for the factory system and brought the industrial revolution in America to New England first, but not without considerable difficulty. English legislation, designed to prevent export of trade secrets, forbade emigration of trained artisans, skilled operators, or mill workers. Later, the emigration of trained miners was forbidden, and the export of tools, machinery, or even blueprints was banned. But they had no control over the export of ideas in men's minds. Samuel Slater, an apprentice of Richard Arkwright (the English inventor of a cotton spinning machine), set up the first textile mill in Pawtucket, Rhode Island, in 1790 (Fig. 9-18). By 1800 there were 30 such mills in New England.

Several factors favored early New England manufacturing. Hundreds of lakes and swamps in the glaciated uplands provided storage for water. These waters, tumbling over numerous rapids and small falls, furnished the power to drive many waterwheels. Moreover, the damp climate, so necessary before air conditioning could supply humid conditions artificially, was ideal for spinning and weaving.

By 1850 the combination of a rapidly growing nation, expressed needs, imagination and inventiveness, and the availability of water power and skilled workers had built New England into the most highly industrialized area in the country. Operating in a land with few natural resources, Yankee managers counterbalanced their costs of importing raw materials and exporting finished products by their innovations in manufacturing methods, the dexterity of their employees, and the drive and shrewdness of their salesmen.

The success of early firms promptly bred competition and New England progressed geometrically: machine begot machine, firm begot firm, and industry begot industry. Manufacturing growth forced the development of faster transportation facilities. These two, working in harness, steadily swelled the volume and accelerated the rate of exchange of goods and services.

The power advantages derived by New England from its rivers vanished with the development of steam and electricity. The center of population moved westward and the industries created in its wake served new markets increasingly remote from New England manufacturers. Initially, at least, labor was cheaper in some new industrial areas than in already mature New England.

THE MODERN PERIOD

For generations, the prime source of New England's revenue has been the processing of

FIGURE 9-18. *The Slater Mill, Pawtucket, Rhode Island—birthplace of the American textile industry. (Rhode Island Development Council)*

imported raw materials into an incredible array of products sold to the nation and the world. High value (quality) type of manufacturing continues to dominate the New England scene. The use of "know-how" and skilled labor have enabled New England to offset her competitive disadvantage with other manufacturing regions in the United States.

Today there are more than 11 million persons in the area, 2 million of whom were added during the last 10 years. The decade ahead is likely to add still another million. Probably no other single economic fact will be of more importance to the region. This growing population will provide new markets. In this fact lie both the need and the opportunity for a continuing expansion of economic activity.

Since 1947, the bulk of all new manufacturing jobs added to the economy have been in the electrical machinery and transportation equipment fields. The demand for electronic parts, radar, aircraft instruments, fire control devices, aircraft, and certain naval ships has energized expansion of the metalworking branch of New England manufacturing.

The region has been able to expand its income over the last generation by shifting its manufacturing operations to more productive industries. At the same time, many of the area's traditional industries have survived the transition by means of improved management techniques, by the installment of new equipment in new or modernized plants, and by the development of new methods and new products.

One may expect the New Englander to continue indefinitely the adaptability he has demonstrated for three centuries. As new economic problems arise—and problems are inherent in change—he is certain to find new devices and processes for solving them.

New England is recognized as an outstanding center of advanced research.. Research-based industries offer expanding employment and investment opportunities as well as important new market developments. The area has more than 11 per cent of the nation's industrial research laboratories in the instruments, electrical equipment, and machinery industries.

Thirteen per cent of the nation's colleges and universities awarding higher degrees are located in New England. No other region can boast so many institutions of higher learning. Few schools, if any, can match the academic reputation of Harvard, Massachusetts Institute of Technology, or Yale. Scores of major colleges and universities, teacher training institutions, small private colleges, and preparatory schools dot the New England landscape. These add revenue to the area's economy and enhance New England's position as a research center.

New England has one of the densest transport networks in the nation, with full rail, water, highway, and air facilities. Nevertheless, the region suffers from several disadvantages in transportation that result in high unit freight costs. These are: (1) isolation at one corner of the country, (2) short hauls (averaging 130 miles compared to 230 nationally), (3) semi-monopoly by two railroads over the area's most densely populated parts, (4) the need to cover losses on commuter services, (5) heavy terminal charges, (6) diversity of routes, and (7) diffusion of traffic. These disadvantages are offset somewhat by proximity to the Atlantic and the concentration of about one-third of the nation's population within a radius of 500 miles. Unfortunately, the rise of labor costs and other costs has so reduced local coastal shipping in recent years that New England has been deprived of a substantial part of the advantage of tidewater location.

THE TEXTILE INDUSTRY

The American industrial era had its beginning in New England's early cotton mills, with the factory system attaining prominence by the end of the Civil War. Despite the tremendous diversity of products made in New England, a high concentration of manufacturing employment in the textile industries developed. As late as 1919, nearly 30 per cent of all the region's manufacturing jobs were in textiles; in more than 100 New England cities and towns the textile industry was either the sole or the leading employer. Today the composition of the textile industry may be divided into three main categories: (1) heavy—woolens, worsteds, and wool carpets, rugs, and yarn; (2) light—cotton, rayon, and silk; (3) miscellaneous—dyeing, finishing, knit goods, hats, and lace goods. Of these, cotton textiles and woolens have been especially significant in New England manufacturing.

New England possessed several early advantages for cotton textile manufacture. All these early advantages, however, with the possible exception of skilled labor, have been offset by the South.

Simple statistics tell the tale. Between 1919 and 1939, New England lost 12.3 million cotton spindles, two-thirds of its total; today there are fewer than 4 million. Industrial misfortune on such a scale is almost without precedent in American life. The drama of New England mill closings, of community after community racked with unemployment, fascinated writers and editors for nearly a generation.

By 1962, with under five per cent of the nation's active cotton spindles, and accounting for only three per cent of all cotton consumed in the U.S., New England could claim but small status as a cotton textile producer. Fall River, New Bedford, Lowell, and Lawrence, cities whose names were synonymous with textiles, were forced to build new economies, solidly based on diversified products (Fig. 9-19).

New England is the heart of the woolen industry, employing more than half the nation's workers engaged in this enterprise. The woolen mills are located chiefly in the Merrimack Valley, north of Boston, although concentrations are also found in Rhode Island. Boston is the great wool importing port of the nation. Nearly half the region's mills are located in Massachusetts, with the balance shared by Maine and Rhode Island.

APPAREL INDUSTRY

New England is the fourth largest regional employer of workers in the apparel and related industries. Although apparel plants are scattered, the major concentrations are in or near certain large urban centers. Over half are in Massachusetts, especially Boston, Fall River, New Bedford, Lowell, Lawrence, Worcester, and Springfield. Boston accounts for about a third of the apparel plants in New England, and the Fall River-New Bedford area adds 15 per cent more. Providence, New Haven, and Bridgeport have lesser concentrations. There has been some movement of apparel plants into northern New England, but most garment makers prefer city locations.

THE SHOE INDUSTRY

The rise of the textile industry and its resultant effect on urbanization stimulated the shoe industry, and for decades it ranked second only to textiles in the economy. Today it is usually regarded as second to textiles only as a regional problem industry. The lures of lower wages, tax-free land, and free or low-cost plants to the west and south have caused a decline in employment in New England's shoe

FIGURE 9-19. *Employment changes in the New England textile industry, 1956–1965 (after New England Business Review).*

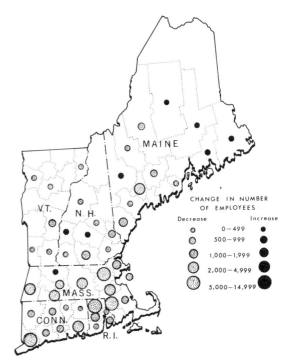

CHANGE IN NUMBER OF EMPLOYEES

Decrease   Increase

○	0–499	●
◔	500–999	●
◕	1,000–1,999	●
◕	2,000–4,999	●
◉	5,000–14,999	●

industry. Despite this, New England still leads the nation in shoe production, accounting for about one-fourth of the national output compared to a peak of 75 per cent in the post-Civil War era (*Fig. 9-20*).

The industry is highly concentrated in eastern Massachusetts. Whole communities are engaged in the manufacture of shoes. So great is this specialization that Brockton produces men's shoes; Haverhill and Lynn, women's shoes. New England's position has been strengthened further by expansions in Maine and New Hampshire.

METALWORKING INDUSTRIES

Thousands of men and women, a large percentage of them toolmakers, machinists, and skilled mechanics, work in hundreds of New England metalworking shops. Jet engines, postage meters, parts for auto engines, automatic lathes, builders' hardware, refrigerators, typewriters, machine guns, printing presses, and textile machinery are only a few of the many items in this industry.

New England's most important metals industries are those that roll, draw, and alloy nonferrous metals. Establishments of this kind account for slightly more than one-third of the industry's total employment, and wire drawing and iron and sheet steel foundries each account for one-sixth. The region has only one blast furnace located at Everett, Massachusetts, with an annual capacity of 195,000 tons.

Most of the market requirements must be filled by purchasing steel from distant mills and shipping it to New England fabricators. Past attempts to secure a large integrated steel mill for New England have been based upon a recognition of the serious gap in the region's industrial plant. The discovery and development of extensive foreign iron ore bodies lent encouragement to the possibility. Such a mill, however, would come into direct competition with newly expanded East Coast steel facilities, which have at least two million tons of additional capacity a year. These expansions have taken place principally at

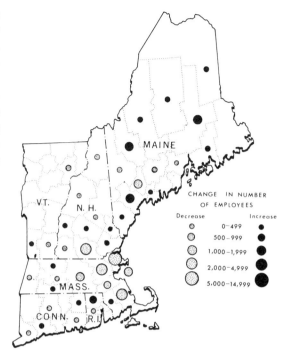

FIGURE 9-20. *Employment changes in the New England shoe and leather industry, 1956–1965 (after* New England Business Review).

Sparrows Point, Maryland, and Morrisville, Pennsylvania.

A small mill, designed to serve part of the New England market for specialty steel, may well be economically feasible. Such a mill could be profitable if sensibly based on new analyses of market demand, competing sources of supply, and well-controlled production costs.

Machinery. The manufacture of nonelectrical machinery is the second-ranking industry in New England in number of persons employed, salary payments to individuals, and in value added in manufacture. Market orientation was one of the dominant factors in the industrial growth of New England, and textile machinery, shoe machinery, and other companies were in a particularly advantageous position during the last century. With a shift to newer industries, such as electronics, the machinery industry must adapt itself to this new market if it is to continue to grow.

Brass and hardware industries. New England has long had an enviable reputation in the brass and hardware industries because of the recognized quality of its output. It supplies one-quarter of the nation's needs for these products by combining highly skilled labor and management. The industry began in 1802, with the making of brass buttons. Today the items may total half a million, including such diversified products as brass rods, tubes, bearings, brushes, wire, shells, lamp sockets, flashlight parts, garden sprinklers, cosmetic containers, snap fasteners, valves, nozzles, diving helmets, and buttons. The bulk of the brass industry is centered in the Naugatuck Valley of Connecticut from Ansonia to Torrington. Waterbury, Connecticut is one of the nation's leading brass centers. New Britain, Connecticut, is the leading hardware center of the region.

Clockmakers started an industry in Bristol about 1850, originating the cheap clock. Connecticut brass clocks, shipped to foreign countries, helped to lay the foundation for America's export trade in the early years of the last century. Today more than 50 per cent of America's clocks are made in Connecticut alone.

Nearly two-thirds of the nation's production of sporting firearms and ammunition is made in Connecticut and those parts of Massachusetts adjacent to Connecticut, with Bridgeport, New Haven, and Hartford, Connecticut, and Springfield, Massachusetts, the leading centers.

JEWELRY

New England is the nation's leading center for the manufacture of low- and medium-priced jewelry. About 90 per cent of the production is concentrated in the Providence metropolitan area. More jewelry and related items are turned out here than in any other city of the nation, if not of the world. Continued high demand for jewelry coupled with aggressive sales action strengthens the industry's position for the future.

TRANSPORTATION EQUIPMENT

The transportation equipment industry is well adapted to New England because of its requirements for a comparatively high level of manufacturing skill and the moderate or below-average requirements of industrial power.

Aircraft industry. Most of the growth in transportation equipment is accounted for by the airplane industry. United Aircraft Corporation and its divisions (Pratt and Whitney Aircraft and Hamilton Standard Propellers at East Hartford, and Sikorsky Aircraft of Stratford) dominate the industry.

Shipbuilding. With the advent of iron and steel ships, New England lost some of its former advantages for shipbuilding. Since the modern ship is built out-of-doors or under huge sheds, the region's frequent rains, heavy snows, and cold weather cause layoffs, interfere with efficiency, and generally handicap shipbuilding.

Most yards, such as those at Bath (Maine) and Portsmouth (New Hampshire) and in Rhode Island and Connecticut, are engaged chiefly in the manufacture of small ships— yachts, torpedo boats, schooners, and motorboats—in which speed is significant. The Electric Boat Company's yard at Groton, Connecticut, is well known for the manufacture of submarines. New England yards produce about ten per cent of the nation's total tonnage.

THE CHEMICAL INDUSTRY

The chemical industry represents less than two per cent of New England's manufacturing employment. Nevertheless, its growth rate places it among the most rapidly expanding industries of the region. New England provides a substantial diversified regional market for chemical products, but the industry faces a serious problem in the decline of the textile and leather industries, which have been major consumers of chemicals. There is a lack of most of the basic materials for the chemical industry in New England, and relatively high power rates prevent the manufacture of such products as chlorine, caustic soda, and calcium carbide.

The present strength of the region's chemical industry lies in two fields: (1) bulk products, such as sulfuric acid, fertilizers, and paints, for local consumption; and (2) specialty chemicals, characterized by a high value added in processing, the rise of skilled labor, management experience in small plant operation, and use of technological support. Examples of specialty chemicals are household products—special soaps, cleaners, and polishes—and such industrial materials as emulsifiers, accelerators, and anti-oxidants.

PLASTICS

New England is today the foremost section of the country for plastics fabrication, accounting for one-third of the nation's output. The region offers the following advantages to the plastics fabricator: (1) its reputation as a center of well-established firms, (2) availability of skilled die workers who can manufacture the molds necessary for plastics molding, and (3) access to a large market. It has many plastic-consuming industries, such as artificial leather and coated fabrics, electrical appliances, floor coverings, electrical wiring devices, and luggage.

ELECTRONICS

After the extraordinarily rapid rise in the importance of the electronics industry during and following World War II, and because a large share of the original development work has come from New England, this industry merits attention.

New England accounts for about 15 per cent of the nation's electronics industry. In fact, 90,000 people are employed in Massachusetts alone in this industry. The strength of its position is traceable to the factors of research, development, and engineering per-

sonnel engaged in electronics. Massachusetts Institute of Technology and research laboratories in the Boston area are the hub of electronics developments (*Fig. 9-21*).

New England electronics manufacturers make tubes and semiconductors, resistors, capacitors, subassemblies, coils, hardware, transformers, insulated wire, and relays. There are no large manufacturers of mass-produced domestic equipment such as radio and television receivers. A number of manufacturers make measuring and control devices, computing and clerical apparatus, and large units such as the Van de Graaff generator for X-ray therapy. There is also considerable manufacture of specialized military supplies.

Two major trends in the electronics industry are toward miniaturization and the use of printed circuits instead of wiring. Using smaller parts favors the more skillful workers, particularly watchmakers, who are largely concentrated in New England. The use of

FIGURE 9-21. *Employment changes in the New England electrical machinery industry, 1956–1965 (after New England Business Review).*

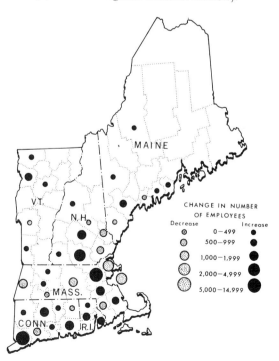

printed circuits as a substitute for wiring involves a number of techniques not formerly associated with the electronics industry, but some of which have much in common with processes like etching and silk-screen printing used in the graphic arts and textile fields. Such skills are available in New England.

Manufacturing in Maritime Canada

Geography and politics have militated against the development of large-scale manufacturing in this area because: (1) it is far removed from Canada's center of population and markets, and (2) high American tariffs bar entry of manufactured goods into densely populated New England and the Middle Atlantic region.

Manufacturing activities are based mainly on the forests and the sea. Pulp and paper, fish processing, sawmilling, and primary iron and steel predominate, accounting for 43 per cent of the region's total production.

The falls and rapids on the St. Lawrence River and its tributaries provide water power potentially capable of furnishing a dependable flow of low-cost hydroelectric energy for the development of forest industries and mines in the more remote areas.

This energy is fundamental to the industrial activities of Canada and is the basis upon which its essential industries have been built. The pulp and paper industry ranks highest in the use of hydraulic and hydroelectric power. Mining and its attendant metallurgical industries are also large users of hydroelectricity, particularly in the final processing of aluminum, of which Canada is a very large producer (*Fig. 9-22*).

NOVA SCOTIA

Closely associated with coal mining in Cape Breton is the iron and steel industry centered in Sydney. Local coal, iron ore from the Wabana mines in Newfoundland, and limestone for open-hearth flux from Newfoundland in-

FIGURE 9-22. *The Arvida, Quebec, plant of the Aluminum Company of Canada, Ltd, which has a capacity of about 10 per cent of the world's production. (Aluminum Co. of Canada, Ltd.)*

sure low-cost steel production. Among the products are steel plate, wire, nails, rails, gun mountings, marine shafting, forgings for warships and cargo ships, locomotive and passenger car axles, and steel railway cars.

Other manufacturing enterprises are varied and small. Amherst is a manufacturing center specializing in heavy and light engineering works, enamelware, textiles, and boot and shoe manufacturing. Truro, the hub of Nova Scotia, is the chief center of the woolen textile industry, the main products being underwear, woven yardage, and hosiery. Noteworthy also are firms producing electronics equipment, aircraft assemblies, repair and maintenance apparatus, and finished fish products.

NEW BRUNSWICK

One of Canada's eastern provinces, New Brunswick, has a fully equipped harbor (St. John's) on the Atlantic Coast open to shipping all year. Direct rail connections from the seaboard to the rest of Canada and the United States markets are shorter than from any other such port.

New Brunswick reflects the increased industrial production evident across the country. About one-half of the province's manufactured goods are derived from the forest, and of this amount, at least two-thirds are manufactured as pulp and paper products.

Diversified manufacturing makes up the other half of total production and includes such articles as foods, ships, fish products, textiles, heating equipment, and boots and shoes.

PRINCE EDWARD ISLAND

Prince Edward Island depends almost entirely for its livelihood on farming and fishing. Several secondary industries, notably canning of fish and farm foods, flourish in urban centers and smaller villages throughout the province. The island offers further opportunities for the development of light industries, particularly for food processing, such as the cucumber pickling plant in Charlottetown.

The island is limited in terms of heavy industry. It is too far from the source of raw materials and the question of transportation is such that it might discourage any move in that direction. There are machine shops, foundries, and woodworking plants in the province, all of which operate on a small scale.

St. Lawrence-Champlain Lowlands Manufacturing

THE UNITED STATES

The geographic features of this area have exerted a strong influence on its economic development. The Adirondack Mountains to the south provide the basis for many unique enterprises. Their forests supply the raw material for the chief industrial pursuits.

The St. Lawrence River provides an outlet from this district to the Great Lakes and the Atlantic Ocean. Ogdensburg, a deep-water port, is the only American city on the river and an important port of entry for trade with Canada. Principal cargoes include pulpwood, paper, coal, and petroleum products. Water transportation is supplied to the eastern part of the area through Lake Champlain, which connects with the Hudson River by a branch of the New York State Barge Canal and with the St. Lawrence River by way of Richelieu and Plattsburgh.

Paper and paper products plants account for about 40 per cent of the total manufacturing employment. These plants are located in a large number of communities in the area. The availability of water power and pulpwood account for the early development of paper production here, although today much of the pulpwood is imported.

Lumber and lumber products and machinery are also important manufacturing industries. Wood products include curtain rods, shade rollers, radio cabinets, doors, and millwork.

Watertown, the center of the machinery industry, manufactures air brakes, papermaking machinery, and other machine shop products. Presses and machinery are manufactured in Champlain. Other manufactured products include razor blades made in Plattsburgh, footwear in the Malone area, and aluminum ingots and other aluminum products at Massena.

CANADA

The Canadian portion of the St. Lawrence-Champlain Lowlands is one of the most densely populated and heavily industrialized areas of Canada. Here are located the leading elements of heavy industry — railway shops (repair shops for locomotives and rolling stock), from foundries, locomotive works, shipbuilding yards, steelworks, and the like; for it is here that raw materials, cheap power, and excellent transportation may be combined most advantageously.

Montreal, Quebec. Situated at the confluence of the St. Lawrence and Ottawa Rivers, Montreal, a thousand miles from the sea, is the national seaport of Canada. Here cargoes from the Great Lakes and from the Atlantic Ocean are transshipped. The harbor accommodates more than 125 oceangoing vessels. It is not only Canada's leading grain port, but also Anglo-America's second-ranking port for steamship passenger travel to Europe.

The city is the financial, commercial, and industrial metropolis of Canada. There are more than 4,500 industries, the most important of which produce locomotives, railway cars, structural iron and steel, tobacco products, textiles, chemicals, airplanes, and electrical appliances. The largest flour mill in the Commonwealth is here, with a capacity of 6,000 barrels in 24 hours. The city is also the center of tremendous power resources.

For generations, industry and manufacturing have also been located in Three Rivers and Sherbrooke. The early 1900's saw an expansion to such points as Kingston, Brockville, Cornwall, Valleyfield, St. Hyacinthe, Shawinigan Falls, Sorel, Drummondville, and Hull.

Quebec City. One of the oldest and most historic settlements in North America, Quebec is, after Montreal, the greatest industrial center of Quebec Province. Its leading industries are canneries, paper mills, breweries, foundries, fur processers, and manufacturers of shoes and other leather goods, candies and chocolate, drugs, clothing, and tobacco products.

The Ottawa Valley. The Ottawa Valley is noted for chemicals. The Electric Reduction Company, Ltd., at Buckingham, was established during the 1890's and is one of the oldest chemical firms in Quebec Province. Originally, phosphorus (manufactured from crude phosphate rock mined locally) was the most important product, but now sodium chlorate, phosphoric acid, calcium, and sodium phosphates for the food and cleaning industries also are made here in large quantities. Not far from Buckingham, at Gatineau, is the modern ethyl alcohol factory of Commercial Alcohols, Ltd. This plant is of interest because it is one of a number of factories making use of waste sulfate liquor, an important by-product of the sulfate pulp industry.

Ottawa, Ontario, capital of Canada since 1858, dominates the trade and manufacturing of the Ottawa Valley. Founded by Champlain in 1613, it became important upon the completion of the Rideau Canal, which was built originally for military purposes.

Pulp, paper, and lumber supplied by power from Chaudiere Falls are the backbone of the city's diversified economy. There is a preponderance of printing, publishing, engraving, and bookbinding. Planing mills, metallic products, textiles, and chemicals are also important.

The Resort and Vacation Industry

The Northeastern Uplands possesses a number of assets for recreation. Its rugged topography, cool climate, heavy snowfall, lakes, streams, trails, and campsites make possible a variety of activity. Its town halls, churches, commons, and shaded villages are rich in historical tradition. Its small towns, cleared farms, and vast forest wilderness are inviting retreats from urban life.

The "recreation industry" has mushroomed with the postwar boom until it now leads all other economic enterprises. The number of summer and winter visitors has been increasing rapidly. Large numbers of people have bought vacation homes. The greatest growth has been in the small cabin and motel type of establishment. Even permanent residents who have large houses frequently rent rooms, however, and large bedrooms in ski areas often become dormitories on winter weekends.

Many summer tourists return as regular visitors and there has been a considerable growth in the number who establish permanent residences after retirement. Such development may offer opportunities for the use of marginal land in some places, since people of retirement age generally prefer small acreages, and are usually not dependent on income derived from the land.

The central and southern parts of the Northeastern Uplands have the heaviest concentration of recreational facilities. The areas north of the White Mountains have not been reached by large numbers of summer residents yet, mainly because of the easier accessibility of desirable sites closer to the urban centers of southern New England.

The Adirondacks contain hundreds of mountain peaks, 46 of them over 4,000 feet high, which makes the area a famous vacation land. Lake Placid is the scene of international winter events. Saranac Lake is a world-renowned health center. Hunting, fishing, and skiing make this section a year-round playground. The largest of the numerous ski centers is the state development on Whiteface Mountain.

Winter sports are becoming increasingly popular in the Berkshires of Massachusetts and the Green Mountains of Vermont. Ski trains run from New York City to the better areas where many ski trails and other facilities have been developed (*Fig. 9-23*).

The White Mountains of New Hampshire form one of the most popular mountain resort regions. Scenically, the area is most famous for its notches, especially Franconia and Jefferson. Most of the mountains may be climbed by foot trail, and some by cable car or motor road. Numerous lakes and streams afford good fishing. There are eight ski trail centers, over a thousand miles of foot, ski, and horse trails, and a number of overnight shelters for hiking and skiing parties.

The Uplands of northeastern Canada are also becoming more important as a vacation area. Fishing and hunting have for many years provided outdoor recreation for the area's residents. Now, more and more, its rivers, lakes and forests are visited by fisher-

Figure 9-23. Skiers at Snow Valley, near Manchester, Vermont. Many skiers are lured to resorts like this on week ends and holidays. (Vermont Development Commission)

men and hunters from other countries, but especially from the United States. The forests abound with deer, bear, rabbits, and birds, and the streams and lakes are well stocked with a wide variety of game fish. Camping, boating, picnicking, hiking, and swimming are some of the many recreational opportunities.

Year-round recreational programs are now playing a vital role in the economy of the New England-Canadian Lowlands. The flow of traffic from centers of population to winter resorts during the winter months is beginning to approach the massive proportions of summer traffic to summer resorts during the summer.

Historic forts, battlegrounds, trails, churches, and museums all lure tourists to this subregion. Boston attracts many sightseers, as does Quebec City, a focus and symbol for all French-speaking North Americans.

Outlook

The Northeastern Lowlands and Uplands Region, with the exception of the St. Lawrence-Champlain Lowlands district, has few natural resources or locational features to attract and support industry and agriculture. Except for pulpwood, limestone, iron ore, and granite, the region contains no substantial sources of raw materials, and most of the area's agricultural land is useful primarily because of its nearness to population centers, not because of its inherent productivity. Construction costs are also higher here than in most other regions. Finally, because of their distant location, manufacturers in the region have a cost disadvantage when shipping to the rapidly growing consumer markets in the Midwest or Far West.

As a result, the typical manufacturer in this region is forced to specialize in products requiring high skill, labor-intensive techniques. These new labor-intensive industries, such as electronics, are highly prized by industrial developers because they provide high income levels and do not have to be located near sources of raw materials or mass consumer markets.

It appears, therefore, that the region's economy rests with the new technologically-oriented manufacturing and service industries rather than with old-line industries, such as textiles, shoes and leather, and apparel. So far as public policy is concerned, this suggests that the Northeastern region should place increasing emphasis on providing high-quality secondary school and college training to provide the necessary high-skilled labor force for the region's growing industries. For example, the St. Lawrence Seaway has generated a number of new industries in the northern part of New York State through its hydroelectric power potential. Chevrolet has constructed a plant for casting aluminum auto parts and Reynolds Aluminum Company has built a multimillion-dollar facility near Massena, New York.

The St. Lawrence-Champlain Lowlands is placed in a highly strategic position between the Great Lakes and the Atlantic Ocean. Because of the St. Lawrence Seaway, its importance as a transportation hub will continue to attract more industries and people; it is indeed, a major gateway to the interior.

Tourism will continue to play a major role in the Northeastern Lowlands and Uplands. Cape Cod, with its sandy beaches and protected waters for boating is a major tourist attraction. The area from Hyannis to Chatham is already saturated with recreational attractions. The ocean, the lakes, and the mountains all combine to make this region an even more important vacationland in the future.

Selected References

ALEXANDER, LEWIS M., "The Impact of Tourism on the Economy of Cape Cod, Massachusetts," *Economic Geography*, Vol. 29, October, 1953, pp. 320–326.

———, *The Northeastern United States*, Princeton, N. J.: Van Nostrand Co., Inc., 1967.

BIRD, J. BRIAN, "Settlement Patterns in Maritime Canada," *The Geographical Review*, Vol. 45, July, 1955, pp. 320–326.

BLACK, JOHN D., *The Rural Economy of New England*, Cambridge, Mass.: Harvard University Press, 1950.

BLACK, W. A., "The Labrador Floater Codfishery," *Annals of the Association of American Geographers*, Vol. 50, September, 1960, pp. 267–295.

BRIGHT, A. A., JR., *Economic State of New England*, New Haven, Conn.: Yale University Press, 1954.

CLARK, ANDREW H., *Three Centuries and the Island*, Toronto: University of Toronto Press, 1959.

DINSDALE, EVELYN M., "Spatial Patterns of Technological Change: The Lumber Industry of Northern New York," *Economic Geography*, Vol. 41, July, 1965, pp. 252–274.

ESTALL, R. C., *New England: A Study in Industrial Adjustment*, New York: Frederick A. Praeger Publishers, 1966.

———, "The Electronic Products Industry of New England," *Economic Geography*, Vol. 39, July, 1963, pp. 189–216.

GENTILCORE, R. LOUIS, "The Agricultural Background of Settlement in Eastern Nova Scotia," *Annals of the Association of American Geographers*, Vol. 46, December, 1956, pp. 378–404.

GIBSON, J. SULLIVAN, "Prince Edward Island—Gem of the Maritimes," *The Journal of Geography*, Vol. 59, October, 1960, pp. 301–307.

GOTTMAN, JEAN, *Megalopolis*, New York: Twentieth Century Fund, 1961.

———, "Megalopolis, or the Urbanization of the Northeastern Seaboard," *Economic Geography*, Vol. 33, July, 1957, pp. 189–202.

HARRIS, SEYMOUR E., *The Economics of New England*, Cambridge, Mass.: Harvard University Press, 1952.

HIGBEE, E. C., "The Three Earths of New England," *Geographical Review*, July, 1952, pp. 425–438.

ISARD, WALTER, and CUMBERLAND, JOHN H., "New England as a Possible Location for an Integrated Iron and Steel Works," *Economic Geography*, October, 1950, pp. 245–259.

KLIMM, LESTER M., "The Empty Areas of the Northeastern United States," *Geographical Review*, July, 1954, pp. 325–345.

LAING, JEAN, "The Pattern of Population Trends in Massachusetts," *Economic Geography*, July, 1955, pp. 265–271.

MANCHESTER, LORNE, "Science in Fisheries," *Canadian Geographical Journal*, Vol. 41, 1950, pp. 189–209.

THOMPSON, JOHN H. (ed.), *Geography of New York State*, Syracuse, N. Y.: Syracuse University Press, 1966.

10 *Atlantic-Gulf Coastal Plain and Piedmont Region*

Between the Appalachian Highlands and the Atlantic Ocean lies the Atlantic-Gulf Coastal Plain and Piedmont Region. This elongated region stretches for some 2,000 miles from New York State to the Rio Grande (*Fig. 10-1*). Physiographically it extends an additional 1,200 miles in Mexico. The boundary between the Piedmont and the Coastal Plain is called the fall line, because, in crossing it, streams develop rapids or falls.

The great differences in climate, natural vegetation, soils, population distribution, and cultural and economic activities warrant a further division of the region into three distinct subregions: the Middle Atlantic Coastal Plain, the South Atlantic-Gulf Coastal Plain, and the Piedmont.

Surface Features

THE MIDDLE ATLANTIC COASTAL PLAIN

Long stretches of sandy beaches and tidewater marshes characterize the Middle Atlantic Coastal Plain of the New York, New Jersey, Maryland, and Delaware ocean coasts. The eastern shore of Chesapeake Bay consists of low, flat, almost featureless plains, with numerous irregularities and small islands. The western shore is a gently rolling upland. Tidewater Virginia encompasses numerous flat peninsulas, wide estuaries, and many swamps. The landscape farther inland rises in an irregular pattern, with hills mostly in the inner Coastal Plain near the streams. Elevations range from sea level along the many tidal streams and bays to a little more than 300 feet in southern Maryland and from 300 to 500 feet above the Hudson River across from New York City.

THE SOUTH ATLANTIC-GULF COASTAL PLAIN

The South Atlantic-Gulf Coastal Plain ranges from perfectly flat near the sea where the erosion cycle has not yet begun, to maturely dissected, distinctly hilly, and, even at some places, peneplained terrain near the inner margin. The local relief in some parts is 200 feet. The inner edge was first (longest) out of water, and is therefore most eroded. Moreover, it is only here that the altitude is sufficient to allow deep valleys. In general the relief increases from the coast inward (*Fig. 10-3*).

Some streams flow almost directly toward the sea. Most tributaries are dendritic. The outcrop

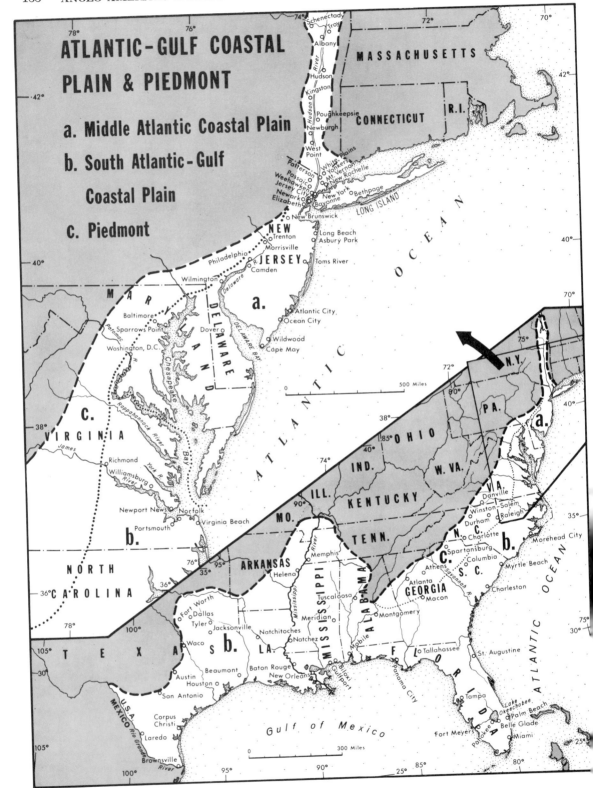

ATLANTIC-GULF COASTAL
PLAIN & PIEDMONT

a. Middle Atlantic Coastal Plain

b. South Atlantic-Gulf
   Coastal Plain

c. Piedmont

FIGURE 10-1.

of a strong stratum may constitute a ridge between valleys. This ridge is generally a "cuesta," with a relatively steep scarp slope and a long, gentle dip slope. The "inner lowland" on weak rocks at the foot of the scarp slope often is followed by a stream. Coastal plains thus characterized are "belted."

The seaward border is marked by: (1) many estuaries, (2) deltas (most of which still are only "mud flats") at the heads of estuaries, (3) bars and lagoons, (4) barrier beaches, (5) sand dunes, (6) salt marshes, and (7) freshwater swamps, such as the great Dismal Swamp of Virginia.

In the embayed section north of Cape Lookout (North Carolina), subsidence of the land had drowned many valleys, making estuaries and islands. Local relief in this section rarely exceeds 50 feet.

The Sea Island (Georgia) section has subsided less, but still enough to form the characteristic islands that give names to the section. The topography is that of a young plain near the coast. Erosion increases inland to maturity near the fall line, around which the local relief may reach 200 feet.

Florida is mainly a newly-emerged, uneven sea bottom with lakes and swamps (everglades). In the north-central part many basins are made by solution (limestone sinks). The "Keys" are a broken coral reef (*Fig. 10-4*). A long barrier beach on the east encloses the so-called "Indian River."

The Gulf Coastal Plain is flat near the sea. Slight subsidence forms bays, as at Mobile, for example. Relief increases inland to several hundred feet at some points. Southern Alabama is typical belted coastal plain, with Montgomery and Tuscaloosa in the inner lowland. This is the Black Belt of dark-colored soils on weak, chalky limestone, formerly one of the most important cotton districts of the United States.

The alluvial plain of the lower Mississippi and certain tributaries embraces large areas subject to overflow except where they are protected by natural and artificial levees.

The section to the west of the Mississippi River includes the Mississippi Delta, which stretches from Cape Girardeau, Missouri, to the

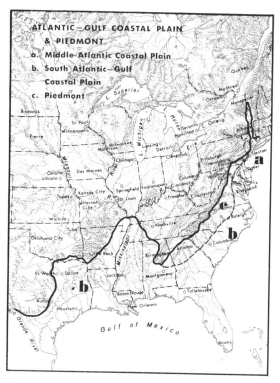

FIGURE 10-2. *The Atlantic-Gulf Coastal Plain and Piedmont Region, physical relief.*

Gulf Coast, and the coastal prairies of southwestern Louisiana and southeastern Texas. The elevation increases northward from sea level at the Gulf of Mexico to about 320 feet above sea level in Missouri. The surrounding loessial terraces rise 20 to 50 feet higher than the flood plain. The flood plain consists of low meander belts of ridges and intervening irregular flood basins.

Most of the surface features reflect the depositional activities of running water. The ridges and basins of the upper part of the deltaic plain are somewhat more uniform than the flood plain, with the ridges standing higher above the general surface. The lowlands often are covered with water. Between ridges the lowlands give way to coastal marshes and bays, and the marsh areas are affected by wave action.

The Coastal Plain in southwestern Louisiana and in southeastern Texas is a long narrow band of marshland lying generally within 50 to 70 miles of tidewater and almost paralleling the coast of the Gulf of Mexico. The topography

FIGURE 10-3. *An aerial view of North Carolina's Coastal Plain country. (North Carolina News Bureau)*

FIGURE 10-4. *An aerial view of one of the Florida Keys. (Florida News Bureau)*

appears to be flat over wide areas, but the land slopes gradually to the Gulf. The maximum elevation above sea level is slightly more than 100 feet, although most of the area is less than 50.

THE PIEDMONT

The area between the Appalachian Mountains and the Atlantic Coastal Plain is called the Piedmont, or "foot of the mountain." It differs from both the mountains and the plain in topography and elevation. The outer border is 100 to 200 feet above sea level in New Jersey, increasing in height southward to about 800 feet in Georgia. The inner border is 200 to 400 feet high in New Jersey, rising to 900 feet in Virginia, and 1,500 feet in the Carolinas and Georgia.

Climate

Two climatic zones, the humid continental long summer and the humid subtropical, predominate in the region.

HUMID CONTINENTAL
LONG SUMMER REALM

All of the region north of about 39° North latitude except the northern Hudson River Valley falls within the humid continental long summer realm (*see Fig. 1-16*). Climatic characteristics in the humid continental long summer realm result from the lack of moderating influence of bodies of water and moist atmosphere. Winter anticyclones bring waves of cold weather; summer cyclones cause hot, humid weather and heat waves. The short-period weather changes are brought about by the invasion of large masses of air of different characteristics—warm, moist air from the Gulf of Mexico; dry, hot air from the southwest; cool, rather dry air from the northern Pacific Ocean; and cold, dry air from the interior of Canada (*Fig. 10-5*).

Temperature. Summers are hot and humid, with the nights almost as hot as the days. Daytime temperatures average 75° to 80° F.; night temperatures seldom drop below 60° F. Maximum temperatures above 100° F. have occurred throughout the region in the summer months.

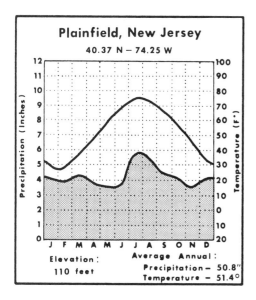

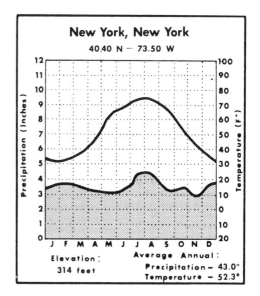

FIGURE 10-5. *Climatic graphs, humid continental long summer realm.*

From about the first of July to the middle of September, this area occasionally experiences uncomfortably warm periods, four or five days in length, during which light wind movement and high relative humidity make conditions oppressive. Relative humidity ranges between 64 and 68 per cent. Frequent thundershowers are interspersed with sunny weather. Occasional one- or two-day spells of cloudy weather—usually cooler at first, but soon turning to clear and hot weather with infrequent waves of severe prolonged heat—may be expected. The growing season here varies from five to six months.

Autumn days are invigorating and clear. Nights are cool, and frosts are frequent. Occasional spells of Indian summer in October, or even November, result in warm, dry periods lasting one or two weeks.

Severe cold is occasionally experienced in the winter season, although on the whole, the three winter months are characterized in the majority of years by mean temperatures of 25° F., only slightly below the freezing point. Much crisp, sunny weather is characteristic. Spells of snow, occasional thaws, and, sometimes, blizzards or cold, driving wind on the tail of a snowstorm are to be expected.

The warm spring weather soon transforms the bleakness of winter into a green landscape. Trees, grasses, and flowers blossom quickly. Cold waves often sweep the region, however, causing considerable damage to fruits and vegetables.

Precipitation. Precipitation occurs throughout the year, but a somewhat greater amount is received during the summer months. Convectional rainfall results in heavy thundershowers, bringing copious precipitation to the region. It is not uncommon for several inches of rain to fall during a single storm. Many of the summer showers are accompanied by thunder and lightning, and a few are accompanied by very heavy downpours of rain, light-to-heavy hail, or wind squalls, all of which do considerable damage to crops and buildings. Occasionally, a tornado strikes some small section during May, June, or July. Cyclonic winter precipitation often consists of snow. Annual snowfall ranges from as little as 5 inches at the southern extremity to as much as 45 inches in the northern. The average annual precipitation, 40 to 50 inches, has a July and August maximum of 5 inches or more each month, and an autumn minimum of 3 to 4 inches each month. Severe droughts are infrequent; periods of three days without rainfall during the growing season occur only during a third of the year. The relative humidity averages 70 to 80 per cent morning and evening, and 60 to 70 per cent in the afternoon; it is a little higher in summer and winter, and lower in spring and fall. This moderate humidity is a favorable condition for the many resorts along the coast.

HUMID SUBTROPICS

All the region south of about 39° North latitude except the southern tip of Florida and the southern coastal plain of Texas is classed as a humid subtropical climate (see Fig. 1-16). It is characterized by abundant rainfall during all months and seasons; by maximum rainfall in the warm season; by tropic-like summer heat; by sharp, quick, summer thundershowers;

by violent soil erosion; and by a cool, moist winter. Light snowfalls may occur occasionally during the winter. There are periods of fairly cold weather associated with winter cold waves that move into the realm from regions farther poleward. The number of frost-free days ranges from 200 in the northern portion of the region to 320 along the Gulf Coast, and many winters—sometimes several in succession—pass without frost or freezing in southern Florida. The average winter temperature is about 45° F. throughout the area. The average annual precipitation is 50 to 60 inches (Fig. 10-6).

Natural Vegetation

Most of the Atlantic-Gulf Coastal Plain and Piedmont was once heavily forested; some areas still are. Several kinds of forest occur, depend-

FIGURE 10-6. Climatic graphs, humid subtropics.

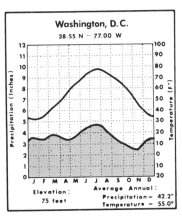

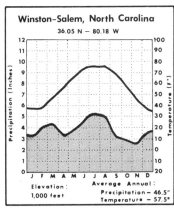

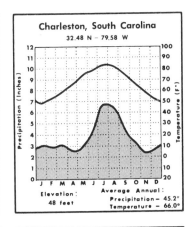

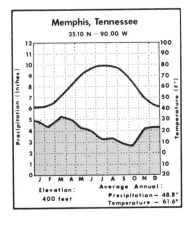

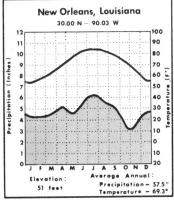

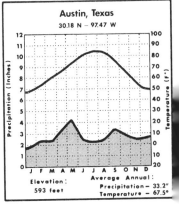

ing upon soil, drainage, and length of growing season. In the most southerly portions, there are a good many broadleaf evergreen trees, such as magnolia and live oak.. Solid growths of yellow pine are found on the sandy plains; cypress stands occur in the swamps and river bottoms (*Fig. 10-7*). In the northerly portions, broadleaf deciduous forests abound. A great variety of hardwoods, such as oak, maple, ash, beech, and birch, are characteristic. There are also many cone-bearing trees, including spruce, hemlock, and white pine.

Soils

The highly variable material of the Atlantic Coastal Plain was transported from the higher elevation of the Atlantic slope and deposited in layers of unconsolidated beds, which vary in texture from fine-grained silts and clays to coarse sands and gravels. The deposits are thought to be a mixture of marine, alluvial, and glaciofluvial materials. Sandy soils with little profile development are characteristic of the outer Coastal Plain.

Over large portions of the humid subtropics, red and yellow soils are characteristic. They develop under a forest cover in the hot, humid environment and are low in humus, phosphate, and alkaline materials. The red color of much of the soil indicates the presence of ferric hydroxide. The yellow color indicates iron deficiency and poor drainage. These soils require much fertilization and careful cultivation.

Along the old stream channels the soils generally are fine sandy loams or loams. The broad, flat basins are mostly clay soils. The intermediate areas, between the basins and the ridges, are silt loams and silty clay soils. As streams overflowed, the sand particles settled out along the stream. The silt and clay particles were held in suspension much longer and finally were deposited by relatively still water in broad, flat areas. The sandy soils allow earlier maturity of plants, and thus are preferred for many kinds of crops. They contains a fair amount of organic matter and mineral plant nutrients and are medium-to-strongly acid in reaction.

FIGURE 10-7. *A scene in Georgia's Okefenokee Swamp. Note the heavy moss covering on the trees.* (Fish and Wildlife Service, U.S. Dept. of Interior)

The most intensive cultivation is on the alluvial soils deposited in the Mississippi Delta. These soils come from a variety of materials. Soil texture ranges from sand to clay. These soils are, for the most part, inherently fertile and, where drained and protected from overflow, are highly productive.

Settlement

The first permanent English-speaking settlement in the Atlantic-Gulf Coastal Plain and Piedmont Region was at Jamestown, Virginia, in 1607. Farther north, there were Dutch and Swedish settlements, in New York and Delaware, respectively, in the early 17th century; but by 1664, they were under English control. The first permanent Spanish settlements were at St. Augustine, Florida, in 1565, and at San Antonio, Texas, in 1718. In 1718, also, the French made their first permanent settlement at New Orleans.

Since the first great waves of settlement had been English waves, the Atlantic Coastal Plain remained almost purely English. In the 18th century, however, there were two other heavy emigration movements from Europe—the German and the Scotch-Irish. It was the German element that first became important. Some settled in William Penn's domain as early as 1683, making Germantown a seat of thriving handicrafts. But the real emigration began after 1700. Some went to the Mohawk Valley in New York, but most of them went to Pennsylvania.

The Scotch-Irish, a more aggressive stock, furnished the chief pioneering element in Pennsylvania and the uplands of North Carolina. Other non-English groups were smaller but not unimportant. French Huguenots settled in South Carolina, Virginia, and New York. A sprinkling of Swiss came with the Germans; there were substantial numbers of Swedes and Finns along the Delaware, and small groups of Italians and Portuguese Jews, primarily in the towns.

The early explorers and settlers expected to make money in almost any other way except agriculture, but they were soon driven to farming to keep from starving. Even so, they might have starved if they had not quickly adopted Indian agricultural methods and crops. European agriculture was based on grain and livestock; it involved cleared and plowed fields, seeded in rows or by broadcasting, and was entirely unsuited to a densely forested land. The Indians had worked out the best way to farm such land with a minimum of labor and practically no equipment except a digging stick or mattock. They killed the trees by girdling, burned them over, and planted their crops— mostly corn, beans, squash—in mounds among the stumps.

In the southern colonies, two money crops of tropical origin soon dominated—tobacco and cotton. Virginians discovered that their climate was well adapted to the growing of tobacco— and they made the discovery just as the English were acquiring the tobacco habit. Eventually, tobacco culture spread all the way across the upper South. Another great discovery was that the southern climate was also well adapted to cotton—both Sea Island cotton, introduced around Charleston from the Barbados, along with sugarcane, indigo, and rice, and upland cotton, a Mexican plant introduced probably from southern Europe. Cotton growing under the plantation system gradually spread westward across the South—and with it, Negro slavery.

Negroes had taken part in several of the early European explorations of North America; Pedro Alonzo Niño, for example, served as one of Columbus' navigators. Later, in the English colonies, Negroes served along with Europeans as indentured servants. It was not until after 1650 that slavery became established in the eyes of the law.

The basic pattern of the American farm is derived chiefly from the middle colonies, which saw the greatest influx of settlers who were true tillers of the soil. Here there were neither southern plantations nor close-knit New England townships, but scattered single-family farmsteads. Swedes and Finns contributed the log cabin. The Dutch added better breeds of livestock, European grasses and clovers, and an interest in dairying. The Irish and Scots contributed intrepid backwoodsmen and potatoes; the Germans, improvements in grain growing and stock breeding, the basic American barn, the rifle, the Conestoga wagon, and the stove instead of the fireplace.

In the middle colonies, the Old World pattern of general farming, with emphasis on the feeding of livestock, was transferred to the New World with one major modification—Indian corn, which greatly increased livestock production. Farming, as it spread westward, became the corn-hog economy of the Prairie States and the dairy-potato-small-grain agriculture of the Great Lakes region.

Agriculture

MIDDLE ATLANTIC COASTAL PLAIN

Covering less than 12 per cent of the land area of the United States, the Middle Atlantic Coastal Plain produces about 3 per cent of the value of all farm products sold in the nation.

Variety is the word for the area's agriculture. Truckloads of produce pour into the world's largest soup plant at Camden, New Jersey. The nation's largest grower and packager of frozen vegetables in southern New Jersey employs several thousand people, who process millions of pounds of vegetables yearly from seed to freezer.

What are some characteristics of agriculture in the Middle Atlantic region? First, much of the importance of agriculture is due to the area's dense population. Good highway and railway facilities lead to excellent markets in the cities adjacent to the region. More than 20 million people live within its borders; inside its perimeter are the metropolitan areas of New York, Philadelphia, Baltimore, and Washington, D.C.

Cities are important to farming not only for their distribution centers, market places, and consuming populaces, but also for their influence on the types of farming prevailing within their orbit. For example, bulky, perishable products like vegetables, and products requiring relatively little land, like poultry and eggs, are produced close to cities—as is the case in New York, Delaware, New Jersey, and eastern Pennsylvania (Fig. 10-8). Milk, another perishable product, is produced and shipped in from farms somewhat further away. Hogs, sheep, beef cattle, butter, and cheese are concentrated and may be shipped long distances at relatively little cost.

Truck crops. The Middle Atlantic trucking region owes its existence primarily to three conditions: (1) The series of large cities extending from Washington, D.C., to Boston, Massachusetts, and affording the greatest market for fresh vegetables and fruits in Anglo-America. The population of this string of cities and adjacent towns exceeds 40 million—more than 18 per cent of the total population of the United States and Canada. (2) Sandy to loamy soils that warm up rapidly in the springtime, are readily cultivated, respond well to fertilizers, and produce vegetables of high quality. On the other hand, these sandy soils are not as well adapted to hay or the small grains as the heavier soils inland. (3) A mild, semimaritime climate, having a long frost-free season and springs so warm that vegetables and small fruits may be shipped to the large urban markets one to three weeks in advance of the crops from inland districts at the same latitude.

More than 60 different vegetables are grown commercially each year in the Middle Atlantic

FIGURE 10-8. *Duck farm at Flanders, near Great Peconic Bay, Long Island. Long Island ducks have much more than a local reputation. The raising of poultry and the production of poultry products is highly developed and is an important source of farm income. (NYSPIX–Commerce)*

trucking belt. Suffolk County, New York, and Monmouth County, New Jersey, are two of the foremost potato-producing counties in the United States (*Fig. 10-9*). Among the other truck crops, tomatoes lead; indeed, the acreage of tomatoes in New Jersey is almost as great as the acreage in potatoes. Three-fourths of the farms producing vegetables other than potatoes grow tomatoes. More than 300 million bushels of tomatoes are processed into pulp annually for soups, sauces, and puree, or are canned whole. Tomatoes are by far the chief product canned in New Jersey.

Vegetable production requires a large amount of labor per acre and therefore the acreage per farm is small. The long growing season makes it possible to double-crop much of the land. Truck farms vary from a few acres to 20 or more. The chief outlets for the truck

FIGURE 10-9. *An aerial view of a typical, well-managed potato farm in New Jersey. (U.S. Dept. of Agriculture)*

crops of this area are the large Eastern markets and local canning houses. Truck routes extend to all the leading cities, and vegetables harvested in the afternoon are at the market the next morning to provide the consumer with fresh produce.

SOUTH ATLANTIC-GULF COASTAL PLAIN AND PIEDMONT

Cotton. After existing almost a century and a half in the English colonies, slavery was, at the time of the framing of the federal Constitution, on the road to extinction. Cotton proved to be the crop that made slavery profitable. After Eli Whitney invented the cotton gin in 1793, cotton became a profitable crop. Once it became possible to produce cotton at reasonable cost, its high adaptability for textile manufacturers gave it a market.

The cotton planter stripped the fertility from his land. He planted cotton, and only cotton, year after year. There was no rotation and no manure from livestock to be spread upon his fields. The best cotton soil was so fertile that for many years it continued to produce large

crops in spite of this treatment, but the moment always came when the return began to diminish. Nothing in the history of American agriculture is less attractive than the plantation going downhill. The decline meant poverty for the planter's children and dissipation of land and slaves. Foreclosures came in their inevitable course, and too often what had been flourishing cotton fields reverted to wilderness. The small, poor, white farmer, who could and would live upon a few acres that had once been part of a plantation, had no surplus of either means or intelligence. The plantation era, with its soil destruction, passed over many an area, leaving it desolate.

Cotton, the great crop of the South, is on the decline. However, it is still a major crop in many areas, especially in fertile alluvial lowlands where modern machinery can be employed (*Fig. 10-10*).

The Cotton Belt was a name given to an area covering the greater part of the Southern states where geographical conditions were suitable for growth of cotton and where a large percentage of the agricultural population derived some or most of its cash income from the cotton crop.

Though many still think in terms of a "cotton belt," and such a belt does exist to some degree, such great changes in the land economy of the South have taken place within the past 30 years that some qualification of the term is necessary.

Cotton is no longer the leading source of Southern farm income. Today's gross return from cotton represents less than 25 per cent of total farm income; 40 years ago it accounted for about 50 per cent. Acreage reductions have affected the old Cotton Belt, but yield increases have offset acreage decreases; gross regional income from cotton is therefore about what it was 40 years ago.

The yield increases have come about mainly from: (1) a greater use of fertilizer, (2) a shift to higher-yielding areas, (3) a more careful selection of land on individual farms as well as in each area, (4) a more widespread use of improved varieties, and (5) the planting of larger legume crop acreages. Since these changes have affected the various production areas differently, considerable acreage shifts have occurred.

The South's decline as a cotton-producing region results partly, of course, from healthy

FIGURE 10-10. *A two-row, self-propelled cotton picker at work in Mississippi. (International Harvester Co.)*

changes in its farm economy. Economic pressure and education are two of the important forces responsible for a more diversified farming system, one that places less reliance on cotton as the principal source of income. It is certain that these forces will continue to exert their effects. It is equally certain, on the other hand, that cotton will remain a basic component of Southern farm economy for many years to come. The relatively disadvantageous position of Southern cotton production, therefore, makes the need for increased efficiency even more acute than it is in other producing areas (*see Fig. 6-11*).

The chief cotton-producing areas include: (1) the alluvial soils of the Mississippi and other river bottoms in Mississippi and Louisiana, (2) the inner coastal plain of the Carolinas and Georgia, (3) the Tennessee Valley in northern Alabama, (4) the northern black prairies of Texas, (5) the south Texas coastal plains, and (6) the high plains of western Oklahoma and Texas.

Tobacco. The cultivation of tobacco was begun in 1612. This was not the harsh native tobacco used by the Indians of the eastern woodlands, but the cultivated tobacco of the American tropics. During the sixteenth century, Spaniards and Portuguese had introduced this Indian ceremonial plant to European trade and its seed to European gardens. The use of tobacco spread rapidly into France and England. In both countries it was planted to some extent before the founding of Virginia. It is not definitely known how this tropical plant came to Virginia. Probably the very first plantings were of seed that had been brought from England.

The inner Coastal Plain and Piedmont from Chesapeake Bay to northern Florida produce two-thirds of the United States tobacco crop; north-central Florida's Gadsden County specializes in cigar wrapper tobacco. North Carolina, Kentucky, South Carolina, and Virginia are the leading tobacco-producing states, in the order named. Tennessee and Georgia also are important producers (*see Fig. 6-12*).

Climate and soil probably influence tobacco more than any other plant. So marked are the influences of these factors that two regions rarely produce exactly the same type of leaf. The effect of slight differences is evident when comparing the tobacco of the Piedmont with that of the Coastal Plain. The leaf of the latter is whiter than the Piedmont, which grows a considerable quantity of mahogany leaf. The tobacco of the Coastal Plain ripens earliest because it lies farther south and nearer the ocean and the large amount of sand in the soil helps raise the temperature (*Fig. 10-11*).

The culture of tobacco is difficult and demanding; tobacco has been called the most intensively cultivated annual crop grown on any large acreage. The seedlings, fragile and subject to many kinds of damage, are started in cold frames, then transplanted; between 5,000 and 10,000 plants are set out on each acre. A constant round of cultivating, topping, suckering, and spraying keeps the farmer and his family completely occupied until the tobacco leaves are mature. Then the ripe leaves are harvested and hung up for curing in the barn.

The life of the tobacco grower is not an enviable one. The work involved is disagreeable—hard, dirty, and in some respects unhealthy. Workers often contract skin irritations and sicknesses from the odor of the plants. In addition, gum on the plants can adhere to the worker.

The tobacco plant is destructive to soil because it is a clean-tilled crop that induces erosion. Moreover, its root system has a tendency to suck rather than to hold the soil in place.

It is obvious, then, that the continuous culture of tobacco is not without its problems. Common practice calls for resting shade tobacco land after four or five years when yields and quantity decline. Some fields remain in high production only two or three years. Rotation of crops may be employed if tobacco is grown in the right order in the rotation. If grown immediately after a legume or other soil-building crop, the quality will be affected adversely. It is therefore necessary to grow a crop such as corn or cotton before planting tobacco.

Types of tobacco are grouped largely according to three curing methods—flue-cured, air-cured, and fire-cured. The first two methods

FIGURE 10-11. *Tobacco planted on contour in Virginia. Attention to proper soil conservation methods has resulted in increased plant yields. (U.S. Dept. of Agriculture)*

are most widely used. Curing of tobacco is the tensest time of all. The weather during the curing period, especially for flue-cured types, may have a profound effect on the excellence and price of the leaves.

After the leaves are cured, the farmer begins the tedious and exacting job of sorting them for proper bundling and selling. Tied and packed, the leaves go to the warehouse sales floor. In about 170 auction markets in tobacco areas there are some 900 of these sales floors. Here a small knot of buyers from the major companies walk along aisles lined with baskets of tobacco while the auctioneer chants his sing-song and knocks down each basket in six to ten seconds' time.

The tobacco then is repacked in the hogsheads and stored away for two to four years; during this time it passes through a certain degree of fermentation and other chemical changes important to its final taste and mildness. The huge quantities of tobacco stored in the sprawling brick warehouses of the great companies account for roughly four-fifths of the companies' total physical assets. At the peak season, the average inventory is about a 30 months' supply.

Drawing upon properly aged stock, tobacco companies process the leaves into various forms for the consumer. In a lengthy series of highly mechanized steps, some 90,000 production workers in different factories rehumidify the leaves, pass them into machines that spray them with hydroscopic (moisture retaining) liquids and with "casings" containing flavor ingredients that have ranged from chocolate to oil of juniper, and then feed them into shredding and cigarette-forming machines that roll out up to 1,500 regular cigarettes or 1,200 filter-tips each minute. In succeeding mechanized steps, the cigarettes are wrapped, sealed, labeled, stamped, and packed in cartons for shipping.

Durham, Raleigh, and Winston-Salem, North Carolina, and Danville, Lynchburg, and Richmond, Virginia, are the South's leading tobacco centers. Roughly a fifth of the nation's cigarettes are produced in Durham. About 50 million pounds of tobacco are auctioned annually at the Durham tobacco market. Raleigh is the wholesale and retail center for a wide territory devoted agriculturally to flue-cured tobacco. Lynchburg is one of the largest dark-tobacco markets in the country. Richmond is not only one of the greatest tobacco markets in the United States, but also has various tobacco factories producing chewing and smoking tobacco, snuff, cigars, and cigarettes.

Filler tobacco for cigars is the big money crop in Lancaster County, Pennsylvania. It pays the farmers' big expenses—the new tractor, another automobile, the hospital bill, or a big slice off the mortgage. Yet tobacco is a minor crop in terms of acreage, accounting only for about one out of every four or five acres tilled.

Most farmers in Lancaster County use a four-year rotation cycle—tobacco, wheat, grass, and corn. This system not only preserves the fertility of the soil but also helps to prevent the soil from being blown away. It has other advantages, too: the corn provides both grain and fodder for cattle feed, the wheat provides bedding for the cattle, and the cattle provide manure for the fields.

OTHER CROPS

Other important crops include corn, hay, sorghum, soybeans, peanuts, rice, commercial vegetable truck crops, fruits, and sugarcane.

Corn. Grown throughout the South, corn is used on the farm for feeding cattle, hogs, and poultry; less than one-third of the crop is sold as grain. Grain sorghums take the place of corn in the drier parts of the Cotton Belt.

Peanuts. These are a leading cash crop on the coastal plains of North Carolina, Virginia, Georgia, Alabama, and northern Florida. They are planted for hog feed, for oil mills, and for the confectionery trade. Peanut cake or meal, a by-product of peanut-oil crushing, is high in protein and serves as an excellent feed for all classes of livestock and poultry.

Soybeans. Nearly 30 per cent of the soybean acreage harvested for beans and nearly 60 per cent of the acreage grazed or plowed under is in the South. Areas of greatest concentrations are the Mississippi Delta, northern Alabama, and the Georgia-Carolina Piedmont.

Rice. The coastal prairie of Louisiana and Texas and the Grand Prairie of Arkansas account for about 55 per cent and 20 per cent respectively of the U.S. rice crop. The rice lands in each area are fertilized and rotated. From the planting of the pre-sprouted seed by airplanes to harvest by combines, rice is the most mechanized of the major domestic crops (*Fig. 10-12*).

Commercial vegetable truck crops. Truck crops in central and southern Florida have a greater value than those of any other state except California. Tomatoes are the most valuable truck crop. Farmers also grow large crops of snap beans, potatoes, celery, and corn.

Florida is 1,500 miles closer to the large Eastern metropolitan markets than is California. Rapid highway and railway transit favors Florida growers, who can market winter vegetables in New York, Philadelphia, Boston, and other cities at a time when they command the highest prices.

Technological changes are largely responsible for a phenomenal expansion in Florida vegetable production: (1) Mechanization has provided more efficient production and harvesting techniques, (2) research has given rise to improved varieties and better fertilization practices, (3) more effective insecticides and fungicides have increased yields, and (4) market outlets have multiplied as both rail and truck transportation have become equipped with more adequate refrigeration.

Packing houses in Belle Glade and Pahokee first grade, then wash, pack, precook, and ship fresh vegetables to all parts of the United States and Canada. At the peak of the harvesting season, as many as 150 carloads a day are shipped out of this area.

Texas grows large amounts of vegetables in the lower Rio Grande Valley and around Laredo, San Antonio, Corpus Christi, Jacksonville, and Tyler. The chief truck crops include carrots, tomatoes, spinach, onions, cabbage, and sweet potatoes. Beans, sweet corn, and

FIGURE 10-12. *A rice combine in Louisiana. Diking, plowing, planting, and threshing are all done by machines. (Louisiana State Dept. of Commerce and Industry)*

lettuce also are produced abundantly. Texas stands third, after California and Florida, in the production of vegetables.

Apples. A small, but very important orchard belt runs through a cluster of Pennsylvania counties—Adams, Cumberland, Franklin, and York—along the southern border of the state just west of the Susquehanna River. These counties have little in common other than the fact that they grow a lot of apples, and even the apple orchards differ from one county to another within this group. Two neighboring counties, Berks and Lehigh to the northeast, are also big apple producers.

The topography and soil are just right for apples and other fruit. The peaks and crests are forested with a mixture of soft and hard woods, and on the intermediate elevations—seldom over a thousand feet—the orchards stand. Fruit trees on the slopes and hillsides get the benefit of good air and water drainage. Cold air currents settle in the lowlands; apple blossoms escape the damaging effect of late spring frosts, and maturing apples have a better chance to avoid the hazards of early fall frosts.

Apple varieties produced here fall into two broad classes: those best for cooking (York, Rome Beauty, Rhode Island Greening, and Yellow Transparent) and apples for eating fresh (Delicious, McIntosh, and Winesap).

Subtropical fruits. The most important of the subtropical fruits are the citrus group—oranges, tangerines, limes, grapefruits, and lemons. Avocados may also be included, although they are less resistant to cold than the others.

Florida is the leading U.S. producer of oranges, grapefruit, tangerines, and limes. Of the more than 500,000 acres in citrus groves, about three-fourths are devoted to orange trees, more than one-fifth to grapefruit trees, and the remainder to tangerines and lime trees. The chief orchard areas are in central and southern Florida (*Fig. 10-13*).

The Florida citrus industry presents one of the most varied economic patterns of all major agricultural enterprises. During the history of commercial citrus production, rapid expansion

FIGURE 10-13. *In the heart of Florida's vast citrus industry, near Clermont, the rolling hills are planted with citrus trees as far as the eye can see. (Florida News Bureau)*

and technological changes necessitated far-reaching economic changes. Perhaps the most salient features of the present economic organization are the widespread separation of grove ownership from grove operation, the importance of cooperative organizations, and the integration of the growing and processing functions.

The principal varieties of Florida oranges are Parson Brown and Hamlin, shipped mostly in October and November. Mid-season varieties are the Pineapple and Temple, shipped during January, February, and March. Valencias and Lou Jim Gongs, late varieties, are shipped in the March to July period.

Citrus fruit consumption has increased greatly in recent years because of: (1) emphasis on vitamins generally, and especially vitamin C, found so abundantly in Florida oranges and grapefruit; (2) processing and packaging of juice in liquid, powdered, and frozen forms, which permit a much wider distribution on a year-round basis; and (3) recognition of citrus fruits in any form as a staple food product.

Texas stands third, after Florida and California, in the production of oranges, and ranks second as a grapefruit grower. Lemons and tangerines are also important in Texas. The lower Rio Grande Valley ships trainloads of oranges, grapefruit, lemons, and tangerines from its orchards to northern markets.

South Carolina and Georgia stand second and third to California in the production of peaches. Peach-growing is centered around Spartanburg and Macon.

Nuts. The pecan, a native of the southeastern United States and Mexico, is extensively cultivated in Texas, Georgia, Louisiana, and Virginia. Pecans are unique in having a higher fat content—more than 70 per cent—than any other agricultural product. The trees are easy to grow, start to bear within three to four years, and their nuts sell for a high price. Exports, however, are not large.

Sugarcane. Sugarcane was one of the last staple agricultural crops to be introduced successfully in the South. Jesuits introduced the crop from Santo Domingo. Acadians later took up cane cultivation and spread its production westward. Commercial production became important after 1825.

Florida and Louisiana are the principal cane sugar growing areas of the mainland United States. Florida has over 150,000 acres of cane under cultivation, most of it in the Lake Okeechobee area, where Cuban immigrants are applying their considerable knowledge of sugarcane cultivation.

Louisiana supplies about five per cent of the nation's yearly sugar requirement. Cane is grown on large mechanized plantations in the lower part of the state. Despite level topography and rich silty clay loam soils, the short growing season (nine months) makes cane production a gamble (*Fig. 10-14*).

FIGURE 10-14. *Sugarcane planting in Louisiana. Louisiana sugar could not compete with sugar imported from the tropics, where the yield per acre is greater, were it not for the tariff on imports. (Louisiana State Dept. of Commerce and Industry)*

particularly the number of beef cattle, has increased rapidly since 1950.

Several factors have contributed to an expansion in the Southern grazing and livestock industries. Chief of these are: (1) more general use by farmers of recent technological developments; (2) advances in animal sciences, and production of feed crops, pasture, and other forage crops resulting from increased research and extension activities in these fields; (3) improved financial status of a large number of Southern farmers; and (4) an increasing consciousness of the real possibilities in livestock enterprises among farmers, farm organizations, and land-grant college personnel.

The general trend in numbers of livestock on Southern farms has not differed significantly from national trends. However, the relative increase in livestock numbers in the South since 1950 has exceeded the national average.

The Livestock Industries

Grazing and livestock industries represent the greatest changes in the South's postwar agriculture. The number of livestock on farms,

DAIRY CATTLE

Middle Atlantic Coastal Plain and Piedmont. The climate, topography, and soils of the Middle Atlantic region are particularly well suited to grassland dairying. The chief economic advantage enjoyed by dairy farmers, however, is the density of population in nearby markets. For this reason, approximately three-quarters of the milk produced here goes to market for consumption as fluid milk, in contrast with one-third in the great north-central dairy region (the Michigan-Wisconsin area). In this region, a much larger proportion of the milk goes to market in the form of manufactured products, such as butter, cheese, ice cream, evaporated milk, condensed milk, or powdered milk.

Philadelphia is the largest fluid milk consuming market in Pennsylvania. The Philadelphia "milkshed" runs from the Atlantic Coast in New Jersey westward as far as Altoona, Pennsylvania. Delaware and Maryland dairy farmers also ship into the Philadelphia market because these states are a natural part of the Philadelphia milkshed. The New York milkshed comprises a large section of Pennsylvania and partially overlaps the Philadelphia milkshed.

Fluid milk must get to market in a hurry because it is highly perishable. Where an individual farmer will ship his milk, then, depends upon which markets will accept his milk, what price he can get for it, and what it costs to haul it there. That is why milkshed boundaries sometimes seem to follow illogical lines.

South Atlantic-Gulf Coastal Plain and Piedmont. Partly because of the adjustment features of national farm programs and partly by virtue of research work on the growing of feed and forage carried on by experiment stations, dairying seems to be getting its long awaited start on Southern farms. Many problems, however, remain for Southern farmers to solve before any large number of dairymen become efficient producers.

For the most part, low production rates are the results of poor herd sires and inadequate or uneconomical feed production programs. Owners of small herds, who predominate, cannot afford proven bulls. Significant and rapid improvement in breeding, therefore, must come about largely by means of artificial insemination. This service is now available to many Southern farmers and calves artificially sired are beginning to replace mediocre cows in more and more herds.

About 49 per cent of all the milk cows in the South are on farms where there are only one or two cows; two-thirds are on farms where there are fewer than five. Dairying, therefore, is of little significance. Large commercial herds are common in Florida, however, where over a third of all milk cows are in herds of 50 or more. With the exception of Florida, the area is one in which commercial dairying has not yet developed enough to affect greatly the average dairy data for individual states or for the South as a whole.

BEEF CATTLE

Middle Atlantic Coastal Plain and Piedmont. About a half-million head of livestock go through the Lancaster, Pennsylvania, market annually This is a market where local farmers buy lean cattle shipped in from 37 states and from Canada.

The Lancaster livestock market grew right out of the corn fields that surround it. Its location is ideal for fattening Western and Southern cattle headed for the heavily populated Middle Atlantic seaboard markets. Bred and grass-fed on the Western ranges and plains and in the hill country of the South, the cattle move into the Lancaster area where, on the "cafeteria principle," a final intensive corn feeding gives the proper fat and finish, after which the cattle are moved into the nearby markets. Radiating from Lancaster County is an area consisting of 18 counties in southeastern Pennsylvania and in Maryland, where most of the stocker and feeder cattle going through the Lancaster market are converted into fat cattle. This area, sometimes called the "Eastern feeding district," is in reality a little corn belt. Each of these counties grows a tremendous amount of corn. In addition to its use as food for cattle, a large part of the corn is converted into pork. Dairying is also important in this area.

Cattle feeding is geared to the previously mentioned four-year system of crop rotation.

By marketing his corn in the form of beef at the rate of about 16 bushels of corn required to produce 100 pounds of beef on the hoof, the farmer sells his corn at a higher price; at the same time a large part of the crop stays on the farm in the form of fertilizer.

Steer feeding in conjunction with the corn-tobacco-wheat-grass cycle is an unbeatable combination if the weather does not conspire against the farmer; this it seldom does in Lancaster. In fact, steer feeding in the county has assumed such large proportions that Lancaster farmers must supplement their huge local corn crop by purchasing from outside almost half as much again as they grow.

South Atlantic-Gulf Coastal Plain. Since World War II, beef cattle raising has become increasingly important in this subregion. Large acreages have been shifted from cultivated crops to grass. New breeds have been developed by the crossing of Hereford and Aberdeen-Angus strains with Brahman cattle from India. Santa Gertrudis, Charbray, Brangus, and Beefmaster are all new breeds that have been tailored for Southern conditions.

Texas is the nation's leading producer of beef cattle, although Florida, South Carolina, Mississippi, and Georgia have converted thousands of acres of land to pasture. Florida's largest cattle-raising region lies in the lowlands between Lake Kissimmee and Lake Okeechobee (*Fig. 10-15*). Orlando, north of Lake Kissimmee, is an important horse-raising area.

Neighboring states ship cattle to Florida for fattening. Approximately 1,100,000 acres of improved pasturage have been developed at a cost varying from $20 to $60 an acre. Some of Florida's improved pastures will support a head per acre. The average is one animal to three acres.

With the development of dehydrated citrus pulp, citrus molasses, and sugarcane blackstrap molasses, cattle feeding methods have

FIGURE 10-15. *The vast, sprawling plains of south-central Florida are cattle country. Many of the animals have Brahman blood, as may be noted in the drooping ears and humped backs. (Florida News Bureau)*

changed radically. Pulp contains high nutritive values desirable for cattle diets; citrus and sugarcane molasses are excellent fattening and finishing feeds. All three are low in cost and available in large quantities.

POULTRY

Middle Atlantic Coastal Plain. Delaware is part of the so-called Delmarva Peninsula, which includes the Eastern Shore parts of Maryland and Virginia, almost separated from the mainland by the bay waters of the Delaware and Chesapeake. This is still the country's pre-eminent broiler-fryer land.

A broiler is a 12-week-old domestic fowl, exceptionally good to eat if grown for human consumption as tender meat. Formerly a luxury that was served only when the family had guests, the broiler is beginning to challenge pork as the poor man's meat.

Delaware is rather typical of the broiler peninsula; the state accounts for about 60 per cent of the birds produced. Numerous reasons are cited for the rapid rate of growth in the peninsula, but three stand out rather prominently. First, the area is near big Eastern markets that appreciate fresh-killed chicken meat. Delmarva broilers slaughtered in Georgetown, Delaware, on Thursday are the *pièce de résistance* of New York City menus on Friday. Second, World War II gave a sharp stimulus to the consumption of chicken, because red meat was scarce, rationed, and high-priced. Third, nature provided a short reproduction cycle, so that the broiler output could be stepped up quickly. Whereas it takes three to four years to increase the breeding and production of edible beef, one year to raise lamb and pork, it takes only 15 weeks to make a broiler—from egg to pan.

South Atlantic-Gulf Coastal Plain. Broiler production is an important industry in the Southeast, accounting for about 50 per cent of the commercial broilers in the United States. Associated with the growth of this industry are a number of important factors: (1) a demand situation favoring production of relatively low cost meat; (2) an area having a large number of farmers with limited alternative uses of land and labor; (3) a willingness on the part of individuals, feed dealers, processors, hatchery men, banks, and others to supply the capital necessary for large-scale broiler production; and (4) changes in technology of production and marketing that have reduced costs to the consumer.

The increase in hatchery capacity in the Southeast has paralleled the increase of commercial broiler production and is dynamic in nature. Hatcheries in Louisiana are concentrated primarily in the rice area; in Mississippi, in the Tupelo and Jackson areas. Hatcheries in North Carolina are located mainly in the eastern part of the state, particularly Duplin County.

The Piedmont. Poultry production in the Piedmont has had a significant increase since World War II. In particular, northern Georgia has become important, and hatchery production from this area has made a definite impact upon the economy.

Forests and Forest Industries

Forests make up one of the basic resources of the Atlantic-Gulf Coastal Plain and Piedmont Region. Despite their rapid exploitation, forest lands now cover more than half the total land area. Favorable climate and soil conditions combine to make this extensive region ideal for growing timber.

On the Coastal Plain, forests are predominantly pine—including longleaf, slash, loblolly, and shortleaf varieties. There are also bottomland hardwoods along the many rivers and cypress and tupelo in the swamps.

Rainfall is heavy, usually averaging about 60 inches along the Gulf Coast but dropping off gradually from the Mississippi westward to the treeless prairies. This, in addition to a warm climate, and a long growing season, assures excellent conditions for both the establishment and rapid growth of trees. Most soils are reasonably well drained and can store water and plant nutrients. Logging is relatively easy and inexpensive except in the swamps and deeper river bottoms or during periods of prolonged rain. The large private holdings of the South are located mostly in the Coastal Plain and in the rolling uplands of Texas, Arkansas, Louisiana, and Mississippi. Throughout the region, trees are the paying crop for 57 per cent of the land. With proper attention, this could be one of the most productive timber regions in the nation.

The Delta embraces about 32 million acres. Its forest is composed largely of hardwood species, and growth is rapid. Annual floods are the rule in this area but the water does not remain on the land long enough to affect growth or regeneration adversely. Floods are obstacles to logging, however, which must be done in the summer and early fall. In some years this logging period is shortened materially by the summer rains. The heavy, large timber obtained from the Delta forests requires heavier and more expensive logging equipment than is ordinarily needed in the pine forests of the South.

Many of the Delta soils are quite fertile, and in the past, many good soil areas have been cleared for agriculture. Although there may be some additional clearing in the future for this purpose, it seems probable that 40 to 50 per cent of the area will remain in forests. Ownership tracts are medium to large. There are a number of sawmills that own more than 500,000 acres. Large farms or plantations are more typical of the area than small ones, and many of them include forest lands in excess of 1,000 acres.

The Delta is a productive timber area where, with good management, tree crops can be made an increasingly important part of the local economy. Although the Delta's forest is least understood by foresters, it has the potential to furnish substantial employment and income to the people, and many useful forest products to the nation.

Forest industries rank next to agriculture in their contribution to the economy of the region. In nearly every community, operating units of the forest industry employ workers, buy products, and pay taxes. The contribution is so general and of such long standing that most people assume it will remain forever, not realizing that the timber resources on which the industry depends might play out some day.

PULP AND PAPER MAKING

The Southeast has millions of softwood trees (nearly two-thirds of its forest land) that provide a rich source of pulpwood *(Fig. 10-16)*.

The sulfate process, adaptable to the pulping of resinous woods, made possible the use of large acreages of Southern pine. Yielding a pulp of great strength, this process, first developed in Sweden, is known as the "kraft" process (the Swedish word for strength).

Pulp produced from Southern pine is used primarily for the manufacture of wrapping paper, bag paper, and paper-board, where its strength is an asset and its characteristic brownish color is no drawback. A rapid increase in the demand for paper as a packaging and shipping material, therefore, acted as a stimulus to the Southeast's pulp and paper industry. Techniques developed for bleaching sulphate pulp broadened its uses. Also, the adaptation of the groundwood process to Southern pine has led to the production of newsprint in this region.

With the necessary raw materials available in large quantities and stimulated by strong

FIGURE 10-16. *A stand of Southern pine. Besides accounting for most of the subregion's lumber, the Southern pine provides raw materials for other industries, such as naval stores and paper.*

economic forces, the area's pulp and paper industry has grown phenomenally in the last 30 years. In 1930, the production of wood pulp, then concentrated in Louisiana, accounted for roughly 6 or 7 per cent of the United States total. Today, about 60 per cent of our wood pulp comes from this area.

With the industry's expansion in the Southeast exceeding that in the nation, an increasing proportion of new capital expenditures has occurred here. There are more than 90 pulp and paper mills in the area, with the largest concentration in Georgia, Florida, Alabama, and Louisiana.

The pulp and paper industry has been the biggest boon to Florida's forest economy. The first major pulp mill was set up in Panama City, on the Gulf of Mexico, in 1931. Since then, many large companies have established pulp and paper mills in Florida. In fact, in 1960, Florida became the number one pulp state in the nation, with a total daily mill capacity of 8,280 tons. It replaced Washington, which had been the leader since 1939.

CYPRESS—THE LAST OF THE GIANTS

The ancients preferred cypress wood because it was straight and close-grained, soft and easily worked, and resistant to rot and decay. These qualities have made cypress a very popular wood in the United States.

Although the North American habitat of the bald, or deciduous cypress ranges from Delaware to Texas and up the Mississippi River basin as far as Indiana, most of the great virgin cypress timber stands (trees 1,000 years old, 8 feet thick at the base, and often 100 feet or more high) are in the tidewater and river swamp areas of the Atlantic and Gulf Coasts.

Southern mills produce about 146 million board feet, or $8 million worth of cypress lumber annually. Nearly half of this output is in Florida; about one-quarter of it is in Louisiana.

Despite a large decline in available supply, cypress lumber is still used to produce a wide variety of items. The highest grade of reddish-colored heartwood, which comes from large trees growing in the tidewater or deep-swamp

forests and which is especially resistant to rot, is used to build shrimp boats along the Gulf Coast.

Lower grades of tidewater red cypress and much of the white or yellow cypress that comes from upland areas are used to manufacture interior trim, doors, sash, and blinds for homes.

With little basis for expecting artificial reforestation to be carried far, and with natural replenishment very uncertain, the prospect is that the cypress industry's supply of raw material will continue to dwindle as the drain from the forests exceeds the new growth.

NAVAL STORES

The naval stores industry (the production of turpentine, rosin, and pitch) has been an integral part of the Southeast's economy since the first colonists landed there more than 350 years ago.

The name "naval stores" was given to these products because they were used principally to calk boats, treat ropes, and in similar applications. Today, the term is a misnomer, for the uses of these products are many.

The United States normally supplies over one-half the world's needs for turpentine and rosin, mostly by tapping second-growth longleaf and slash pines in southeastern Georgia and northern Florida. However, the naval stores belt extends along the Coastal Plain from the Savannah River to the Mississippi River.

Fishing

Nature has made the coastal waters of the Atlantic Plain a haven for shellfish. The drowned coast with its many bays, coves, estuaries, and shallow tidal flats is ideal for the propagation and culture of several shellfish varieties. Freshwater streams, which reduce salinity; relatively warm, shallow water; and weak tides further aid in making this area an outstanding producer of shellfish. Oysters and crabs are the most highly prized, bring the highest return, and engage the greatest number of fishermen. Mackerel, rosefish, salmon, and shad are also sought.

NORTHERN WATERS

Oysters. Chesapeake and Delaware Bays historically have accounted for nearly one-half of the nation's oyster supply. Continuous fishing on natural beds has caused a decline in oyster production, however. State governments were careless in enforcing laws designed to give oysters a fighting chance to maintain their population. Oyster gardeners themselves were careless in harvesting oyster clusters and in failing to return the small undersized oysters to the grounds. Upstream municipalities polluted the rivers with sewage, and industrial concerns poisoned the water with factory wastes. As a result of such malpractices, along with the destruction caused by natural enemies of the oyster, some oyster beds have been almost totally destroyed.

Fortunately, oyster culture in New Jersey and Delaware is in a much better condition than in other oyster areas. This is because growers in Delaware Bay are partly dependent on the existence of public reefs from which to obtain seed for planting on privately owned beds. The state of New Jersey polices its seed beds and also maintains a laboratory with a corps of scientists who have made notable progress in helping growers to fight the oyster's natural enemies.

Clams and crabs. Clamming is carried on extensively in the waters from Long Island to Chesapeake Bay. Familiar to seafood gourmets are Cherrystone clams on the half shell. Cherrystone is a trade name used by the U.S. Fish and Wildlife Service to denote the size of the clam. Claw-like rakes with long handles are employed to dig for clams in the shallow waters near shore. Rowboats are used in deeper water.

The "soft shell," or Blue crab, is a highly prized shellfish in the Middle Atlantic region. Chesapeake Bay abounds in this variety (*Fig. 10-17*).

FIGURE 10-17. *A fisherman removes soft shell crabs from a float in Tangier Island's harbor. The economy of the lower Chesapeake Bay area is almost entirely dependent on fishing. (Virginia Dept. of Conservation)*

SOUTHERN WATERS

Fishing is one of the oldest industries of the South Atlantic-Gulf Coastal Plain. Most fish are confined to the waters of the gently sloping portion of the ocean floor (called the continental shelf) or to bays and inlets of the coast. In these waters a greater variety of fish and shellfish abound than anywhere else off the shores of the United States.

The continental shelf is wide along much of the coast and far out along the Florida Keys. The deeply-indented bays, the coastal marshes and inland lagoons—especially those along the coasts of Louisiana, Mississippi, and Alabama—provide ideal growing conditions for oysters, as well as shelter for young shrimp and fish that come in from the open sea to grow to maturity (*Fig. 10-18*).

In contrast with other types of fish, most of the shellfish caught in Southern waters are processed before they are marketed. Oysters marketed fresh have their shells removed before shipping. Louisiana and Mississippi together process oysters valued at almost four-fifths of the total United States production. Biloxi, Mississippi, is the world's center for canned oysters.

Fish. The United States Fish and Wildlife Service lists almost 60 varieties of fish caught commercially off Southern shores. Seven varieties, however, account for 75 per cent of the total fish sales (excluding shellfish). Mullet, caught principally by Florida fishermen, yield about 28 per cent of the total returns. Other important varieties include Spanish mackerel, sea trout, menhaden, catfish, groupers, and red snappers. When four other varieties are added —drum, pompano, bluefish, and flounders—the list accounts for over 90 per cent of the total fish sales exclusive of shellfish.

Menhaden. The most important fish on the basis of volume caught is menhaden, which amounts to 60 per cent of the volume of com-

FIGURE 10-18. *A haul of shrimp along the Gulf Coast.*

mercial catch of 180 million pounds annually. Most of the menhaden is taken from the waters off the Florida, Louisiana, and Mississippi coasts.

This fish is used primarily for the manufacture of meal and oil. Meal made from menhaden, very high in protein content, is fed to hogs and poultry. The oil has industrial importance in the manufacture of paints, varnishes, insect sprays, soaps, and as a lubricant for certain specialized uses. It also is used to fortify poultry feeds with vitamins.

At one time, menhaden-processing was concentrated in New England, but because of the longer fishing season, many of the newer plants are now in the South. Approximately 60 fish by-product plants, many of them processing menhaden, are found in Florida, Louisiana, and Mississippi.

Boats generally from 85 to 150 feet long, carrying a crew of around 20 men, supply the plants. Some of these boats venture as far as 100 miles into the Gulf, although occasionally large schools of fish may be found nearer the shore. Airplanes are sometimes used to spot the schools. When the boats arrive at the plants, they may be carrying as many as a million fish, with each of the fish weighing approximately a pound.

Trapping

The southern part of Louisiana is famed for the millions of fur pelts taken there every year. The large area especially adapted to the raising of fur-bearing animals makes Louisiana one of the leading states in the nation in this respect. Muskrat, otter, mink, raccoon, opossum, coypu, and other fur-bearing mammals abound. From a commercial standpoint the muskrat occupies the place of greatest importance.

Most of the trapping in Texas is carried on in a desultory manner, becoming active in first one community and then another, and depending on natural reproduction for the game supply. In the vicinity of Beaumont, however, the muskrat production is carried on under a range management program.

Minerals

The character of minerals found in a given region is often related to its geologic history and therefore to the types of rocks in which the minerals are found.

The relatively flat-lying, poorly consolidated rocks of the Coastal Plain contain phosphate, asphalt, bauxite, clay, sand, gravel, lignite, fuller's earth, bentonite, iron, gypsum, chalk, marl, ocher, natural gas, petroleum, sulphur, and brines containing salt and bromine (*Fig. 10-19*).

Petroleum and natural gas have provided much of the energy that made possible the industrial development of the Gulf Coastal Plain. This area, including parts of Louisiana, Mississippi, and Texas particularly, but also portions of Alabama and Florida, now ranks second in the nation in petroleum output, contributing some 22 per cent of the total. Texas and Louisiana jointly account for 68 per cent of U.S. production and are credited with 67 per cent of the proved reserves.

The world's principal sulfur-mining region is coastal Texas and Louisiana. This area has a combination of characteristics favorable for sulfur mining: (1) enormous reserves; (2) high quality sulfur; (3) location near tidewater; (4) low cost of mining (Frasch process); (5) impervious strata above and below the sul-

fur deposits, which permit maintenance of the necessary water temperatures and pressure; and (6) abundant supply of petroleum and natural gas.

Texas and Louisiana are important producers of salt. The largest deposits lie in underground salt domes in east Texas and west Louisiana. Eastern Texas is noted for its high-grade lignite. Arkansas produces more than 95 per cent of the bauxite mined in the United States.

Manufacturing

MIDDLE ATLANTIC COASTAL PLAIN

Many factors account for the concentration and dominance of industry in this portion of the United States. Chief of these are: (1) a large labor pool with diversified skills; (2) available cheap fuel and power in the form of coal, natural gas, petroleum, and falling water; (3) geographic location—containing many of the major population centers of the United States; (4) cheap and efficient forms of land, sea, and air transportation; and (5) large, deep, commodious harbors along the Atlantic Coastal Plain, with access to the interior through the Hudson-Mohawk Depression via the New York State Barge Canal.

In terms of industry, commerce, and agriculture this is one of the best-balanced areas on earth. Every important ingredient is either here or is readily available: transportation, natural resources, location, labor, supplying industries, and markets. Nowhere is there such a meeting point of raw materials for processing into manufactured goods.

The outstanding feature of the subregion's industry is its diversification. At the same time, many of the industries are also large. This is illustrated by the fact that the area leads all other industrial districts in the nation in the fabrication of many items (*see* pages 214-224).

SOUTH ATLANTIC-GULF COASTAL PLAIN AND PIEDMONT

The South Atlantic-Gulf Coastal Plain and Piedmont is experiencing a new industrial revo-

FIGURE 10-19. *A phosphate mining operation near Barstow, in central Florida. This area has the largest deposit of phosphate in the Western Hemisphere. (Florida News Bureau)*

lution. The remarkable advance of manufacturing in this region is not merely a matter of expanding volume in the few old, established industries—textiles, wood products, and tobacco—but, more significantly, a vigorous branching out into chemicals, hydroelectric energy and refined mineral fuels, transport equipment, electrical goods, metal products, and other technically advanced enterprises. Simultaneously, the older industries have upgraded their products, introduced more complex forms of manufacture, and, as in the case of the Southern entry into synthetic textiles, explored new fields.

Textiles, tobacco, and furniture dominate the industrial structure of the North and South Carolina Piedmont. Wooden furniture manufacturing is especially important in the vicinity of High Point, North Carolina. Industrial activity in Florida extends over a wide range, from ships and paper to cigars, food, and novelties. The long list of products manufactured in Florida includes: building materials, guided missiles, electronics equipment, machines, chemicals, glass, hardware, clothing, and communications equipment (*Fig. 10-20*).

The Gulf Coast is one of the nation's major producers of alumina and aluminum and a leader in petroleum refining and petrochemicals. The area from Baton Rouge south past New Orleans is becoming one huge chemical plant, linked by webs of pipelines, strings of tank cars, and fleets of barges (*Fig. 10-21*).

FIGURE 10-21. *The Humble Oil Company refinery at Baytown, Texas, near Houston. Both the Houston-Galveston Bay and Beaumont-Port Arthur areas possess refineries with a total crude oil capacity in excess of 700 million barrels per day. Other important refining centers are Baton Rouge, Lake Charles, Corpus Christi, and New Orleans. (Humble Oil and Refining Co.)*

Space-age triangle. A major generator of growth in the South is the important government space program. The latter includes the rocket research center at Huntsville, Alabama, the spacecraft center at Houston, Texas, and the launching facilities at Cape Kennedy, Florida.

FIGURE 10-20. *This modern plant in Orlando, Florida, is typical of the new industries locating in the South. (Martin Aircraft and Missiles Co.)*

Recreation and Tourism

MIDDLE ATLANTIC COASTAL PLAIN

Visitors to the shore resorts of New Jersey spend between a quarter of a billion and a half-billion dollars annually. Although the resorts offer numerous attractions, the outstanding feature common to all is the climate. When the days get hot and sticky in the cities of the interior, it is always cooler and more comfortable

at the shore. This is borne out by official records of the Weather Bureau, going back three-quarters of a century. The mean monthly temperature averages 53° F. throughout the year. It drops to an average of only 34° in the winter and rises to an average of only 73° in summer. Compared with New York, Philadelphia, and Washington, the temperature is usually six to ten degrees cooler during the summer and warmer during the winter. Another climatic factor favoring the seashore is the abundance of days with sunshine.

Summer vacationing is easily and quickly available to the millions of people living in the heavily industrialized New York-Philadelphia-Baltimore-Washington axis, the country's largest cluster of people. When a heat wave strikes Philadelphia, tens of thousands of people leave their places of business at the end of the workday and motor to the shore for a dip in the ocean. The market gardens, in the immediate hinterland of the seashore, supply fresh vegetables and fruits for the summer multitude, and commercial fishermen supply fish and other seafoods to add variety to seashore dining rooms.

From Highland Park, north of Trenton, New Jersey, to Cape May, at the state's southern end, there are more than 50 resort communities, ranging in size from less than 1,000 to over 50,000 permanent residents. Some communities have quaint names, like Ship Bottom and Love Ladies; others boast such famous names as Atlantic City and Cape May. Some of these communities, Asbury Park and Long Branch, for example, are at the water's edge on the mainland; others, like Toms River and Pine Beach, are a short way upstream; but most of them are on islands separated from the mainland by innumerable bays and inlets that dot the ragged New Jersey coastline.

The resort communities have many characteristics in common—bathing beaches, boardwalks, back bays, seagulls, hotels, restaurants, apartments for rent, and saltwater taffy. Yet no two are alike, and each attracts its own particular clientele.

Cape May is the oldest and southernmost. Sitting on the very edge of the cape, the town has been host to a century and a half of patrons. In days gone by, it entertained the country's leading citizens—presidents, congressmen, merchants, and socialites. It has charm, individuality, folklore, and tradition—old houses with "widows' walks" on the roofs where skippers' wives kept vigil for their husbands returning from year-long expeditions; a freshwater pond hard by the bay where British men-of-war and pirate vessels stopped to replenish their stores of drinking water; and legends of buried treasure cached by Captain Kidd.

Wildwood, just a short distance above the cape, is different. It is livelier and larger. Including the adjacent communities, Wildwood has a population of 10,000 permanent residents. Claiming the "World's Finest and Safest Bathing Beach," this resort has been growing rapidly. Its growth is attributable to excellent bathing facilities afforded by a wide and moderately sloping beach, a variety of boardwalk amusements, and good fishing. It is only a short run from Wildwood to a number of excellent fishing banks off the coasts of New Jersey, Delaware, and Maryland. Many of the fishing boats are equipped with ship-to-shore communication facilities so that masters of the vessels may determine the best market for quick sales of their catch to representatives of the buyers waiting at the wharves.

Ocean City, further up the coast and within sight of Atlantic City, is a resort of still another type. With a permanent population of 6,000 that swells to an estimated 60,000 at the peak of the season, Ocean City takes pride in being "The Country's Greatest Family Resort." This grows out of the fact that it was started as a Methodist camp meeting, and in line with that tradition, the sale of alcoholic beverages is still forbidden within the city limits. Placing somewhat less emphasis upon commercial forms of entertainment than its neighboring communities, Ocean City is steadily gaining in the size of its permanent population.

Atlantic City is in a class by itself. It has been described as "an amusement factory operated on the straight-line, mass production pattern." The belt is the boardwalk, along which each specialist adds his bit to assemble the finished product—the departing visitor, sated, tanned, and bedecked with souvenirs. Founded on sand, surrounded by water, and flooded with sunshine, Atlantic City is endowed with all the natural advantages that go with the seashore resort. What puts the city in a class by itself are the added attractions built in by its enterprising promoters (*Fig. 10-22*).

Atlantic City entertains 12 to 14 million visitors annually. To take care of such numbers requires physical and entertainment facilities in the grand manner, and Atlantic City has them. It is a city of hotels—hundreds of them, big hotels with capacity of up to 1,000 rooms. In addition to the hotels there are about 1,600 guest houses. The Convention Hall is big enough to seat the entire population of the city. The boardwalk is one of the country's most famous fashion highways, where Easter styles go on parade each year.

Amusement and diversion facilities are almost endless—sports and entertainment compete with stores for space on the five large piers jutting out into the ocean. In addition to entertainment and recreational opportunities at the theaters, on the golf links, at the race track, on the dance floors, or in the night clubs, there are also fishing, yachting, boxing, wrestling, ice hockey, basketball, steeplechasing, surf bathing, and sun bathing.

By reason of its ideal climate and all its added attractions, Atlantic City is a great con-

vention city. Americans are probably the world's greatest "conventioneers." Whether bankers, doctors, teachers, or diamond cutters, they all have their annual convention—and sooner or later they convene at Atlantic City, simply because the city has the facilities to house them, feed them, and entertain them. Atlantic City gets about a fifth of the country's annual conventions.

SOUTH ATLANTIC-GULF COASTAL PLAIN

Few regions in the nation excel the Southeast in the number and variety of tourist attractions. The whole periphery is ringed by vacation areas and centers of tourist traffic. In many cases these already are highly developed; in others they are merely potential resources, the future of which will depend upon the wisdom, energy, and imagination displayed by public and private agencies in their development.

Of all the vacation areas in the Southeast, Florida is by far the most important. The whole state is virtually one great playground. Enjoying an unusually favorable climate, spangled by its 30,000 lakes, washed by the Atlantic on its eastern shore and by the waters of the Gulf along its western shore, for centuries the state of Florida has exercised a powerful attraction on people seeking health and recreation. The Florida of the '60's has no one tourist season; golfing, swimming, fishing, and plain relaxation are catered to the year 'round. Miami, Marathon, Palm Beach, and Ft. Myers, to name a few, are places that mean warm sun, white beaches, and fun to millions (*Fig. 10-23*).

Northward from Florida, the islands lying off the Georgia coast already attract considerable numbers of tourists and vacationists. Their full possibilities, however, are yet to be developed. Westward from Florida, the Gulf Coast provides another natural vacation area. Alabamans dream that some day Baldwin County will rival Miami, Gulfport, and Biloxi as a vacation center.

Evidences of the nation's historic past are perhaps more numerous in Virginia than any-

FIGURE 10-22. *Steel Pier and the Boardwalk on Atlantic City's beachfront. (Atlantic City Convention Bureau)*

FIGURE 10-23. *Aerial view of Miami Beach and Miami. (Florida News Bureau)*

where else in the region. Thousands annually visit Williamsburg, where the old Courthouse, the Capitol, Public Gaol, Raleigh Tavern, Ludwell-Paradise House, Governor's Palace, Wythe House, Powder Magazine, and Guardhouse, among others, have been restored. Other historically significant places are Monticello, home of Thomas Jefferson, and Jamestown, site of the first permanent English settlement in America. Numbered among North Carolina's historic attractions are the Fort Raleigh national historic site on Roanoke Island, where the first English attempt to found a colony in America was made by Sir Walter Raleigh, and the County Courthouse at Charlotte, where the Mecklenburg Declaration was signed. In South Carolina are located the home of John C. Calhoun on the Clemson College campus and old Fort Jackson, where the first shot of the Civil War was fired on Fort Sumter.

Seashore, mountain, and health resorts, some catering to the budget-minded and others to the wealthy, are to be found throughout the region. Outstanding on the coast are Virginia Beach and Ocean View (Norfolk), Virginia; Carolina Beach, Morehead City, and Wrightsville Beach, North Carolina; and Myrtle Beach, South Carolina.

The Southeast has a large financial stake in the tourist trade. Florida claims four to four and a half million tourists a year who spend about a billion dollars annually. This exceeds the value of Florida's manufactured products and the annual production of its forests, mines, or fisheries. Obviously the tourist business is the state's most important industry.

Megalopolis

The Middle Atlantic Coastal Plain is predominantly a land of cities. It includes New York City (the heart of megalopolis), Long Island, the Hudson Valley, the city belt west of the Hudson River in New Jersey, the Philadelphia metropolitan area in southeastern Pennsylvania, the Delaware Valley, Baltimore, Maryland, and Washington, D.C. Nowhere else in Anglo-America is there such a cluster of factories, skyscrapers, land and sea transportation routes, and people. Practically every type of industry is represented here, with products so diverse that it would be difficult indeed to think of many articles that are not manufactured in this region. Manufacturing and commerce dominate the economy, abetted by the area's nearness to: (1) raw materials, (2) markets, (3) fuel and power, (4) a supply of skilled labor, and (5) a well-developed system of transportation and communication.

Population density per square mile is greater on the inner Coastal Plain than on the outer Coastal Plain, with densities of 700 and 160, respectively (*Fig. 10-24*).

NEW YORK CITY

The scale and variety of New York's economic activity make it unique among the cities of Anglo-America. Its business is of such magnitude that a new standard of measure is almost required, for what is comparatively small by New York City standards would be huge in a community of average size.

The nearly eight million residents of New York City occupy only slightly more than 300 square miles. They comprise the largest and most concentrated consumer market in the country, as well as one of the most diversified in terms of tastes, skills, and economic status. The city also leads the nation in industry, banking, insurance, wholesale and retail trade, and specialized business services.

Although catering to the varied demands of its own population is a big business in itself, the city, to an even greater extent than most metropolitan areas, also exports a large proportion of its goods and services. It imports almost all its food. Many of its products—furs, apparel, millinery, scientific instruments, cosmetics, leather goods, and printed matter—are known throughout the nation and the world. New York's concentration of high-ranking specialized business services in such fields as law, advertising, engineering, research, finance, shipping, and other technical lines, makes it an ideal center for the head offices of large corporations.

FIGURE 10-24. *Population density of the urban Eastern seaboard (after Eckardt).*

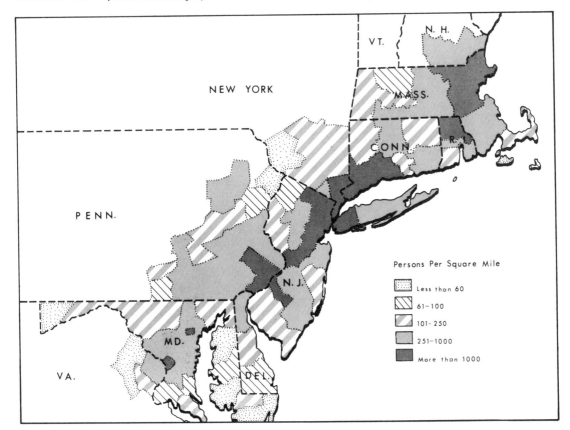

FIGURE 10-25. *Aerial view of New York City and its hinterland. Manhattan is in the center, the Bronx in the center background, New Jersey to the left, Queens to the upper right, and Brooklyn to the lower right. (Port of New York Authority)*

KEY TO NEW YORK'S IMPORTANCE

Soon after the completion of the Erie Canal in 1825, New York dwarfed all other cities of the nation. The basic elements making New York so important a community are: (1) its excellent location, (2) its unrivaled port and facilities, (3) its concentrated population with widely diversified skills, professions, and occupations, (4) its highly developed industry and commerce, and (5) its far-reaching network of transportation and communication.

Strategic location. Situated on an arm of the sea at the mouth of the Hudson River and lying about midway between Boston and Baltimore, New York City is the terminus of the major sea, land, and air routes of the nation, the continent, and the world (*Fig. 10-26*). The Hudson River links the Port of New York with the Great Lakes via the New York State Barge Canal system, which provides a cheap means of transportation for bulk commodities. No other Atlantic seaport enjoys so favorable a route to the interior. The Mohawk depression is the only break in the Appalachian Uplands, which otherwise continue without interruption from the St. Lawrence Valley to north-central Alabama. This almost sea level route owes its existence to the region's geology. The softer limestone rocks that lie between hard crystallines of the Adirondacks and Catskills have been eroded, creating an easy route through central New York. The Hudson, which lies at the eastern edge of this depression, is a drowned river valley. Land subsidence here permits ocean-going vessels to penetrate inland to Troy, a distance of 150 miles. From Troy the New York State Barge Canal links the Hudson River with Lake Erie at Buffalo. Because of cheap water rates, this 340-mile system handles the bulk of the interior's eastbound freight. Railroads parallel the canal; their rates are kept low by water freight competition. The more recently developed New York State Thruway, a toll express road following the same route, provides rapid service for passenger automobiles and trucks.

New York City dominates not only the trade of the interior but also coastal and foreign trade. The city is the funnel through which commodities flow from the New England fisheries and factories. From the South come an array of raw materials for processing, and oil and gas for power and domestic fuel.

Strategic location favors New York in foreign trade. Its position in the North Atlantic Basin facing Europe, the world's largest market, gives rise to an unequaled exchange of unlike commodities between the two continents.

INDUSTRIAL PATTERNS

For many decades, trade and services have played a more significant role in the economy of New York City than in that of most other metropolitan centers of the country.

One of the most persistent legends about New York is that it is only a city of consumers and middlemen, an unproductive parasite that lives off the labor and substance of others, a buzzing marketplace where the goods of outsiders are exchanged (for exorbitant fees), and a wasteful pleasure center where talents,

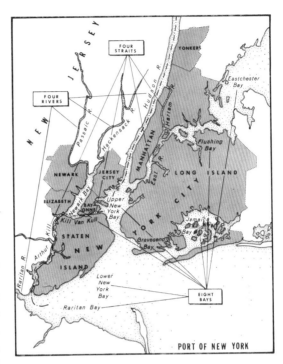

FIGURE 10-26.

services, and money are squandered without concern. In fact, New York is the greatest manufacturing center in the world.

Every major manufacturing group is represented, but the heaviest concentration is in nondurable goods industries, which employ over 75 per cent of the area's manufacturing workers. Despite the concentration of employment in nondurables, there is a wide diversity of industry. This contributes an economic stability lacking in many other urban centers. Emphasis on production of consumer soft goods serves to cushion the shock of any economic decline, since the demand for such items is usually more constant than the demand for hard goods.

Small firms dominate. The average number of persons employed per establishment, 19 workers, is substantially below the national figure. Taken individually, the area's manufacturing enterprises are so diminutive that foreign visitors seeking the heart of American mass production hurry through New York and go out to see the giant automobile plants that dominate Detroit, the steel mills that darken the skies near Pittsburgh, or the sprawling aircraft factories of California. New York has nothing to match these industries, yet the combined output of its thousands of tiny shops is so much greater than that of other large cities that there is not even a close competitor.

These tiny shops are more representative of metropolitan industry than the huge enterprises with headquarters in the Empire State Building or Rockefeller Center. More than 235,000 separate enterprises exist in New York's five boroughs. Of these, only 500 businesses employ over 500 persons, and 210,000 are owner-operated or have fewer than 20 workers on their payroll.

THE GARMENT INDUSTRY

The largest single segment of New York's economy is the ladies' garment industry. This strange business, based on fickle feminine taste and requiring small capital outlay, provides jobs for some 250,000 workers, produces about 70 per cent of all women's and children's clothing in the United States, and has made New York a world fashion center (*Fig. 10-27*). More

FIGURE 10-27. *A typical loft scene in New York City's garment district. Women operators using multipurpose sewing machines turn out clothing to suit every taste and every pocketbook. (International Ladies' Garment Workers' Union)*

than that, it has created a city within a city, the Garment Center—a crowded district bounded on the north by Forty-second Street, on the south by Thirty-fourth Street, on the east by the Avenue of the Americas, and on the west by Ninth Avenue.

Few industries are as ideally suited to a city where space is at a premium. Garment making lends itself readily to division of labor. Only small and relatively inexpensive equipment is needed, with little capital or risk required. But the most important factor of all is the unequaled local market—a metropolitan area population of more than 14 million, with a per capita income higher than the national average, in a climatic area demanding four seasonal wardrobe changes. What could be more advantageous than a site where clothes are made on the fourteenth floor and sold on the first?

OTHER INDUSTRIES

New York is the nation's leading printing and publishing center. Machinery and metal products rank third in the city's industrial hierarchy. In order of importance, the list also includes: scientific instruments, chemical products, leather goods, paper products, furniture and wood products, and textile products.

FINANCIAL AND COMMERCIAL CAPITAL

The area around Wall Street contains the world's greatest concentration of finanical institutions, including: insurance, commercial, industrial, and savings banks; investment trusts; insurance companies; security dealers and underwriters; commodity brokers; exchanges; mortgage, loan, and installment finance companies; personal loan companies; and holding companies.

LONG ISLAND

Long Island extends a finger eastward into the Atlantic Ocean for some 120 miles from New York Bay. Its north shore, overlooking

Long Island Sound, is a product of many deposits laid down during the last glacial period. It is one of the most remarkable islands anywhere, with great diversity of community, character, geography, and industry.

The island is linked to Manhattan and the Bronx by six great bridges and several vehicular and subway tunnels. Through the tunnels and over the bridges flows the greatest intercommunity traffic in the world. Two of the biggest of New York's five boroughs—Brooklyn and Queens, with population in excess of 4,000,000 people—are a part of Long Island (*Fig. 10-28*).

Its geography ranges from rugged, wooded hills, cupped with deep bays along the north shore, to flat salt marsh along the south behind barrier islands of sand. These barrier dunes—a chain of island splinters more than a hundred miles long—give Long Island some of the finest beaches in the world.

The industry of Long Island is enormously varied—from huge aircraft and aircraft parts industries like Grumman at Bethpage, Republic at Farmingdale, and Sperry Gyroscope at Lake Success to the manufacture of scientific and engineering instruments, electronic equipment, toys, curtains, lace goods, apparel, laboratory furniture, and high precision aeronautical and marine instruments.

East of the great urban area around New York City, the island is a veritable garden—growing huge quantities of potatoes, cauliflower, lima beans, and corn. Its duck farms are famous, and from the shallow waters along its shores are raked great quantities of clams, oysters, and scallops.

THE CITY BELT—WEST OF THE HUDSON

At one end there is New York, at the other there is Philadelphia. Between, on either side of a thin railroad corridor linking them, live more than two-thirds of all the people in New Jersey. Here is the area of cities—Jersey City, Newark, Elizabeth, Camden, and the state capital at Trenton. This is the City Belt, where trains thunder over the busiest stretches of

FIGURE 10-28. *Rush hour scene at a Brooklyn station of one of New York City's subway lines. (New York City Transit Authority)*

railroad tracks in the world, where heavy trucks and hundreds of thousands of automobiles each day grind away at cement and macadam on the highways and superhighways and turnpikes, and where factories and chemical plants combine to make New Jersey one of the leading states in industrial development.

The upper half revolves around New York; the lower half has Philadelphia as its axis. This is the City Belt where "dormitories'" for New York and Philadelphia have become a pattern. This is the land of industry, of city slums, of suburban housing developments, of progress, of noise, and of culture. This is the land Benjamin Franklin likened to a barrel "tapped at both ends."

Four bridges and two tunnels financed and constructed by the Port of New York Authority are in operation between New Jersey and New York City. Two bridges, the Goethals Bridge and the Outerbridge Crossing, were opened to traffic in 1928. Both the Bayonne Bridge and George Washington Bridge were opened to traffic in 1931. The Holland Tunnel, connecting Manhattan to Weehawken, New Jersey, was opened in 1937. These transportation arteries make the Jersey shore opposite Manhattan another economic borough. The northern counties are part of the New York metropolitan complex and share many of its problems—problems dealing with traffic and other aspects of growth and decay.

Located across Newark Bay from Jersey City, and eight miles from Manhattan, Newark is the metropolis of New Jersey, a port of entry and one of the world's great manufacturing centers. To the south of Newark is Elizabeth, the nation's leading producer of sewing machines. To the north is Passaic, the largest handkerchief center in the United States, and a center for the manufacture of woolen and worsted goods. Nearby Paterson, straddling the falls of the Passaic River, is noted for its silk, rayon, and woolen mills.

THE HUDSON VALLEY

The Hudson Valley, an area of rich farms, industrial cities, and vacation areas, is the Northeast's natural gateway to the interior. Ocean-going vessels penetrate inland to Troy, and the major rail and highway routes converging upon New York City provide valley towns with ready accessibility to the city's markets.

The lower Hudson. More than half of the population within the lower Hudson Valley lives in four large suburban cities—Yonkers, Mount Vernon, New Rochelle, and White Plains—with their economy closely linked to New York City. Manufacturing establishments produce nationally known brands of rugs, automobiles, copper wire, elevators, and hearing aids. Clothing manufacturing is the area's largest industry, employing about one out of every six factory workers. Textile mill products, primarily carpets and rugs, rank a close second to apparel in employment. Chemicals and allied goods are also well represented.

The mid-Hudson. The mid-Hudson Valley's population has a greater proportion of its labor force dependent on agriculture, trade, and services than the areas previously mentioned. Its fertile soils support extensive fruit orchards, vineyards, and dairy farms. Apples, pears, plums, cherries, grapes, and currants are important crops.

Poughkeepsie, Newburgh, Kingston, and Hudson are the principal manufacturing and retail trading centers. The machinery industry is the most important source of manufacturing employment. Major products include electric typewriters, ball bearings, recording equipment, and gauges.

Brickmaking, centered around Kingston, owes its origin to the combination of large deposits of clay on the banks of the Hudson River and cheap water transportation to the New York City market. The manufacture of Portland cement near Hudson is another industry based on local water resources.

Numerous places of historic interest attract tourists, among them: the United States Military Academy at West Point, Washington's headquarters in Newburgh, the old Senate house in Kingston, the Hyde Park home of Franklin D. Roosevelt, and the magnificent estates along the Hudson above Poughkeepsie (*Fig. 10-29*).

The upper Hudson. This section is dominated by Troy, located at the head of navigation on the Hudson River. An important industrial city and the eastern terminus of the New York State Barge Canal, Troy claims national leadership in manufacturing men's shirts, engineer-

FIGURE 10-29. *Cadets on parade at the United States Military Academy, West Point, New York. (U.S. Military Academy)*

ing and surveying instruments, sandpaper, and emery cloth.

Albany, capital of New York, is located south of Troy on the west side of the Hudson. It is one of the most important inland ports accommodating oceangoing vessels (*Fig. 10-30*).

Schenectady, located on the Mohawk River, 13 miles northwest of Albany, has been a noted center of the electrical industry since 1886. It has the world's largest plant for the production of electrical equipment and radio and television sets. It has extensive research laboratories, including an atomic research laboratory at nearby Knolls. The city also is a major producer of electric and diesel locomotives, and has several smaller industries.

PHILADELPHIA METROPOLITAN AREA

Unlike Pittsburgh, which is predominantly a steel city, or Detroit, which is automotive and metropolitan, Philadelphia has a great diversity of manufactures. Industrial establishments are clustered along the Delaware River in adjoining Bucks and Delaware Counties and have crossed the river into Camden, Burlington, and Gloucester Counties in New Jersey (*Fig. 10-31*).

Textiles. Textile mills of all classes flourish in the Philadelphia area. They include such major genera or subdivisions as scouring and combing plants that clean and prepare fibers for processing, yarn and thread mills that do the spinning, weaving mills that make only broad fabrics, and other mills that specialize in ribbon, braid, and related narrow fabrics. Other divisions are: dyeing and finishing mills, knitting mills, hat factories, and carpet and rug mills.

Metals—iron and steel. The heavy industries are assuming an ever-increasing prominence in the Philadelphia metropolitan area. The basic members of this large family group are the primary metal industries—the steelworks and rolling mills, the iron and steel foundries, and the smelters and refiners of copper, brass, and other nonferrous metals.

FIGURE 10-30. *Albany, the capital of New York, spreads along the west bank of the Hudson River. (New York State Dept. of Commerce)*

The Delaware Valley is becoming a new center of the steel industry because: (1) the high-grade (50 per cent plus) iron ore of the great Mesabi Range in Minnesota is running out; and (2) to replace Mesabi ore, the steel companies are importing ore from South America and Canada, especially the Venezuela and Labrador-Quebec deposits; this ore can be brought to the mills most economically by water transportation. The location of an integrated mill on the riverside, such as the Fairless plant at Morrisville, Pennsylvania, affords advantages peculiar to the steelmaking process. The manufacture of one ton of steel requires four tons of raw materials—two tons of ore, one ton of coke, a half-ton of limestone, and about a half-ton of ferroalloys. In other words, roughly four pounds of raw material must be assembled and processed to make a pound of steel worth an average of about four cents. It is obviously advantageous for a steel mill to be located on a navigable waterway where the raw materials can be brought to the furnace in bulk by low cost water transportation. Few other industries are as dependent upon navigable waterways as those of iron and steel.

FIGURE 10-31. *Philadelphia, Pennsylvania, the second largest city of megalopolis, dominates the populous, wealthy, and productive Delaware Valley and lands to its east and west.*

Other important steel-using industries include locomotive construction at Chester, Pennsylvania, and railroad cars at Wilmington, Delaware. Newark, Delaware, is the site of a Chrysler automotive assembly plant.

BALTIMORE—WASHINGTON

The port of Baltimore is situated on a northern estuary of Chesapeake Bay, the Patapsco River, and other streams. This port is 150 miles from the Atlantic Ocean via the Virginia capes. However, approximately 20 per cent of the deep draft ships putting in at Baltimore come through the Chesapeake and Delaware Canal. This route shortens the distance to the ocean by 25 miles. It is also a link in the Atlantic Intracoastal Waterway that extends from Boston to Miami. All main ship channels leading into the harbor are capable of handling deep draft ships, the

depth varying from 35 to 39 feet at low tide. Its inland location gives Baltimore the distinctive advantage of being the Atlantic port nearest the industrial center of the nation. Its hinterland, therefore, includes the Middle West, a large part of the Central Freight Association territory (that area east of the Mississippi River, north of the Ohio River, west of the Alleghenies, and south of the Great Lakes), and the Great Lakes region, as well as nearby territory. Connections are afforded by four railways: the Baltimore and Ohio, the Pennsylvania, the Western Maryland, and the Maryland and Pennsylvania. The advantageous location of Baltimore in relation to water, rail, and trucking transport has aided its development into a diversified center of production and trade.

Iron and steel. Iron was one of Baltimore's early products. At first the ore was obtained within the state, but as the supply dwindled and transportation facilities developed, ores were brought into the state for smelting. In the source of this development, the first modern steel plant was built at Sparrows Point in 1889. Today this plant of Bethlehem Steel is one of the largest tidewater steel mills in the world.

For many years mills at Sparrows Point have been fed imported ore brought to Baltimore at lower freight rates than were charged for transportation of domestic ore. For some time Bethlehem Steel has imported iron ore from Chile and Venezuela.

Other industries. Baltimore has a score of industrial giants, some of which are the largest of their kind in the world, with others rating high in their respective fields. It is a leading producer of tin cans, bottle caps, spices, copper, stainless steel, bichromate, electric tools, high tension insulators, copper sulphate, paint brushes, weather instruments, and Christmas tree ornaments. Sugar refining and commercial fertilizer production are also important. Baltimore's ship-repairing activity is extensive. Her shipping trade is legendary, as befits a maritime city that began its early life as the haven of the privateering fleet of the new nation. Later the Baltimore-built clipper ship was the outstanding vessel in international trade.

Washington. The 69-square-mile area of Washington, D.C., the nation's capital, is a world political and cultural center (*Fig. 10-32*). Government dominates the economy. The city is facing increasing pressures in the areas of urban renewal, suburbanization and its attendant problems on city fiscal structure, and transportation difficulties.

Outlook

The growth of manufacturing has given rise to many industrial centers, making the Middle Atlantic Coastal Plain the most densely populated region of the United States. The big cities offer many advantages, among them being a wide choice of jobs, varied educa-

tional opportunities, many forms of entertainment, and a wide selection of manufactured goods and services. Great industrial concentrations, they are also centers of finance and commerce. Geographic location and markets will continue to favor expansion within this region. Such expansion will make it more difficult for government to solve the region's already serious problems. Too often the large Eastern city has been planless in pattern, uncontrolled in size, crowded and congested, and lacking in contacts with nature. The absence of planning has produced dirt and ugliness.

Only through large-scale planning, such as that now being sponsored by the Twentieth Century Fund to analyze urban problems from Washington, D.C., to Boston, can more people be absorbed into the urban landscape and still enjoy a reasonable living pattern. This calls for wholesale slum clearance, smoke control, zoning restrictions, and green belts on a scale unprecedented in America.

Industrial expansion in the South Atlantic-Gulf Coastal Plain and Piedmont has given rise to large population gains since 1960. A variety of new materials, ample power resources, and low-cost labor provide a good base for textile manufacturing, for iron and steel, for pulp and

FIGURE 10-32. *The Washington Monument towers above government buildings in Washington, D.C., a city of great beauty and charm and a mecca for tourists. (The Washington* Post)

paper, for chemical industries, for aluminum refining, for meat packing, for the canning and freezing of foods, and for many other industries.

The Old South no longer exists. Monoculture is a thing of the past. Diversification is the key to agriculture, mining, forestry, and manufacturing. Mechanization has revolutionized the farm. Better seeds, more fertilizer, higher yields per acre, and scientific breeding of livestock are but a few of the many innovations in the South. Large urban centers are taking over the countryside in many places. These changes are healthy signs of prosperity, of a region on the move.

Selected References

AHNERT, FRANK, "Estuarine Meanders in the Chesapeake Bay Area," *The Geographical Review*, Vol. 50, July, 1960, pp. 390–401.

BROWN, RALPH H., *Mirror For Americans*, New York: The American Geographical Society, 1943.

BRUSH, JOHN E., "The Hierarchy of Central Places in Southwestern Wisconsin," *The Geographical Review*, Vol. 43, July, 1953, pp. 380–402.

———, *The Population of New Jersey*, New Brunswick, N. J.: Rutgers University Press, 1956.

BURTON, IAN, and KATES, ROBERT W., "The Floodplain and the Seashore, a Comparative Analysis of Hazard-Zone Occupance," *The Geographical Review*, Vol. 44, July, 1964, pp. 366–385.

CROSS, CLARK I., "The Parramore Island Mounds of Virginia," *The Geographical Review*, Vol. 44, October, 1964, pp. 502–515.

DOLAN, ROBERT, "Beach Changes on the Outer Banks of North Carolina," *Annals of the Association of American Geographers*, Vol. 56, December, 1966, pp. 699–711.

DORAN, EDWIN, "Shell Roads in Texas," *The Geographical Review*, Vol. 45, April, 1965, pp. 223–240.

DUNBAR, GARY S., "Thermal Belts in North Carolina," *The Geographical Review*, Vol. 46, October, 1966, pp. 516–526.

DURAND, LOYAL, JR., "The Historical and Economic Geography of Dairying in the North Country of New York State," *The Geographical Review*, Vol. 47, January, 1967, pp. 24–47.

FORD, ROBERT N., *The Everglades Agricultural Area* ("University of Chicago Research Paper No. 42"), Chicago: University of Chicago, 1956.

HANCE, WILLIAM A., and VAN DONGEN, IRENE S., "General Cargo Hinterlands of New York, Philadelphia, Baltimore, and New Orleans," *Annals of the Association of American Geographers*, Vol. 48, December, 1958, pp. 436–455.

HART, JOHN FRASER, *The Southeastern United States*, Princeton, N. J.: Van Nostrand Co., Inc., 1967.

HOYT, HOMER, *An Economic Survey of New Jersey*, Trenton, N. J.: State of New Jersey, 1950.

ISAAC, ERICH, "Jamestown and the Mid-Atlantic Coast: A Geographic Reconsideration," *The Journal of Geography*, Vol. 57, January, 1958, pp. 17–29.

LEMON, JAMES T., "The Agricultural Practices of National Groups in Eighteenth-century Southeastern Pennsylvania," *The Geographical Review*, Vol. 46, October, 1966, pp. 467–496.

LONSDALE, RICHARD E., "Two North Carolina Commuting Patterns," *Economic Geography*, Vol. 42, April, 1966, pp. 114-138.

NELSON, J. G., "Some Effects of Glaciation on the Susquehanna River Valley," *Annals of the Association of American Geographers*, Vol. 55, September, 1965, pp. 404–448.

PADGETT, HERBERT R., "Some Physical and Biological Relationships to the Fisheries of the Louisiana Coast," *Annals of the Association of American Geographers*, Vol. 56, September, 1966, pp. 423–439.

———, "The Sea Fisheries of the Southern United States: Retrospect and Prospect," *The Geographical Review*, Vol. 53, January, 1963, pp. 22–39.

PRUNTY, MERLE, "The Woodland Plantation as a Contemporary Occupance Type in the South," *The Geographical Review*, Vol. 53, January, 1963, pp. 1–21.

RESEN, F. LAWRENCE, "The Gulf Coast Today: Its Billion Dollar Petro-Chemical Industry," *The Oil and Gas Journal*, Vol. 51, No. 6, 1952, pp. 190–192.

SHARER, CYRUS J., "The Philadelphia Iron and Steel District," *Economic Geography*, Vol. 39, October, 1963, pp. 363–367.

VANCE, RUPERT B., and DEMERATH, NICHOLAS J. (eds.), *The Urban South*, Chapel Hill, N. C.: University of North Carolina Press, 1954.

11 Appalachian-Ozark Region

The Appalachian-Ozark Region includes several subregions: (1) the Blue Ridge, (2) the Ridge and Valley, (3) the Appalachian Plateau, (4) the Interior Low Plateau, and (5) the Ozark-Ouachita Highlands (*Fig. 11-1*).

The great diversity of topography in these subregions is due to a variety of factors. Chief among these are: (1) structural differences, (2) differences in lithology, (3) varying diastrophic histories and associated differential uplift, (4) unequal distances from the sea, related to whether the drainage was to the Atlantic Ocean or the Gulf of Mexico, (5) different degrees of baseleveling, and (6) varying states of preservation of old erosional surfaces. (*Fig. 11-2*).

Surface Features

BLUE RIDGE

The Blue Ridge is the first mountain range inland from the Atlantic Coast. It extends from southern Pennsylvania to northern Georgia. Most of it lies in western North Carolina but parts of it spread into Pennsylvania, Maryland, Virginia, Tennessee, Georgia, and South Carolina. North of Roanoke Gap the subregion averages 10 to 15 miles in width. Its greatest width, 70 miles, is at the south end. There the name Blue Ridge applies only to the first ridge seen from the Piedmont section. This is also the divide that limits the Ohio drainage basin.

North of the Roanoke River, this subregion (called Blue Ridge in Virginia and South Mountain in Maryland and Pennsylvania), consists of generally rounded mountains of gentle slope and fairly even skyline when seen from a distance. Several parallel ridges separate steep valleys in the southern portion. These ridges flatten out toward the north to form a long, sweeping curve across Pennsylvania in a southwest-northeast direction. The ridges stand from 1,500 to 3,000 feet above sea level, with the top an old imperfect peneplain, older, of course, than the lower adjacent peneplains.

South of the Roanoke River, the older peneplains become less perfect and monadnocks on them are more abundant. In western North Carolina, peneplanation was barely begun along the large streams. This part of the subregion consists mainly of subdued mountains rising 1,000 to 3,000 feet above the peneplain, or 3,000 to 6,000 feet above the sea. Twenty to 25 peaks rise above 5,000 feet; eight, above 6,000 feet. Mount Mitchell (6,684 feet) is the highest point in the eastern United States.

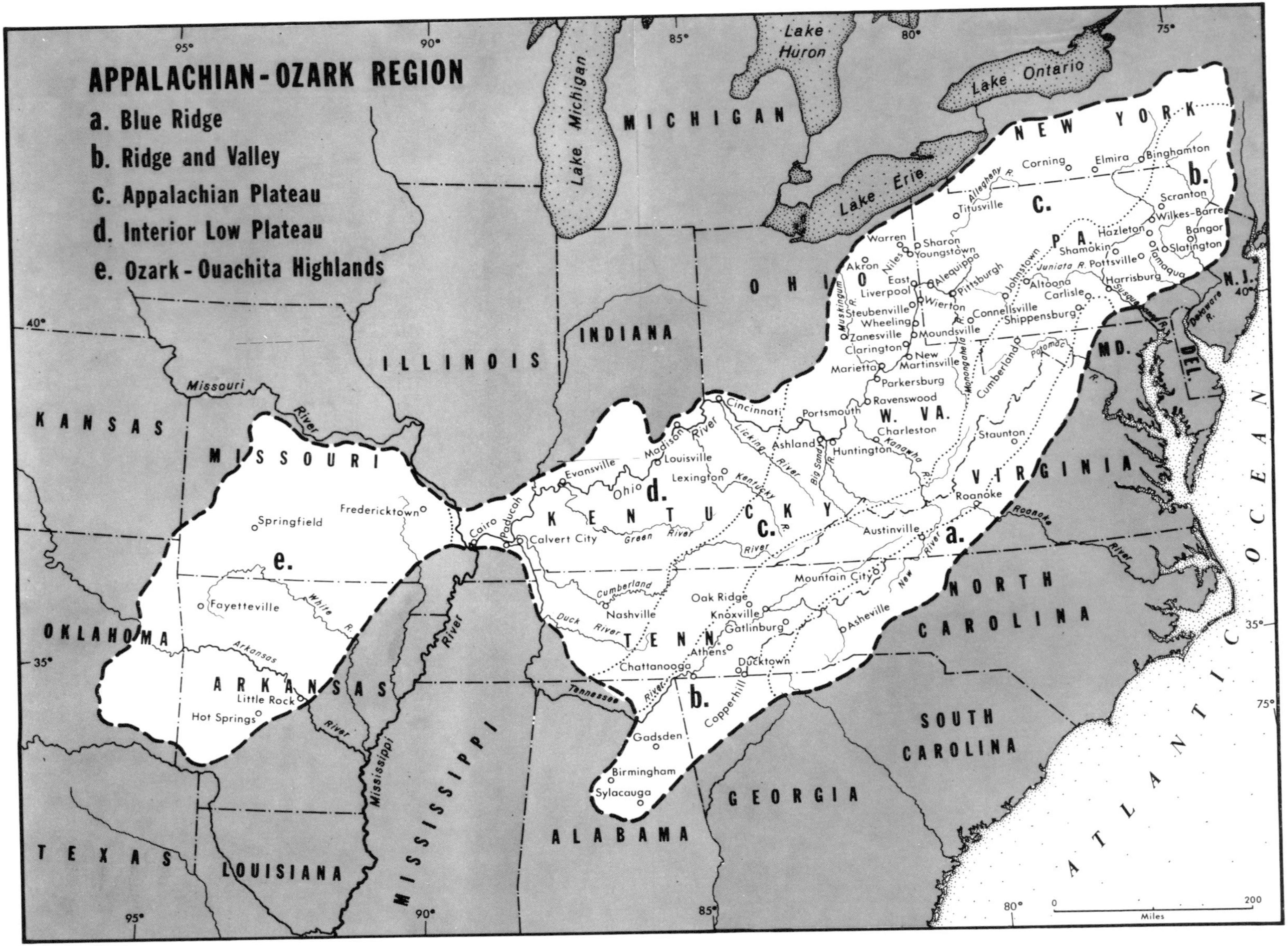
APPALACHIAN - OZARK REGION
a. Blue Ridge
b. Ridge and Valley
c. Appalachian Plateau
d. Interior Low Plateau
e. Ozark - Ouachita Highlands
MICHIGAN
Lake Michigan
Lake Huron
Lake Erie
Lake Ontario
NEW YORK
PA.
OHIO
INDIANA
ILLINOIS
KANSAS
MISSOURI
OKLAHOMA
ARKANSAS
TEXAS
LOUISIANA
MISSISSIPPI
ALABAMA
GEORGIA
TENN.
KENTUCKY
W. VA.
VIRGINIA
MD.
DEL.
N.J.
NORTH CAROLINA
SOUTH CAROLINA
ATLANTIC OCEAN
Miles
0
200
Springfield
Fredericktown
Fayetteville
Little Rock
Hot Springs
Cairo
Paducah
Calvert City
Evansville
Louisville
Lexington
Cincinnati
Portsmouth
Ashland
Huntington
Charleston
Nashville
Chattanooga
Knoxville
Oak Ridge
Gatlinburg
Athens
Ducktown
Copperhill
Gadsden
Birmingham
Sylacauga
Asheville
Mountain City
Austinville
Roanoke
Staunton
Parkersburg
Ravenswood
Marietta
Clarington
New Martinsville
Moundsville
Wheeling
Steubenville
Zanesville
East Liverpool
Wierton
Akron
Warren
Niles
Sharon
Youngstown
Aliquippa
Pittsburgh
Connellsville
Johnstown
Altoona
Titusville
Corning
Elmira
Binghamton
Scranton
Wilkes-Barre
Hazleton
Shamokin
Pottsville
Tamaqua
Bangor
Slatington
Harrisburg
Carlisle
Shippensburg
Missouri River
White R.
Arkansas
Mississippi River
Tennessee River
Duck River
Cumberland River
Green River
Ohio
Madison River
Licking River
Kentucky R.
Big Sandy R.
Kanawha R.
Muskingum R.
Monongahela R.
Allegheny R.
Juniata R.
Susquehanna R.
Potomac R.
Cumberland
Delaware R.
New River
Roanoke River
95°
90°
85°
80°
75°
40°
35°

FIGURE 11-1.

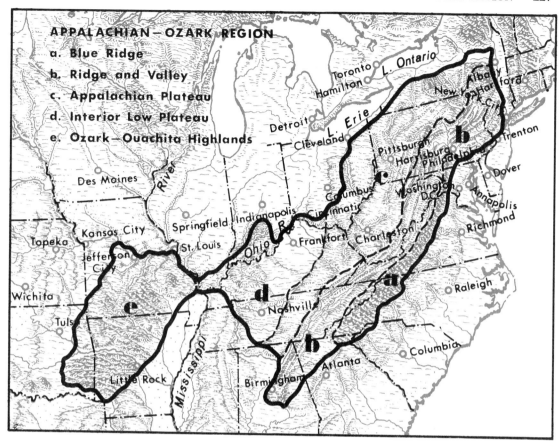

APPALACHIAN — OZARK REGION

a. Blue Ridge
b. Ridge and Valley
c. Appalachian Plateau
d. Interior Low Plateau
e. Ozark—Ouachita Highlands

FIGURE 11-2. *The Appalachian-Ozark Region, physical relief.*

Main streams run northwest from the Blue Ridge in deep valleys separating mountains into groups bearing local names (Bald, Smoky, Unaka, Iron, etc.). Near their heads these streams run in flat-bottomed valleys one to four miles wide, the mere beginnings of the older peneplain, now raised 2,000 to 3,000 feet above the sea. The rejuvenated streams (those that have had their rate of fall increased) have cut so deeply in their lower courses as to destroy the old, flat bottoms (*see Fig. 1-7*).

RIDGE AND VALLEY

Running for nearly 900 miles from the Mohawk Lowland in the north to around Birmingham, Alabama, is one of the most persistent and most striking relief features of Anglo-America. It is the Great Valley, which lies to the west of the older rocks of the Blue Ridge Mountains. The geologist and the physiographer maintain that the Champlain and Hudson Lowlands are a part of this Appalachian Valley, but the geographer shows that man cannot use these two parts of the valley in the same way.

The Great Valley itself is the easternmost of a whole succession of valleys separated by long, narrow sandstone ridges; hence, "Ridge and Valley" is used as a descriptive name for the whole. The valley or valleys are usually excavated along outcrops of limestone or various "weak" strata, contrasted with the sandstones of the ridges. Though the main valley is a continuous feature, it is occupied in different parts by many different rivers—by part of the Hudson in the north, then by various tributaries of the Delaware, Susquehanna, Potomac, and Tennessee Rivers. It has different local names (*Fig. 11-3*).

APPALACHIAN PLATEAU

In general, the Appalachian Plateau is a partly or wholly dissected plateau with a northwesterly slope. On its southeast, or higher side, the area is limited almost throughout by an escarpment called the Allegheny Front in Pennsylvania and West Virginia, and the Cumberland Front in Tennessee. It also is limited by an escarpment on the west side in Kentucky and Tennessee and on the north in New York, Pennsylvania, and Ohio.

The several parts of this subregion differ in elevation, in degree of dissection, and in their underlying rocks. A part also was glaciated. Two sections on the high and deeply dissected eastern margin are always called mountains—the Allegheny Mountains and the Cumberland Mountains. The strata are somewhat folded, even making ridges within the plateau districts. Most of western Pennsylvania, West Virginia, eastern Ohio, and eastern Kentucky are maturely dissected. The highest elevations are in the central part of West Virginia, where much of the land lies between 1,500 and 3,000 feet; the maximum elevations exceed 4,000 feet (*Fig. 11-4*). Local relief may be 500 to 1,000 feet on the east and south but diminishes toward the west and north. The escarpment on the north, 500 to 1,000 feet high, overlooks the Mohawk Valley, which is a strike valley not as low and smooth as the Hudson Valley or the plain south of Lake Ontario. This escarpment extends west to northeastern Ohio, overlooking the Central Plains. At the south end is the Cumberland Plateau, in which large areas of nearly flat upland remain between young valleys—except at the southern extremity.

INTERIOR LOW PLATEAU

The Interior Low Plateau subregion is a west-sloping plateau 1,500 feet high and young on the east side, 500 feet high and mature on the west. It is separated from the higher Appalachian Plateau by an eroded escarpment nearly 1,000 feet high in northern Tennessee but lower at both ends. Where it borders the

FIGURE 11-3. *The rich farm lands of the Shenandoah Valley of Virginia resemble a giant crazy quilt.* (*Virginia Dept. of Conservation and Economic Development*)

Coastal Plain, the latter is lower and has less relief. It extends north to the Interior Lowlands, which are smoother though no lower than this subregion.

The rocks are nearly horizontal and in large part older than those of the Appalachian Plateau, which once extended farther west and is being narrowed by erosion. The strata underlying the area are bulged slightly upward. When these low domes were baseleveled, lower strata were exposed. After uplift, these lower areas, being of soluble limestone, eroded faster.

The Bluegrass section consists of two separate areas, one in Kentucky, centering on Lexington, and the other in west-central Tennessee. Their outstanding feature is the soils of high phosphate content, which largely account for the abundant growth of bluegrass and other pasture plants that are considered characteristic of this general subregion. (*Fig. 11-5*).

The Tennessee portion of the subregion,

referred to as the Nashville Basin, is mostly level; its average elevation is about 600 feet. It is surrounded by the Highland Rim, which is several hundred feet higher in elevation. Outliers and ridges of the Highland Rim are numerous at the border of the basin. Major drainage systems are the Cumberland River, which empties into the Ohio, and the Duck River, which empties into the Tennessee.

The Kentucky part of the subregion has elevations up to 1,000 feet. A belt of rough land of higher elevation, called the Knobs, encircles the subregion in Kentucky except in the north, where the Ohio River is the boundary. The major drainage systems are the Kentucky and Licking Rivers, which empty into the Ohio. Stream dissection is deep along the Ohio and Kentucky Rivers. The elevation of the Ohio River in northeastern Kentucky is below 500 feet. Much upland adjacent to the streams, particularly in the northern section, is unsuited for cultivation. The land in the central portion (inner Bluegrass) generally is smooth.

The Pennyroyal section in southern and southwestern Kentucky is undulating to rolling. Near streams and areas of underground drainage it is hilly or karsted. Mammoth Cave Park, noted for its subterranean chambers formed by dissolution of limestone, is in the area. The limestone section of the western Pennyroyal is mostly undulating, but some small parts are rolling or even hilly. Subsurface drainage has created limestone sinks and karst terrain in much of the area. The eastern Pennyroyal is an upland, higher than the rest of the subregion, and has a great variation of relief. Most of the terrain is rolling; some is undulating. In places it is hilly or karsted and, near streams, may be rough or precipitous. There are wide bottoms along the Cumberland River.

OZARK-OUACHITA HIGHLANDS

The Ozark-Ouachita Highlands, with a total area of more than 50,000 square miles, lie mainly in southern Missouri and northern Arkansas, but extend westward to include

FIGURE 11-4. *A hill farming section in Pendleton County, West Virginia. In the background is Spruce Knob (4,860 feet), the highest point in West Virginia. (West Virginia Dept. of Commerce)*

FIGURE 11-5. *Lush pastures and thoroughbred horses have become symbolic of the Bluegrass district of Kentucky. (Kentucky Travel Division)*

parts of eastern Oklahoma and the extreme southeastern tip of Kansas.

These highlands, located only a few hundred miles southeast of the center of the conterminous United States, are the most centrally situated upland of the country. They rise gradually (except for a short distance at the south end) from the Interior Lowlands on the west and north, and abruptly from the Gulf Coastal Plain on the east. Because of their greater relief, poorer soils, and forest vegetation, the Ozark-Ouachita Highlands have a culture and economy which differ considerably from that of the surrounding lowlands.

From north to south the subregion naturally divides into: (1) the Ozark Plateaus, including the Salem and Springfield Plateaus; (2) the Boston Mountains, separated from the Ozarks by the White River; (3) the Arkansas River Valley; and (4) the Ouachita Highlands (the Arbuckle and Wichita Mountains in south-central and southwestern Oklahoma are western outliers of the Ouachitas).

The Ozark district is a dissected plateau developed upon domed rocks, which are, for the most part, highly resistant to erosion. According to Sauer, " It (the district) has been uplifted very unevenly, and being composed of different rocks situated at exceedingly varying distances from vigorous drainage lines, its various portions have been modified in different ways and to different degrees by erosion."[1]

[1] Carl O. Sauer, *The Geography of the Ozark Highlands of Missouri*, Bulletin 7, Chicago Geographical Society (1920), p. 7.

The western part of the Missouri Ozarks, although highest on the whole, is most remote from the major drainage lines. Therefore, it has been eroded only slightly, whereas most of the eastern region is maturely dissected. Nearly flat remnants range in height from less than 1,000 feet at the edges to 1,700 feet near the center. In the northeastern part of the plateau, granitic rocks are exposed in some places. In this area of crystalline outcrops, known as the St. Francis (François) Mountains, the topography is especially rough and rugged. (*Fig. 11-6*).

The Boston Mountains, 200 miles long and 35 miles wide, have been sculptured into truly mountainous forms by the Arkansas River and White River systems. Elevations as high as 2,300 feet occur in this section, with an average crestline of about 1,800 feet. The district presents a bold, rugged, forested escarpment to the north and a general slope to the south.

The Arkansas Valley, located between the Boston and Ouachita Mountains, varies in width from 30 to 40 miles and extends in an east-west direction, providing easy access through the Highlands. It is a gently undulating plain, most of which lies between 300 and 600 feet above sea level.

South of the Arkansas Valley, the Ouachita Highlands consist of numerous ridges and narrow valleys that, in general, lie in an east-west direction. They were made by close folding, like the Appalachians, and at the same time. In the central part of Arkansas, near the city of Little Rock, the ridges are not well defined and have elevations of about 500 to 700

FIGURE 11-6. *Cross-section of the Ozark-Ouachita Highlands.*

feet above sea level. They increase in altitude to the west, and mountains of more than 2,000 feet above sea level are common. Much of the land is too rugged for farming; a large part of this area is in the Ouachita National Forest.

Climate

Considerable climatic contrasts occur within the region because of the latitudinal distance from north to south (ten degrees) and the range in elevation to over 6,000 feet. The predominant climates are humid continental long summer and humid subtropical (*see Fig. 1-16*).

BLUE RIDGE—RIDGE AND VALLEY

From Maryland through Pennsylvania into central New York State, these subregions are not rugged enough to have anything like a true mountain type of climate, but they do have many of the characteristics of such a climate in modified form. The mountain and valley influences on the air movements cause somewhat greater temperature extremes than are experienced on the Coastal Plain, and the daily range of temperature increases somewhat under the valley influences. The growing season varies from 130 days in the mountains to an average of 165 days in the valleys. The average annual precipitation for the subregions is 40.74 inches. The seasonal snowfall is moderately heavy (about 54 inches) and fields are normally snow-covered about three-fourths of the time during the winter season.

The mean temperature of the northern section decreases about six degrees from south to north. In the northern highlands the summer mean is about 67° F. and the winter mean about 24°. Temperatures of 100° or higher occur in the southern counties of Pennsylvania, for example, nearly every summer season; midwinter temperatures of 20° to 25° below zero are occasionally recorded in the northern highlands.

From northern Virginia southward the principal climatic characteristics are: (1) rigorous but not severe winters; (2) warm summers, except at the higher elevations in the Blue Ridge and Great Smoky Mountains; (3) a rather heavy annual snowfall in the western part of the section; (4) usually ample precipitation; and (5) abundant sunshine. Dry or wet spells of long duration are infrequent. The average seasonal snowfall ranges from about 15 inches in middle Virginia to about 24 inches in the Shenandoah Valley of northern Virginia and 3.3 inches in the Tennessee Valley (*Fig. 11-7*).

APPALACHIAN PLATEAU— INTERIOR LOW PLATEAU

The northern Alabama and Tennessee portions of these subregions are not in the path of any of the principal storm tracts that cross the country; instead they come under the influence of the storm centers that pass along the Gulf and then up the Atlantic Coast, and also of those that pass from Oklahoma northeastward to the Great Lakes and then to the coast of Maine. Weather changes are therefore frequent compared with the remarkably stable conditions of the far Southwest, but not nearly as frequent as in the Lakes Region and the Northeastern States.

Very changeable temperature conditions prevail in winter. Zero temperatures occur, on the average, about once a year over the lowlands in Tennessee, but they are comparatively frequent in the mountains. Occasionally the temperature falls considerably below zero. Maximum temperatures exceeding 100° F. are very rare. In the highlands, the conditions of heat and humidity are modified somewhat, the nights being cooler and the air movement greater.

Kentucky's climate, generally, is temperate. Sunlight, heat, moisture, and winds are all in moderation, without prolonged extremes. Rainfall is abundant and fairly regular throughout the year, usually as short showers. Heavy snowfalls are rare. The seasons differ markedly, yet warm to cool weather prevails, with extremes of heat and cold occurring only in short spells.

Topographic characteristics considerably

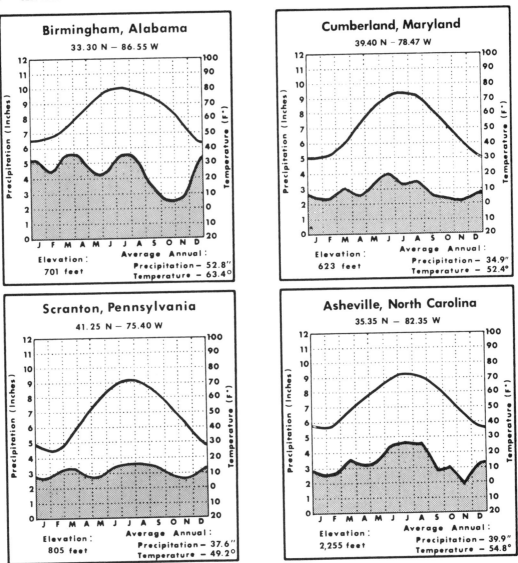

FIGURE 11-7. *Climatic graphs of the Blue Ridge and the Ridge and Valley subregions.*

modify the latitudinal control of the climate of West Virginia, with the result that marked variations in temperature and precipitation occur between different parts of the same counties. The seasons are nearly of equal length, and strongly contrasted. In most sections of the state, the winters are moderate to rigorous, and severe only occasionally, except in the mountains. Cold waves occur on an average of three times during the winter, but severe cold spells, as a rule, last only two or three days.

The northern portion of these subregions—

southern and eastern Ohio, western Pennsylvania, and southern New York—has adequate precipitation and marked seasonality.

Because hilly topography permits uneven heating of land surfaces and allows colder air to settle to lower points, local differences in climatic conditions are more apparent than differences on an area-wide basis. Although the northern third of these subregions is slightly cooler and drier than other portions, the differences involve a temperature range of some six degrees and a six-inch precipitation variation.

The annual temperature range is marked but not excessive. The average January temperature for the area is 29.3° F.; the July average is 72.6°. Extremes of −28° and 109° have been recorded, but average annual extremes range from −10° to about 90°.

The growing season lasts from 130 to 140 days in the states of New York and Pennsylvania, 140 to 150 days in Ohio, 130 to 180 days in West Virginia, and 180 to 190 days in Kentucky and Tennessee.

The total precipitation varies from 38 to 40 inches in New York, Pennsylvania, Ohio, and the northern sections of West Virginia, to 50 or 55 inches in Tennessee. Summer maximum is the rule, but the rain is not well distributed. Evapo-transpiration is high, and drought periods in some sections—Kentucky, for example —are frequent. Snow blankets much of the northern portion of these subregions during the months of December, January, and February (*Fig. 11-8*).

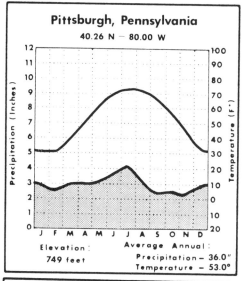

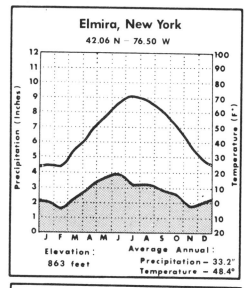

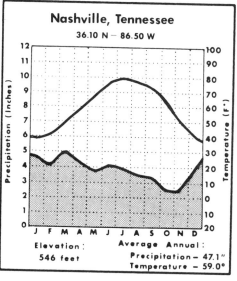

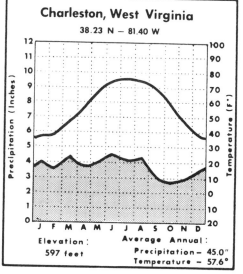

FIGURE 11-8. *Climatic graphs of the Appalachian Plateau and the Interior Low Plateau subregions.*

OZARK-OUACHITA HIGHLANDS

In general, the Ozark-Ouachita Highlands' climate is controlled by two air masses: (1) the dry, cold, continental air that moves from the west and northwest to the east across the northern part of the highlands; and (2) the warm, moist air that comes in from the Gulf, affecting mainly the southern part. Since the highlands stand out from the lower surrounding plains, they are subject to the prevailing winds. There is no nearby mountain range to act as a barrier against the fronts (*Fig. 11-9*).

Natural Vegetation

BLUE RIDGE—RIDGE AND VALLEY

Forests of spruce, fir, and northern and central hardwoods, characterize these subregions, with hardwoods predominating. The principal species are oak, maple, pine, gum, beech, and poplar.

Each year the forests provide the raw material for pulp and paper, lumber, railroad ties, veneer, firewood, furniture, excelsior, piling, and many other products.

APPALACHIAN PLATEAU— INTERIOR LOW PLATEAU

Forests mantle the hills of the Appalachian Plateau and the Interior Low Plateau subregions. Red, black, and white spruce; balsam fir; white, red, jack, and pitch pine; Eastern hemlock; maple; oak; beech; birch; and aspen predominate on the Allegheny Plateau in New York and Pennsylvania and in the uplands of central West Virginia. Eastern Ohio, the extreme western portion of Pennsylvania, the western half of West Virginia, and most of Tennessee lie within the Central Hardwood Forest. Several species characterize the area. In the northern portion, oak, hickory, ash, elm, maple, beech, black walnut, pine, and cottonwood occur; the southern portion contains red and black gums, Eastern red cedar, and yellow poplar, in addition to such trees as oak, hickory, ash, black walnut, and beech.

Private ownership is divided almost equally between individual farmers and industrial concerns, utilities, and other organizations. No commercial forest stand of consequence is in virgin condition, and most stands are in need of better management, especially modern conservation methods. All forest land in the two subregions can grow merchantable timber.

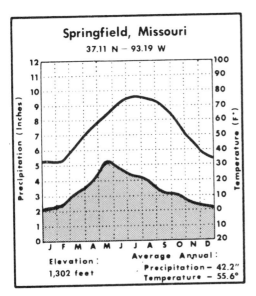

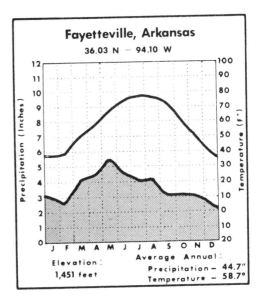

FIGURE 11-9. *Climatic graphs of the Ozark-Ouachita Highlands subregion.*

OZARK-OUACHITA HIGHLANDS

Still retaining a primeval quality, the Ozark-Ouachita Highlands are thickly wooded. Their vegetation is more nearly akin to the oak-hickory forests of the Eastern and Central states *(Fig. 11-10)*. Varying conditions of soil and exposure account for many differences among the species covering the slopes. The only pine native to the area, the loblolly or short-leaf, is not nearly as frequent in the Ozarks as in the Ouachitas and on the flats farther south.

Forests cover almost two-thirds of Arkansas. The state leads the nation in the production of red gum, oak, and hickory lumber. Yellow pine is an important source of pulpwood.

Federal interest in the conservation of the region's timber was first demonstrated in 1907, when President Theodore Roosevelt defined the boundaries of the Arkansas National Forest, later renamed the Ouachita. Since 1907, the original tract has been greatly expanded until it now includes more than 1.3 million acres extending into Oklahoma from about 20 miles west of Little Rock. The Ozark National Forest, 300,000 acres in Oklahoma and west Arkansas, was created in 1908.

FIGURE 11-10. *A virgin stand of hardwoods in the Ozark National Forest in Arkansas. (U.S. Forest Service)*

Soils

Soils vary greatly within the region, depending upon local conditions. Some are relatively shallow, acid, and low in natural fertility. Over large portions of the area, the bedrock is mostly sandstone and shale, with limestone occurring occasionally *(Fig. 11-11)*.

Reddish-colored soils occupy the broad till-mantled hills of the Allegheny Plateau in New York State where glacial action has mixed red and gray shale and sandstone. The dominant soils are strongly acid and low in fertility.

Soils in the unglaciated parts are fairly good where topographically favored, such as in the smoother parts of the Ohio Valley, but beds that cap the plateau, being mainly siliceous, generally are not good soil makers.

FIGURE 11-11. *Erosion of silt loam soil in Benton County, Tennessee. (U.S. Dept. of Agriculture)*

The inner Bluegrass district of Kentucky contains some of the most fertile soils in the region. Limestones, many of which are phosphatic, represent the dominant rock formations. Shales occur also, often interbedded with limestone. Surface soils are brown silt loams, and subsoils are reddish-brown silty clays of good structure and drainage. A thin deposit of glacial till occurs in the extreme northern portion in Kentucky. There is evidence of shallow loess in places near the Ohio River.

Soil series low in phosphate are found in the central part of the Nashville Basin. Similar soils are present in Kentucky, where they have more random distribution.

The soils of eastern Ohio generally are rather thin, but respond well to fertilization and care. Soils of the valley bottoms are usually more limited in extent. Silty loams derived primarily from shaly rock are characteristic of the area. They are deficient in organic matter and lime content, and require moderate to heavy fertilization.

The soils in the Ozark Plateaus were formed largely by the weathering of limestone and dolomite. In this process, the calcium and magnesium carbonates were leached out and residual materials were left to form soil with a high chert content, particularly on steep slopes. Chert interferes with tillage and mowing and reduces the water-holding capacity of the soils so that crops suffer sooner from lack of moisture. On the other hand, the cherty fragments on the surface protect the soils against the beating effect of raindrops and slow down the movement of water over the surface.

In the Ouachita Highlands, the soils derived chiefly from the weathering of sandstone soils are relatively unproductive because of their course texture and deficiency of plant food. The residue from the shales and slates consists of fine clay particles that form heavy soils with poor drainage characteristics.

The alluvial soils in the flood plains of the Arkansas and White Rivers are the most fertile. Clearing the land of timber and providing adequate drainage and protection from peri-odic overflow have been the principal problems in utilizing these lands for farming purposes.

Settlement

APPALACHIANS—INTERIOR LOW PLATEAU

Topography conditioned travel and settlement in early America. By 1700, settlement had reached the fall line in most parts of the English colonies. In those colonies south of New York, the settlers above the falls were already well on their way inland.

There were essentially three focusing points for the routes through the Appalachian barrier: the Forks of the Ohio, the Cumberland Gap, and the Valley of East Tennessee. Pennsylvania, Virginia, and Carolina trappers first made their way into the Ohio Valley about 1701; they followed the Roanoke River in Virginia to the New River Gorge and then moved along the Kanawha River to the Ohio. Later, other settlers followed the Juniata River westward across Pennsylvania to its headwaters at Fort Bedford and to the Loyalhanna, which flows westward to the Conemaugh River. They followed the Conemaugh to the Allegheny to the Ohio. Still later, a more direct route was taken from Harrisburg to Carlisle to Shippensburg to Fort Bedford at the upper end of the Juniata River. From there, settlers traversed the same route as before to the Allegheny River; this latter route became known as Forbes Military Road.

In taking up new land in the Appalachian subregions, the qualities of the soil for agriculture played a dominant role; settlers also considered the possibilities of grazing, the wealth of nearby forests, and the availability of a good supply of water. Coal and iron ore were discovered in various areas within the region by 1750. These were industries allied to agriculture.

In 1775, Daniel Boone crossed the Cumberland Gap. Westward movement was then under way. The Kentucky Bluegrass area was settled by Maryland and Virginia settlers; the Nashville Basin, by people from North Carolina. Statehood came rapidly. Kentucky was admitted to the Union in 1792; Tennessee, in 1796; and Ohio, in 1803 *(Fig. 11-12)*.

OZARK-OUACHITA HIGHLANDS

Historically, the Ozark-Ouachita subregion belonged alternately to the French, the Spanish, and the French again. The French have left their mark on names, as have the Indians. Many small streams are "bayous" (dead streams) in this subregion. Many towns bear the French suffix "ville." Some are named for French explorers. Some names, though, have been changed so that their French origin scarcely is discernible.

The first non-Indians to see the subregion were Spaniards under Hernando de Soto, who explored the area in 1541, but did not settle. More than a hundred years later (1673), two French Jesuit missionaries, Jacques Marquette and Louis Joliet, appeared. In about 1682, Robert de La Salle laid claim, in the name of the king of France, to all the country watered by the Mississippi and its tributaries.

More Frenchmen came, but few stayed. The French were not efficient colonizers. Their pioneering groups were small, their numbers were not maintained by sufficient recruits from the homeland, and few of them sought to establish homes in the New World. They came to find wealth or adventure or to Christianize the natives, and then wanted to return to their homeland.

Lead ore, salt springs, and, to some extent, furs were sought. Later the search for silver attracted settlers. Temporary visits in quest of these commodities soon led to permanent habitation. Organized mining began in 1720; the earliest land grant was recorded in 1723. Before 1763, however, there was very little population increase. Few grants of land were made, and these were designed mainly to embrace mineral riches.

The Treaty of Paris (1763) ended French colonial rule in the New World. Many of the French families left. After the Louisiana Purchase (1803), there was an influx of American settlers from the East. The early immigrants were mostly of Southern stock, a majority coming from Tennessee and Kentucky.

From 1830 to 1850, the westward migration from the Southern states received a new impetus. The decline of prices of cotton and tobacco in the South, together with the exhaustion of the soil, sent many thousands of persons—including not only the poorer small farmers, but also the more affluent planters caught by the general financial depression—northwest and southwest.

Most of those who migrated as far as Arkansas and Missouri did not settle in the highlands, but sought the lowlands farther south. The more restless frontier type, leading a seminomadic life of hunting and farming, and moving to newer lands whenever the older region became fairly well settled, was attracted to the highlands.

The plateau and hill regions of the central Ozarks were settled last, in part because of their poverty, but principally because of their isolation. Only where river valleys established connection with the outside world and furnished good land were settlements made contemporaneously with those of the Ozark borders.

FIGURE 11-12. *This cabin in the Great Smoky Mountains of Tennessee is 125 years old. (Tennessee Conservation Dept.)*

Agriculture

In general, the Appalachian-Ozark Region is one of the poorer agricultural regions in the United States. Much of the land is hilly or mountainous. A little less than half the total farm land is cropland. About a third is woodland. The average farm has about 50 acres of cropland and less than 20 acres of other land that may be used for pasture. The small average size of farms and the steep and irregular topography in many parts of the region militate against the adoption of large-scale operations.

BLUE RIDGE

Farms are small here. The average holding is about two-thirds the size of that in the rest of the region, and its cropland is about one-third as much. This is an important dairy section, with the emphasis being on grassland farming. Burley tobacco is the leading cash crop. Corn, small grains, and forage crops do well. Temperature and moisture conditions are favorable for the production of high-quality vegetables, too. For example, Mountain City, Tennessee, is a major market for green beans. Cabbage is another important crop. Some lettuce is grown in the Georgia section.

Agriculture throughout the upper Tennessee Valley is characterized by small general and part-time farms. Much of the cultivation is on a subsistence basis. A wide diversity of crops is grown, with emphasis on corn, small grains, tobacco, and hay. Irish potatoes, strawberries, cabbage, and fruits are important crops in certain counties. Dairying, poultry, and truck gardening have developed around major urban centers. Range-type livestock production occurs in some counties that are remote from markets. Forestry is a major land use in many counties, although agriculture continues to play the dominant role in determining the level of farm income.

RIDGE AND VALLEY

Agriculturally, the Ridge and Valley subregion is the impoverished part of the region.

The valleys are often so narrow as to be almost V-shaped gorges. There the farmer must wrestle with the slopes of shale hills, or at best find but a small field or two on the valley floor.

General farming, scarcely much more than subsistence farming, is the general rule—some wheat, some corn, some cattle, occasionally some hogs, with a small amount of dairying.

In some places there are fortunate exceptions to the general rule. Here limestone formations appear, the valleys widen, and the soil is rich, like small sections of the Great Valley (*Fig. 11-13*). A considerable acreage is in apple orchards in the Shenandoah Valley. "Apple Pie Ridge," an almost continuous series of apple orchards, stretches from Frederick County, Virginia, to Berkeley County, West Virginia. Westchester, Virginia, is a center of apple growing and packing. Burley tobacco is the important cash crop in the southern two-thirds of the valley, although the average allotment per farm is less than one acre.

Forage crops, notably lespedeza, clover, and alfalfa, are relatively important to the livestock economy, particularly cattle and sheep, which represent 10 per cent and 9 per cent of the totals for the region.

Several distinct cropping systems often are used on the same farm. Steep, stony, or shallow soils are planted in trees or permanent pasture and meadow. Soils on moderate slopes are used for a rotation, such as corn, small grains, and meadow. Smooth areas, including alluvial soils, are used intensively for corn or tobacco, with or without a cover crop.

APPALACHIAN PLATEAU— INTERIOR LOW PLATEAU

Agriculture, one of the oldest occupations in these subregions, began with the Indians, mainly in the northern portions. In a very limited way the early Iroquois tillers grew Indian corn, common beans, pumpkins, squash, artichokes, gourds, and tobacco. Maple sugar was produced in quantity; from the forest such products as groundnuts, leeks, and wild onions were gathered.

FIGURE 11-13. *Land used for general farming along the Susquehanna River in north-central Pennsylvania. Note the rolling hills in the background. (U.S. Dept. of Agriculture)*

The agriculture of the early settlers was equally primitive. Progress in clearing land occupied mainly by dense virgin forest was painfully slow. The frontier was pushed northward and westward only a few miles a year. It was not until after 1800 that urban markets for farm products began to develop, stimulating the expansion of agriculture as a more specialized and commercial enterprise and encouraging the use of better tools and more scientific methods.

The Erie Canal, opened in 1825, brought steadily increasing quantities of foodstuffs to Eastern markets from the new states. The development of the railroads, which shortly followed the canal's opening, meant even better transportation. By 1860, changes in the region's agriculture definitely were under way because of freight competition.

More emphasis was given to bulky and perishable foodstuffs that, because of large and growing nearby markets, could partly escape Western competition. Pork, lamb, cash grains,

and wool began to decrease in importance in relation to milk, poultry, market hay, and somewhat later—fresh fruits and vegetables.

Dairying. Dairying is the major agricultural enterprise in the plateau areas of New York, Pennsylvania, and northeastern Ohio. The investment in a typical commercial dairy farm exceeds $100,000, about half of which is in land and buildings and the balance rather evenly divided between livestock and machinery. The principal building is the barn, which houses cattle and provides storage for hay and other feeds. Adjuncts to the barn, conveniently located, are the silo and the milk house. In addition, there is likely to be a hen house, a machinery storage shed, and a building for the machine shop. Farm buildings are electrified to run such laborsaving devices as a water pump, milking machines, a milk cooler, a hot water heater, a hay hoist, and perhaps a gutter cleaner. Thirty-five to 40 head of stock are usually kept, about 25 of which are likely to be cows in milk. The farm machinery inventory includes a tractor, plows, a harrow, a grain drill, a corn planter, a fertilizer spreader, a sprayer, wagons, and a truck. In addition, a hay baler, forage chopper, or combine are not unusual.

Surrounding the farm buildings is the land, perhaps 150 acres in extent in the larger operations, in addition to woodland. About 75 acres are in crops, mostly hay, oats, and corn silage, and another 75 in pasture. Cash receipts annually on such a dairy farm ordinarily amount to about $9,000 or less, the principal item for sale being the 80,000 or so quarts of milk delivered to a nearby dairy plant. The chief expense items are concentrate feeds and machinery, including depreciation. Although home-grown grains supply straw for bedding and a certain amount of high-energy feed for the dairy cows, farmers purchase the bulk of their grain and additional proteins. Most of these products come from Western states.

Poultry. Ranking next to dairying is poultry. Like the dairy cow, the chicken is well dispersed throughout north-central and southern New York, western and southern Pennsylvania, and northeastern Ohio. Poultry returns total more than ten per cent of farm cash receipts; the money comes mainly from the sale of eggs, although the raising of broilers, turkeys, and ducks for market are important ventures.

Sheep. Although the grazing of sheep is a well established enterprise in the subregions, Ohio is the only state east of the Rockies that has long been known for the quantity and quality of its wool. Sheep are raised on the general farm. Formerly most Ohio sheep were of the Merino breed, but an increasing number of the mutton breeds now are found. In many counties the winter feeding of Western lambs has become a sizable enterprise.

General farming. General farming is practiced throughout much of the central and southern portions of the two subregions. Potatoes and vegetables are grown on about seven per cent of the cropland. Irish potatoes are cultivated on some of the better drained soils on the broad

ridges in Steuben and adjoining counties in southern New York.

Many of West Virginia's farms are small and, therefore, comparatively easy to maintain. Livestock and livestock products account for three out of every four dollars of the farm cash income. Poultry production and dairying are also important. Corn, wheat, oats, barley, buckwheat, hay, and a variety of fruits are grown on most farms. In Kentucky, the farm economy, long based principally on tobacco, corn, and beef production, has experienced a shift in recent years to a greater dependence upon a wider variety of income-producing elements. Tobacco remains king, although strong emphasis is being placed on dairy products, swine, broilers, soybeans, fruits, and vegetables. Agricultural income in Tennessee is derived almost equally from crops and livestock. Leading in extent and value within this region are corn, tobacco, small grains, potatoes, and soybeans.

Many large residential farms, particularly near Lexington, Kentucky, and Nashville, Tennessee, are devoted primarily to grassland and meadow for production of race horses and other registered livestock. The high phosphate content of the soils on most of these farms encourages a vigorous growth of bluegrass and white clover.

Tobacco. Burley tobacco, a thin-bodied tobacco, generally very light in color when cured, is grown for chewing tobacco, cigarettes, and smoking mixtures. It is a specialty crop in the Bluegrass district of Kentucky, the Nashville Basin of Tennessee, and in the Ohio River counties bordering Kentucky. It is grown mainly on silt loams of limestone origin, because of the crop's demand for highly fertile soils (see Fig. 6-12).

Kentucky is second only to North Carolina in total tobacco output, accounting for about 20 per cent of the national total. Three classes of tobacco are produced: light air-cured, fire-cured, and dark air-cured. Yields are high, averaging roughly 1,600 pounds per acre.

Only a small percentage of the land within the tobacco area is planted to tobacco itself.

Farms in the belt average 190 acres in size. Of this acreage only 5 per cent is in tobacco, and 6 per cent in corn; 16 per cent, or nearly all the remaining crops harvested, is used for hay and small grain. Pasture occupies most of the tillable land and 60 per cent of the total acreage.

OZARK-OUACHITA HIGHLANDS

Isolation has been the keynote to the backward economy of the Ozark-Ouachita Highlands. Dissected plateaus and mountainous terrain have always made transportation difficult. Much of the region is too rough for railroad building, except at great cost. Moreover, the uplands are too steep for cultivation, and because of their slope and low fertility, they offer few freight possibilities.

With few exceptions highways follow the crests of the ridges. From the ridge roads, private roads lead to the farms in the valleys. The latter often are impassable because of flooding. In such situations a subsistence economy has prevailed. Here the inhabitants are still independent—proud of their skill with fishing rod, shotgun, and rifle; apt at ballad singing and fiddling; and aloof from the outside world.

Because of larger resources and easier communication, the border areas, namely the Springfield Plateau of southwest Missouri and the Arkansas Valley, are exceptions to this isolation. The once-popular image of the Ozarks as a country of simple mountaineers leading a picturesque but stark life is no longer a true one in these two districts.

The Springfield Plateau. A good place to see the new Ozarks is in southwest Missouri. Springfield, a growing trade and transportation center, is the area's metropolis. Farms spreading out from Springfield form one of the nation's larger milksheds and are also major suppliers of livestock and poultry.

The Arkansas Valley. Agriculture in the Arkansas Valley is quite varied and is best described as mixed farming. Although raising livestock, mainly beef and dairy cattle, is the leading farm enterprise, local areas are notable for the production of peaches, strawberries, green beans, tomatoes, peanuts, cucumbers, and watermelons.

Nearly 35 per cent of all land in farms is in woodland, and an even greater percentage is in pasture. Principal changes in agriculture in recent years have been a general increase in beef cattle production, in milk cows, and in the sale of fluid milk rather than cream. Broiler production has grown rapidly in the central part of the district.

The typical farm includes both bottom land and upland. The bottom land is used for intensive cropping; the upland, largely for pasture.

A significant trend has been the decline of cotton production. Soybeans and small grains, mainly wheat and oats, which can be handled with machinery and by less labor than required for vegetable production, are becoming more important.

Fruit. Northwest Arkansas and southwest Missouri are the center of a region once rich in apple orchards and still rich in vineyards. As early as 1885, the Shannon apple was taking prizes in world expositions. In 1887, the first carload shipments were made from Benton County, Arkansas. Orchardists set out millions of trees during the next 20 years. A crop of 7 million bushels was picked and over 4,500 carloads were shipped in 1919. Two years later, drought and parasites damaged the orchards heavily and the 1919 peak has never been regained. Transparent, Jonathan, and Delicious are the most common apple varieties being marketed from this area today.

The concentration of grape growing was inspired in part by Italian and German settlers prior to World War I. Much of the nation's grape juice supply comes from this area. Strawberries and peaches have been grown commercially here since 1900.

Mining and Quarrying

Mining and quarrying, though less important than farming, occupy a key role in portions of the region.

APPALACHIANS—INTERIOR LOW PLATEAU

Cement. The Great Valley has long been an important cement-manufacturing region. Nearness to New York, Philadelphia, and Scranton, abundant labor, and access to raw materials (limestone, coal, and slate) combine to make the Lehigh Valley towns in eastern Pennsylvania important cement-producing centers.

By 1900, the Lehigh Valley district was producing almost three-fourth of the nation's cement. Although it still makes more cement than any other region in the country, its share of the national total has dropped to about seven per cent. The establishment of regional mills to serve markets more economically has affected producers in the Lehigh Valley.

Quarrying. Slate is metamorphic rock derived from clay or shale. It is characterized by almost perfect cleavage, so that it can be split readily into thick, smooth slabs. Dimension slate is quarried, slabbed, and split to size for making cemetery vaults, billiard table tops, and electrical apparatus. About three-fifths of the nation's supply of slate is quarried in Pennsylvania between Bangor and Slatington.

Marble, also a metamorphic rock, is noted for its beauty. Tennessee marble, world famous as an interior decorative material, is quarried in the Knoxville area. Sylacauga, Alabama, produces the greater portion of the ornamental marble used in buildings, memorials, and homes in the Western Hemisphere. Sylacauga marble is accepted as the nation's white marble standard because of its cream-white appearance.

Scattered throughout these subregions are limestone quarries, which provide agricultural lime and material for cement plants, iron furnaces, and highway construction. Fire clay, mined in western Maryland, is used mainly to make bricks for furnaces.

Iron ore. Sedimentary iron ore beds outcrop in the Appalachians from New York southwestward to Alabama. Although iron ore mining has been carried on in several places throughout the region, large-scale production has occurred in Alabama. Vast deposits of iron ore in the Birmingham and Gadsden areas lie near coal and fluxing materials used in the iron and steel industry.

Copper and zinc. Copper ores are smelted to blister copper at Copperhill, near Ducktown, Tennessee, but all subsequent refining and fabrication are done outside the state. Sulfuric acid is recovered in this smelting of the copper ores. Normally the annual acid output is about 500,000 tons, the bulk of which is used by the state's largest phosphatic fertilizer and rayon industries.

The zinc mining industry of eastern Tennessee, centering near Knoxville, is one of the largest in the eastern United States and annually produces about 1,500,000 tons of ore, none of which is smelted or refined in the area. Zinc also is mined at Austinville, Virginia, where the New Jersey Zinc Company produces about two per cent of the United States total.

Anthracite coal. Almost all the hard coal in the United States is concentrated in a 480-square-mile area in five northeastern Pennsylvania counties—Lackawanna, Luzerne, Carbon, Schuylkill, and Northumberland. Three anthracite regions—the Wyoming, the Lehigh, and the Schuylkill—are drained by the Susquehanna, Lehigh, and Schuylkill Rivers, respectively. Most of the coal comes from the Wyoming region *(Fig. 11-14)*.

Mining anthracite is a highly skilled, hazardous occupation. The veins of coal are sometimes thin, often irregular, usually steep, and eventually deep. Most of the shafts are dark, damp, dirty, and dangerous.

Coal is dug (if not stripped) out of the mine, hauled to the surface breaker where bone, slate, and other impurities are removed, and sorted into eight different sizes for market. In these processes, machinery is being used more and more for such operations as undercutting, loading, cleaning, grading, and, more recently, stripping (*Fig. 11-15*).

Anthracite production reached its peak of 100 million tons in 1917. Competition of other heating fuels—coke, gas, and especially fuel oil—has resulted in a steady drop in tonnage.

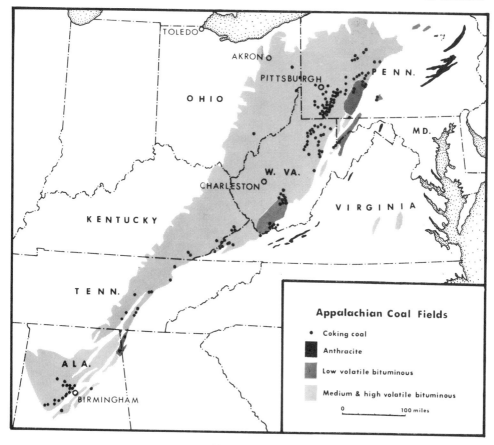

FIGURE 11-14.

The anthracite coal section is heavily populated as a result of early settlement. The million people now living in the five counties include a large number who are of Welsh, Italian, and Polish origin. Scranton, the area's biggest city, is the fourth largest in Pennsylvania, ranking after Philadelphia, Pittsburgh, and Erie. Other prominent mining towns are Wilkes-Barre, Hazleton, Tamaqua, Shamokin, Pittston, and Pottsville.

Communities throughout the anthracite region are making heroic efforts to survive. The Northeast Pennsylvania Industrial Commission, set up to attract new industries to the area, has succeeded in creating hundreds of new jobs. Meanwhile, the Anthracite Institute has labored to retard the extension of natural gas lines into the anthracite marketing area. It also conducts laboratory research to find new uses for hard coal.

FIGURE 11-15. *Strip mining anthracite coal in northeastern Pennsylvania. (U.S. Bureau of Mines)*

Bituminous coal. Bituminous coal is the primary energy resource upon which the nation's phenomenal industrial and economic growth has been based. It underlies most of the region northeastward from Alabama almost to the northern edge of Pennsylvania (*see Fig. 11-14*). Pennsylvania alone has nearly 15,000 square miles of bituminous coal land, and that is less than half of the amount in the Appalachian coal field (*Fig. 11-16*). These reserves, enough to last a thousand years at current rates of consumption, make possible an abundance of cheap power. Power stations may be located close to the mines or along the many streams, in which case the stations are supplied economically by barge.

Over the years there have been wide variations in production in several states. West Virginia, Kentucky, and Pennsylvania currently are the leading coal-producing states, in the order named. For nearly a quarter of a century, West Virginia has led the nation in its output of high-grade bituminous coal. Bituminous coal mining is the principal mineral industry in Pennsylvania, despite a 21 per cent decline in output since 1957, its lowest point since 1898. Pennsylvania coal production has followed closely the ups and downs of national

FIGURE 11-16. *Miners placing explosives in a hole in a coal face preparatory to blasting.* (*U.S. Bureau of Mines*)

coal output. More than 500 years' supply remains at the present rate of consumption. Kentucky has large coal reserves. Less than 4 per cent of the total estimated deposits (123 billion tons) has been depleted. Ohio's reserves are small but the eastern part of the state is an important coal mining area. Tennessee, with small coal reserves, is a minor producer.

Petroleum. The American oil industry began in 1859 with a shallow, spring-pole well near Titusville in northwestern Pennsylvania. It was financed, rather inadequately, by a small, adventurous group in New Haven, Connecticut, who believed that petroleum had a use and a future. The drilling was supervised by a former railroad conductor, "Colonel" Edwin L. Drake. After many trials and tribulations, the Drake well struck oil at a depth of 69.5 feet. It was not a big well but its results were stupendous; it launched an industry now among the world's largest.

Oil production boomed in the Pennsylvania fields after Drake's discovery. Production, by 1863, was up to 2.6 million barrels; in 1870, it was 5.3 million; in 1874, it hit 11 million; and early production peaked at 31 million barrels in 1891. Since that time crude output has declined steadily in the Pennsylvania fields, except for a brief period during World War II when the use of secondary recovery methods resulted in a second peak of more than 35 million barrels. Most wells in the district are now extremely small, averaging between an eighth and a quarter of a barrel per day. The oil is high grade, has a paraffin base with few impurities, and consequently commands the highest price of all petroleum. It is of particular value in the making of high-quality lubricants.

Natural gas. The utility of natural gas was known and commercially exploited in the United States long before Colonel Drake drilled his oil well in 1859. Pennsylvania today ranks eleventh among the states in natural gas production and eighth in total dollar value of production, showing a decrease in both quantity and value since 1957. West Virginia ranks seventh in production; Kentucky, twelfth. New York and Ohio, the only other producing states within the region, have minor outputs of natural gas.

OZARK-OUACHITA HIGHLANDS

The principal minerals of economic importance in the Ozark-Ouachita Highlands are zinc, near the Missouri-Oklahoma-Kansas border; coal in western Missouri and east-central Arkansas; lead, north of the St. Francis Mountains in Missouri; and iron ore, at Iron Mountain and Pilot Knob in southern Missouri. Limestone, clay, gravel, and sand are widely distributed. The subregion has an important share of the nation's production of bauxite, manganese, and fluorspar (*Fig. 11-17*).

Additional minerals of the Ozark-Ouachita Highlands include barite, a heavy white mineral used in oil drilling, chemicals, glass, paint, and rubber; and cobalt, a by-product of lead mining at Fredericktown, Missouri.

Power Development

THE TENNESSEE VALLEY AUTHORITY

The greatest single power development in the region lies in the southern part of the Great Valley. Created by Congress as a United States government corporation charged with carrying on a widespread and unified program of natural resources development, the Tennessee Valley Authority was instructed to develop the Tennessee River system to control floods on the Tennessee and lower Ohio and Mississippi Rivers, to provide a navigable channel from the mouth of the river to Knoxville, Tennessee, and to generate electric power. It was also directed to engage in activities for the agricultural and industrial development of the Tennessee Valley, to operate facilities built in World War I at Muscle Shoals, Alabama, and to aid in the national defense (*Fig. 11-18*).

When President Franklin D. Roosevelt, on May 18, 1933, put his signature on the act creating the Tennessee Valley Authority, he envisioned a far-reaching electrical network based on water power. Today the T.V.A. makes full use of water power, but it is also the world's largest buyer of coal, with three-fourths of its power produced by steam.

Thirty-two major dams regulate the Tennessee River and its tributaries (*Fig. 11-19*). T.V.A. has built 21 of these dams and acquired 5 others. Six belong to the Aluminum Company

FIGURE 11-17. *A typical lead mining operation in the Ozark-Ouachita Highlands subregion, which produces about 30 per cent of the lead mined in the United States. (Massie, Missouri Resources Commission)*

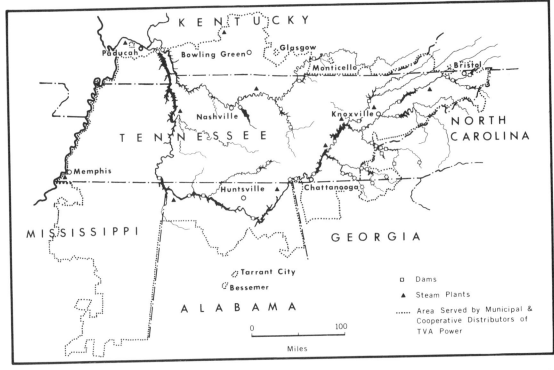

FIGURE 11-18. *The Tennessee Valley Authority district (after Tennessee Valley Authority).*

FIGURE 11-19. *The Tennessee Valley Authority's Hiwassee Dam on the Hiwassee River in western North Carolina. This multiple-purpose dam impounds a lake 22 miles long, with a shoreline of 180 miles. (Tennessee Valley Authority)*

of America but are operated by agreement as part of the T.V.A. system. Nine T.V.A. dams along the mainstream of the river assure a navigation channel for vessels of nine-foot draft traveling between cities as far west as Knoxville, Tennessee, and the Gulf Coast and inland river ports of 20 states. River traffic ton-mileage is about 60 times as great as it was before T.V.A. (*Fig. 11-20*).

POWER DEVELOPMENT OF THE OZARK-OUACHITA HIGHLANDS

Because of the rugged terrain, considerable head for hydroelectric power is provided by the Arkansas and White Rivers. Their development was authorized by Congress in the Flood Control Act of 1950. The authorized plan for the Arkansas River consists of an integrated system of projects to improve navigation, to develop hydroelectric power, and to provide for flood control. An installed capacity of 577,000 kilowatts eventually will serve the urban centers on the plains border and central lowlands of Kansas and Oklahoma.

The White River and its tributaries drain an area of about 27,765 square miles. The northern and western parts of the basin, comprising approximately three-fourths of the area, are in the Ozark Plateaus. Future development of hydroelectric power calls for construction of 14 authorized multipurpose dams, an estimate based upon an ultimate installed capacity of 1,386,000 kilowatts.

Manufacturing

The products of mines and quarries support a variety of manufacturing industries within the Appalachian-Ozark Region, from handicrafts to light processing, ceramics, chemicals, furniture, aluminum, and heavy steel goods.

MISCELLANEOUS INDUSTRIES

Manufacturing in the Blue Ridge subregion is limited largely to mountain crafts, such as handmade fabrics, pottery, brooms, dolls, and wood carvings. Gatlinburg, Tennessee, is perhaps the best known of the Southern Appalachian handicraft centers, although there are numerous others.

The Ridge and Valley has attracted a variety of industries because of its power and resource base. Perhaps the most notable is the Bethlehem Steel Corporation, in the Lehigh Valley, which operates one of the nation's largest rolling mills. The industries include silk mills, sheet metal works, shirt factories, woodworking, buiding materials, and the manufacture of sport shoes. The Radio Corporation of America has a large semiconductor and materials division facility at Crestwood Industrial Park near Wilkes-Barre. Altoona, Pennsylvania, is the home of the car shops of the Pennsylvania Railroad. It is also the center of a wide array of manufacturing industries.

Tennessee Valley power has attracted many manufacturers to that area. Since 1923 several industries have located there. The Aluminum Company of America was a pioneer in the area, building hydroelectric dams and factories years before T.V.A. was created. Today, the Alcoa, Tennessee, plant covers 135 acres of manufacturing space.

FIGURE 11-20. *Barging freight on Wheeler Lake. More than twelve million tons of freight a year are shipped on the Tennessee River system. (Tennessee Valley Authority)*

The Atomic Energy Commission selected the T.V.A. site at Oak Ridge, Tennessee, for its three nuclear plants because of available blocks of hydroelectric power. The Oak Ridge National Laboratory is one of the largest research centers in the nation. It is engaged in nuclear research and development, with emphasis on fundamental studies in support of applied technology.

The Binghamton area in the southern portion of New York State produces shoes and business and photographic equipment. Elmira is noted for its typewriters, computers, compressors, valves, engines, aircraft, machine tools, and structural steel, all of which add to the region's industrial importance.

Synthetic fibers. Man-made fibers are significant props in the economy of western and southwestern Virginia. Fiber and rayon acetate processing and nylon hosiery plants have been attracted to the area because of low-cost female labor and available coal for power and raw material.

Glass manufacturing. This industry is widely distributed throughout the region. The Chattanooga Glass Company at Chattanooga, Tennessee, is a large manufacturer of soft-drink bottles. Corning, New York, leads in the manufacture of technical glass in volume and diversification, including laboratory and pharmaceutical apparatus; marine and railroad signals; home and industrial lighting ware; tubing for fluorescent, neon, and incandescent lighting; and the famous Steuben Ware. Other important glass centers are Athens, Tennessee, and Asheville, North Carolina.

BIRMINGHAM

Within a 25-mile radius of Birmingham, Alabama, are large deposits of iron ore, coal and limestone. The availability of these raw materials, plus the presence of a market for steel products led to the establishment of mills in that area, and the successful manufacture of steel by the Carnegie Company and others brought the construction of open hearth fur-

naces. In 1905, the Republic Iron & Steel Company and the Tennessee Coal, Iron & Railway Company consolidated. Two years later, the U.S. Steel Corporation acquired the operation. Since then it has poured millions of dollars into the Birmingham district, constructing many plants at Birmingham and Gadsden to produce an ever-widening range of finished steel products. Total annual steel capacity slightly exceeds five million net tons.

PITTSBURGH

The Pittsburgh steel district accounts for 17.4 per cent of the nation's steel. Only the Chicago area, with 19.2 per cent, surpasses it.

Pittsburgh's location, which includes the fact of its nearness to coal, has made it a titan of industry. The city exists because two great rivers, the Allegheny and the Monongahela, come together to form the Ohio. The result is a marvelous system for the collection and assembly of vast quantities of the bulky raw materials, namely iron ore, limestone, coal, and coke, needed to make steel. Transportation is supplied by fleets of barges and by trunk line railroads (*Fig. 11-21*).

The lack of level land has forced a large majority of the basic industries up the Allegheny and Monongahela, almost without a break for distances of 40 and 25 miles, respectively, and down the Ohio for 30 miles. Pittsburgh is the heart of an industrial empire, but its limbs sprawl along the banks of its rivers into many other communities (*Fig. 11-22*).

The strategic location at the junction of two rivers early led to bringing together at Pittsburgh the materials for making hardware and other iron products. The up-river areas furnished adequate supplies of coal and iron ore. During the early part of the nineteenth century most of the pig iron manufactured in western Pennsylvania was made in local charcoal furnaces scattered throughout that portion of the state. Later, coal became the major fuel and furnaces were constructed near coal mines further to the south and west. The pig iron usually was brought to Pittsburgh by river, and rolled, forged, or recast in the city. Necessary

FIGURE 11-21. *Pittsburgh's Golden Triangle, where the Monongahela (right) and the Allegheny (left) join to form the Ohio River. (Allegheny Conference on Community Development)*

FIGURE 11-22.

coal for working the iron was brought from nearby mines, often by water.

When the market for raw iron became primarily industrial, as contrasted with a previously agricultural demand, it was necessary to produce large amounts of cheap metal of uniform quality. By 1850, the nature of the market for pig iron was changing; the requirement for smaller amounts of high-grade bar iron to be used in local forges or foundries was being supplanted by a requirement for large quantities of cheap iron to be made into industrial products at the factory. This change forced the rolling mills in Pittsburgh to control production of pig iron itself. After 1860, therefore, blast furnaces were built in connection with the local rolling mills. In order to produce good quality iron consistently, these plants found it advantageous to use the high-grade iron ore of the Lake Superior district. Thus the iron industry first became integrated in Pittsburgh, where Connellsville coking coal was used with Lake Superior ore. The main geographic advantage of the city as an iron producer was its location near large supplies of high-grade coking coal and near enough to Lake Erie to obtain the necessary supplies of ore at relatively low freight costs.

Since the Civil War period, the growth of iron and steel manufactures in the United States has been prodigious. The Pittsburgh area took an early lead as the center of this industry and for decades enjoyed an almost complete monopoly in iron and steel production. Other factors, however, soon began to offset many of the favorable advantages once held by this district. Perhaps Pittsburgh's greatest asset was its nearness to coal, for Pennsylvania bituminous has always been dependent to a large extent on an industrial market, especially the railroad and steel industries. The downward trend in these industries, with the added influence of a pronounced increase in the economy of combustion, led to a slowing-up in the rate of growth in coal output. Less dependence of other regions on western Pennsylvania coal for manufacturing steel caused other steel centers to rise and expand and eventually to challenge the supremacy of the Pittsburgh district in iron and steel production.

In spite of increased competition from other steel centers, the relative importance of the several geographic characteristics of Pittsburgh —low-cost fuel, power, raw steel, and water transportation—has changed little in the past three-quarters of a century. Nearness to coal and comparative proximity to the Great Lakes remain of crucial importance. The production of primary metals, chiefly steel, continues to dominate; blast furnaces account for about 17½ per cent of national pig iron capacity. Steel rolling mills in the Pittsburgh area turn out every line of steel products, ranging from heavy structural components to fine wire. Some steel is also made into forgings and castings. Other commodities include coal chemicals, ferroalloys, and titanium products.

Most of the steel mills are in Allegheny County; several of these employ more than 5,000 people each. Smaller plants in the primary metals group, employing from 500 to 1,000, produce zinc, sheet copper, brass, bronze, and aluminum basic shapes.

The comparative position of the Pittsburgh district in iron and steel manufacturing will depend on the extent to which local producers take a leading part in exploiting new markets, in recovering their relative position in old markets in which the area once was much stronger, and in increasing their share of sales in markets in which the area has been comparatively weak.

Aluminum. Although bauxite ore from which aluminum is made is not mined in the Pittsburgh district, the Aluminum Company of America, by far the largest unit in the industry, always has had its home office there, along with one of its larger fabricating plants.

Glass. Pittsburgh is a city of glass as well as of steel and aluminum. This is because the sand of which glass is made and the coal or natural gas used for fuel in its production have been abundant there from the start. Glass plants, large and small, are scattered up and down the three rivers, but the largest producer is the Pittsburgh Plate Glass Company.

Westinghouse Electric. It was in Pittsburgh in the early 1870's that George Westinghouse started to manufacture the air brake and the railroad signals he had perfected. Because the signal system required electric controls, he soon found himself making electrical equipment; the vast Westinghouse interests have been in Pittsburgh ever since.

From its giant plant, Westinghouse ships each year more than 20,000 carloads of basic electrical equipment, much of it tailor-made. Among the products are motors for industrial use and electrical equipment for mine cars and railroad trains.

H. J. Heinz Company. One of the comparatively few large industries within the city limits of Pittsburgh itself is the H. J. Heinz Company. Heinz is the largest maker of ketchup in the world, the second largest maker of canned soups, and one of the four largest makers of baby foods. There are from 120 to 127 varieties, not just the fabled "57," and the chief products, besides those mentioned above, are baked beans, pickles, spaghetti, and condiments.

YOUNGSTOWN DISTRICT

Situated about midway between Cleveland and Pittsburgh, the Youngstown metropolitan area is even more specialized than Pittsburgh in steel production. Youngstown is the third largest steel center in the country and one of the oldest of the major American steel centers. About nine per cent of the nation's pig iron and steel capacity is located here. Finished steel is largely of the flat rolled variety used in automobiles and appliances, but some heavier items are also rolled in Youngstown mills. In the city and its environs, steel works and rolling mills manufacture pipe and tubing, sheets, strips, rod and wire products, and plates and shapes. Ingot molds are produced at Hubbard. Mills in Warren and Niles turn out flat rolled steel and pipe. Furnaces and steel mills in and near Sharon produce pig iron, steel sheets, strip, pipe, and tubing; foundries in Sharon and elsewhere in Mercer County turn out ingot molds and miscellaneous castings.

JOHNSTOWN

At the junction of the Conemaugh and Little Conemaugh Rivers about 60 miles east of Pittsburgh is the Bethlehem Steel Corporation's Johnstown mill. The city, in the center of an area producing both iron ore and bituminous coal, probably has contributed more than any other city to the development and technology of the steel industry. This congested valley, a miniature Pittsburgh, presents a striking picture of intensive industrial use.

THE KANAWHA VALLEY

The Kanawha Valley of West Virginia, especially in the area around Charleston, is the site of an important chemical manufacturing district. The availability of local deposits of coal, natural gas, and salt has attracted a number of plants wishing to combine raw materials with good transportation facilities in terms of river shipment. Metal products, synthetic rubber, textiles, glass, and antifreeze combine with a variety of basic industrial chemicals to give the area an important economic base.

THE OHIO VALLEY

The Ohio River, beginning at Pittsburgh with the confluence of the Allegheny and the Monongahela and winding north, then south and west 981 miles to the Mississippi at Cairo, is technically the property of Kentucky, West Virginia, and Pennsylvania, but it flows past three other states—Ohio, Indiana, and Illinois. Narrow and bordered by mountains at the beginning, the Ohio Valley is crammed with steel mills, coke ovens, power plants, and brick kilns for its 40 miles in Pennsylvania. For another 60 miles, West Virginia and Ohio duplicate the Pennsylvania industrial pattern on a somewhat smaller scale. Then the cities and towns, narrow ribbons of humanity pressed between the river and the Allegheny foothills, begin to separate; long stretches of open farmland intervene. The countryside is essentially rural with only a sprinkling of metropolitan centers to dominate the hundreds of miles of river—Wheeling and Huntington, West Virginia; Cincinnati and Steubenville, Ohio; Louisville, Kentucky; and Evansville, Indiana.

Space, coal, and power have attracted new industries and given rise to expansion of old facilities in the Ohio Valley. The Ohio now surpasses the Rhine, Europe's "chemical river," in chemical plant investment; nearly three times as much steel is produced on the Ohio as in the celebrated Ruhr Valley, and over three times the coal. The Ohio's fissionable material plants rival those at Oak Ridge. A group of power companies has invested over half a billion dollars in new facilities to supply these Atomic Energy Commission plants, and nearly three times as much to keep pace with the demands of private users. Within the past few years the aluminum industry has made a significant break away from Northwest sites offering cheap hydroelectric power to Ohio River sites based on coal. Producers believe savings in transportation that result from having the metal produced nearer its markets will more than offset the two mill per kilowatt-hour higher cost for coal over water power. Among the new aluminum producers in the Ohio Valley are: (1) Alcoa's 150,000-ton smelter near Evansville, Indiana; (2) Kaiser Aluminum's Ravenswood, West Virginia, facilities, with an annual smelter of 220,000 tons; and (3) Olin Mathieson's (120,000 tons) aluminum smelter near Clarington, Ohio (*Fig 11-23*).

The Atomic Energy Commission has invested $1.7 billion in three plants: a uranium processing plant at Fernald, Ohio, and gaseous-diffusion plants at Paducah, Kentucky, and Portsmouth, Ohio. To supply the diffusion plants, there are four new power plants located at Joppa, Illinois; Paducah, Kentucky; Madison, Indiana; and Cheshire, Ohio.

Salt, over a hundred feet thick in places, along the upper Ohio Valley attracted chemical industries to the area. To producers of chlorine and chlorine products, few places offer as many advantages as the Ohio Valley. Brine deposits, salt, and the water essential to

FIGURE 11-23. *Aerial view of the giant aluminum rolling mill of Olin Mathieson Chemical Corporation (left) and the primary reduction plant of Ormet Corporation (right) on the Ohio River near Hannibal, Ohio. (Olin Mathieson Chemical Corp.)*

chlorine operations are abundantly present. Chemicals valued at a third of a billion dollars are produced, mainly in new plants at Calvert City, Kentucky, home of the Pennsylvania Salt Manufacturing Company's sulfuric and hydrofluoric acid operation, and in New Martinsville-Moundsville's chemical facilities in the vicinity of Parkersburg and Marietta.

Steel industries along the Ohio River have expanded plants by nearly $1 billion since 1956, an increase primarily represented by the expansion up-river of National Steel at Weirton, West Virginia; of Wheeling Steel from Steubenville, Ohio, south; and that of Jones & Laughlin Steel at Aliquippa, Pennsylvania. Down-river there is Armco's $75 million facility at Ashland, Kentucky, and the $90 million expansion of Detroit Steel at Portsmouth, Ohio.

The Wheeling-Steubenville metropolitan area, which is located along the upper Ohio River a short distance west and south of Pittsburgh, is made up of two Ohio counties and four West Virginia counties. Steel mills are the largest employers in all six counties. Well over 5,000 workers are employed by mills in Weirton, Steubenville, and Benwood; they produce structural steel, tin plate, sheets and strip, and galvanized sheets and pipe. Riverside locations make possible the use of low-cost barge transportation on the Ohio River for the industry's bulky raw materials, most of which come from outside the area, as well as for its heavy finished products. The river also furnishes water for industrial processing and cooling.

Traffic on the Ohio River. More than 96 million tons of shipping traveled the Ohio in 1966—more than passed through the Panama Canal. The importance of the Ohio River as a commercial route may be attributed to: (1) its proximity to the nation's largest soft coal deposits; (2) its all-water connection, via the Mississippi, with the very large petroleum reserves of the central South; and (3) the industrial growth of the country, particularly that portion lying generally to the north of the river. The value of the river as an inexpensive avenue for bulk commodity movement could not have been realized without a stabilized flow of water and a guaranteed minimum channel depth. The federal government, recognizing this requirement at the turn of the century, assumed the responsibility for the full canalization of the river in the interest of furthering interstate commerce. Today the river is canalized and channeled for its entire length, with a controlling depth of nine feet. The river is navigable all year. Its chief tributary in Ohio, the Muskingum, also is canalized to permit navigation from Zanesville in central Ohio to the Muskingum's junction with the Ohio at Marietta.

Tributary streams of the Ohio River—the Tennessee, the Cumberland, the Green, the Kentucky, the Big Sandy, and the Kanawha—and the so-called headstreams, the Monongahela and the Allegheny, add some 1,340 miles of navigable channel with nine-foot draft.

The chief port on the Ohio River is Cincinnati; other important ports are East Liverpool, Steubenville, Wheeling, Marietta, Portsmouth, Louisville and Paducah.

Cincinnati. This city has long been known for its machine tool industry, but in the period since World War II the production of automobiles, automobile parts, aircraft engines, and truck trailers has grown so rapidly that the manufacturing of transportation equipment now is as important as the long-dominant machine tool industry. Two of the major automobile manufacturers have large plants in the area, each of which employs more than 3,000 people *(Fig. 11-24)*.

Virtually every kind of metalworking machinery, with its accompanying tools and dies, is manufactured in Cincinnati, as well as a variety of special purpose machinery and equipment. Machine tool plants, employing more than 500 persons each, turn out valves, laundry machinery, and power transmission equipment. Fabricated metal plants, employing between 500 and 1,000 each, manufacture plumbing supplies and metal containers.

The chemicals and chemical products group contains one of the largest plants (Procter and Gamble) in the area; it produces soaps, detergents, toilet articles, and vegetable shortening.

FIGURE 11-24. *Cincinnati, Ohio, a major manufacturing center and the premier port of the Ohio River. (Cincinnati Gas and Electric Co.)*

Louisville. Furniture, distilled products, and large tobacco plants are major props of Louisville's industrial economy. Other types of manufacturing include aluminum sheet, rod, and extruded products; ordnance; explosives; aircraft parts; automobile parts; and butadiene for synthetic rubber.

NASHVILLE

This city has diversified industries: shoe manufacturing (General Shoe Corporation, with headquarters in Nashville, is one of the leading shoe manufacturers of the world), cotton, flour and feed, lumber, brick, snuff, chemicals, foundries, meat-packing plants, stone and cement works, printing and publishing, rayon mills, cellophane, and fertilizer industries. Nashville also claims to have the largest titanium plant in the United States. Such a list suggests a wide industrial base and is in keeping with the rapid growth in manufacturing throughout the South.

Recreation and Tourism

Within a few hundred miles of the Atlantic Coast are the Blue Ridge and Allegheny Mountains, with the beautiful Shenandoah Valley between them. The Skyline Drive along the crest of the Blue Ridge within Shenandoah National Park connects with the Blue Ridge Parkway to form a continuous mountaintop drive across the state of Virginia. Scenic wonders of this area include limestone caverns, the Natural Bridge, and the Breaks of the Cumberland.

The Great Smoky Mountains National Park is one of the nation's most popular tourist attractions. It is on this "roof of eastern America," embracing an area 54 miles long and 19 miles wide, that tourists see 29 peaks more than a mile high and 16 more than 6,000 feet high. The heavily forested slopes, cascading streams, and many waterfalls provide impressive scenery. The lakes and lakeshores of the Tennessee Valley Authority offer boating, swimming, fishing, camping, and other outdoor activities. The Finger Lakes section in New York also attracts tourists, and other water bodies and varied land-forms in the region are within easy reach of the densely populated lowlands. Segments of the agricultural landscape offer some scenic attractions to tourists, too.

The Ozark-Ouachita Highlands are the only major hill areas between the Appalachians and the Rocky Mountains. Consequently, they offer an attraction to the surrounding population centers. Residents of such cities as St. Louis, Kansas City, Tulsa, Oklahoma City, Little Rock, and Shreveport are within a 300-mile radius of resort facilities.

Tourists are not new to the area. Indeed, the isolation that originally retarded its development has long been one of its main attractions to hunters and fishermen. Eldorado Springs was one of the several southwest Missouri cities that attracted health seekers by the hundreds before the turn of the century. Lake Taneycomo was formed by the building of Powersite Dam during World War I; it has been a tourist attraction ever since. Lake of the Ozarks was created in the 1920's (*Fig. 11-25*).

FIGURE 11-25. *Bagnell Dam, a hydroelectric power dam on the Osage River, forms Lake of the Ozarks, Missouri's largest lake and one of the most extensively developed resort areas in the United States. (Massie, Missouri Resources Commission)*

Recreational advantages are heightened by the location of two national forests: (1) the Ouachita, oldest in the United States; and (2) the Ozark, a series of high ridges punctuated by deep valleys. Within the two forests are several government-built recreation areas.

Hot Springs, Arkansas, created as a national reservation in 1832, is the oldest national park in America. The apparently endless flow of mineral waters from 47 springs attracts thousands of people from all over the world.

Outlook

The Appalachian-Ozark Region has a fairly small number of districts solidly devoted to manufacturing. Of these, the Pittsburgh industrial complex best exemplifies some of the major problems facing the region. Many of its industries are old, congested, and obsolete. Higher living standards, more leisure, and greater population mobility make it increasingly important for any community to provide a far higher level of convenience, sightliness, public services, recreation, and cultural and educational opportunity than was ever before the case; and this trend will continue.

Pittsburgh is currently in a state of transition from an economy based on coal, iron, and steel, to one in which light industries, skilled services, automation, research, education, and nuclear technology will play important roles. It faces, however, a major challenge in the field of civic amenities. The Pittsburgh Renaissance (urban renewal and smoke control measures) has had a tremendous impact, but a great deal remains to be done. The costs will be high, but the district's most valuable asset—its future—is at stake.

People living in the poor and isolated sections of the Appalachian-Ozark Region inhabit a world scarcely recognizable, and rarely seen, by the majority of us. It is a world apart, one in which the inhabitants are isolated from the mainstream of American life and usually alienated from its values. In this world, the people are literally concerned with day-to-day survival--a roof overhead, the source of the next meal, and obtaining sufficient clothing. Here, a minor illness is a major tragedy; pride and privacy must be sacrificed to get help; honesty can become a luxury and ambition is myth. Worst of all, the poverty of the fathers is visited upon the children in unbroken cycles.

Equality of opportunity is the American dream, and universal education is our noblest pledge to realize it. But for many children of the region, education does not provide the answer. Many are too ill-motivated and too ill-prepared at home to learn well in school.

In the long run, headway against poverty in areas so inaccessible as parts of the Appalachian-Ozark Region will require attacks on many fronts. Education and income-producing opportunities must go hand in hand.

Selected References

CARLSON, FRED A., "Traffic on the Ohio River System," *The Journal of Geography*, Vol. 59, November, 1960, pp. 357–359.

COLLIER, JAMES E., *Agricultural Atlas of Missouri* (University of Missouri Agricultural Experiment Station Bulletin 645), Columbia, Mo.: University of Missouri, 1955.

———, *Geography of the Northern Ozark Border Region in Missouri*, Columbia, Mo.: The Curators of the University of Missouri, 1953.

DEASY, GEORGE F., and GRIESS, PHYLLIS R., "Coal Strip Pits in the Northern Appalachian Landscape," *The Journal of Geography*, Vol. 58, February, 1959, pp. 72–80.

———, "Effects of a Declining Mining Economy on the Pennsylvania Anthracite Region," *Annals of the Association of American Geographers*, Vol. 55, June, 1965, pp. 239–259.

———, "New Maps of Underground Bituminous Coal Mining," *ibid.*, Vol. 47, December, 1957, pp. 336–349.

DURAND, LOYAL, JR., "Mountain Moonshining in East Tennessee," *Geographical Review*, April, 1956, pp. 168–181.

DURAND, LOYAL, JR., and BIRD, ELSIE T., "The Burley Tobacco Region of the Mountain South," *Economic Geography*, July, 1950, pp. 247–300.

FORD, THOMAS R. (ed.), *The Southern Appalachian Region*, Lexington, Ky.: University of Kentucky Press, 1962.

FOSCUE, EDWIN J., "Gatlinburg: A Mountain Community," *Economic Geography*, 1945, pp. 192–205.

GOTTMAN, JEAN, *Virginia at Mid-century*, New York: Holt, Rinehart & Winston, Inc., 1955.

GUERNSEY, LEE, "Strip Coal Mining: A Problem in Conservation," *The Journal of Geography*, Vol. 54, April, 1955, pp. 174–181.

———, "The Reclamation of Strip Mined Lands in Western Kentucky," *ibid.*, Vol. 59, January, 1960, pp. 5–11.

HARPER, ROBERT A., "River Junction Communities of the Lower Ohio Valley—a Study of Functional Change," *The Journal of Geography*, Vol. 59, November, 1960, pp. 364–370.

HEWES, LESLIE, "Tontitown: Ozark Vineyard Center," *Economic Geography*, April, 1953, pp. 125–143.

KERSTEN, EARL W., JR., "Changing Economy and Landscape in a Missouri Ozarks Area," *Annals of the Association of American Geographers*, Vol. 48, December, 1958, pp. 398–418.

LOUNSBURY, JOHN F., "Industrial Development in the Ohio Valley," *The Journal of Geography*, Vol. 60, September, 1961, pp. 253–262.

MAGIN, IRVIN D., "The Wilderness Road," *The Journal of Geography*, Vol. 57, April, 1958, pp. 191–195.

MILLER, E. WILLARD, "Some Aspects of Population Trends in Pennsylvania," *The Journal of Geography*, Vol. 54, February, 1955, pp. 64–73.

———, "The Southern Anthracite Region: A Problem Area," *Economic Geography*, Vol. 31, October, 1955, pp. 331–350.

NELSON, J. G., "Man and Geomorphic Process in the Chemung River Valley, New York and Pennsylvania," *Annals of the Association of American Geographers*, Vol. 56, March, 1966, pp. 24–32.

RIGGS, FLETCHER E., *Income Levels in the Upper Tennessee Valley: A Comparative Analysis*, Knoxville, Tenn.: Division of Agricultural Relations, Tennessee Valley Authority, 1957.

RODGERS, ALLAN, "The Iron and Steel Industry of the Mahoning and Shenango Valleys," *Economic Geography*, October, 1952, pp. 331–342.

RUDD, R. W., and SHUFFETT, D. M., *Trends in Kentucky Agriculture* (Kentucky Agricultural Experiment Station Bulletin 653), November, 1957.

12 *Interior Lowlands Region*

The Interior Lowlands encompass one of the largest regions of Anglo-America. It includes portions of three Canadian Provinces and all or parts of 16 states (*Fig. 12-1*).

Because of the vast size of the Interior Lowlands, their economy is extremely varied. Some portions, such as the urban belt on the borders of the Great Lakes, are made up of teeming cities and industries; others are primarily devoted to dairying or to the growing of grain used to finish livestock.

Surface Features

With but few exceptions the surface of the Interior Lowlands is level to gently rolling (*Fig. 12-2*). In absolute elevation the Interior Lowlands Region ranges from 1,500 or even 1,800 feet on its western border to 450 feet in southern Illinois and to less than 300 feet on the shores of Lake Ontario. The average elevation is perhaps a thousand feet (*Fig. 12-3*).

The rocks are almost horizontal, a characteristic that accounts for the monotonous landscape in large portions of the region. They are largely of limestone and shale deposited in the interior sea before the Appalachian revolution. The northern part of the Interior Lowlands was covered by glacial drift from a few feet to 800 feet thick, which is composed mainly of till, but also much waterlaid drift.

The Interior Lowlands Region was subject to erosion during the entire time the older and younger peneplains were being made in the East. The whole has reached base level at least once. Most of it now stands above local base level, having been raised and eroded not long before the glacial epoch. The continental ice advanced over the region several times, each advance making a glacial stage.

The sections of this region are distinguished with respect to the effects of glaciation and the degree of erosion, since two widely separated areas, the Osage and Wisconsin Driftless sections, were never glaciated. Two (the Western Lake and Eastern Lake sections) have a topography characterized by all the features of recent glaciation, i.e., moraines, lakes, swamps, kames, outwash plains, and poorly developed drainage. These features are not uniformly distributed, but they are not absent from any great area either. Two sections (the Till Plains and the Dissected Till Plains) are till plains with little morainic topography and no lakes and swamps. The Till Plains section is still young; the Dissected Till Plains section is older and submaturely eroded (*Fig. 12-4*).

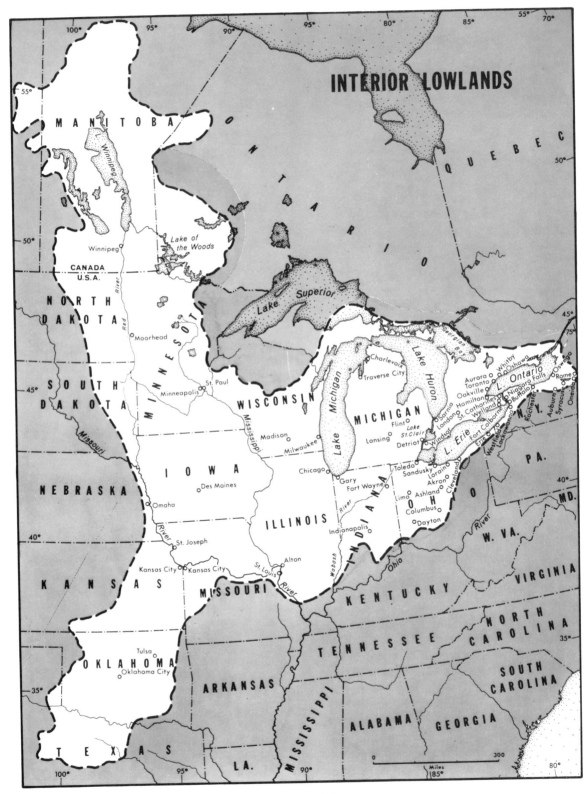

FIGURE 12-1.

Climate

The Interior Lowlands region encompasses such a large land area (more than 1,800 miles from north to south and over 1,200 miles from east to west) that temperature, precipitation, and length of growing season vary greatly. There is a measure of uniformity throughout the region only in terms of seasonal distribution of precipitation and the influence of the continental land mass on temperatures (*see* Fig. 1-16).

The average annual temperature varies from 65° F. in the extreme southern portions of the region (northern Texas) to 18° in northern Manitoba. The January average is 50° in the south, −5° in the north; July, 80° in the south, 65° in the north. Average annual minimum temperatures vary from 15° along the southern border to −40° north of Lake Superior. A much narrower range occurs in summer, however; there is only a 10-degree differential in average annual maximum temperatures between the southern (105°) and the northern (95°) parts of the region.

The region as a whole is characterized by small variations in precipitation from year to year, frequent alternations of above and below normal, and comparative absence of prolonged drought periods. Precipitation increases from west to east (25 inches to 40 inches) and from north to south (25 inches to 50 inches). Winter is the driest period of the year; precipitation falls in the form of rain in the south and snow in the north. Cyclonic storms traverse the region and bring changeable weather on the

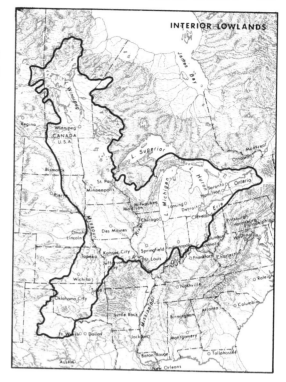

FIGURE 12-2. *The Interior Lowlands Region, physical relief.*

average of every three to five days. The wettest period is from April to September, inclusive. Convectional rainfall throughout the region provides adequate moisture for crops without irrigation. Nowhere is less than 16 inches of moisture received, and over most parts, a minimum of 20 inches is recorded during the six-month period. The frost-free season varies considerably—from less than four months in

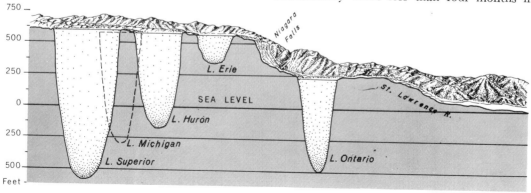

FIGURE 12-3. *Cross-section of the northeastern Interior Lowlands Region.*

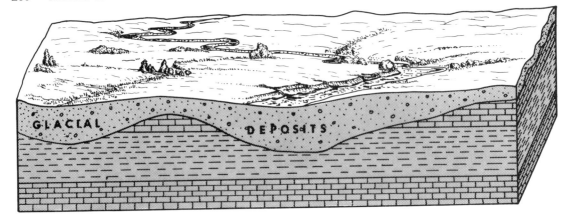

FIGURE 12-4. *The effects of glacial action in the Interior Lowlands (after Tarr and Von Engeln).*

the extreme north to more than seven months in the extreme south (*Fig. 12-5*).

Soils and Natural Vegetation

Soils range from chernozem in the drier portions of the region to prairie soils in the grassland areas, and to gray-brown soils in the wetter sections, where they have developed under a forest cover. The latter are lighter in color and generally lower in organic matter and in bases than the soils of the prairie grasslands.

The prairie soils occcur in the greater part of the Middle West. They are dark in color and high in organic matter and total nitrogen. Having been formed predominantly from medium-textured parent material, either of glacial origin or of related windblown silts or loess material, the soils are generally permeable and quite favorable for tillage operations under a wide range of moisture conditions.

The Interior Lowlands have a wide variety of flora because of their wide latitudinal extent. In the drier sections, treeless grassland of the prairie or meadow type is characteristic, whereas the rainier sections are covered by dense forests. To the south are mixed deciduous hardwoods, such as oak, maple, black walnut, hickory, beech, and others. To the north, these hardwoods give way to forests of pine and other conifers. From Illinois west to Nebraska and Kansas, the country has slightly less rainfall; hence, luxuriant prairie grassland replaces forest.

Settlement

By 1850 the first period of American colonization, that of the forest, was at an end, and the second, that of the grasslands, was beginning. Originally, the prairies were covered with grass that grew three to ten feet high and was studded with wildflowers. Trees were rare except among the "oak openings" on the eastern boundary and along the river valleys, where the subsoil was moist enough to support forest. Perhaps trees could not survive on the prairie because of prairie fires and grazing buffalo. Many pioneers from the East were afraid of this too-bright, too-level land where there were so few friendly trees and so little shade and water. They eased into it by first settling in the river valleys and oak openings, which seemed familiar.

Before they could successfully settle on this new type of land, they needed to develop new techniques for farming and living. Houses had to be made out of sod instead of logs. Cow chips and knots of twisted grass had to serve as fuel. Wells, sometimes 200 feet deep, needed to be dug with pick and shovel. Windmills had to be made to harness the strong winds for

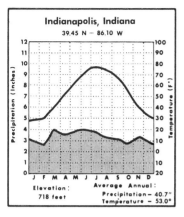

Indianapolis, Indiana
39.45 N – 86.10 W
Elevation: 718 feet
Average Annual: Precipitation – 40.7"
Temperature – 53.0°

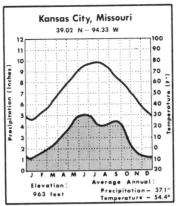

Kansas City, Missouri
39.02 N – 94.33 W
Elevation: 963 feet
Average Annual: Precipitation – 37.1"
Temperature – 54.4°

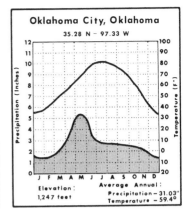

Oklahoma City, Oklahoma
35.28 N – 97.33 W
Elevation: 1,247 feet
Average Annual: Precipitation – 31.03"
Temperature – 59.4°

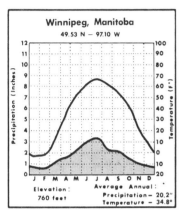

Winnipeg, Manitoba
49.53 N – 97.10 W
Elevation: 760 feet
Average Annual: Precipitation – 20.2"
Temperature – 34.8°

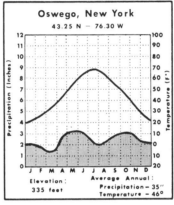

Oswego, New York
43.25 N – 76.30 W
Elevation: 335 feet
Average Annual: Precipitation – 35"
Temperature – 46°

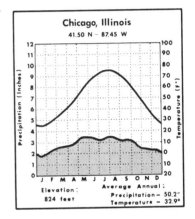

Chicago, Illinois
41.50 N – 87.45 W
Elevation: 824 feet
Average Annual: Precipitation – 50.2"
Temperature – 32.9°

pumping. Barbed-wire fencing was required as a substitute for the almost nonexistent split rails. Steel plows were needed—plows that would not stick the way iron and wooden plows did. One by one, these were provided.

Once conquered, the prairies yielded enormously. It was not necessary here to grub out trees laboriously and endlessly; a man could have the land producing within a year. There seemed little need to conserve this soil—it looked inexhaustibly fertile. Eastward, great industrial cities were growing up that needed to be fed cheaply. The prairies, with cheap land and large-scale methods of production, could do the job. Quickly, they swung into the production of wheat, corn, cattle, and hogs on a vast scale. The prairies were an agricultural treasure-trove such as has seldom existed in the world, and they lived up to their destiny.

Agriculture

The livestock and grain section of the American Middle West is one of the world's most important agricultural regions. Its fertile land, relatively level topography, ample precipitation, and favorable temperatures over a large area make an exceptional combination of natural resources. This region's land and climate give it an advantage over other areas in the production of many crops, including several different grains, legumes, and grasses. Although corn is the major grain, other crops are grown in smaller quantities (*Fig. 12-6*).

KING CORN

Corn is well suited to the area, for the corn plant thrives on its deep, black, fertile soils.

FIGURE 12-6. *Types of farming in the Wabash Basin, a typical section of the Interior Lowlands Region.*

Furthermore, the high organic content of the prairie soils is associated with desirable characteristics of cultivability, aeration, water-holding capacity, and available nutrients; the relatively flat topography permits an intensive corn cropping program without excessive soil erosion; and the climate in the area is almost perfect for the crop (*Figs. 12-7* and *12-8*).

Optimum corn yields are obtained under the following conditions: (1) ample moisture in early spring, followed by a warm dry spell in the first half of May so that the corn may be planted about that time; (2) a minimum of eight inches of rainfall during June, July, and August; (3) prolonged hot weather during the growing season (74° to 78° F. during the day, and nights above 58° F.); (4) fairly dry weather before harvest; and (5) the absence of killing frost through the month of September.

There probably has never been a perfect corn year, but the weather conditions delineated above are approximated in most years in the livestock and grain section where about three-fourths of the nation's corn harvested for grain and about one-half of the world's output of corn is produced. The so-called Corn Belt

includes Iowa, Illinois, Minnesota, Indiana, Nebraska, Ohio, Missouri, and South Dakota. Iowa produces the most corn; Illinois ranks second, and Minnesota is third.

The fairly definite boundaries of the Corn Belt restrict the corn supply and tend to maintain its relative value. Farmers within the area can profitably produce corn at a price and in a supply that is relatively impossible in most other places. Even such new developments as hybrid corn and the greater use of commercial fertilizers have achieved their greatest results in the area that was most favored originally— the heart of the Corn Belt.

More than nine-tenths of the corn grown in the Corn Belt is hybrid (*Fig. 12-9*). Hybrid corn plants produce up to one-third more corn

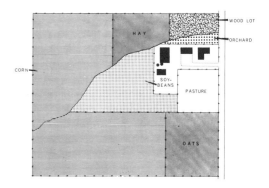

FIGURE 12-7. *A typical Corn Belt farm in Iowa.*

FIGURE 12-8. *A picker and sheller harvesting corn in Illinois. (U.S. Dept. of Agriculture)*

FIGURE 12-9. *A field of hybrid seed corn in eastern Iowa. New corn hybrids yield about ten per cent more per acre than those grown less than ten years ago. (U.S. Dept. of Agriculture)*

than do the best varieties developed by other methods of breeding. Hybrids are also bred to have a greater ability to withstand drought, diseases, and pests. All the ears of hybrid corn ripen at the same time, the plants are more uniform and stand up better, and the ears can be more easily harvested with modern machinery.

The development of hybrid corn and improved farming methods have helped increase corn production from about 25 bushels per acre in the early 1930's to about 60 bushels an acre today. High yields are essential for profits; many farmers merely break even with a corn yield of 40 to 50 bushels per acre. The average Corn Belt farmer now spends approximately nine times as much for fertilizer as did the average farmer in 1940. This intensive use of commercial fertilizer has all but eliminated crop rotations in the Corn Belt; indeed, some of the more progressive farmers today regard crop rotation as obsolete. Corn is now grown year after year on the same land.

The demand for corn is derived largely from strong consumer preference for high-quality meats. This has resulted in relatively high values for grain-fed livestock. About 60 per cent of the corn crop normally is fed to animals produced primarily for their meat. If

dairy cattle and laying hens are included with meat animals, nearly 90 per cent of the demand for corn is accounted for. The importance of corn as a livestock feed is further emphasized by the fact that it accounts for more than half of all grain fed to livestock. Livestock, therefore, makes up the superstructure of the farm economy and accounts for almost three-fourths of that region's farm income.

The principal types of livestock—hogs, beef cattle, and farm flocks of chickens—require relatively small investment in specialized buildings and equipment. Moreover, the production cycles for these kinds of livestock are relatively short. This permits farmers to adjust rather quickly to the changing economic conditions.

Hogs. About half the corn fed to all livestock in the United States goes to hogs, and about two-thirds of the nation's hogs are raised and fed in the Corn Belt. Corn is excellent for fattening because of the high percentage of digestible nutrients and the high percentage of fats. The area is densely populated with hogs, but the greatest concentration occurs in the eastern half of Iowa and the northwest quarter of Illinois (*Fig. 12-10*).

The price that farmers receive for their corn helps them decide what to do with it. As corn

FIGURE 12-10. *Corn fattened hogs on an Illinois farm. (U.S. Dept. of Agriculture)*

prices rise, for example, farmers usually sell more corn and raise fewer hogs. They receive more money by selling the corn than they would by feeding it to the hogs and then selling the hogs. If corn prices fall, farmers generally raise more hogs and feed the corn to them, because the hogs would bring in more money than the corn.

Beef cattle. Between 10 and 15 per cent of the corn fed to livestock in the United States is fed to beef cattle; about half of these "feedlot" cattle are fed in the Corn Belt. Their sale usually accounts for approximately one-fourth of the cash receipts of farmers in the area. The feeding of beef cattle is rather common throughout the Corn Belt, but this activity is concentrated most heavily in two areas—northwestern Illinois and northeastern Nebraska-northwestern Iowa (*Fig. 12-11*).

The bulk of the cattle fattened in Corn Belt feedlots are born on the Western ranges in the spring. Some of them are shipped to the Midwest as feeder calves in the fall. Others are wintered in their homeland and spend their second summer on the open range, after which they may have achieved a weight of 600 to 700 pounds. Then they are bought by corn farmers and shipped to the feedlots. The heaviest movement usually occurs in October. The feed-

Figure 12-11. *A typical Corn Belt feedlot in Illinois.*

lot diet is rich with corn, and cattle are fed to varying weights and degrees of fatness before being sold for slaughter. Many of the animals are marketed in the late spring and early summer, with the largest volume usually coming in June. The cattle feeding operation has a production and investment period that ranges typically between 3 and 12 months, 6 to 8 months being the most common. The period within which substantial production adjustments can be made does not differ greatly from that for hogs.

Cattle feeding, as it is carried on in the Corn Belt, typically involves the outlay of a substantial amount of cash for the purchase of feeder stock. Hogs, on the other hand, usually are bred and raised by the farmer who feeds them to market weight. Credit, therefore, plays a more important role in the cattle enterprise than it does in hog raising. Most of the credit is provided by commercial banks.

The substantial investment required to purchase animals causes cattle feeding to be somewhat more exposed to risk from price changes. Whereas the hog feeder must concern himself largely with two prices—hog and feed, the cattle feeder must consider three—fat cattle, feeder cattle, and feed. A change in the price of fat cattle while animals are being fattened affects the selling price of the portion of the final weight that was purchased as feeder cattle, as well as the portion that was added in the feedlot. Since the weight of cattle purchased as feeders usually will be equal to 40 per cent or more of the weight at the end of the fattening period, price changes while cattle are being fattened may result in substantial cash losses or profits.

Southern Iowa, northwestern Missouri and the adjacent counties in Illinois make up an area of rolling land in which considerable numbers of beef cattle are raised. Over one-third of the land in that area is kept in pasture utilized for maintaining herds of beef cows. The soil in the flatter parts is well adapted to corn, however, and enough corn is raised in the area so that the feeder cattle produced there can be fattened along with animals obtained from other areas.

Poultry. About 15 per cent of the corn fed to livestock in the United States is consumed by poultry. Only one-fourth to one-third of the poultry is located in the Corn Belt, however. Sale of poultry and products accounts for about one-tenth of the cash receipts of farmers in that area.

Corn Belt poultry production is widely diffused; most farms have at least a few chickens. Only a small fixed investment in buildings and equipment is required for the average farm flock, and the poultry enterprise is thought to utilize some labor that otherwise would be wasted. The period of production is one year or less, and this livestock enterprise can be adjusted quite readily to changes in markets and market prospects.

FIGURE 12-12. *Holstein cattle in an alfalfa-ladino improved pasture in Wisconsin.* (*U.S. Dept. of Agriculture*)

THE DAIRY BELT

To the north of the Corn Belt lies the Midwestern section of the Hay, Forage, and Dairy Belt. These two belts shade into each other geographically. Milk is produced in the Corn Belt, especially in the northern part. Corn is harvested for grain in the Dairy Belt, particularly in the southern part. But, taken as a whole, the two belts differ substantially in soil and climate and, consequently, in their agricultural economies (*Fig. 12-12*).

The boundaries, related primarily to temperature, generally follow the July 72° isotherm. In only two localities does the Dairy Belt extend much south of the line—in southwestern Wisconsin, where the rough topography encourages dairy farming, and around Chicago, which provides a large market for fluid milk.

For the Dairy Belt as a whole, the land and climate are such that its advantage over other areas extends to the production of only a few widely grown crops. Much of its cropland may be used most effectively for the production of roughage—hay and silage—and in the remainder of the area the crop alternatives available are not much more profitable than hay. The yield of roughage is relatively high, although lower than in the Corn Belt.

Silage is bulky and heavy relative to its value, and deteriorates rapidly when removed from the silo. It cannot be transported economically for any significant distance and therefore has no commercial market. Usually it must be fed on the farm where it is produced and stored. Likewise, the commercial market for other types of roughage, such as hay, is predominantly local, and for the same reasons.

Thus, the value of roughage is determined by the value of livestock products that can be produced through its utilization as feed in the area where the roughage is grown. This is in sharp contrast with corn, which, although predominantly fed on farms where it is grown, has a sufficiently high value per pound to be shipped readily into areas where additional feed is needed. While the low value per pound of roughage insulates farmers from the competition of other areas, there is a well-developed nationwide market for the livestock products they produce. In this way the products from the Dairy Belt come into competition with those from other areas. Hence the Dairy Belt cannot escape the competitive effects of production advantages enjoyed by the Corn Belt.

Oats. The climate of the Dairy Belt is favorable to the growth of oats, a cool weather, early maturing crop. Consequently the district has a modest advantage over the Corn Belt in its production. The average yield of oats is 39 bushels per acre in the Dairy Belt, whereas only 35 bushels per acre are produced in the Corn Belt.

Oats are an acceptable feed for most types of livestock. But the digestible nutrients in 39 bushels of oats in the Dairy Belt are less than half the amount contained in 45 bushels of corn, the average yield of that crop. Since other grains that can be grown in the Dairy Belt also produce much less nutrients per acre than does corn grown in the Corn Belt, the Dairy Belt is at a disadvantage in the grain fattening of meat animals. However, oats are very useful as a supplement to the primarily roughage diet of dairy cattle, and in the Dairy Belt about a quarter of the tillable land is planted to it.

Hay and pasture. The cool climate of the Dairy Belt is well suited to the growth of short-rooted grasses. For the deep-rooted legumes, however, the fertility of the Corn Belt soils more than offsets the disadvantage of that area's hot summer temperatures. Despite this disadvantage in the production of legumes, the Dairy Belt plants as many acres to alfalfa as does the Corn Belt, even though the latter has almost three times as much cropland.

The grasses that supply much of the roughage in the Dairy Belt grow on nontillable land, in permanent pastures and meadows. In addition, both grasses and legumes are planted on cropland and harvested and preserved as hay or silage. In terms of acreage, hay is the leading crop in the Dairy Belt.

Primarily because of the rougher topography and poorer soils in the Dairy Belt, only 60 per cent of the land area is in farms. The proportion of the land in permanent pasture, woodland, and waste is considerably larger than is the case for the Corn Belt. The land not in farms has little agricultural value and is utilized largely as recreational areas and for the production of wood products.

The adaptability of permanent pasture and hay land is restricted severely. Pasture can be utilized effectively by only a few types of farm animals, dairy cattle included. Thus the

rougher topography of the Dairy Belt is a factor contributing to the specialization of the area in milk production. Nowhere is this better illustrated than in southwest Wisconsin. Climatically that area should be part of the Corn Belt. Nevertheless, southwest Wisconsin is predominantly a dairy area, primarily because of its rough topography. The average farm here has about twice as much permanent pasture as farms in adjacent areas to the east, south, and west (*Fig. 12-13*).

Dairy breeds. Although nearly all the European dairy breeds are represented in the Dairy Belt, Holstein cows are the most numerous. This is not surprising since they are large animals and heavy milk producers. However, they tend to give milk averaging somewhat lower in butterfat content than the milk of some other breeds. Guernsey cattle rank next to Holsteins in importance. Guernseys on the average are smaller in size but usually produce a relatively greater amount of butterfat in their milk; they therefore are most popular in the butter area of Minnesota and the cheese manufacturing portion of Wisconsin. Sometimes it is the practice to include some Guernseys in Holstein herds to increase the average butterfat content of the milk.

Smaller numbers of Jersey cattle and Brown Swiss are scattered throughout the area. Minor breeds, such as Dutch Belted and Ayrshire, also are found, along with some dual-purpose

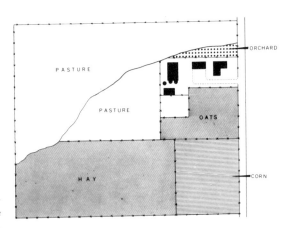

FIGURE 12-13. *A typical Wisconsin dairy farm.*

breeds. Wisconsin now leads all states in dairying (*see Fig. 6-15*).

Demand for milk. As is the case with meats, the demand for milk originates in consumer preferences and incomes. Consumers like the flavor and texture of dairy products. They seem to be less inclined to shift their demand for dairy products in response to income or price changes than in the case of meat, i.e., the demand for dairy products is less elastic. However, the demand for dairy products appears to be more vulnerable to technological change. For example, the flavor and texture of butterfat can be duplicated quite readily by the processing of vegetable oils, but it is difficult to conceive of a good vegetable substitute for a steak or a rasher of bacon. Because of the nature of consumer preferences and the competition from other commodities, the demand for milk probably will grow at a somewhat slower rate than the demand for meats.

Milk may be used fresh or it may be manufactured into a number of other dairy products. These two sources of demand for milk are of approximately equal importance.

Dairy products. Wisconsin manufactures a large amount of all types of dairy products but specializes in cheese and evaporated milk. Michigan is the leader in ice cream production, while Minnesota specializes in butter. The largest share of Minnesota's milk is manufactured. In Wisconsin and Michigan the proportion of manufactured milk is smaller because those states supply fresh fluid milk for the large Chicago and Detroit markets.

With about 45 per cent of the nation's cheese output, Wisconsin has no close competitor in production of natural cheese. Over 40 per cent of its milk goes into cheese, and the bulk of this is made into American cheese. Swiss cheese is also a very important product in some Wisconsin counties. In 1950 a record Swiss cheese output was achieved, as production reached over 52 million pounds (*Fig. 12-14*).

Cheddar cheese production is widespread, but heaviest concentrations are in the east-central and central sections. Italian, Munster, blue, and limburger cheeses also are made.

FIGURE 12-14. *Brining and salting Swiss cheese in Wisconsin. (Monroe Chamber of Commerce)*

MICHIGAN

The outstanding area of fruit and vegetable production in the Interior Lowlands Region is located along the eastern shore of Lake Michigan, where the influence of the lake moderates temperature variations to produce a favorable climate. Smaller areas are scattered throughout the region. The production of commercial fruits and vegetables in the region is limited by two factors, however: (1) the climatic conditions favorable to some of these crops are quite localized, and (2) the market for these crops is not extensive enough for the region as a whole to specialize profitably in their production. Consequently these crops are only occasionally an attractive alternative to the present economy, although they provide some element of diversity in the salable output of the area.

Apples. Michigan has ranked third among the states in apple production in recent years. Apple orchards are concentrated in a strip 10 to 15 miles wide along Lake Michigan northward from Oceana County to Charlevoix. Jonathan, Delicious, McIntosh, and Northern Spy are the leading varieties.

Peaches. Five southwestern and western counties produce the bulk of Michigan's annual peach crop. In these areas, and elsewhere in the southern counties of the lower peninsula where peaches are grown, production is favored by relative freedom from temperatures that result in winter and spring frost injury, length of growing season, and nearness to markets.

Cherries. Production of both sweet and red-tart cherries is concentrated in select areas along the Lake Michigan shore. Michigan is the leading state in the production of red-tart cherries and third in sweet cherry production. Tree numbers have declined in the past 15 years but the bulk remaining are red-tart, concentrated in the Grand Traverse area.

Others. Other fruits, nuts, and berries are also of importance in Michigan's agriculture. Pears, plums, grapes, and strawberries are vital adjuncts within the "fruit belt." Raspberries, blueberries, blackberries, and dewberries round out fruit production in the southwestern part of Michigan.

ONTARIO PROVINCE

Southern and eastern Ontario are by far the most important agricultural sections of the province. Several large, sandy tracts are extensively used for tobacco growing. The soils of part of the lake plain and the St. Clair River area have a high organic content and are well suited to the growing of cash crops. The whole of the upper Thames area, particularly Oxford County, is effective for dairying.

The narrow strip of land surrounding the western end of Lake Ontario, protected by the Niagara escarpment and favorably influenced by the large body of water, enjoys a long growing season and is largely devoted to fruit and vegetable growing. Although the Niagara area is suitable for producing all types of vegetables, only asparagus, tomatoes, and mushrooms are grown extensively because other vegetables do not mature early enough to receive high prices early in the season. Grapes, cherries, peaches, pears, and plums are the most widely grown fruits. St. Catharines and Welland are centers of the Niagara fruit belt and of the wine-making industry.

LAKE ERIE'S SOUTH SHORE

The land in most of the lake plain is well suited to the growing of grain crops such as corn, wheat, oats, and soybeans. Even though corn and wheat together comprise only one-fourth of all cash income, more farm land is planted in these crops than in any others. Much of the grain is used as feed for dairy cows, hogs, poultry, and beef cattle; in large measure, the grain shows up indirectly as cash income from the marketing of livestock products. Agriculture in the area is marked by the prevalence of crop rotation and the use of other up-to-date farming techniques, including a heavy investment in machinery.

A basic crop in the western portion of this area is soybeans. This crop accounts for roughly 15 per cent of the income from agricultural products. All six of the leading soybean counties of Ohio are located in the Lake Erie south shore district.

Agricultural activity in the central and eastern portions of the lake plain reflects its proximity to the Cleveland and Buffalo metropolitan areas. Dairying and the raising of hogs, poultry, and beef cattle, together with complementary enterprises, represent balanced farming.

The southeastern shore of Lake Erie in Ohio, Pennsylvania, and New York is the center of a very important fruit belt. The climate near the lake retards the early blossoming of fruit trees until the danger of frost is past. Rolling-to-hilly land permits the drainage of cold air from the cherry orchards, peach orchards, and grape vineyards on the beach ridges.

A wide variety of deciduous fruits is grown in Ohio. The leading orchard counties are Ottawa, with peach and pear trees, and Sandusky and Lake Counties, which have large cherry orchards. Vineyards dominate near the lake and on the islands within the state of Ohio. Grapes are sold for fresh table use and for wine making. North East, the northernmost community in Pennsylvania, is situated in the heart of the Concord grape belt and a large fruit orchard area.

Westfield, New York, is situated in the Chautauqua grape belt. Although Chautauqua County has only a few hundred square miles of its land in vineyards, the productivity is so high that it ranks among the leading grape-growing counties in the nation. Many grape juice-producing plants are located within this region.

ONTARIO LAKE PLAIN

Fruit, vegetable, and dairy farms occupy about three-fourths of the acreage on the plain south of Lake Ontario. Sales of dairy products, principally milk, provide the largest source of agricultural income; they account for more than half of all farm products sold. Other livestock products, including poultry, represent the second most important source of farmers' cash income. The area's truck farms yield fresh beans, sweet corn, cabbage, tomatoes, spinach, beets, and onions. A large proportion of this produce is delivered to local canneries. With large dairy herds to feed, the area also has an extensive acreage of forage crops. Alfalfa production ranks high nationally.

New York's largest fruit region is just south of Lake Ontario. Although cherries account for roughly 15 per cent of the total value of fruit in the Lake Ontario plain, apples are by far the most important single fruit enterprise in the area.

A climate free from sudden changes in temperature, which results in a relatively long growing season, and accompanying soils with a good internal drainage favor the production of fruit. The Ontario Lake Plain area, although it lies in the northern half of New York, has more frost-free days than any other region in the state, excluding metropolitan New York and Long Island. The tempering effects of Lake Erie, Lake Ontario, and the Finger Lakes have a strong influence on fruit production there. Grape vineyards and orchards of apples, pears, cherries, peaches, and plums extend all along Lake Ontario's shoreline in this district.

Mineral Resources

COAL

The Interior Lowlands contain parts of four important bituminous coal fields. These are: (1) the Northern Region of Michigan; (2) the Eastern Interior Region of southern Illinois and the adjacent part of Indiana; (3) the Western Interior Region of northern Missouri, Iowa, eastern Nebraska, southeastern Kansas, and east-central and northeastern Oklahoma; and (4) the Southwestern Region in north-central Texas (*see Fig. 3-6*).

Only southern Illinois produces good coking coal in sufficient quantity to supply the iron and steel industry. Gary, Indiana, and other Midwestern steel centers provide a market for coal from this field. Considerable tonnage is used for steam purposes as well. One major technological shift, the "dieselization" of the railroads, has resulted in a considerable decline in domestic demands. Illinois usually ranks fourth in soft coal output behind West Virginia, Pennsylvania, and Kentucky.

The Western Interior Region, although extensive, is not only low grade, ranging from lignite to subbituminous, but also is rather remote from the major centers of population. Production is small. For example, Oklahoma mines less than two million tons annually. The coal is utilized as industrial fuel throughout the Southwest and Midwest.

The coal of the Southwestern Region ranges in quality from middle to inferior bituminous. During the last few years coal production has amounted only to about 50,000 tons annually. Petroleum and natural gas are cheaper and better fuels in Texas.

PETROLEUM

No sooner had Drake completed his well near Titusville, Pennsylvania, than a rush for oil deposits started. The search for oil soon spread throughout the Midwest, first in Ohio, where a well was sunk by spring pole at a spot one and a half miles southeast of Macksburg during the winter of 1860. Drilling spread through the years to other parts of the region (*see Fig. 3-7*).

Northeast Indiana-Ohio field. The largest producing formation has been the Trenton in northwestern Ohio, which for a short time was the greatest in the world. During 1896, Ohio's peak year, 23,941,000 barrels were produced, of which 21 million came from the Trenton formation. For many years, Ohio's oil production has been generally on a steady decline. Production in Indiana reached a peak in 1904, and has been declining steadily ever since. Although the oil is of a high-grade paraffin base, it contains considerable sulphur, making it more difficult to refine.

The Michigan field. This field came into production around 1925, and experienced a phenominal rise from 4,000 barrels in that year, to a peak of 23 million barrels in 1939. Since then, production has dropped to about 14 million barrels annually. The Michigan field is located in the central part of the southern peninsula to the west of Saginaw Bay. New fields are being developed elsewhere in the state.

Illinois-Southwest Indiana field. Southeastern Illinois is the center of an oil field that continues eastward into the adjacent portions of Indiana and Kentucky. Production began in 1889, and output was small for a number of years until, in 1910, more than 33 million barrels were taken from the ground. The field then experienced a rapid fall to less than 5 million barrels. Deeper drilling caused a second peak to be reached in 1940, when some 147 million barrels were produced. Like most highly productive oil areas, the field again declined rapidly and presently contributes 4 to 5 per cent of the national output.

Midcontinent field. Only a part of this largest of all oil fields, namely north-central Texas, Oklahoma, and eastern Kansas, lies within the Interior Lowlands. (*Fig. 12-15*).

The first oil output of consequence occurred at Corsicana, Texas, where oil was discovered in 1894, while drillers were seeking water. This find, however, was merely a prelude to

FIGURE 12-15. *A pumping station in the Midcontinent field. There are more geologists, more drilling companies, and more oil companies — and there is more crude oil produced — in this field than in any comparable area. It accounts for about 60 per cent of total United States production of crude oil.* (*Philips Petroleum Co.*)

the development of the field's resources. It was the tremendous gusher at Spindletop, near Beaumont in the Atlantic-Gulf Coastal Plain Region, on January 10, 1901, that opened up oil exploration. This well, flowing at an initial rate of 75,000 to 100,000 barrels per day— about one-half the total of all other wells in the nation—stirred world-wide interest and made people aware of the great oil potentialities in Texas.

For several years after the Spindletop discovery, exploration tended to be concentrated on the Gulf Coast, but the discovery of the huge Glenn Pool near Tulsa in 1905 shifted attention from the Gulf Coast to Oklahoma. Many important discoveries were made in Oklahoma in subsequent years, and this state led the Midcontinent field in oil production from 1906 to 1928. After the Cushing field began production in 1915, yielding 305,000 barrels daily, oil and gas became Oklahoma's greatest income producers. The Seminole field, opened in 1928, was one of the biggest. Today, oil derricks stand in front of the state capitol in Oklahoma City, amid corn fields, and in backyards.

Oil brought a great industry to the state, giving Oklahoma City and Tulsa metropolitan status. The state ranks fourth nationally in oil production and in oil reserves (behind Texas, California, and Louisiana). Total yearly output has exceeded 100 million barrels for several decades. Peak production was reached in 1927, with 216.5 million barrels.

Since 1928, Texas has maintained its position as the leading petroleum state. In the past ten years, crude oil production has almost doubled. This increase has been caused by a combination of factors: (1) the sustained growth in the nation's demand for petroleum products, (2) the relative success of the industry in locating rich oil pools accessible to markets, and (3) an economic climate that has induced investment in oil exploration and production activities. The Midcontinent field is unique in contributing oils with a paraffin base, with an asphalt base, and with a mixed paraffin-asphalt base; some of the oils are heavy, others light.

Transportation of oil. Transportation influences oil development in a particular region in several ways. It constitutes a major factor determining which markets can be reached profitably by oil produced in a specific area. All other things being equal, a market is secured by the oil that offers the lowest transportation cost to that market.

In moving oil, almost all the principal media of transportation in this country are utilized —pipelines, tankers, barges, trucks, and railroads. Of these, pipelines are the most important. Nearly 43 per cent of the region's crude oil is moved this way (see Fig. 3-7). Water carriers account for 30 per cent; trucks, 22 per cent; and railroads, 5 per cent.

Petroleum refining. More than half the crude petroleum in the United States in the last 30 years has come from the Midcontinent field, which, in turn, possesses only about ten per cent of total refining capacity. The location of refineries is obviously not determined solely by the geographic occurrence of crude petroleum; it is also influenced by the location of consuming markets and by differences in transportation costs.

Transportation costs constitute an important part of the market value of refined petroleum products. In order to minimize these costs, it has been logical to locate refining activities at the source of crude oil; at marketing centers in the consuming areas; and at intermediate transshipment points between crude oil supplies and markets, where for any reason the journey is broken. The cost of refining petroleum generally has constituted only a minor portion of the final value of refined products, so that geographic differences in the cost of refinery operations have not been of great importance in determining refinery locations.

The ton-mile cost of moving petroleum and petroleum products by pipeline is less than half the cost of shipment by railroad tank car. Movement by tank ship or barge is, in turn, substantially less expensive on a ton-mile basis than by pipeline. It follows that railroad tank car shipments are proportionally small and that water transportation is used wherever available, except in cases where ice prevents winter transport for several months during the year and large storage costs are involved.

Refineries are located in marketing centers and transshipment points on the Great Lakes at Chicago, Toledo, Detroit, Cleveland, and Buffalo. St. Louis refineries have access to a fairly large marketing territory by barge up and down the Mississippi River and its connecting waterways. Kansas City is an important distribution center for petroleum products; it also lies astride crude oil and oil products pipeline routes from the producing fields to the consuming areas. Other large refineries are located near the producing fields.

Manufacturing

THE GREAT LAKES

By its very geography, the land that adjoins the shores of the Great Lakes is extremely suitable for the support of a large population—a population that brought with it a rigorous development in the manufacture of consumer goods. To this normal industrial activity have been added specialties that depend either upon nearness to natural resources or upon the trades generated by them, so that the Great Lakes area has become even more a source of producer's goods than of articles used directly by consumers.

Many factors account for the concentration and dominance of industry in the economy of this area. Chief of these are: (1) a large labor pool with diversified skills, (2) available and cheap fuel and power, (3) geographic location astride the Great Lakes close to the major population centers of the United States, (4) cheap and efficient forms of land, sea, and air transportation, and (5) plenty of room for expansion of existing industries and addition of new ones on flat land.

In terms of industry, commerce, and agriculture, the Great Lakes area is one of the best-balanced areas on earth. Every important ingredient either is here or readily available: transportation, natural resources, location, labor, supplying industries, and markets. Coal from the mines of Ohio, Pennsylvania, West Virginia, and Kentucky is abundant and comparatively cheap as a fuel and as a chemical raw material. Gas and oil also are available, both from wells locally and by pipeline from other areas. The Great Lakes ore fleet literally moves a small mountain of ore down the lakes each year from the Lake Superior district. Corn, wheat, soybeans, oats, and hay, together with dairy products and meat in the form of beef, pork, and poultry, pour into the area from the agricultural hinterland. Clay, shale, limestone, dolomite, sandstone for abrasive use, marl, peat, gypsum, and salt account in large measure for leadership in brick and tile, refractories, potteries, steel mills, and related industries.

The outstanding feature of the area's industry is its diversification. At the same time, many of the industries are also large. This is illustrated by the fact that the area leads all other industrial districts in the nation in the fabrication of many items, including: steel, telephone equipment, automobile parts, machine tools, marine engines, rubber tires and tubes, metal wares, electrical and nonelectrical machinery, sporting and athletic goods, bolts and nuts, forgings, stamped and pressed metal products, framed pictures, mirrors, gloves, mittens, soaps, perfumes, cosmetics, window screens, shades and blinds, tin cans, and tinware.

Manufacturing industries account for about 35 per cent of all employment in the Great Lakes area. Although there is a broad range of industries with a sizable number of workers, metalworking activities predominate. The emergence of the Lake Superior area as the country's main center of iron ore and the convenient access to it provided by Great Lakes waterways, together with the large coal deposits in the region and in nearby regions, resulted in the location of a substantial proportion of the nation's basic steelmaking facilities in the area.

The steel district extends from Buffalo on the east along the shores of the Great Lakes to Chicago on the west. It produces more than one-third of the nation's steel. Pittsburgh, traditionally the nation's top steel-producing center, yielded first place to Chicago in 1953. Across Lake Ontario, the lakefront city of Hamilton makes most of Canada's steel.

Because of its role in steelmaking and because of its extensive water and land transportation facilities, the area took a leading role in the rapid growth of metal forming and fabricating industries that began shortly after the Civil War and that has continued to the present.

These factors helped the area become a center of industrial employment. Today, the greatest number of employees in blast furnaces, steelworks, and the rolling mills industry is found here. With this concentration of steelmaking facilities and with its central location among the industrial and household markets in the country, it was natural that the area should become the largest fabricator of metal goods. Automobiles are a striking example; the section accounts for the great bulk of the production and employment in this manufacturing field.

Nonelectrical machinery manufacture also is quite prominent, with the area having almost half the nation's employment in this category. The area is also the main producer of agricultural machinery and tractors, possessing more than three-fifths of that industry's total employment, a large part of it concentrated in Illinois, but with Wisconsin also claiming a substantial number of employees. The thousands of workers in the electrical machinery, equipment, and supplies industry partly reflect the substantial employment in radio, television, and electronics manufacturing concentrated in the Chicago metropolitan area.

The importance of the motor vehicles industry is emphasized by the fact that it accounts for about one-sixth of the area's manufacturing employment. Michigan is the major producer. Its workers make up over two-thirds of those employed in automobile manufacturing and assembly in the area, and over half of the national employment.

Outside of metalworking, food and kindred products make up the most important manu-facturing industry, to account for about a quarter of the total national employment in the industry. Part of the Great Lakes area's importance as a food processor results from its strategic location with regard to transportation facilities and consuming markets.

Agriculture, forest, and fisheries account for a somewhat smaller proportion of the area's employment, with 8.9 per cent, followed by professional and related services (8 per cent), and transportation, communication, and public utilities (7 per cent). Each of the other industry divisions employs 5 per cent or less.

Chicago metropolitan area. The Chicago industrial area, embracing five counties in Illinois (Cook, DuPage, Lake, Kane, and Will) and one in Indiana (Lake County), has experienced a greater industrial, commercial, and financial expansion since World War II than any other metropolitan area in the nation (*Figs. 12-16* and *12-17*).

The outstanding feature of Chicago industry is diversification—about 94 per cent of all types of industry are found there. Steel production, the foundation upon which other in-

FIGURE 12-16. *Chicago is the center of one of the world's richest markets. Within a 500-mile radius of the city is a large share of Anglo-America's wholesale trade, population, farms, and industrial and retail establishments.*

FIGURE 12-17. *An aerial view of Chicago. The Chicago River is in the foreground. Lake Michigan can be seen in the background. (Chicago Association of Commerce and Industry)*

dustries rest, not only leads all other industries in the Chicago area, but is, in turn, the largest in the nation. Chicago's prominence as an iron and steel center depends on the fact that iron ore, coal, and limestone can be brought to Chicago cheaply by water. The largest single producer in the metropolitan area is U.S. Steel Corporation's gigantic operation at Gary, Indiana, built in 1907.

Chicago, once the nation's leading meat-packing center, has been replaced by Omaha. Both Swift and Armour have ceased their slaughtering operations in Chicago; Wilson dropped out ten years ago. Rehabilitation of existing facilities is deemed economically unsound.

Chicago still retains its position, however, as the world's largest competitive market for salable livestock. Several factors favor its importance in this industry: (1) its geographical location on the shore of Lake Michigan provides cheap water transportation via the Great Lakes; (2) all major railroads and highways crossing the nation focus on Chicago; (3) inland from Chicago in all directions is the livestock-grain area, where corn is grown primarily for feed for finishing animals for market; and (4) the metropolitan area, second only to New York City in size, provides a huge market for meat products.

Food products are the second largest category in the Chicago area, followed by non-electrical machinery and electrical and electronic machinery and equipment. Other major categories of industrial production are fabricated metal industries (tin cans, stamped and structural shapes, and other products), petroleum, chemicals, and transportation equipment.

Chicago is a leader in industrial research, with more than 1,200 laboratories in the metropolitan area. Moreover, the Chicago district continues to lead all other metropolitan centers in both number and value of contract awards for new manufacturing facilities.

Milwaukee, Wisconsin. Because of its size and maturity, as well as its capital goods specialization, Milwaukee differs in a number of important respects from most other Midwestern industrial cities.

Milwaukee's largest industry is the manufacturing of equipment for generating, transmitting, and distributing electric power. The local firms in this industry produce items ranging in size from the smallest electric motor controls to 305,000-kilowatt steam turbine generator units capable of producing enough electricity to serve an industrial city of half a million people. The largest local producer is the Allis-Chalmers Manufacturing Company.

Ranking second and third in the industry are the Allen-Bradley Company and Cutler Hammer, Inc. Milwaukee producers account for close to a fifth of the nation's output of electrical control apparatus.

Detroit, Michigan. Detroit was founded as the fur trading post of the strait (*de troit*) by the Frenchman, Cadillac, in 1701. From its population of 285,704 in 1900, it was raised by the motorcar industry to be the fifth largest city in the United States, with a total population of 2,250,000 in its metropolitan district.

Michigan is the center of the automobile industry, and Detroit the epicenter. Although there is a tendency toward some dispersal of automobile manufacturing, over 70 per cent is concentrated in a triangular area extending from Lansing, Flint, and Detroit, Michigan, to Cleveland, Ohio (*Fig. 12-18*).

The triangle owes its importance in this industry largely as the result of an historical accident. Detroit, the automotive center, for example, is no better situated geographically for such production than are several other cities bordering the lower Great Lakes. Fortunately for Detroit, Henry Ford, the first successful automobile manufacturer, was born in Michigan and elected to locate his plant there.

Once the industry began, there were many favorable factors within the area to keep it

FIGURE 12-18. *The Ford Motor Company's River Rouge Plant at Dearborn, Michigan, one of the world's largest manufacturing units. (Ford Motor Co.)*

there. The early models were little more than motored (horseless) carriages, and the carriage trade was a well established local industry because of the presence of hardwood as a raw material. Marine engine building was also important, facilitating the adaptation of an engine suitable for use in automobiles. A skilled labor pool likewise was available. Fortunately, too, the flat terrain made it easier for these low-powered vehicles to win public acceptance. Presence of a hilly landscape possibly would have retarded development or discouraged the pioneer builders entirely. Finally, metal fabricating was well established and has expanded to keep pace with the growth of the automotive industry.

Other manufacturers followed in Ford's footsteps, and mass production of automobiles began on a large scale. Volume production combined with low prices put the automobile within reach of all classes. This feat was accomplished through division of labor, the use of interchangeable parts, and standardization. Actual production stages include: (1) the manufacturing of parts from raw materials, (2) primary assembly, and (3) final assembly. In 1951, the one-hundred-millionth American automobile was produced. Annual output has now topped the seven million mark.

The automobile industry creates a huge market for tools, dies, gauges, and jigs and fixtures —all indispensable to the trade. Because of Detroit's concentration on automobile manufacturing, these supporting industries are also centered in that city. The same applies to manufacture of paints, varnishes, upholstery, chemicals, copper wire, brass, iron, and steel.

Toledo, Ohio. Toledo is the fourth largest city in Ohio and an important manufacturing center. In total tonnage of Great Lakes shipping, it ranks first among Ohio's ports; shipment of iron ore, coal, lumber, and grain rank high. The city is an important rail and truck center, with terminals linking port facilities. Toledo has made special efforts to accommodate new trade generated by the St. Lawrence Seaway.

Cleveland, Ohio. Industrial activity of the Cleveland district is closely related to the city's historic importance as an industrial lake port. Located on the Lake Erie Plain at the mouth of the winding Cuyahoga River, Cleveland is a splendid site for industrial activity. Access to the upper Great Lakes iron ore deposits by way of water has made Cleveland an important steel center. The St. Lawrence Seaway opens the way to the rich deposits of iron in Labrador, which assure a continuous supply of high-grade raw materials to the steel mills of the area (*Fig. 12-19*).

Unlike centers dominated by one major industry, Cleveland's industrial complex has grown as a collection of many small or medium-sized plants, mainly under local ownership. Precision metalworking historically has been the strong point of Cleveland industry.

Transportation equipment, the leading industry, includes production of motor vehicles and parts, as well as aircraft, aircraft parts, and auxiliary equipment. Machinery, excluding electrical machinery and equipment, is the second most important industrial enterprise. Primary metals industries—smelting, rolling, casting, and forging of metals—also are significant. Located in the area are blast furnaces, steelworks, and rolling mills of sev-

FIGURE 12-19. *Cleveland's excellent inner and outer harbors constitute one of the finest ports on the Great Lakes. (Cleveland Chamber of Commerce)*

eral of the nation's largest steel producers, and also numerous foundries and forge shops, both ferrous and nonferrous, including an aluminum foundry and forging plant.

Other important industry groups that account for a substantial volume of employment include: chemicals, food processing, printing and publishing, and apparel.

Sandusky-Ashland, Ohio. This district lies west and south of the Cleveland, Lorain, and Akron metropolitan areas. The largest plants manufacture a variety of goods—ball bearings, auto parts, radio and television sets, washing machines, and paper products. Sandusky is important as a lake port, especially in coal shipments, boat building, commercial fishing, and the summer resort business. The city is also a center of the wine industry. Ashland has a large plant for the manufacture of water pumps and sprays and several plants producing a score of rubber products.

Akron, Ohio. The Akron rubber industry employs more than 50,000 people, or one-fifth of the nation's total employment for the industry. Products include motor vehicle tires and inner tubes, synthetic rubber, reclaimed rubber, and a large variety of fabricated rubber goods.

Aircraft parts, machinery (including precision tools and special industrial machinery), ordnance equipment, cereal breakfast foods, sporting and athletic goods, gray-iron castings, millwork, pottery products, and machine shop products are also important in this area.

Erie, Pennsylvania. Situated near the eastern end of the lake that bears its name, Erie's major industrial group is machinery, including electrical. Metals and metal products also rank high, both in terms of value added and total employment. Other large plants employing 1,000 or more workers manufacture such items as: locomotives, paper products, steel forgings and castings, electronic components, and cranes and power shovels.

Buffalo-Niagara district. The Buffalo-Niagara district lies at the junction of the Great Lakes and the New York State Barge Canal. It is within economical shipping distance of Lake Superior iron ore and Pennsylvania coal and enjoys convenient access to low-cost transportation, hydroelectric power generated at Niagara Falls, basic raw materials, and the great consumer markets of the Northwest, the Middle West, and Canada (*Fig. 12-20*).

The district has a wide diversity of industry, led by the manufacture of iron and steel products, chemical and metallurgical supplies, and foods. Agricultural activity is substantial, with almost 70 per cent of the total acreage made up of farmlands.

Buffalo's iron and steel industry, which has a total blast furnace capacity in excess of three million tons, is one of the largest in the country. The giant Bethlehem Steel Company plant at Lackawanna, just south of Buffalo, has nearly four-fifths of New York State's basic steel and over half its pig iron capacity.

The chemical and metallurgical industries, utilizing the cheap power available from Niagara Falls, have huge factories making aniline dyes, aluminum, carborundum, drugs, soaps, and oil. Buffalo, an important transfer point for both American and Canadian wheat, is also one of the world's greatest milling centers.

The Genesee Valley. This is one of the leading industrial sections of New York State. Population, industry, trade, and commerce focus on Rochester, the valley's trade center and third largest city in the state. Early known as the "Flour City," Rochester has added many industries, several of them as a result of the inventiveness of its citizens. The city is famous for the manufacture of cameras and photographic supplies, optical goods, electrical machinery, instruments, and apparel. It also produces radio and television equipment, shoes, gears, laundry and dry cleaning equipment, gauges, and baby foods.

Situated on Lake Ontario, the Genesee River, and the New York State Barge Canal, Rochester is a port of entry for trade with Canada. The principal transportation routes of New York State traverse the area. Ample and dependable electric power is available throughout the section.

FIGURE 12-20. *This view of Niagara Falls shows the American Falls on the left and part of Horseshoe Falls on the right. Four miles below the falls, the Robert Moses Niagara Power Plant generates almost two million kilowatts of electricity.* (*New York State Dept. of Commerce*)

Syracuse district. Syracuse is advantageously situated at the intersection of the major traffic corridors of New York State. It is a highly industrialized, machinery and metalworking center. Industrial products include: china, worsted fabrics, typewriters, air conditioning equipment, pneumatic conveyors, washing machines, and laundry and dry cleaning equipment.

Within a radius of 35 miles of Syracuse are Auburn, the site of one of the leading manufacturers of diesel engines; Oswego, noted for paper and matches; and Oneida, known for its quality furniture.

Utica is the hub of the region's transportation system and one of the largest redistribution centers in the United States for less-than-carload freight. Although textile production is still an important industry, most of the manufacturing is now oriented toward durable goods. Four of the major industry groups—electrical machinery, nonelectrical machinery,

primary metals, and fabricated metals—account for over 56 per cent of employment.

Rome is an important manufacturer of copper products. The largest single employer there is the Griffiss Air Force Base, with a high percentage of civilian employees.

Ontario. The southern or triangular part of Ontario, sandwiched between the lower lakes and the Ottawa River, supports Canada's greatest concentration of population and is recognized as one of the world's major industrial areas. Almost 3,500,000 people, 68 per cent of Ontario's population and 22 per cent of the population of Canada, live and work in the urban centers and rich farming areas south of a line running from near Oshawa, just east of Toronto on Lake Ontario, to Georgian Bay. Approximately one-third of these live in the metropolitan area of Toronto.

Located across the river from Detroit, Windsor shares the bulk of Canadian automobile manufacturing with Oakville, Hamilton, and Oshawa. These four cities account for most of Canada's auto and auto parts industries (*Fig. 12-21*).

Ontario's important petrochemical industry is centered around Sarnia, the "Chemical Valley" of Ontario. Most of the province's chemical production comes from this area and in it are the province's major oil refineries. Among the chemicals of which Sarnia is the only Canadian manufacturer are carbon tetrachloride (an important industrial solvent) and glycol (used in making antifreeze, explosives, and cellophane). Imperial Oil, Dow Chemical, and the Polymer Corporation (manufacturer of synthetic materials) are the big three of Sarnia's industrial empire. Other companies—Cabot of Canada, Sun Oil, and Canadian Oil—recently have located new plants in the area.

Oil from the west is brought to Imperial Oil's refinery at Sarnia by pipeline and lake tanker; oil from the south comes by pipeline. It is broken down and its components rearranged with those from fresh water and salt, which is mined locally in large quantity. The resulting products range from wax to antifreeze; some shipped from Sarnia by rail,

FIGURE 12-21. *The assembly line of the Ford of Canada plant in Windsor, Ontario.* (*National Film Board of Canada*)

others by water, and still others by pipeline to all parts of Ontario.

Ontario's Golden Horseshoe, 50 miles wide and 150 miles long, is comprised of the area from Oshawa westward around Lake Ontario to Niagara Falls. It includes Toronto, the capital of Ontario and second largest city in Canada, with a metropolitan population of more than one million (*Fig. 12-22*). Toronto ranks among the business and financial centers of the world. Its Stock Exchange is second only to Wall Street's in transactions. More mining companies, banks and investment companies have their head offices here than in any other city of Canada. Toronto, like Montreal, is an important distribution and transportation city for eastern Canada. It produces a wide diversity of manufactured articles—meat products, electrical appliances, metal products, machinery, clothing, processed food, and refined oil.

Forty miles to the west is the lakefront city of Hamilton, which makes most of Canada's steel. The Steel Company of Canada, Ltd., was formed in 1910 by the amalgamation of the Hamilton Iron and Steel Company with nearly all the important hardware-producing firms in Canada. Its Hamilton plants are situated midway between coal and iron resources; the United States ore and coal companies in which it has an interest furnish a large part of its requirements, while limestone is obtained from a subsidiary 50 miles from Hamilton. Its largest markets are in the immediate vicinity. To the southeast is St. Catharine, a noted health resort and a shipbuilding, rubber, and paper products center.

Dispersal of industry outside the metropoliton area of Toronto has begun, indicating a pattern for Ontario's industrial development in the years ahead. Up until 1950, the majority of new industries settled in the Greater Toronto district, an area extending from Oakville to Whitby and north to Aurora. Since then, decentralization of industry has increased in momentum.

London, Ontario, is a highly diversified manufacturing center specializing in radios, refrigerators, sheet metal products, knitted goods, machinery, and printing.

FIGURE 12-22. *Toronto, Ontario, with the harbor area in the foreground. (National Film Board of Canada)*

Other centers symbolizing the spread of manufacturing in Ontario are Thorold, a pulp and paper center, and Port Colborne, which is noted for nickel refining because of excellent transportation facilities and cheap hydroelectric power from Niagara Falls.

Kingston, Brockville, and Cornwall are the most important Ontario cities along the St. Lawrence. Kingston was founded in 1673 as a fur trading post and strategic military stronghold. It is situated at the point where Lake Ontario empties into the St. Lawrence River, and at the head of the Thousand Islands. The city is an important lake port connected to Ottawa by the Rideau Canal. Kingston also is noted for its locomotive shops, shipyards, textile factories, and aluminum refining. Brockville, midway between Kingston and Cornwall, is another important link in the St. Lawrence corridor, turning out hats, hardware, abrasives, marine engines, and boats. Cornwall specializes in paper, chemicals, textiles, furniture, and clothing.

Ontario has been termed "the fabricator" of materials for the rest of Canada. Its plants manufacture steel, electrical goods, heavy machinery and mechanical equipment needed for resource development. In addition, the province is an expanding source of iron ore, petroleum, essential minerals, and other basic materials.

United States manufacturers see great advantages not only on the basis of a Canadian market of more than 19 million people, but in Ontario's 2,362 miles of shoreline on the St. Lawrence Seaway and the Great Lakes. Branch plants may be located in Ontario within convenient distances from their parent plants in the major industrial areas of the United States, particularly in New York, Ohio, Michigan, Illinois, and Pennsylvania. Of the some 1,500 United States branch plants in Ontario, three-quarters originated from firms located in the Cleveland-St. Louis-Minneapolis triangle.

CENTRAL OHIO-INDIANA

Sometimes referred to as the "East-central Lowland," central Ohio-Indiana is transitional between the highly urbanized manufacturing belt of the Great Lakes on the north and the sparsely populated, rough, hilly land overlooking the Ohio River Valley on the south. A dense rail and highway network provides rapid transportation from one part of the area to the other. Although predominantly a farming area, the presence of large coal deposits, oil and gas pipelines, and ready markets favors industry, especially in such metropolitan centers as Columbus and Dayton, Ohio, and Indianapolis, Indiana.

Fort Wayne, Indiana. Unquestionably the most mature of the cities on the northern fringe of the central Ohio-Indiana district, Fort Wayne is directly astride the country's main belt of population, transportation, and industry. Well over a third of the city's export earnings are derived from the production of insulated magnet wire for electric motors, transformers, coils, and electronics equipment.

Columbus, Ohio, metropolitan district. Because of its position as a state capital and the location there of one of the nation's largest state universities, public employment in the

Columbus area accounts for a sizable part of the labor force.

Leading manufactures are airplanes, appliances, and auto parts. Foundry and machine shop products, packed meat, shoes, printing and publishing, railroad cars, and food products also rank high.

Dayton, Ohio, metropolitan area. Dayton is a center for the production of office and store machines and devices. The federal government also employs a sizable work force in the Dayton metropolitan area, most of it at the Wright-Patterson Air Force Base and other military installations.

Indianapolis, Indiana, metropolitan district. Indianapolis consists predominantly of branch plants of national corporations. Like so many other American cities, Indianapolis was transformed when World War II brought into being many new enterprises and expanded old ones—for example, Allison Division of General Motors, Bridgeport Brass, and the Naval Ordnance Plant.

ST. LOUIS METROPOLITAN DISTRICT

St. Louis began as a fur-trading post hacked out of the wilderness in 1764. It became the gateway to settlement of the West and was a major transportation center, first by river, then by rail. Transportation and furs are still important, but the city's stability and growth in the past half-century may be attributed to its broad industrial base (*Fig. 12-23*).

Besides being a major market for raw furs, St. Louis is noted for its production of sugar mill machinery. It is a leader in the manufacture of stoves and ranges, harvest hats, woodenware, and brick products. The city is also the hub of the shoe industry, rising to national importance after 1900 when shoe manufacturers located there to be nearer the source of raw material—leather tanned from cattle hides, a by-product of the meat-packing industry.

Chemicals, drugs, aircraft and auto parts, apparel, and related items round out a long list of industrial materials made in St. Louis. East St. Louis, the largest satellite, is the center of aluminum refining. The area between Alton and East St. Louis is important for petroleum refining.

MINNEAPOLIS-ST. PAUL

The Twin Cities are located on the bend of the upper Mississippi River at the head of navigation. Founded as a fur trading post (Fort Snelling), the early history of the area was associated with flour milling, which was powered by the Falls of St. Anthony. The combination of furs, water power, and strategic location with respect to east-west and north-south trade routes was sufficient stimulus for early and rapid growth.

Food processing leads among Minneapolis industries, followed by machinery, precision instruments, and printing and publishing. Still famous for flour production, it is headquarters for General Mills, International, Pillsbury, Commander-Larrabee, and Russell-Miller. Its chemical industry processes Minnesota's large flax crop for linseed oil and oil cake. Meat packing is another important industry, along

FIGURE 12-23. *The Jefferson National Expansion Memorial, on the St. Louis waterfront. Its center feature is the 630-foot Gateway Arch. (Chamber of Commerce of Metropolitan St. Louis)*

with the manufacturing of electrical machinery, heating equipment, agricultural machinery, and fertilizer (Fig. 12-24).

St. Paul, the capital, is among the larger transportation centers of the nation. The city is served by several first-class railroads for ready access to markets throughout the country. Only New York and Chicago handle more freight in more trucks and deliver to more cities than the hundreds of vehicles constantly loading and unloading in St. Paul's Midway district. The Mississippi River provides excellent low-cost water transportation to all points on the Mississippi system of inland waterways.

KANSAS CITY-OMAHA

In manufacturing, as in transportation and trade, these two cities are part of a belt of industry extending from Omaha down the Missouri Valley to St. Joseph and Kansas City.

Kansas City, Missouri. Kansas City is the natural capital of the tremendous agricultural region surrounding it. Crops produced are diverse in character, in keeping with the general economy of Missouri. Wheat, tobacco, corn, potatoes, fruit, soybeans, and livestock, together with oil, natural gas, coal, and other mineral resources, combine to furnish a stable economy for the area.

The meat-packing industry is only one of the many big enterprises in the city. Food processing, flour milling, steel and steel products fabrication, petroleum refining, garment manufacturing, automobile and truck assembling, and aircraft and aircraft accessories production are among the leading industries.

Kansas City, Kansas. This city is a major grain storage and milling, livestock, and meat-packing center. Food processing, oil refining, the manufacture of structural-steel products, soap, and airplanes and airplane parts are important industries.

FIGURE 12-24. *The Mississippi River waterfront in Minneapolis, Minnesota. Flour mills are located along both sides of the river. (Minneapolis Chamber of Commerce)*

Omaha, Nebraska. Situated on the west bank of the Missouri River, almost midway between the mouth and the source, Omaha is the nation's largest livestock and meat-packing center. Other important industries include oil refining, lead smelting, farm implements, paint, mechanical appliances, flour milling, and dairy products.

OKLAHOMA CITY-TULSA

Oklahoma, in common with the rest of the nation, has had a rapid increase in the number of cities. With its central location, Oklahoma City is a political center. In addition, the discovery of oil and the development of manufacturing, wholesaling, and retailing have contributed to its growing economy; meat-packing, textiles, food processing, chemicals, and fabricated metals are all important industrial activities.

Tulsa is headquarters for many oil companies and a center for the manufacture of oil field supplies. Wholesale trade, along with industry, formed the basis of Tulsa's growth. The city is the trade center for the northeastern part of Oklahoma, and for the adjacent parts of Kansas, Arkansas, and Missouri.

Recreational Resources

A region as large and diverse as the Interior Lowlands offers countless opportunities for tourism and recreational development. A network of modern highways opens an ever-changing panorama of attractions, and the range of selection is wide. There are vast forests, natural and man-made lakes, and sparkling fishing streams. State, provincial, and national forests offer the enchantment of vast, unspoiled playgrounds; summer and winter health resorts; and camping, boating, swimming, hiking, picnicking, skiing, and sledding facilities throughout many parts of the region. Many of these facilities, however, are sandwiched between industrial towns and cities. To reach them often involves a long drive and heavy traffic. The parks are crowded with thousands of other human beings with the same purpose in mind, relaxation.

Only in the northern portion of the Interior Lowlands is there sufficient land area that is relatively undeveloped or unspoiled by cities so that it might be termed a true vacationland. Upper Minnesota, Michigan, and Wisconsin offer outstanding recreational outlets (*Fig. 12-25*). There are several thousand square miles of virgin forest and some 50,000 square miles of lakes, rivers, and streams—the natural haunt of a wide variety of fish and wild game —interspersed with many fine towns and villages. Summer and winter health resorts are ideally located in beautiful natural settings.

Outlook

The Interior Lowlands Region is the agricultural and industrial heart of Anglo-America. Its factories and farms provide a high standard of living for the people who dwell there. In keeping with the national trend, a great increase in the urban pattern of living can be anticipated as more and more industries arise. Already the population density along the Great Lakes exceeds that of any part of Anglo-America except in the megalopolis portion of the Atlantic Coastal Plain. It is here that the railways, highways, waterways, airways, and means of communication become most concentrated.

FIGURE 12-25. *Richmond County Park, Wisconsin. (Wisconsin Conservation Dept.)*

Selected References

ALEXANDERSSON, GUNNAR, "Changes in the Location Pattern of the Anglo-American Steel Industry: 1948–1959," *Economic Geography*, Vol. 37, April, 1961, pp. 95–114.

BORCHERT, JOHN R., "The Twin Cities Urbanized Area: Past, Present, and Future," *The Geographical Review*, Vol. 51, January, 1961, pp. 47–70.

BROWNELL, JOSEPH W., "The Cultural Midwest," *The Journal of Geography*, Vol. 59, February, 1960, pp. 81–85.

BURGHARDT, ANDREW F., "The Location of River Towns in the Central Lowland of the United States," *Annals of the Association of American Geographers*, Vol. 49, September, 1959, pp. 305–323.

DURAND, LOYAL, JR., "The American Centralizer Belt," *Economic Geography*, Vol. 31, October, 1955, pp. 301–320.

——, "The Migration of Cheese Manufacture in the United States," *Annals of the Association of American Geographers*, Vol. 42, December, 1952, pp. 263–282.

GARLAND, JOHN H., *The North American Midwest—a Regional Geography*, New York: John Wiley & Sons, Inc., 1954.

GOLLEDGE, R. G., RUSHTON, G., and CLARK, W. A., "Some Spatial Characteristics of Iowa's Dispersed Farm Population and Their Implications for the Grouping of Central Place Functions," *Economic Geography*, Vol. 42, July, 1966, pp. 261–272.

HENDERSON, JAMES M., and KRUEGER, ANNE O., *Natural Growth and Economic Change in the Upper Midwest*, Minneapolis, Minn.: The University of Minnesota Press, 1965.

HEWES, LESLIE, "The Northern Wet Prairie of the United States: Nature, Sources of Information, and Extent," *Annals of the Association of American Geographers*, Vol. 41, 1951, pp. 307–323.

HEWES, LESLIE, and FRANDSON, PHILLIP E., "Occupying the Wet Prairie: The Role of Artificial Drainage in Story County, Iowa," *Annals of the Association of American Geographers*, Vol. 42, March, 1952, pp. 24–50.

KAUPS, MATTIE, "Finnish Place Names in Minnesota: A Study in Cultural Transfer," *The Geographical Review*, Vol. 46, July, 1966, pp. 377–397.

KERR, DONALD, "The Geography of the Canadian Iron and Steel Industry," *Economic Geography*, Vol. 35, April, 1959, pp. 151–163.

LAIDLY, W. T., "Submarine Valleys in Lake Superior," *The Geographical Review*, Vol. 51, April, 1961, pp. 277–283.

LEWTHWAITE, GORDON R., "Wisconsin Cheese and Farm Type: A Locational Hypothesis," *Economic Geography*, Vol. 40, April, 1964, pp. 95–112.

MERRIAM, WILLIS B., "Reclamation Economy in the Holland Marsh Area of Ontario," *The Journal of Geography*, Vol. 60, March, 1961, pp. 135–140.

OLMSTEAD, CLARENCE W., "The Application of a Concept to the Understanding of a Region: People, Time, Space, and Ideas in the Economic Core Region of Anglo-America," *The Journal of Geography*, Vol. 59, 1960, pp. 53–61.

PROUDFOOT, MALCOLM J., "Chicago's Fragmented Political Structure," *The Geographical Review*, Vol. 47, January, 1957, pp. 106–117.

REEDS, LLOYD G., "Agricultural Regions of Southern Ontario, 1880 and 1951," *Economic Geography*, Vol. 35, July, 1959, pp. 219–227.

RUDD, R. D., "The Red Ember Coal Mine: An Illinois Stripping Operation," *The Journal of Geography*, Vol. 59, January, 1960, pp. 11–15.

SCHMUDDE, THEODORE H., "Some Aspects of Land Reforms of the Lower Missouri River Floodplain," *Annals of the Association of American Geographers*, Vol. 53, March, 1963, pp. 60–73.

WEAVER, JOHN C., "Crop-combination Regions in the Middle West," *The Geographical Review*, Vol. 44, April, 1954, pp. 175–200.

YEATES, MAURICE H., "Some Factors Affecting the Spatial Distribution of Chicago Land Values, 1910–1960," *Economic Geography*, Vol. 41, January, 1965, pp. 57–70.

YATES, THOM, "Toronto—City of Superlatives," *Ethyl News*, November–December, 1960, pp. 4–7.

13 *Great Plains Region*

The Great Plains Region, extending in a continuous belt from Mexico into Canada, comprises the largest uninterrupted area in Anglo-America with a semiarid climate (*Fig 13-1*).

Surface Features

The Great Plains is a region of nearly horizontal rocks and has a topography, varying from young through mature to old, that stretches 400 to 500 miles across and slopes eastward eight to ten feet per mile (*Fig. 13-2*). It is 4,000 to 6,000 feet high where it abuts the Rocky Mountains on the west. Its eastern edge is 1,500 to 2,000 feet high, generally passing into the Interior Lowlands by a steeper slope. In some places there is a 300- to 400-foot escarpment, which is dissected in other places into a belt of hills. The sections are distinguished mainly by the stages reached in the erosion cycle (*Fig. 13-3*).

The Great Plains from Nebraska to Texas are essentially flat except where crossed by streams (not numerous) or blown into sand dunes (western Nebraska). The largest flat is the Llano Estacado (Staked Plain) in western Texas, a surface made by alluviation by overloaded streams pouring from the mountains. This flat once occupied the entire width of the region. When erosion succeeded the

deposition, the eastern margin was first dissected. The central lowlands and the marginal hilly belt are expanding westward at the expense of the high plains. South of central Kansas this marginal hilly belt is narrow; to the north, it widens and is represented by the Smoky Hill section.

At the same time a more arid strip near the mountains in eastern Colorado and New Mexico was eroded because vegetation was insufficient to protect it. Only in west Texas, where the grass forms a tight sod, was the flat surface preserved. Farther west in the Colorado piedmont are bunch grass and an eroded surface. The Raton section (northeastern New Mexico) has been raised a little higher and its streams run in canyons, some of them 1,000 feet deep. It has prominent volcanic features: great lava-capped mesas,[1] many volcanic "necks,"[2] and a few very young volcanoes.

[1] A flat, table-like mountain that falls away steeply on at least three sides and is formed from a plateau in an arid region. The word in Spanish means "table." The flat surface is due to the fact that the harder top layers of rock have resisted denudation and, being nearly horizontal, have maintained a uniform surface parallel to the stratification.

[2] A rocky crag consisting of solidified lava that formerly filled the central opening of a volcano and has been left isolated when the remainder of the cone has been worn away by weathering.

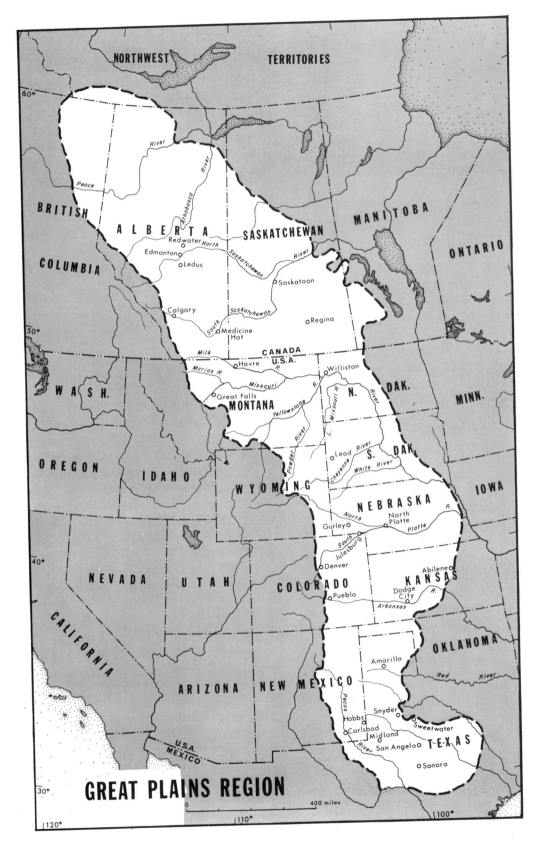

GREAT PLAINS REGION

FIGURE 13-1.

Part of the Pecos section (east-central and southeastern New Mexico) is reduced to a new peneplain 500 to 700 feet below the Raton section on the north. Much of its northern part is quite rugged.

At the south end of the Llano Estacado the alluvial cover gives out. The Edwards Plateau is a limestone plateau with dissected edges that overlook the Interior Lowlands and the South Atlantic-Gulf Coastal Plain. There is little left of the plateau surface in central Texas. Much of this section is eroded enough to be rugged (mature or past mature) and considerable areas are approaching old age.

The Pine Ridge Escarpment overlooks the Missouri Plateau. The plateau on the north, subject to long erosion, is much lower than the high plains to the south (1,000 feet lower on the Wyoming-Nebraska boundary), and is expanding southward. It is not a perfect peneplain because the erosion cycle has been interrupted by occasional periods of uplift. Fragments of peneplain are found at different levels. There are also extensive areas of old river terraces developed at different stages of uplift. Recently revived erosion has made gigantic badlands[3] east and south of the Black Hills and along certain streams, especially the Little Missouri River (*Fig. 13-4*). There are

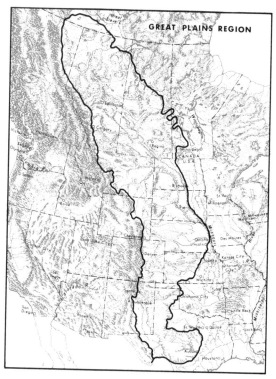

FIGURE 13-2. *The Great Plains Region, physical relief.*

several isolated mountain uplifts; the Black Hills uplift is the largest and farthest east.

The northern and eastern margins of the Missouri Plateau were glaciated. The course of the Missouri River was determined by the edge of the ice, which blocked former drainage toward the east. The river has since cut out a trough much like that of the Ohio River. The strip of the Missouri Plateau between the Missouri River and the Interior Lowlands (James River Valley) is surmounted by strong terminal moraines called the "Couteau of the

---

[3] An elevated, arid region that is seamed and lined with innumerable deep gullies by the occasional torrential rain, the normal precipitation being insufficient to support an adequate protective covering of grass or other vegetation. The unequal resistance of the rocks often causes tall columns and platforms to stand out above the surrounding land. So completely are the badlands gullied or bared by rain that they are almost valueless for agriculture or for pasture land.

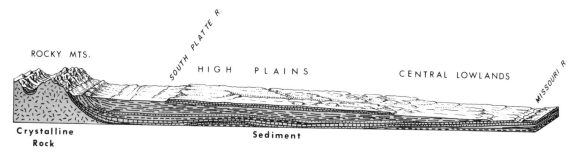

FIGURE 13-3. *Cross-section of the Great Plains Region (after Raisz).*

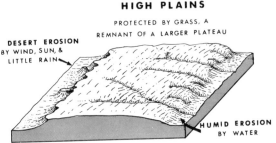

FIGURE 13-5. *The high plains as a survival, or remnant (after Webb).*

FIGURE 13-4. *The Badlands National Monument, South Dakota, is a 170-square-mile area of castellated spires, colorbanded cliffs, and sharp ridges — a classic example of erosion by wind and water. (South Dakota Dept. of Highways)*

Missouri." There are numerous ponds, swamps, and stony hummocks; this is a grazing country, bordering farm lands on the east (*Fig. 13-5*).

The Black Hills are a dome-like mountain range 3,000 to 4,000 feet above the plain and 7,000 feet above the sea. Granite is exposed in the center where the overlying sedimentary rocks are eroded away, leaving the former monoclinal[4] ridges and valleys. The larger local rainfall causes forests to grow and feeds streams which are used for irrigation on the nearby plains.

Natural Vegetation and Soils

Originally the Great Plains Region was like a vast, close-cropped meadow, with short

[4] A fold in which the bend is in only one direction; the rock stratum changes its dip by increasing its steepness of inclination, and then levels out again or resumes its gentle dip.

grasses that could stand prolonged drought. Because moisture was inefficient, this was not a rich, tall, prairie grass, but rather was a number of short grasses, such as buffalo, grama, side oat, bunch, needle, and wheat grass. These, together with many kinds of herbs, made up the plant cover (*Fig. 13-6*).

Broad zones of soils correspond to broad differences in climate and vegetation. The chernozem, chestnut, and brown soil zones are aligned in a generally north-south direction corresponding to climatic belts. The chernozem soils, largely devoted to crops, occupy the most humid part. They have thick, black horizons and a large amount of organic matter. The brown soils occur in the driest parts and

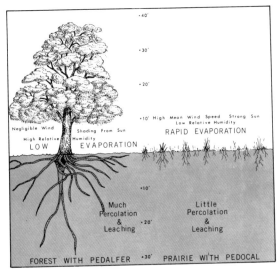

FIGURE 13-6. *Contrasting hydrological conditions for trees and grasses.*

are devoted primarily to grazing. The chestnut soils, between the chernozem and brown soils and intermediate in their features, have thin black or dark-brown surface horizons and moderate organic matter.

Climate

The 20-inch isohyet is not far from the eastern limit of the region. In Kansas and Nebraska the region extends east to the 25-inch isohyet. Farther north along the boundary there is less rainfall, but it is almost equivalent to 25 inches in Kansas because of reduced evaporation. The maximum precipitation comes in the growing season, so that the eastern margin of the region is farmed without irrigation. Westward, rainfall decreases to 10 to 12 inches. In general the wind velocity, evaporation, and percentage of sunshine are high (*Fig. 13-7*).

The climate of the Great Plains is very similar throughout. Its general features are: a low relative humidity; a large amount of sunshine; a light rainfall, confined largely to the warmer half of the year; a moderately high wind movement; and a large daily range in temperature with high daytime temperatures in summer. The major climatic difference within the region from south to north is that of temperature, which results from a latitudinal spread of over 30 degrees. The southern portion generally has mild winters with little snow and few protracted cold spells. Winter in the northern section is lengthened at the expense of spring and autumn. Snow falls frequently in May, and, occasionally, in small amounts in June. In September the autumn snow begins. The average date of the last killing frost in spring is May 21, while the average for the first killing frost in autumn is September 18 (*Fig. 13-8*).

The passage of many centers of high or low pressure near or through the northern Great Plains in the course of a year occasions some decided and sudden changes in weather conditions. Perhaps the most notable are the cold waves. In the more severe of these the temperature may range from −20° to −50° F. for

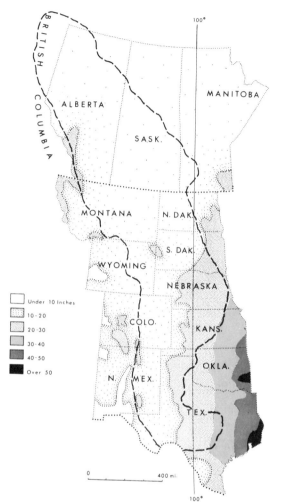

FIGURE 13-7. *Annual precipitation in the Great Plains Region.*

days at a time, though intervals of extreme cold are frequently terminated by chinooks (warm dry, foehn-like winds that descend the Rocky Mountains).

Maximum summer temperatures in excess of 100° F. have been experienced nearly everywhere in the Great Plains, and records of 117° have been reported from both Texas and Montana. Below-zero temperatures have occurred throughout the region, but the minimum drops lower with increase in latitude, to reach a record of −68° at Havre, in northern Montana (*Fig. 13-9*).

The hazards of hail, frost, and hot winds are all particularly severe in the Great Plains,

FIGURE 13-8. *Average length of frost-free period in the Great Plains Region.*

rally divides the region into three major land-use patterns: (1) commercial grain farming, (2) grazing, and (3) irrigated farming.

Settlement

COMMERCIAL GRAIN FARMING

For some time after the geography of the West was fairly well known, much of the Great Plains was believed to be suitable for habitation only by nomadic Indians. Even after settlement of the eastern part of the area had begun, it was thought that the western portion never could become an agricultural country. Most maps of the 1840's and 1850's showed an area called the "Great American Desert," which frequently was compared with the Sahara. The location was rather indefinite, with the earliest maps including all the area between Missouri and the Rocky Mountains, and later ones giving the eastern boundary as approximately the center of Kansas.

If the facts had been known, the geographers would have put the desert districts west of the Rocky Mountains, where they still may be found. The two great divisions of the plains, as applied to natural production, are well defined. They are separate, one from the other, and entirely unlike in physical aspect. They are the Prairies (Interior Lowlands) and the Great Plains. The Prairies extend from the Missouri border to an irregular line passing through Council Grove, Kansas, in Morris County—something less than one-third the distance to the western boundary of the state. It is rolling country with streams fringed with trees. For some thousands of years, at least, the Prairies have been grass-clad, well watered, and fertile. In historic times they never possessed any of the characteristics of desert.

The Great Plains extend from the western border of the Prairies near Council Grove to the Rocky Mountains. This is a country of disappearing streams. There was little or no timber originally. Stretches of drifting sand were to be found, but these were not deserts in the true sense. Covered almost entirely with buffalo grass, the Great Plains were the pastures,

and are caused by alternate inundations of the region by various types of air masses and their interactions. A vigorous upward displacement of warm air along the advancing front of a cold polar air mass is responsible for most of the hailstorms, which are common during the summer. In spring and autumn an advance of polar air may cause killing frost, accompanied by great damage to crops. Equally serious is the hazard presented by the hot, dry winds of summer that are at times experienced in all parts of the High Plains.

The climate of the Great Plains, varying from subhumid in its eastern margin to semiarid in the central and western portions, natu-

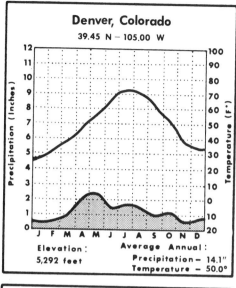

Denver, Colorado
39.45 N – 105.00 W

Elevation: 5,292 feet
Average Annual:
Precipitation – 14.1"
Temperature – 50.0°

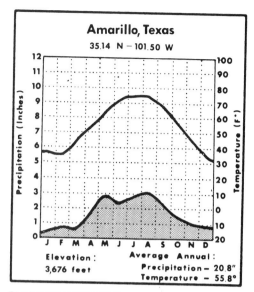

Amarillo, Texas
35.14 N – 101.50 W

Elevation: 3,676 feet
Average Annual:
Precipitation – 20.8"
Temperature – 55.8°

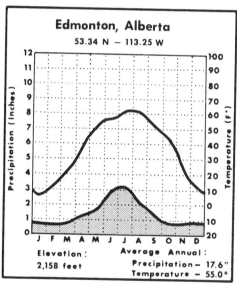

Edmonton, Alberta
53.34 N – 113.25 W

Elevation: 2,158 feet
Average Annual:
Precipitation – 17.6"
Temperature – 55.0°

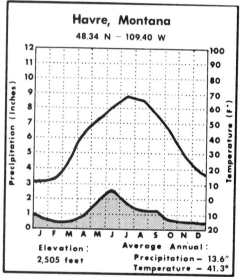

Havre, Montana
48.34 N – 109.40 W

Elevation: 2,505 feet
Average Annual:
Precipitation – 13.6"
Temperature – 41.3°

FIGURE 13-9. *Climatic graphs of the Great Plains Region.*

par excellence, of the buffalo. The antelope, too, was native to the Great Plains, along with deer, wolves, coyotes, rabbits, and numerous birds.

The history of agriculture in this area begins at the close of the Civil War, in the summer of 1865. Cheap land, the return of soldiers from the Civil War, rapid railroad development, improvements in farm machinery, and increasing immigration were important factors in the rapid westward expansion of population. Opposing these features were unfavorable weather conditions, grasshoppers, unadapted crops, and the fact that most of the settlers had come from humid regions and knew little of farming in the low rainfall areas (15 to 20 inches) of central and western Kansas. In addition, few of the newcomers had sufficient resources to survive a poor crop year, especially for the first year or two after their arrival. Yet, by 1875, settlements had been made in most counties in the eastern two-thirds of Kansas.

Corn was the most important crop, with wheat—both spring and soft winter varieties—

in second place. Yet, as early as 1875, agricultural leaders were pointing out that winter wheat was better adapted to local conditions than spring wheat. One of the most important events in wheat production was the introduction of hard winter wheat. This generally is credited to the Mennonites who came from southern Russia to settle in Kansas in 1874.

By 1890 a vanguard of settlers had pushed beyond Kansas and Nebraska into eastern Colorado. The majority had come from the humid Northeastern states, and previous experience had in no way prepared them for the climatic hazards they now encountered. The initial settlement occurred during one of the more rainy periods, and the settlers were predisposed to believe that the climate was becoming more humid—a delusion that was destroyed by the drought of the 1890's (Fig. 13-10). The drought not only stopped further immigration but also caused a considerable emigration of earlier settlers. In some of the western Kansas counties, two-thirds of the farm population was forced to leave because of the drought. Many towns were abandoned completely.

One almost immediate reaction to the drought was a phenomenal increase in dry

FIGURE 13-10. *Desert conditions and improper use of the land took their toll of livestock on the Great Plains in the late nineteenth century and the early part of this century. Scenes like this were not uncommon. (U.S. Dept. of Agriculture)*

farming throughout the Great Plains. Dry farming was hailed as the solution to all agricultural problems within the region, and settlers again began pouring into the area.

All dry farming practices focused upon the single aim of conserving the scant moisture supply by reducing or eliminating run-off and evaporation, and by increasing to a maximum the absorption and retention of moisture by the soil. It was thought that this could be accomplished by summer fallowing and by maintaining a dust mulch through cultivation after every summer rain. The mechanical treatment considered necessary for moisture conservation resulted in rapid deterioration of the soil structure and destruction of humus; its consequence introduced wind erosion as a menace to permanent settlement. Before the beginning of World War I the enthusiasm for dry farming had waned and it was recognized that climatic risks still existed in the Great Plains.

The skyrocketing of agricultural prices during the 1914-1918 period tended to expand cattle production rather than crop production in the Great Plains, but, with the crash of the cattle market during the depression of 1920-1922, many ranchers were ruined financially. In the years following World War I rapid progress was made in agricultural mechanization. Various machines designed for use on the level land, including a manageable tractor, a disk plow, a disk drill, and a small combine harvester, made it possible to plant and harvest wheat in the Great Plains at less than half the cost incurred on the smaller rougher farms to the east.

The economic distress of the rancher, the development of power machinery for planting and harvesting wheat, the maintenance of high prices for wheat, and a series of wetter-than-average years resulted in renewed land speculation. At a time when land values the country over were falling toward pre-war levels, land in the Great Plains, purchased from the ranchmen at $2 to $4 an acre, was resold for $30 to $40 to investors and speculators from as far east as Iowa and Illinois who were ignorant of the physical deficiencies of the area. Despite the speculative nature of much land purchase and the fact that a great deal of the crop production was by "suitcase farmers" who did not live on the farms and frequently stayed in the region only long enough to harvest one crop and sow the next, the population throughout the Great Plains continued to increase until 1931.

In 1931, a disastrous drought was experienced in the northern and central Great Plains, with desert climate prevailing in western Kansas. From then on, in every year until the end of the decade, some part of the area was affected by serious drought; in 1934 and 1936, the region was scourged with drought from end to end (*Fig. 13-11*).

The depression, coming simultaneously with the onset of the drought, carried prices of agricultural products down to the lowest levels on record. Great Plains farmers, burdened with expensive farm machinery and land that had been overcapitalized, were bankrupted almost immediately. Federal relief in many forms had to be poured into the region. Despite the fact that the administration of relief tended to discourage movement of the population, there was a tremendous emigration from the Great Plains between 1930 and 1940.

Man has learned to farm the eastern, more humid portion of the Great Plains, however, and through use of adaptable crops and dry farming techniques, he has been able to establish a rather stable form of agriculture. Nevertheless, plains farming is not entirely a bonanza. Nature is not always smiling. In summer, drought and hot winds too often wither the flourishing crops, and insect pests too often take a heavy toll. In late summer and autumn, disastrous prairie fires may sweep the grasslands, destroying crops, fences, and sometimes farmsteads as well. In winter, blizzards often take huge tolls among animal herds. Despite these handicaps the Winter Wheat district (the eastern edge of the Great Plains) is one of the world's superior farming areas.

The Spring Wheat district, to the northeast, is a sparsely populated land. There are no large cities. Three out of five people live on farms or in towns of less than 2,500 population. The average density of population is approximately

FIGURE 13-11. *An abandoned farmstead in eastern Colorado in the 1930's. The old turning plow in the foreground was left at the end of the row in the field. (Soil Conservation Service, U.S.D.A.)*

six persons to the square mile within the American portion, and less than two in the Canadian Prairie Provinces (Alberta, Saskatchewan, and Manitoba), whose population arrived mainly in the wave of settlement that swept westward during the first two decades of the present century.

About 25 per cent of the land is under cultivation, but the cropland is not distributed evenly. In some areas more than 80 per cent of the land is under cultivation; in others, less than 1 per cent. The proportion of cropland decreases generally from east to west, but not in regular belts. Between cultivated areas are large expanses of native grassland that have not been plowed and should not be plowed. Production varies greatly from year to year and from locality to locality because of the limited and variable precipitation.

Opportunities for industrial developments are restricted by long distances to central markets, high transportation costs, and a sparse population. Long and severe winters, high winds, and early spring and late fall storms that frequently destroy promising crops and range livestock are part of the environment. But drought that strikes at unpredictable intervals has been the nemesis of thousands of farm and ranch ventures. The rural population continues to decline.

GRAZING

Mexican land grants in Texas initiated the ranching practice there prior to Texas' independence. Following admission to the Union, enormous ranches grew up, but cattle were priced so low just before the Civil War that many ranches were abandoned and the cattle ran wild. Then, as war caused prices to rise from four or five dollars a head to fifteen to eighteen dollars, the boom set in.

Following the Civil War, Texas ranchers began driving northward in search of a market and soon there were hundreds of drovers moving their herds over the "long drive" (Fig. 13-12). At first, relatively small herds were driven into southeastern Kansas and the adjacent areas of Missouri, but by 1867 the Kansas Pacific Railroad reached Abilene, which became the most famous of the "cow towns." More than 600,000 head were driven to western Kansas in 1871, the last year a cattle business was done in Abilene. Then Fort Harkness, 65 miles farther west, became the shipping point. In 1871, too, the Santa Fe Railroad reached Newton, which became a competitor

FIGURE 13-12. *Nine miles west of Dodge City, Kansas, the old Santa Fe Trail ruts appear as dark streaks in the ground. (Kansas Dept. of Economic Development)*

for part of the trade, since this route represented a somewhat shorter drive. In 1872, a branch of the Santa Fe reached Wichita and, soon thereafter, Dodge City. For the next several years, the latter became one of the most important shipping points for Texas cattle.

The growth of population in the East and the advance of the railroads into the Great Plains provided both a market and a means of shipping the cattle. This combination of circumstances enabled the range cattle industry to dominate the Great Plains from the late 1860's to the late 1880's.

From 1890 until 1930, the cattle raiser retreated before the crop farmer in all except the rougher and drier parts of the Great Plains. Since that date there has been a re-establishment of beef cattle raising in many areas that at one time seemed permanently given over to crop growing. The retreat of the farmer from much marginal cropland was one reason for the change, but improved breeding and feeding, together with the rapid urbanization of the United States, was the principal cause. The Great Plains farmer and cattleman have found ways to produce more and better meat for a bigger market.

IRRIGATED FARMING

The first Anglo-Americans to practice irrigation on an extensive scale in the United States were the Utah Mormons, who, in about 1847, began the practice of utilizing water in crop production as a necessary means of livelihood. The Mormons extended their colonization activities into neighboring states, among them Colorado and New Mexico, and their irrigation institutions and practices went along with them.

Commercial Grain Farming

WINTER WHEAT DISTRICT

Although wheat is grown in localities in Anglo-America having widely different climates, it is a cool weather crop and produces the largest yield of best quality where cool, moderately wet weather prevails during the growing season, and dry sunny weather during the ripening period. Wheat generally is not a safe crop where the mean annual precipitation is less than 15 inches. In the districts of densest production (Kansas) the annual precipitation ranges from 18 to 20 inches. Wheat does not thrive where the rainfall exceeds 45 inches a year, principally because rust and fungus dis-

eases are more prevalent there than in less humid districts (*Fig. 13-13*).

The distribution of the rainfall is as important as the total amount. For instance, even if the rainfall is normal in a given year, crop yields can fall to almost nothing if the spring growing months receive little rainfall.

The Winter Wheat district lies in Kansas, Nebraska, central Oklahoma, eastern Colo-

FIGURE 13-13.

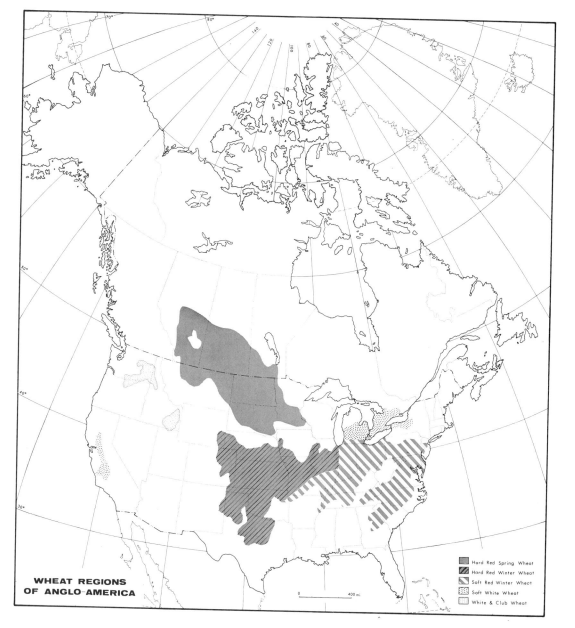

WHEAT REGIONS
OF ANGLO-AMERICA

0   400 mi

Hard Red Spring Wheat
Hard Red Winter Wheat
Soft Red Winter Wheat
Soft White Wheat
White & Club Wheat

rado, and the panhandles of Oklahoma and Texas (*Fig. 13-14*). On the east, wheat gives way to corn as more humid conditions and higher temperatures, especially at night, favor corn growing. On the south, the increasing heat and humidity and the longer growing season make cotton more profitable. The southern boundary of winter wheat production is limited by an average temperature of 68° F. from about April 15 to June 15, or for two months preceding harvest, and coincides rather closely with the northern boundary of cotton growth. The northern winter wheat boundary coincides in a general way with the mean winter isotherm of 20°, and corresponds rather closely to the southern boundary of spring wheat production, or the winter killing of fall-sown

grain. The western limit is set by frequency of failure of wheat crops caused by low precipitation and a high evaporation rate. The annual precipitation within the district varies from about 17 to 20 inches in western Texas to 30 to 35 inches in eastern Kansas and Oklahoma. Winters are moderately cold, especially along the northern border, and generally dry with little or, at best, uncertain snow cover.

Wheat occupies slightly more than a quarter of all the land in farms, or roughly five and one-half times the percentage of farm land in corn, the second most important crop. Sorghums rank third among the grains with less than 3 per cent; hay crops total 4.3 per cent. Oats and barley are minor crops, constituting only 1.7 per cent and 0.5 per cent, respectively.

FIGURE 13-14. *The checkerboard design of strip-cropped wheat fields is common to the Great Plains wheat growing area of Nebraska. This area, near Scottsbluff in the lush Platte Valley, is famous for its hard red winter wheat, which is high in protein and has excellent milling qualities.* (*Nebraska Dept. of Agriculture and Inspection*)

Kansas is by far the largest wheat producer, accounting for more than 200 million bushels in an average year. Oklahoma is a poor second with well over 100 million bushels, followed by Texas, Nebraska, and Colorado.

Winter wheat will grow on a wide range of soil types, but well-drained medium and fine textured soils generally are considered best adapted for wheat production (*Fig. 13-15*).

The usual time for seeding is September 15 to October 15; the optimum is about October 1, since the water requirement of wheat is very high, and wheat yields are influenced materially by the amount of moisture in the soil at seeding time in the fall. The wheat crop attains much of its growth in late fall and early spring when there is usually very little rainfall. During this period, except in seasons when rainfall is plentiful and well distributed during the growing period, growth must depend largely upon the moisture stored in the soil before seeding time. The close correlation between the yield of wheat and the depth of soil moisture at seeding time has been shown in extensive studies by the Kansas Experiment Station.

Growing wheat and handling it are special major industries all across the country from New England to the Northwest and down into the Deep South. Two-thirds of the total output, however, is produced on the plains between the Mississippi River and the Rockies. Of this, about 47 per cent, or approximately 30 million acres, is planted to hard red winter wheat in the central and southern Great Plains. Harvesting begins in central Texas in May just as the hard winter wheat that was planted the previous autumn becomes mature. Up in the Dakotas and Montana, at about the same time, spring wheats that will mature in the late summer are being planted. Twenty-five bushels of wheat, on the average, are taken from every acre. Some rich fields produce 40 or 50 bushels per acre or more.

One man on a self-propelled combine and one man in a truck to pick up the wheat and haul it to storage comprise a harvest crew that handles as many acres as 12 to 15 men could handle in the 1920's (*Fig. 13-16*). Two or three man-hours of labor per acre of wheat, from

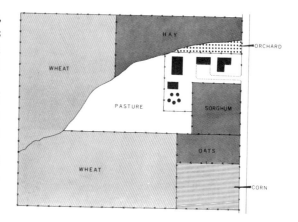

FIGURE 13-15. *A typical Kansas wheat farm.*

tillage to market, are all that are required today, and the result is that one farmer often can handle his own fields, amounting to 500 or more acres, all by himself. Operators who farm two or three times that acreage require only small amounts of help.

FIGURE 13-16. *Harvesting wheat on an east-central Colorado farm. Wheat is a completely mechanized crop. Seeding is done by tractor-drawn, drill-type seeders, some of which fertilize the ground at the same time. Harvesting is performed by combines, the combination reaping and threshing machines that cut the heads from the wheat stalks, shake out the grains of wheat, and discharge the chaff and straw back onto the fields. (Colorado Dept. of Public Relations)*

Harvest time is the final critical period in making a crop, and each owner of grain land wants his wheat safely under cover the moment it is ripe enough to thresh. The Great Plains, in particular, have a tricky climate—a few days delay may bring a high wind or a rainstorm or hailstorm that shatters the heads and knocks the stalks down on the ground, decimating the crop.

Because of this danger, harvesting is always a rush operation and the crews work all day long and far into the night, every day of the harvest season. The emergency exists until the last acres are reaped.

Meanwhile the storage elevators and the railroads fight their annual battles to get the precious grain under a roof or on its way to the big central storage houses and the mills. New concrete elevators have been built every ten miles or so alongside the railroads that cross the wheat country; yet even their capacities are taxed by bumper crops. Some farmers have had to store their wheat temporarily on the ground. At some of the elevators, huge wooden cribs have been built alongside the bins to take care of the overflow.

The railroads are in a similar fix at harvest time. There are never enough cars to meet the demand, even though plans are made six months ahead of time to divert every available boxcar to the prairies. Extra locomotives are brought in from as far away as the Pacific Coast. Additional crews of engineers, firemen, conductors, brakemen, and switchmen are recruited from other divisions. The freight departments of the Santa Fe, Southern Pacific, Union Pacific, and other lines in the wheat territory reschedule many of their operations to give priority to the wheat specials.

Most of the grain that moves by rail goes to huge terminal elevators located in Kansas City, Chicago, Wichita, and other cities. Some of the elevators have a capacity of more than ten million bushels. Suction hoses sweep the cars clean of their loads; the cars then are made up into long strings of empties to go back for more wheat. Several of the largest elevators have automatic car dumps that can pick up an entire boxcar and tilt it so that all its grain is spilled out into a receiving hopper in only seven minutes (*Fig. 13-17*).

Improved plant breeding has brought tremendous increases in yield—up to 50 per cent, in some cases—over the best varieties available in the past. Kansas harvests 30 million bushels more from the same acreage simply because of the success of the prolonged plant breeding program. Over a period of 45 years the original hard red Turkey pioneer wheat of the Great Plains has been given built-in disease and insect resistance, has been refined to produce a higher yield, and has even been redesigned for machine handling. The newest Pawnee strain bears little resemblance to its Turkey ancestor; it almost guarantees a good crop in the particular region to which it is adapted.

Most hard red winter wheat is milled into flour for bread. Bakers want flour having certain characteristics of quality because bakeries must be able to produce a uniform product month after month.

An important problem confronting farmers, bankers, and other persons in the Great Plains is instability of income. Because of weather, insects, disease, and price hazards, farm income varies widely, particularly in those areas where highly specialized wheat farming prevails. These hazards may be minimized to a

FIGURE 13-17. *A 1,320,000-bushel grain elevator in Garden City, Kansas, the heart of the Winter Wheat district. (U.S. Dept. of Agriculture)*

certain extent by properly conserving moisture, by the use of good production practices in growing wheat, and by efficient marketing. However, the problem of instability of income cannot be solved by following a system of highly specialized wheat production.

Farmers realize the advantages of diversification, but in the western Great Plains Region profitable alternatives to the wheat enterprise are limited. Livestock activities cannot be incorporated profitably into the farm business unless feed can be provided at a cost that is comparable to feed costs in other areas of efficient livestock production. If satisfactory provision can be made for such feed supplies, livestock may be produced successfully in this area. Proper combination of livestock and wheat enterprises in the farm organization would enable farmers to utilize available labor more effectively and to increase the amount and stability of income that could be acquired from a given area of land. In periods when labor is expensive and difficult to obtain, planning for better distribution in the use of labor throughout the year is desirable. Furthermore, the availability of livestock on the farm makes it possible to utilize roughage such as wheat pasture and sorghum stubble that otherwise does not have a satisfactory market. Diversification helps to offset damage done by certain insects, weeds, and diseases. It also alleviates wide fluctuations in farm income because of failure of one crop or a relatively low price for a specific commodity.

These and other advantages of proper diversification were partially responsible for the intensive efforts that were made to develop a crop such as grain sorghums that would provide an adequate supply of economically efficient food for the western Great Plains area. Sorghum varieties and their production methods have been improved to such an extent that livestock may now be produced successfully on a major scale in much of the Great Plains area. Grain sorghum also may be produced successfully in competition with wheat as a cash crop in many sectors of this region. In recent years, the production of grain sorghum as a cash crop has become relatively impor-

tant, particularly in the southern Great Plains. This importance is emphasized by the fact that the Chicago Board of Trade established trading in grain sorghum futures in 1951.

SPRING WHEAT DISTRICT

The eastern section of the northern Great Plains is characterized by the dominance of spring wheat. The yields per acre in this subhumid and semiarid region are lower than in the humid regions to the east, but along this marginal belt wheat can compete more successfully with corn and other productive crops, partly because of its adaptation to dry and cool climates, partly because of the extensive use of machinery that the crop permits, and partly (especially with relation to corn) because of the better ability of wheat to stand the cost of transportation to market.

The northern limits of spring wheat are largely determined by the length of the growing season (80 to 90 days) and the mean summer temperature (57° July isotherm). The natural boundary on the east is a zone of transition that may be defined in terms of climate, soil, or natural vegetation. The 98th meridian represents the average of these changing characteristics. Precipitation there averages about 20 inches a year; westward, it is less. The western boundary is the base of the Rocky Mountains in Alberta. The southern boundary is the northern limit for fall-sown grain. Here, winter temperatures are too low to permit the growth of other than spring-sown crops.

The most compelling fact of agriculture in the Spring Wheat district is the irregular and generally deficient rainfall, the greatest limitation on crop production. Moisture comes as slow rains, as cloudbursts sometimes accompanied by hail, as gentle snowfalls, or as blizzards of severe intensity. The average is 27 inches in the southwestern part and less than 10 inches in some places in the northwestern part. Much of the rain falls in the spring and early summer.

Temperatures vary widely from north to south and, in a given locality, from day to day. A range of more than 100° F. often occurs between maximum summer and minimum winter temperatures. For example, a summer temperature of 116° and a winter temperature of −41° have been recorded at Valley City, North Dakota. Great variations in summer temperatures are reflected in the lack of dependability of rainfall. High daytime heat is generally the accompaniment of drought. On the other hand, although the advent of cool waves may bring welcome rainfall, they may also bring scattered frosts, especially in the northwestern part of the subregion. Only a limited portion of the Canadian southern Prairies, for example, has an average continuously frost-free period of 100 days or more, while North Dakota has about 121 days without severe frost—more in the southern part and fewer in the northern.

Chernozem and chestnut soils play a role in wheat production similar to that of the Prairie soils in corn production. Production is less hazardous in the eastern chernozem portion of the Spring Wheat district; rainfall is heavier and the soils are darker and deeper. Yet wheat is relatively a more important crop in the reddish chestnut zones, largely because of their ability to produce grain of excellent quality (high protein content) under the semiarid conditions existing to the west of the chernozem soils.

The spring wheat land is one of tremendous vistas and enormous sky. Unbroken by high or deep natural formations, the land offers no obstruction to the winds that blow more steadily here, on the average, than they do across any other settled part of the continent except the winter wheat land farther south. In wet years the farmers always are conscious of the wind and the pressures; in dry years, they can see them, smell them, and taste them in the form of acrid and bitter dust.

Hard red spring wheat is still the major crop in spite of the many hazards farmers must face during the growing and harvesting seasons. This variety, known for its high protein content and excellent bread-making characteristics, is used extensively for blends with softer wheats in many parts of the world.

The Spring Wheat district also produces annually about 35 to 40 million bushels of durum wheat, a crop concentrated mostly in northeastern North Dakota and extending slightly into South Dakota and, in recent years, into Canada. Because of its greater resistance to stem rust, durum wheat has had, until recently, a yield advantage compared with the prevalent varieties of hard red spring wheat; but this advantage has largely disappeared with the introduction of rust-resistant varieties of spring wheat, notably Thatcher and, more recently, Rival and Regent.

The spring wheat grown here accounts for about 90 per cent of Canada's total wheat acreage and about 30 per cent of that of the United States (*Fig. 13-18*).

Dry land farming techniques have led to the development of large-scale farm units. The flat terrain lends itself to the use of power machinery and the farming of immense plots of ground with a small amount of labor.

Nearly all the flax in the United States and Canada is grown in this district along with much of the rye and barley. Wild hay, too, is a very important crop.

Grain movement and storage. The grain from the Prairie Provinces of Canada concentrates at Winnipeg and, except for a small amount

FIGURE 13-18. *Indian Head, with its skyline of grain elevators, is typical of Saskatchewan's great wheat growing districts. (Canadian Government Travel Bureau)*

to Duluth-Superior via Fort Francis, most of it moves over three railway lines to the terminal elevators in Fort William and Port Arthur in Ontario, where it is graded and held for shipment (*Fig. 13-19*). The grade given the grain here is the one on which it is sold and delivered in both eastern Canadian and foreign markets. By holding the grain at the head of the Great Lakes, the shipper can market it through either Canadian or United States channels. Only Canadian grain is forwarded from Fort William-Port Arthur, whereas some Canadian and a large amount of United States grain moves from the spring wheat area to Montreal from Duluth-Superior. Only United States grain is shipped from Milwaukee and Chicago to Montreal.

The routes of grain shipment from the head of the Great Lakes include: (1) the water route, (2) the water and rail route, and (3) the rail route. These alternative methods serve to keep transportation costs at a minimum. Canada has a further advantage in shipment because of low wheat freight rates resulting from an agreement made by the Canadian Pacific Railway for handling Western wheat in exchange for a charter.

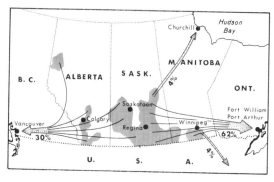

FIGURE 13-19. *Origins and destinations of Prairie Provinces wheat.*

Grazing

The Great Plains were originally the feeding grounds of vast herds of buffalo. During the last third of the nineteenth century the buffalo were replaced by cattle. Today, cattle raising remains the dominant agricultural enterprise in the semiarid and arid portions of the Great Plains. Sheep and goats are also grazed; they are more important than cattle in some sections.

Climatic conditions, especially the supply of moisture, were significant in the determination of this system of land use. Here the product of the pasture becomes of greater value than the crops. The average annual precipitation increases on the eastern boundary southward from 15 inches in Canada and northeastern Montana to 17 inches in central South Dakota and western Nebraska, 18 inches in eastern Colorado, eastern New Mexico, and west-

central Texas, and 25 inches in extreme southern Texas, where the rainfall is more irregular and often torrential.

Great variability in precipitation, both in quantity and form, is characteristicc of this area. Rainfall varies by as much as 30 inches annually from year to year. Upon occasion, a single shower will provide one-third of the total annual rainfall within a day, and as much as one-fifth within an hour.

Other boundaries deserving notice are those delimiting the driest areas where almost no crops are grown without irrigation (except a little corn, kaffir or sorghum, and sweet clover for forage), usually on land that receives flood water from higher lands or that possesses other favorable conditions. This almost purely pastoral agriculture is found also on lands of rough topography or on very sandy soils that preclude cultivation. The districts of arid climate, rough surface, or sandy soil do not form a continuous belt, but include in the aggregate a large area.

In Montana, these grazing lands are found in the warm, dry valleys of the Yellowstone, Missouri, Musselshell, and Marias Rivers, where the average annual precipitation is below 14 inches; they include also much of the valley of the Milk River (*Fig. 13-20*). The badlands of the Little Missouri River in North Dakota constitute the only large area in that state given over exclusively to grazing. In South Dakota, the grazing lands include the badlands along the Cheyenne and White Rivers. Most of northeastern Wyoming belongs to this grazing type of land. The Sand Hills constitute the

FIGURE 13-20. *A grazing scene in Gallatin Valley, Montana. The cattle are being moved in from the range. Note the rolling land, the short grass, and the sleek condition of the herd. (U.S. Dept. of Agriculture)*

principal area in Nebraska. In Colorado, much of the nonirrigated land in the South Platte Valley and most of that in the Arkansas Valley are suitable only for grazing, as is also most of the southeastern portion of the state, in which the average annual precipitation is less than 16 inches. In Kansas, only the Arkansas Valley west of the Hartland and the Sand Hills to the south are included; and in eastern New Mexico, lands included are the Pecos Valley and the drier portions of the upper Canadian Valley. Nearly all the nonirrigated area in Texas west of Midland, Sonora, Carizzo Springs, and Hebronville is suitable for grazing.

CATTLE

The size of the ranch will vary, depending upon the location and carrying capacity of the range, from less than 3,000 to more than 500,-000 acres, and from as low as 22 cattle per section of 640 acres to more than double that number. Maintenance of an acceptable standard of living on the larger ranches necessitates access to telephone, automobile, radio, tele-

vision, and in many cases the possession of a home in the nearest town as well as upon the ranch. The telephone and automobile are invaluable aids in dissipating the monotony, solitude, and seclusion of life far from the nearest town and several miles from neighboring families.

Although conditions of ranch life vary greatly from one end of the Great Plains to the other, the livestock industry almost everywhere follows a similar pattern (*Figs. 13-21* and *13-22*). Problems of water, the need for supplemental feed in the drier portions of the range, marketing, and so on, are fairly similar throughout the area. The farther north the ranch, the less open it is in the winter and the greater the need for shelter and winter feeding of animals. Cattlemen who can avoid or reduce to a minimum the need for supplemental feeding are more likely to realize a profit. The industry, then, is a precarious one, for there are many variable factors beyond a rancher's control. A severe winter can wipe out thousands of head through starvation. By the same token, a rancher who is able to get feed to livestock during blizzards stands a good chance of going broke paying for the feed to keep his cattle alive. Severe droughts, such as those Texas has experienced in the past few years, may ruin rangeland for years to come. If natural hazards do not decimate the industry, there is always the possibility that market prices will. Again, in good years, cattlemen reap huge profits. In the long run a careful entrepreneur can make a good living if he is willing to take the bad years along with the good ones. And the high per capita meat consumption of the American people insures a continued use for millions of acres of land with little, if any, alternative uses.

SHEEP

Sheep are grazed in many parts of the Great Plains. Ranchers often run both sheep and cattle on their range; the cattle usually occupy the portions with better water and grass; sheep graze in the more arid sections, since they can subsist on less water and can graze on shorter grass. Three areas in particular specialize in the grazing of sheep: (1) the Edwards Plateau of Texas, (2) northern Colorado, and (3) eastern Montana.

Texas has long been known as cattle country. Yet, it is interesting to note that the sheep in Texas contribute a much greater proportion to the national total of sheep than is the case with cattle. Texas' cattle and calves contribute less than 7 per cent of the value of all cattle in

FIGURE 13-22. *A small ranch headquarters in Cascade County, Montana. Windmills are still major items of equipment on ranches in the Great Plains Region. (U.S. Dept. of Agriculture)*

the United States, whereas Texas' sheep contribute more than 14 per cent of the value of all sheep. Although sheep are raised throughout the state, ownership is concentrated on the Edwards Plateau and in the eastern Trans-Pecos area. There, sheep production is a major undertaking, the primary or sole source of income to many ranchers.

No clearer illustration of a joint product and joint cost enterprise can be found than sheep raising. In the Western and Southwestern states the ranchers who built great flocks were initially just interested in wool. The animal had little value as meat, although that value was always a significant one among those who ran small flocks. Indeed, it has been this difference in interest that has led to a general preference for "down" breeds of the medium wool class by those who run small flocks in the older and developed areas—breeds that furnish a good wool and, at the same time, a goodly poundage of meat either as lamb or mutton. Upon the open range, however, where in the past the prime or sole interest has been in wool, the "down" breeds have gained slight acceptance; instead, interest has been almost wholly in the fine wool breeds, with one or another of the Merino types widely favored.

FIGURE 13-21. *A typical Great Plains Region cattle ranch.*

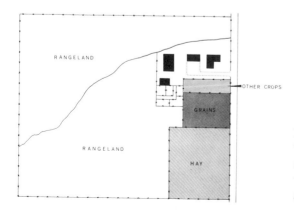

Northern Colorado and eastern Montana sheep ranchers practice transhumance, a seasonal movement of flocks to high mountain grassland meadows during the spring and summer periods. During the winter, sheep are quartered in the protected valleys. Sheep have decreased almost steadily since 1942. Production also has been shifting from range to farm flocks and from the Western states eastward.

One of the causes of the decline in range sheep numbers is the increase in labor costs. To illustrate, the average family-operated sheep ranch in the northern Great Plains had a hired labor cost of $490 per year in the period from 1937 to 1941. Today the hired labor cost is more than $3,000.

The United States is the world's greatest market for wool and woolen products, but, since it produces less wool than it consumes, it is dependent upon foreign supply for at least a part of its raw wool requirements. This fact stimulates wool growers in surplus-producing countries to seek a market in the United States. As soon as the supply available for import into this country exceeds the margin between domestic production and consumption, the domestic producer must either restrict the inflow by selling his product, regardless of cost, at a price that will win the preference of the domestic mill owner, or he must look to the government to check the inflow by tariff barriers, import quotas, or other such artificial restraints, which involve serious conflicts of economic interest between the wool grower, domestic woolen mills, and consumers of textiles.

ANGORA GOATS

For many years a major part of the nation's goat population has been on the Texas range. The great concentration of Angoras in Texas is on the Edwards Plateau and the upper Rio Grande Plain. In this area the vegetation is such as to make poor pasturage for cattle or sheep, but the shrubs and other growth are favorable for goats.

The Angora goat industry differs markedly from sheep raising in that it is only in small measure a joint product and a joint cost industry. The Angora is raised for its fleece; little income is derived from the sale of animals for meat, and at present there seems to be little likelihood that any demand comparable to that for lamb or mutton will develop for the kid as meat, let alone the mature animal. About the only consistent and considerable demand for kid or goat meat is among the Mexican population of the Southwest.

The industry's future is tied basically to the price of mohair, with no alternative source of income available such as that enjoyed by the sheep raiser in the sale of lamb. Mohair is a distinctive textile fiber that is the basic raw material for many types of fabrics. It is used in the manufacture of men's suits and overcoats. It adds to the coolness and wrinkle resistance of summer garments. In tweeds, it combats wrinkles and deepens color. Mohair is used in women's wear—in soft suits, dresses, and coatings—because it adds to color tones, to drape, and to wear. It is used also for other items of clothing, such as sportswear, robes, and sweaters. The chief use of mohair, however, is in the manufacture of upholstery for automobiles, buses, trains, planes, theaters, and the home.

Irrigated Farming

In the arid sections of the West, irrigation has been used for over a century in agricultural production and undoubtedly will become more important with the passage of time. The Spanish settlers brought with them considerable knowledge and experience in instituting and practicing irrigation, which they adapted to conditions they found in the Southwest. Out of the combination of Spanish and Indian methods grew what is called the Spanish-American community acequia—a canal for irrigating land. Acequia groups were widely established in New Mexico. The Spaniards were likewise energetic in extending irrigation into Texas and Colorado.

The Mormons, as previously noted, expanded the territory cultivated through irrigation. Later, as irrigation opportunities through easy and inexpensive methods of diversion of water gradually disappeared, there came a need for larger enterprises and higher per-acre expenditures to obtain water. The combination of a demand for developing the public lands of the United States and the need of federal funds for the large undertakings led to the passage of the National Reclamation Act in 1902. The work done under this act has been extended to include reclamation of private as well as public lands.

Sources of irrigation water are grouped into two classifications: (1) surface water—lakes, rivers, streams, and flowing wells; and (2) ground water obtained from pumped wells. Ground water is used predominantly by single farm enterprises, while surface waters are used by most co-operative farm operations.

The general system of farming in the irrigated districts, like that along the northern margin of the corn area, is based on some intertilled crop, usually corn or sugar beets, followed by a small grain (usually wheat), and then by hay (commonly alfalfa), which may occupy the land for several years and be pastured incidentally. Commonly, both cattle and sheep are brought down off the plains into the irrigated districts during the winter and fed beet pulp or corn fodder, supplemented sometimes with grain.

IRRIGATED FARMING DISTRICTS

North Platte Valley. The North Platte Valley of western Nebraska and eastern Wyoming comprises a half-million acres of irrigated farm land—the largest completely adjacent irrigated acreage in the United States. Pathfinder Reservoir, in the mountains of Wyoming, stores over a million acre-feet of water, and with the auxiliary storage of Guernsey Lake, Lake Alice, and Lake Miniature, assures the moisture to grow crops every year. Corn, small grains, tomatoes, peas, sugar beets, potatoes, beans, and many other crops in increasing importance make up a multi-million dollar farm income for the valley (*Fig. 13-23*).

A highly favorable, mild, dry climate con-

FIGURE 13-23. *An irrigated field of sugar beets in Nebraska. (Nebraska Division of Resources)*

tributes to the success of livestock feeding in the area, as does the production of feed crops. Sugar beet tops from an average acre have a feed value equivalent to 60 bushels of corn. Beet pulp, a sugar factory by-product, is also an important livestock feed, and a tremendous tonnage is available. Corn, barley, and alfalfa are produced in great quantities.

Missouri River Basin. Agriculture in the Missouri Basin is an important part of the national economy. The basin contains about 18 per cent of the land area of the country. Except for the Mississippi drainage area, of which it is a part, the Missouri Basin is the largest drainage area in the United States. Almost a fourth of the nation's farm land and slightly more than a fourth of the harvested cropland lie within it.

The Great Plains contain about half the land area of the basin. Except for irrigated areas the land is suitable for only limited cultivation. However, multipurpose uses—for grazing, timber, recreation, mining—and water yield make the land in this area a highly valued part of the basin's land resources.

More than 87 per cent of the land irrigated in the basin has a surface water supply. Most of this is served by gravity systems, but a small quantity of the surface water is pumped. About 11 per cent of the land is irrigated by pumping ground water from wells. A small acreage has both surface and ground water supplied.

IRRIGATED FIELD CROPS

Sugar beets. Grown in 22 Western and North-central states, sugar beets are not a major crop even in those states that are large producers. Beets have been an important factor, however, in the development of permanent agriculture in the irrigated areas of many Western states. In addition to providing a cash crop, they are suited to several rotation systems and thus complement diversified farming operations.

The overhead costs of irrigation on the Great Plains require a sizeable acreage of crops having a high return per acre. Sugar beets have met this requirement. In a number of the irrigated areas, beets, beans, and potatoes represent important, high-value crops. They are grown in rotation with small grains, alfalfa, and corn. Livestock feeding operations are integrated into the farm program, with beef cattle and lambs being fattened, in part, on the feed crops, sugar beet tops, beet pulp, and molasses.

Cotton. The principal cash crop of the western Texas Great Plains is cotton. Large areas of fertile, level land, a highly mechanized farming system, and irrigation have brought economic stability and prosperity to many cotton growers. Some land that formerly produced an income of a few cents per acre in brush is now yielding more than three bales of cotton with an annual gross income in excess of $500 per acre.

Because of the relatively high costs of irrigation, it is necessary to maintain a high output per acre to reduce unit costs. Consequently, farmers growing cotton under irrigation use heavy applications of fertilizer to boost yields and to offset the loss of plant nutrients leached out by irrigation water.

The lack of water, caused by the drought, has been a serious problem in western Texas during the past few years. Although cotton is a deep-rooted plant that can take much drought and heat, it cannot produce without adequate water when temperatures stay about 100° F. for many days. Therefore every effort must be made to utilize fully every drop of water that falls on western Texas.

Grain sorghum. With irrigation, the significance of sorghum to the economy of the Staked Plains of Texas cannot be overlooked. Wheat, long regarded as the major crop, has declined. With restrictions on wheat, sorghum has become even more important. Some farmers say that grain sorghum is so well established now that even if wheat were unrestricted they would still plant sorghum. Sorghum has about 90 per cent of the feed value of corn, does not compete with wheat for labor or machinery, and, with mechanization, is easy to harvest.

Alfalfa. Irrigated pastures make possible an expansion in dairy and farm-flock sheep and beef cattle production. In the Great Plains, alfalfa is an important crop from Colorado north to Canada. It makes a good hay, pasture, and silage crop for almost all farm animals. It is an excellent soil improver; in combination with grasses it helps stop soil erosion. Alfalfa meal, dehydrated alfalfa, and other similar products are becoming increasingly important. Alfalfa's wide distribution shows a remarkable adaptability but the best yields are attained on deep loams with open, porous, and well-drained subsoil.

Alfalfa may be cultivated and harvested with ordinary farm machinery for hay and seed crops, a characteristic that makes it ideal for rotation with wheat. An ordinary mower or rake is used in harvesting the hay crop; the combine harvests the seed.

Truck crops. With irrigation, truck farming, too, has become important on the Staked Plains. In the Hereford area of Texas many farmers specialize in the cultivation of potatoes, onions, carrots, cabbages, and melons. The main problem in truck farming is marketing.

Extractive Industries

A vast part of the more gently sloping portion of the Great Plains Region consists of sedimentary rock conducive to the formation of such nonmetallic minerals as coal, potash, petroleum, and natural gas. There are several isolated mountain uplifts, of which the Black Hills is the largest and farthest east. The Black Hills make up a dome-like mountain range rising 3,000 to 4,000 feet above the sea. Granite is exposed in the center where the overlying sedimentary rocks have eroded; intruded masses of igneous rock give rise to the formation of metallic minerals—gold, silver, copper, lead, and zinc. Gold is by far the most important metal.

Gold from the Homestake Mine at Lead continues to be South Dakota's number one mining product. First opened in 1876, the Homestake is the largest gold-producing mine in the United States. Uranium, feldspar, mica, bentonite, granite, gypsum, and limestone are other mineral products contributing to South Dakota's wealth.

PETROLEUM AND NATURAL GAS

Petroleum and natural gas are found from Texas to northern Alberta, and some of the most spectacular discoveries in Anglo-America have taken place within the region. The major fields are (1) the Canadian Prairie Provinces, (2) the Williston Basin, (3) the Powder River Basin, (4) the Denver-Julesburg Basin, (5) the Permian Basin, (6) the Texas Panhandle, and (7) the Hugoton field of Texas, Oklahoma, and Kansas (*see Figs. 3-7 and 3-8*).

Canadian Prairie Provinces. Prior to 1947, the Prairie Provinces had only one major oil field with an average daily crude oil production rate of less than 20,000 barrels. In February, 1947, Imperial Oil Ltd. brought in the discovery well at Leduc, Alberta—the beginning of a Canadian oil boom. Other companies rushed into the area, and within a year 43 major producers had been drilled.

The Redwater field was discovered in 1948; its reserves are estimated at a half-billion barrels. This was followed by discoveries at Golden Spike, at Woodland, and in the Edmonton area. Rapid expansion soon spread through the length and breadth of Alberta, reaching the Peace River in 1949. Production soared with these new discoveries. The number of wells producing crude oil has grown from a few in 1950 to more than 500. Reserves of crude oil and condensate have increased to an estimated 1.9 million barrels. Daily output of crude oil now exceeds 250,000 barrels per day.

Oil and gas have been found in numerous localities in Alberta. The principal producing fields are in the central region within a 150-mile radius of Edmonton, namely Pembina, Swan Hills, Redwater, Leduc-Woodbend, Judy Creek, Bonnie Glen, Hondo, and Mitsue. Other important fields dot the prairie between Edmonton and Calgary. Oil-bearing fields are also found extending in a northwesterly direction from Edmonton.

This expansion has produced certain marketing problems. The local Alberta refinery demand was soon saturated by available supplies and, as a consequence, new markets had to be developed. In order to meet this situation plans were made for the construction of a major pipeline outlet. In 1950, the Interprovincial Pipeline, Canada's largest, was completed. It connects Edmonton, Alberta, with Superior, Wisconsin, and Sarnia, Ontario, and has a capacity of 150,000 barrels per day.

The Trans-Mountain Pipeline, completed in 1953, is Canada's second largest; it extends from Edmonton to the West Coast. The Foothills Division, which carries gas consigned to Alberta Natural Gas Company, is part of the system that goes southward through Idaho to Northern California. It has a carrying capacity of 665,000 cubic feet per day.

In addition to these major pipelines there are many gathering systems serving the producing areas. Edmonton is the terminus of lines that bring in oil for refinery use and for shipment to points east and west.

Natural gas has been one of Alberta's major assets for many years. Today, local utility systems supply much of the urban population and also some markets outside the province on a limited scale. Proven gas reserves are estimated at 3.5 trillion cubic feet.

Although Saskatchewan's oil industry has not enjoyed the spectacular success of Alberta's, it has developed into one of major importance and the province is rapidly achieving stature as a major oil reserve region. Its southeastern corner has turned into the most lucrative oil and recovery area in the whole of western Canada outside of the Pembina field. Discovery performance has reached a point where two out of every three wells drilled has produced oil.

Saskatchewan has benefited from its proximity to eastern markets and from strong demand for the medium gravity crude oil which forms a large proportion of total output. Recoverable reserves of crude oil are estimated in excess of 500 million barrels.

Though drilling for oil in Manitoba occurred as early as 1887, interest was only sporadic until two wells drilled in the southwest corner of the province in 1949 revealed for the first time the presence of rocks containing oil. The first recoverable oil in significant quantity was obtained in January, 1951. This discovery led to increased interest in potential oil properties by a number of companies and to the development of the Daly field in southwestern Manitoba. Since that time progress has been rapid.

A number of economic considerations favor the development of Manitoba's oil industry: (1) the oil reservoirs are rather shallow, resulting in relatively low drilling and production costs; (2) the oil fields are close to the Interprovincial Pipeline, making transportation readily available; and (3) both the consumer market and refinery capacity in Manitoba exceed local production, a situation that is likely to continue.

Williston Basin. The discovery of oil and gas in the Beaver Lodge Pool, 32 miles northeast of Williston, North Dakota, in April, 1951, caused a rush of major oil companies to the area. Geologists contend that it may be the greatest sedimentary oil deposit on the continent, with an estimated reserve of 2.5 million barrels. The Williston Basin (18,500 square miles) extends into southern Alberta, southwestern Manitoba, the northern half of South Dakota, eastern Montana, and central North Dakota (*Fig. 13-24*).

The biggest difficulty confronting the industry is distance from large populated markets. Unless the area experiences a tremendous population growth, oil from the Williston Basin will meet serious competition from producing fields closer to consuming centers. At present, most oil shipped out of the region moves by tank car to the Minneapolis-St. Paul metropolitan district.

Powder River Basin. This has been one of the leading oil and gas producing sections in the Great Plains for many years. Located in Wyoming, it has only recently been topped in production by Big Horn Basin, with its Elk Basin field.

Most oil discoveries have been made in the southern portion of the basin. The Salt Creek field, discovered in 1906, has been the most

FIGURE 13-24. *An oil well in the Williston field near Williston, North Dakota. Wells are spaced quite far apart here. Note the uneven topography of this area adjacent to the Missouri River. (W. E. Shemorry, Williston Chamber of Commerce)*

productive. In 1923 it attained a record output of 38 million barrels, the largest producer in the world at that time. It has leveled off in recent years at about 4 million barrels. Since 1948, a number of smaller fields have been discovered, several of them in the million-barrel class.

Gaseous formations have been found under about 9,000 acres of land. Best estimates place gas reserves at 370 billion cubic feet. Salt Creek also dominates here. Teapot Dome, at the south end of the Salt Creek anticline, could be a fairly heavy producer, but the wells have been shut in for a number of years. The gas produced in the Powder River Basin is high in quality and largely free from hydrogen sulfide.

Denver-Julesburg Basin. The Denver-Julesburg Basin encompasses southeastern Wyoming, northeastern Colorado, and southwestern Nebraska. Oil was first discovered in the region in 1962, but the current boom dates from the Ohio Oil Company's 1949 discovery near Gurley, Nebraska. Within a few months, millions of acres were leased on the eastern flank of the basin and wildcat drilling boomed in the Nebraska and Colorado portions.

Although the proximity of the major trunk lines and the rapid development of a crude oil gathering system have done much to encourage activity in the region, a favorable land leasing situation and relatively fast and inexpensive drilling methods also have proven very attractive to operators. The Colorado portion has been the most productive, but the focal point of Denver-Julesburg exploration has shifted to western Nebraska.

Permian Basin. The Permian Basin, a producing field turning out more than one and a half million barrels of oil a day, extends from western Texas into New Mexico. Roughly, it is bordered by Hobbs and Snyder on the north, Sweetwater on the east, San Angelo and Eldorado on the south, and Carlsbad on the west. The basin has an intricate interlacing of pipelines and railroads.

No small part of the present wealth of western Texas has been derived from oil, and oil has contributed generously to the transformation into cities of what must otherwise have been small towns. The farther westward toward the New Mexico border, the more such marks of prosperity and wealth stand upon the cornerstone of oil.

Panhandle-Hugoton fields. The Texas Panhandle began producing oil in 1918. Natural gas long has been more important than petroleum in this area, however. Drillers have found some of the largest and most important gas fields in the world there. The field extends northwest across six counties in the Texas Panhandle until it almost touches the Hugoton field. The Hugoton field underlies most of Sherman County and part of Hansford County in the Texas Panhandle and extends from there northward across Oklahoma into Kansas. The Panhandle and Hugoton gas fields together are more than 200 miles long and from 5 to 40 miles wide.

The real magnitude of the Texas Panhandle field was not realized until 1925. From that time on, the natural gas business in Texas began to develop rapidly. As time passed, additional supplies of natural gas were discovered in the search for oil, and the price of natural gas fell very low because of the much larger available supply in relation to the current demand. This caused great losses and waste.

The extension of long-distance transmission lines from the Panhandle in 1932 by the Eastern Pipeline Company brought Texas gas to many consuming markets in all parts of the country. In that year, gas from the Panhandle and Hugoton fields was carried to Detroit. Since then natural gas has continued to flow to 33 other states, the District of Columbia, Mexico, and Canada.

HELIUM

The Great Plains have a virtual world monopoly on the production of helium, most of which comes from the Texas Panhandle gas field. Helium, in any appreciable amount, is a rare constituent of natural gas. A few fields have been discovered that contain sufficient amounts to permit extraction with a helium content generally about one or two per cent, but ranging as high as eight per cent in one field in New Mexico. Helium is isolated by reduction to a temperature at which the natural gas (methane) liquefies, leaving the helium in a gaseous state. Its present price is less than one cent per cubic foot, but prior to World War I it was a laboratory curiosity obtained from radioactive minerals at a cost of approximately $2,500 per cubic foot.

The world's sole producer of helium is the United States Department of the Interior. For many years its only plant was at the Cliffside gas field near Amarillo, Texas, but to meet the increased demand for helium during World War II, three other plants were built by the government in Kansas and New Mexico. After the war, demand for helium declined sharply. In recent years, however, many uses have been found. The gas is used in the welding of magnesium, aluminum, and stainless steel. It also has come into considerable use in hospitals, where it is employed as an oxygen carrier in the treatment of respiratory cases and for admixture with anesthetic gases to minimize explosion hazards in operating rooms. Helium is a nonflammable gas only a little heavier than hydrogen, and it was employed at first to fill dirigibles, blimps, and other lighter-than-air craft.

COAL

The northern Great Plains contain enormous reserves of unmined coal, varying from lignite to high-grade bituminous (see Fig. 3-6). Competition from petroleum and natural gas, however, has kept its exploitation to a minimum. Where mining does occur, the coal is used chiefly to serve railways, for smelters, and as a domestic heating fuel. Sparse population within the area seems to preclude any large-scale production.

Alberta is particularly rich in coal deposits that range from semianthracite to lignite. For a distance of over 700 miles from the international boundary northward, the Rocky Mountains and their foothills are studded with deposits of coal.

Lignite is found in Saskatchewan and Manitoba. In Manitoba, small deposits occur in the vicinity of Turtle Mountain, and the whole southern portion of Saskatchewan from Manitoba to the Alberta boundary is underlaid with lignite. The principal deposits occur in the Sauris Valley in southeastern Saskatchewan; it is from this area that about 90 per cent of the present production is derived.

North Dakota possesses extensive lignite coal. Completion of a federal lignite research laboratory at the University of North Dakota in 1950 was a big step forward in the development of almost unlimited supplies of this low-grade coal.

Lignite deposits underlie about 32,000 square miles of surface in the state. Beds vary in thickness from a fraction of an inch to 35 feet, while six- to eight-foot veins are common. In places they are so close to the surface that the overlying soil is stripped and the coal mined in open cuts; in other places the room-and-pillar method is used.

The lignite beds of North Dakota extend into eastern Montana, where they underlie more than 35 per cent of the state's surface. Much of it is mined easily, for it lies in thick seams free from waste materials. Recent developments include the construction by Montana-Dakota Utilities of Montana's first steam electric generating plant using lignite at Sidney.

The Powder River Basin of Wyoming is one of the most important areas of subbituminous coal in that state. The coal beds are thick and continuous over relatively large areas. Only a small amount is mined, however, primarily because the coal is younger and of lower rank than coal in other areas of the state.

POTASH

Mineral potash was first noted in the Permian Salt Basin in 1921, in the form of polyhalite, a compound of potassium sulfate, calcium sulfate, and magnesium sulfate. The deposit has not been developed, however, primarily because conventional methods of commercial potash production have been applied principally to sylvite and carnallite, which furnish most of Europe's commercial production. Possible development of Texas polyhalite also was discouraged by the subsequent discovery of a domestic supply of potash in sylvite and carnallite deposits at Carlsbad, New Mexico, now the center of commercial production of potash in the United States. Potash can be produced at a materially lower cost there than in any other area within the nation's boundaries.

Saskatchewan's potash resources, said to be the world's largest known reserves, were first discovered in the 1940's in samples of deposits from oil well drilling. Continuous production has been carried on since 1962 from another conventional mine in the Esterhazy area near the Manitoba border. Represented among the companies in the field are major American potash firms and Canadian, British, and German interests. A $20 million concentrator has been built at the mine site of the Potash Company of America near Saskatoon, Saskatchewan.

Manufacturing

The Great Plains cannot in any sense be considered a prime industrial region. Industries that do exist are scattered widely; in no one place is there any great concentration. Distance from urban markets, a sparse population, and limited resources preclude any large-scale industrial expansion. Nevertheless, manufacturing establishments serving local markets are exceedingly important to the region's economy. Because of space limitation only the most important industries within the region are discussed here.

PETROCHEMICAL INDUSTRIES

Petroleum and natural gas have provided the basis for a limited industrial development in the Great Plains Region, as is attested by the existence of several carbon black plants, the many liquid petroleum gas plants, and a number of refineries varying widely in capacity. The Panhandle of Texas and the Canadian

Prairie Provinces, in particular, are noteworthy for the development of new industries based on petroleum and natural gas.

Geographically, the heart of the American petrochemical industry is in the Gulf Coastal Plain, where an estimated 75 per cent of the total production is concentrated.

Like the American petrochemical industry, the Canadian counterpart has shown a very remarkable growth. The western portion, in Alberta, with energy supplies based on natural gas, has developed largely in the past five years. Since 1950, considerably more than 40 per cent of the new Canadian petrochemical investment has been in Alberta. Nevertheless, long distances from major markets and relatively high plant operation costs caused by severe climatic conditions and the lack of large industrial suppliers will probably be instrumental in preventing any considerable percentage gain in Alberta's petrochemical industry.

FOOD PROCESSING INDUSTRIES

Food processing industries long have been important in the irrigated districts of the Great Plains, especially sugar beet factories. Several food processing plants are located in northeastern Colorado and in the North Platte Valley.

Sugar beet factories in the Great Plains Region produce nearly a third of the nation's beet sugar from refineries in Colorado, Nebraska, Wyoming, and Kansas. Sugar from the region is marketed principally in the West and the Middle West, from the Rocky Mountains to the Mississippi River and Lake Michigan.

Edmonton is the meat-packing center of the Canadian Prairies. Its plants account for a large portion of the area's animal processing industry, a response to the excellent rail transportation network. Calgary is also an important meat-packing center, ranking second to Edmonton.

Flour milling was one of Alberta's first manufacturing industries. Large flour mills are located at Calgary and Medicine Hat; smaller flour mills, which usually operate on a custom basis, are scattered throughout the province.

METALS INDUSTRIES

The smelting of copper, zinc, and manganese at Anaconda (in the American Rockies) and their refining at Great Falls; the refining of alumina into aluminum at Columbia Falls; and the manufacturing of aluminum products at Great Falls are typical of a number of important and growing industries in Montana (*Fig. 13-25*). It is apparent that great industrial diversity and consequent stability of the economy is being achieved through expansion of existing endeavors and the entry into new fields of manufacturing and processing for both national and local markets.

Pueblo, Colorado, often called "the Pittsburgh of the West," has been a producer of iron and steel products since 1882, when a Bessemer converter was established there to supply the Denver and Rio Grande Western Railway with steel. The enterprise, although insignificant compared with the giant steel industries of the Great Lakes or Pittsburgh, occupies an important position in the local economy (*Fig. 13-26*).

FIGURE 13-26. *Coke plant of the Colorado Fuel and Iron Corporation in Pueblo, Colorado. Steel from Pueblo is important in serving the needs of the region. Iron from Wyoming and Colorado and coal, limestone, and fluorspar from southern Colorado supply the raw materials at fairly low freight costs. (Colorado Fuel and Iron Corp.)*

Recreation and Tourism

The Great Plains Region offers little to attract the tourist. The climate tends to extremes. Winter temperatures may fall far below zero over the northern two-thirds of the region; summer days are long and hot. The landscape, for the most part, is a fairly flat and monotonous expanse of semiarid and subhumid plain.

Because of its geographical position between the densely populated Midwest and the Rocky Mountains, the Great Plains Region is spanned by a number of major federal highways running in an east-west direction. Transcontinental railways and airways also cross the region. This transportation pattern does result in some tourist trade, with the majority of tourists staying only overnight on their way to attractions outside the region.

There are a few points of interest within the Great Plains Region that do attract thousands of visitors each year, however. These include: Carlsbad Caverns National Park of

FIGURE 13-25. *Great Falls Refinery, on the Missouri River in Montana. Great Falls is noted for copper smelting and refining, and for coal, natural gas, silver, and lead deposits. (Anaconda Copper Co.)*

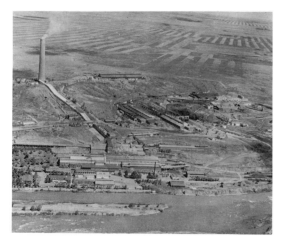

southeastern New Mexico, the dude ranch country of the Edwards Plateau in southwestern Texas, the Black Hills and the Badlands of South Dakota, and, to a lesser extent, the lakes of the Canadian Prairie Provinces. Of these, Carlsbad Caverns, the Black Hills, and the Badlands merit more attention.

CARLSBAD CAVERNS

Carlsbad Caverns National Park is located in semidesert country in the rugged foothills of the Guadalupe Mountains. The cave for which the park is named is of unusual magnificence and size. Although many miles of passages have been explored, development has been limited to the 750-foot and 829-foot levels reached by trail from the natural entrance and by elevator.

When first established, the park surface area was only 700 acres. It since has been enlarged and now contains nearly 46,000 acres of federal lands. Within its bounds are many caves of scenic or archeological interest.

Carlsbad Caverns are unique because of the vast size of the underground chambers and their high ceilings—features brought about partly by rock collapse.

The bat flight is one of the park's great attractions. Flying out through the cave entrance each summer evening, incredible numbers of bats spiral upward, stream southward over the rim, and later separate into flocks for night foraging. Bats return from their nocturnal feeding just before dawn. These bats are quite harmless to human beings; in fact, they are beneficial to man since they destroy harmful insects and also provide guano—a valuable fertilizer.

THE BLACK HILLS OF SOUTH DAKOTA

These are the oldest mountains on the continent and the highest east of the Rockies. Mile-high lakes, pine-clad peaks, verdant mountain valleys, and formations of towering granite often appear in one setting. The Black Hills cover an area of about 6,000 square miles. They rise on an average about 2,000

feet above their base. The mass has an elliptical shape; its long axis, which extends north-northwest to south-southwest, is about 120 miles long, and its short axis about 40 miles long. Carboniferous and older stratified beds still cover the western half of the hills, and the beds have been removed from the eastern half, exposing the granite.

Mt. Rushmore National Monument is a major tourist attraction (*Fig. 13-27*). With great detail, sculptor Gutzon Borglum carved the busts of four great Americans at the base of Mt. Rushmore in the Black Hills. In depicting the prudence of Washington, the vision of Jefferson, the energy of Theodore Roosevelt, and the compassion of Lincoln, the sculptor told a story of America, taking a mountain as his medium. Under his direction thousands of tons of granite were blasted away with dynamite. It is tremendous in concept, sculptured to the scale of men 465 feet tall.

THE BADLANDS

Sixty miles east of the Black Hills is the Badlands National Monument, a startling contrast to the cool forests, sparkling streams, and lush valleys of the hills. Desolate, arid, eerie—almost devoid of vegetation—the Badlands seemingly are no part of the green prairies that surround them. The jagged peaks, turrets, spires, and steep canyons of colored ocean sediments, unadorned by plant or bush, could well be the setting of Dante's *Inferno*.

Sixty million years ago, the Badlands were the floor of a great salt sea. As the waters receded, marshes, dank lagoons, and jungle-like forests emerged. Gigantic animals of strange shapes and habits roamed the land: the saber-toothed tiger, the titanothere (large, odd-toed ungulates related to the rhinoceros), the brontosaurus (a huge herbivorous dinosaur), and the eohippus (a small four-toed horse). As the area became dry and barren, the animals disappeared, but their bones were preserved in the earth on which they once wandered. Today scientists and amateurs alike search for bones and skeletons of these prehistoric animals in the Badlands.

FIGURE 13-27. *Mount Rushmore, South Dakota. More than a million tourists a year visit this impressive memorial. (South Dakota Dept. of Highways)*

Population

Only four widely separated cities—Denver, Edmonton, Calgary, and Amarillo—have a population exceeding 100,000. Distance, then, is a major factor in the development of institutional arrangements in the Great Plains Region.

Denver is the regional capital of the Great Plains. Its location, at the base of the Rocky Mountains, makes it a geographic focus of federal agencies and military installations and a center of national activity in the development of oil and minerals. It is also an oasis of health and recreation activities to which thousands of vacationers and retired people are turning (*Fig. 13-28*).

Edmonton is the most important rail and air center in the Canadian Northwest. The distribution point of a rich farm country and coal mining area, it is also the hub of a large fur trade.

Calgary, as well as being the trading center of an extensive stock raising and wheat region, is the base of supplies for surrounding mining

districts. It has large grist and flour mills, grain elevators, brick and cement works, lumber mills, oil refineries, and packing houses.

Amarillo is the commercial and industrial center of the Texas Panhandle. It is the supply center for oil and helium gas. The city is noted for its zinc smelters, foundries, grain elevators, oil refineries, and meat-packing establishments.

Outlook

The characteristics of the Great Plains Region place permanent restrictions on its occupancy. The great variability in precipitation, both in quantity and form, will continue to limit land use. Grazing must remain the dominant occupation throughout the drier parts of this climatic realm; only by controlled grazing can man hope to maintain a protective cover over much of this region. Irrigation is the key to any extensive agriculture in the area. Clusters of population have already developed on the oases made possible by the use of underground or surface water. Federal and state governments have constructed dams or watersheds to provide hydroelectric power as well as water for irrigation. Thus, man's technology has enabled him to overcome some of nature's handicaps in this dry world. Further population increases may be expected as more and more storage reservoirs and dams are built and as new lands are opened for settlement. Dry farming methods, better seeds, and drought-resistant plants will also extend agriculture into new areas. Shelter-belts, strip-cropping, stubble mulching, and other such attempts to conserve moisture may be expected to increase the amount of cropland available. Discovery of new minerals and better use of those now being extracted will provide a base for new industries in some parts of the Great Plains. Much progress has been made; more is to be expected. Yet, despite man's progress, nature will continue to impede his efforts through the arid restrictions she has placed on the region.

FIGURE 13-28. *Denver, Colorado, with the Front Range of the Rocky Mountains in the background. Denver's great distance from Anglo-America's mass markets has resulted in the gradual selection of high-value industries, such as instruments, precision equipment, and publication services, that are not hampered by cost of transportation.* (Colorado Dept. of Public Relations)

Selected References

BOYCE, RONALD R. (ed.), *Regional Development and the Wabash Basin*, Urbana, Ill.: University of Illinois Press, 1964.

CALEF, WESLEY, "The Winter of 1948-49 on the Great Plains," *Annals of the Association of American Geographers*, December, 1950, pp. 267–292.

CURTIS, JOHN T., "The Modification of Mid-Latitude Grasslands and Forests by Man," *Man's Role in Changing the Face of the Earth*, Chicago: University of Chicago Press, 1956, pp. 721–736.

DOERR, ARTHUR H., and MORRIS, JOHN W., "The Oklahoma Panhandle—a Cross Section of the Southern High Plains," *Economic Geography*, Vol. 36, January, 1960, pp. 70–88.

HAYSTEAD, LADD, and FITE, GILBERT C., *The Agricultural Regions of the United States*, Norman, Okla.: University of Oklahoma Press, 1955, pp. 179–203.

HENDERSON, DAVID A., " 'Corn Belt' Cattle Feeding in Eastern Colorado's Irrigated Valleys," *Economic Geography*, Vol. 30, October, 1954, pp. 364–372.

HEWES, LESLIE, "Causes of Wheat Failure in the Dry Farming Region, Central Great Plains, 1939-1957," *Economic Geography*, Vol. 41, October, 1965, pp. 313–330.

———, "Wheat Failure in Western Nebraska, 1931-54," *Annals of the Association of American Geographers*, Vol. 48, December, 1958, pp. 375–397.

KOLLMORGEN, WALTER M., and JENKS, GEORGE F., "Suitcase Farming in Sully County, South Dakota," *Annals of the Association of American Geographers*, Vol. 48, March, 1958, pp. 27–40.

KRAENZEL, CARL F., *The Great Plains in Transition*, Norman, Okla.: University of Oklahoma Press, 1955.

LEWIS, G. MALCOLM, "William Gilpin and the Concept of the Great Plains Region," *Annals of the Association of American Geographers*, Vol. 56, March, 1966, pp. 33–51.

LOEFFLER, M. JOHN, "Beet-sugar Production on the Colorado Piedmont," *Annals of the Association of American Geographers*, Vol. 53, September, 1963, pp. 364–390.

———, "Colorado Population Syndromes," *ibid.*, Vol. 55, March, 1965, pp. 27–66.

MEIGS, PEVERIL, "Outlook for the Arid Realm of the United States," *Focus*, Vol. 4, December, 1953.

MORRIS, JOHN W., and DOERR, ARTHUR H., "Irrigation in Oklahoma," *The Journal of Geography*, Vol. 58, December, 1959, pp. 421–429.

SIMONETT, DAVID S., "Development and Grading of Dunes in Western Kansas," *Annals of the Association of America Geographers*, Vol. 50, September, 1960, pp. 216–241.

STEVENS, W. R., "Some Causes of Drouths in the Great Plains," *Journal of Geography*, Vol. 54, September, 1955, pp. 304–307.

STOCKTON, JOHN R., and ARBINGAST, STANLEY A., *Water Requirements Survey: Texas High Plains*, Austin, Texas: University of Texas Press, 1953.

VANDERHILL, BURKE G., "Post-war Agricultural Settlement in Manitoba," *Economic Geography*, Vol. 35, July, 1959, pp. 259–268.

VILLMOW, JACK R., "The Nature and Origin of the Canadian Dry Belt," *Annals of the Association of American Geographers*, Vol. 46, June, 1956, pp. 211–232.

WEAVER, J. E., and ALBERTSON, F. W., *Grasslands of the Great Plains: Their Nature and Use*, Lincoln, Nebr.: Johnson Publishing Co., 1956.

WEBB, WALTER PRESCOTT, *The Great Plains*, Boston: Ginn and Co., 1931.

ZAKRZEWSKA, BARBARA, "An Analysis of Landforms of the Central Great Plains," *Annals of the Association of American Geographers*, Vol. 53, December, 1963, pp. 536–568.

14 Rocky Mountain Region

The Rocky Mountain Region includes the Southern Rockies in the United States, the Central Rockies in the United States and Canada, and the Arctic Rockies, or Brooks Range, in Alaska (*Fig. 14-1*). The Rockies are lands of high relief, having a low percentage of near-level land (*Fig. 14-2*). Their land use patterns and population density differ greatly from the other regions of Anglo-America. Rugged terrain, inaccessibility, and severe climatic conditions preclude any dense settlement. Economic activities, for the most part, are either of an extractive nature—hunting, trapping, mining, or logging—or are devoted to grazing or recreational industries.

The Southern Rockies

Like most high mountains, the Southern Rockies have a complex origin and structure, involving folding, faulting, intrusion, eruption, and carving by water and ice. Large areas have been subjected to erosion through two or more cycles.

SURFACE FEATURES

The Southern Rockies are roughly 500 miles long by 150 miles broad, centering in Colorado, the highest state (mean elevation) in the conterminous United States (*Fig. 14-3*). The mountains rise abruptly on all sides from plateaus 5,000 to 7,000 feet high. About 100 peaks rise above 13,000 feet, but none reach as high as 14,500 feet. Between and around the highest ridges are very large areas of granite upland 9,000 to 11,000 feet high, at places plateau-like; elsewhere the region is dissected into mountains.

The most obvious features of the structure are the north-south belts of granite, each belt representing an axis of uplift. Some belts are narrow; others are 40 miles wide. These elevated belts are flanked by upturned strata that dip away from the axes and descend to great depths beneath the adjacent plateaus. They may once have covered the granite axes. Generally the tilted strata make monoclinal or "hogback" foothills.

Front Range. The name "Front Range" is commonly applied to the easternmost range from the Arkansas River north to the Wyoming boundary. More than one-half the area of its granite core is plateau-like, with a maximum height of 11,000 feet in central Colorado. This is a peneplain, much of it again being cut into "mountains" by valleys several thousand feet deep. Rising above it are huge monadnocks

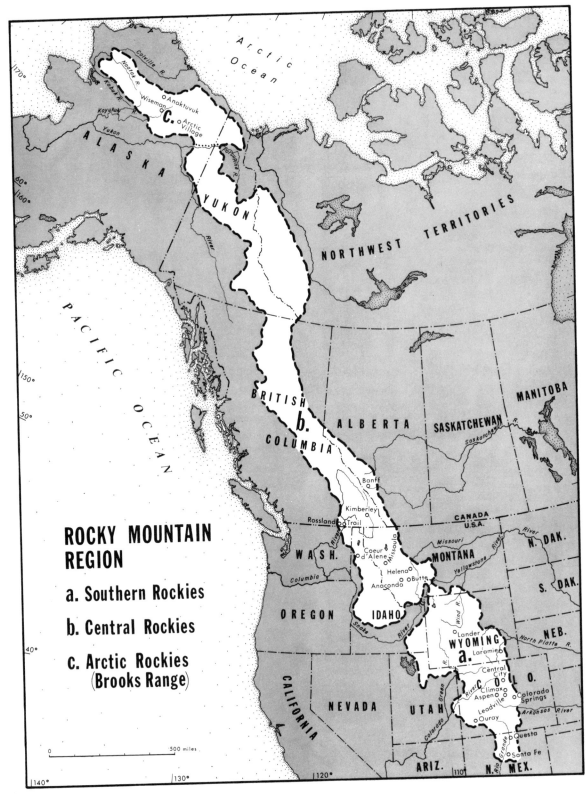

FIGURE 14-1.

like Pike's Peak (4,000 feet higher than the peneplain) and massive residual ridges like the "Continental Divide" (*Fig. 14-4*). These have very "alpine" features due to local glaciation. The Wet Mountains south of the Arkansas River are similar. The range continues north to central Wyoming under the name Laramie, the upland declining to 8,000 feet with few monadnocks. The Medicine Bow Range is a northwesterly branch.

The Park, Sawatch, and Sangre de Christo Ranges are similar in having granite cores, monoclinal foothills, plateau-like uplands and granite peaks. The Sawatch Range is one of the best-marked chains in the Rocky Mountains. The dominating peaks along the whole range exceed 14,000 feet in elevation.

Other ranges. The southwestern extension in Colorado is made by the San Juan Mountains, mainly a plateau-like surface on volcanic rocks that have been cut by water and ice into very rugged mountains. Many peaks are between 13,000 and 14,000 feet high (*Fig. 14-5*). North of the San Juan Mountains an irregular line of uplifts extends northwest toward the Uinta Range. This line includes the lofty Elk Mountains, the West Elk Mountains (mainly laccoliths), and the White River Plateau.

Parks. The "parks" of Colorado are extensive basins between the Front and Park Ranges, the elevation of their floors varying from 8,000 to 10,000 feet and the topography from level to locally mountainous. The first three "parks" (North, Middle, and South) are drained by the Platte, Arkansas, and Colorado Rivers re-

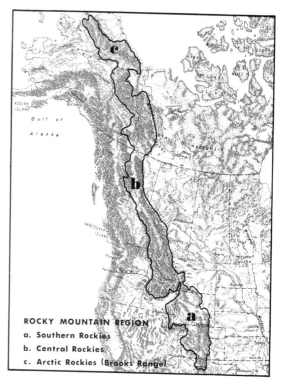

FIGURE 14-2. *The Rocky Mountain Region, physical relief.*

ROCKY MOUNTAIN REGION
a. Southern Rockies
b. Central Rockies
c. Arctic Rockies (Brooks Range)

spectively. The Rio Grande originates in the San Luis Valley—the largest park of them all. From here this river drains southward through New Mexico and Texas, emptying into the Gulf of Mexico.

Wyoming Basin. The folded structure of the Southern Rocky Mountains is continuous with that of the Central Rockies, but the ridges in central Wyoming are low and in large part

FIGURE 14-3. *Cross-section of the Southern Rockies (after Raisz).*

FIGURE 14-4. *Pike's Peak (14,500 feet), as seen from the Black Forest near Colorado Springs, Colorado. The summit of Pike's Peak can be reached by automobile or cog train. (Colorado Springs Chamber of Commerce)*

FIGURE 14-5. *The San Juan Mountains north of Ouray, Colorado. (Colorado Dept. of Public Relations)*

buried by horizontal tertiary sediments. Their tops stand out as low, isolated, east-west ranges between the Laramie and Wind River Ranges, forming a plateau 6,500 to 7,500 feet high. The Wyoming Basin is an extensive semiarid tract, almost 250 miles square, which merges with the Great Plains in the east and the Colorado Plateau in the south and forms a topographical break in the Rocky Mountain system. It is a region of scrub, sagebrush, sand dunes, buttes, and low hills. It is drained by the Green and Sweetwater Rivers.

The basin floor is mainly a peneplain, flat or mildly rolling where the rocks are weak, rougher where stronger beds outcrop; it is interrupted by sandstone escarpments or districts of roughly dissected plateau. As the bordering mountains or isolated domes are approached, low cuestas give way to steeper hogbacks. Some cuestas are cut into badlands; other badlands border entrenched streams like the Green River.

Drainage lines disregard the mountains. The Laramie River drains Laramie Basin, then crosses the Laramie Mountains. North Platte River flows through the mountains to get out of North Park and later cuts its way past two more ranges to reach the Great Plains. Big Horn River crosses mountains to enter Big Horn Basin and again to leave it. Green River traverses the Uinta Range in a 3,000 foot canyon. Bitter Creek crosses Rock Springs Dome. Yampa River leaves the Wyoming Basin to enter the Uinta Mountains where it joins the Green River.

The Uinta Range lies directly west of North Park and is separated from it by the Park Range and by a broad belt of high mesa country. The Uinta is unusual in that it has an east-west trend, and thus forms a connecting link between the eastern edge of the Rocky Mountain system and its western border, of which the Wasatch Range is the most strongly marked division.

As the traveler advances northwesterly, he finds less variety in the scenery, more uniformity in the elevation of the ranges, and almost no dominating peaks. Striking exceptions are the Wind River and Teton Ranges and the Yellowstone geyser region (*Fig. 14-6*). There are also various isolated groups of mountains lying to the east of the main range of the Southern Rockies, especially in Wyoming. Prominent among these are the Absaroka Range and the impressive Big Horn Mountains, separated by Big Horn Basin, a broad bowl-like structural depression.

The Central Rockies

The Central Rockies in the United States and Canada consist of a large number of ranges having a general northwest-southeast trend, although by no means regularly conforming to that direction. As a whole, the central division of the Rocky Mountains is lower and less impressive in scenic terms than the southern (*Fig. 14-7*).

The Montana and Idaho portions of the Central Rockies are more irregular in their development than are all portions of the Southern Rockies. There is, however, a similarity in both areas in the formation of mountain-encircled valleys locally called "parks" or "prairies" (*see Fig. 14-2*). These parks are mostly destitute of timber, except for cottonwoods growing along the banks of streams. The mountains are partially covered with coniferous trees, not of great size but sufficiently large to be useful for ordinary building purposes. Some portions of the parks have a soil suitable for cultivation; others are covered with bunch grass and are well suited for grazing.

FIGURE 14-6. *The Teton Range is one of the most striking mountain masses in Anglo-America. Grand Teton, highest peak in the range, is 13,766 feet above sea level. The southern portion of the range, which includes Grand Teton, is included in Grand Teton National Park. (National Park Service)*

The Bitterroot is an important range that, in a portion of its course, forms the main divide between the headwaters of the Missouri and the Columbia Rivers and which, farther to the northwest, separates the waters tributary to the Snake River from those that help form the Clark Fork of the Yellowstone River.

The Clearwater Mountains lie to the west of the Bitterroot Range and unite the Rockies

FIGURE 14-7. *Cross-section of the Central Rockies (after Raisz).*

CENTRAL ROCKIES   Lewis Overthrust Fault   GREAT PLAINS

with the Blue Mountains. The latter are an important group of ranges that occupy a considerable part of the area lying west of the Snake River (*Fig. 14-8*).

The Canadian Rockies are not as well known as those in the United States, but they contain numerous peaks of equal or greater altitude. Many of the highest peaks in this part of the range have large glaciers, in this respect closely resembling the Swiss Alps. They average 25 to 50 miles in width and extend in a northwesterly direction almost to the Yukon.

Between the Central Rockies and the mountains immediately to the west—the Purcell, Selkirk, and Cariboo Mountains, which are earlier in origin—lies the great Rocky Mountain Trench, running northward from Montana more or less continuously for 900 miles. Seen from the air it looks like a vast trough, with its floor varying from 2 to 10 miles across.

North of Mount Robson the range changes in character, becoming much lower. Where the Peace River flows eastward out of the Rocky Mountain Trench, it is at a minimum width of 25 miles; but beyond, in what is perhaps the least known area of the Central Rockies, its width increases to 85 miles or more. Here are the almost inaccessible Lloyd George Mountains, rising to a maximum of 9,800 feet. About 100 miles northwest of the Lloyd George group and 480 miles from Mount Robson is Terminus Mountain (6,250 feet), which rises above the Kechika River in the extreme north of British Columbia. It is suitably named, for it is the real northern outpost of the Central Rockies.

All the Rocky Mountain ranges of Canada contain magnificent scenery, which accounts for no fewer than seven national parks in this section of the subregion (*Fig. 14-9*).

The Arctic Rockies

The northernmost part of the Rocky Mountains is represented by the Brooks Range in Alaska—a mountain land 600 miles long and 80 miles wide. It comprises several groups of

FIGURE 14-8. *The Sawtooth Mountains, south of the Clearwater Mountains, represent a large group of ranges and masses in south-central Idaho. Many peaks rise over 9,000 feet. (Idaho Dept. of Commerce and Development)*

FIGURE 14-9. *From the 7,000-foot lookout on Mount Norquay in Banff National Park, the top of 9,838-foot Mount Rundle is seen towering in the background. In the distance is the Bow River Valley. (Canadian Government Travel Bureau)*

rugged, glaciated mountains having a relief of 3,000 to 6,000 feet and maximum altitudes of 3,600 to 9,200 feet. The Arctic foothills area is a hilly region between the mountains and the coastal plain. It is divided topographically and geologically into the southern foothills, characterized by irregular topography with isolated hills and ridges that rise 500 to 2,000 feet above areas of low relief, and the northern foothills, characterized by persistent ridges, mesas, and hills generally of 500- to 1,000-foot relief and having approximately accordant summits.

Everything associated with the Brooks Range is Arctic. Caribou roam its uplands, pursued by wolves as large as can be found in Anglo-America, some "Arctic white" and weighing 120 pounds or more. Its native inhabitants are Eskimos and Indians. The willows are stunted by the cold and grow to be only knee high. From the snows and glaciers of the higher slopes, rivers, which are ice-clad for much of the year, flow into ice-covered seas. The Porcupine flows into the fast, cold Yukon, which, in turn, reaches the Bering Sea with its tributary, the Koyukuk; the Kobuk and Noatak empty into the icy sea encompassed by the coasts of Alaska and Siberia; the Colville flows across frozen muskeg into the Arctic Ocean.

Few outsiders have scaled the contorted ridges that rise to the pinnacles of Mount Michelson, visible from the little settlement of Arctic Village, or those culminating in the ice-clad Mount Doonerak. In the west, the Noatak River divides the Brooks Range into two tongues: the rugged Baird and DeLong Mountains, rising to 4,500 feet.

Once the only value of this vast range lay in its furbearing animals; the only form of transport through it was the canoe in summer and the dog team and snowshoe in winter (*Fig. 14-10*). Since World War II, however, bush planes have operated from airstrips and settlements at Wiseman, Arctic Village, and Anaktuvuk in the Endicott Mountains, home of the Nunamiut, a virile tribe of Eskimo hunters who follow and live on caribou herds along the northern side of the passes in the Brooks Range. There is much prospecting for minerals

FIGURE 14-10. *The Alaskan Husky, a valuable work animal to the people living in Arctic Alaska. (Alaska Travel Division)*

and oil, using the airstrip maintained near the Eskimo village of Umiat.

For the rest, the Brooks Range is remote even by Alaskan standards; its predominant sounds are the clicking of caribou feet, the rattle of moose horns, the howl of wolf packs, and the hum of winds that sweep across the Arctic peaks from the ice-clad sea. Much of it is still inaccessible wilderness.

Climate

Because of the diversified topography within the Rocky Mountain Region, there is a remarkable variety of climates, and great differences often occur within short distances. As far as temperatures and precipitation are concerned, altitude is, in general, a more potent factor of control than latitude. The entire region lies within the belt of prevailing westerly winds. Because of intervening north-south mountains to the west, especially the Cascade and Sierra Nevada Ranges, that rob the eastward-moving winds of much of their moisture, precipitation is light except at the higher elevations. There are alternating mountains and lower, comparatively flat intervening areas. These variations greatly affect the amount of precipitation, which varies from a high of 40 inches in the more exposed areas to a low of 8 inches in portions of southern Colorado.

At the lower levels of the western slope, wind movement is light and commonly of the mountain-and-valley type. At the summits of the mountains, the winds are generally from the west and are frequently very strong in winter and spring. High winds often interrupt traffic for considerable periods, and their action in drifting and packing the snow is very important.

There is a tendency for a high pressure area to form in winter and to remain stationary for several days. When such a pressure distribution controls the weather, the sky is clear, the day temperatures are moderately high and uniform, and the nights are cold, though seldom excessively so except where the ground is covered with snow and where air drainage is poor. Night temperatures depend largely on the topography, with air drainage exerting a greater control than actual elevation. The lowest readings, from −40° to −54° F., are observed in the mountain valleys and parks, where the air tends to become stagnant. In such localities there is almost always an inversion of temperature during cold spells, when the greatest cold is generally confined to the lower strata of air whose upper limits do not always reach the higher altitudes. The mildest weather during the cold spells is found below, or near the mouths of the larger canyons (*Fig. 14-11*).

Because of the varied topography, the length of the growing season differs markedly from a minimum of 30 days in some parts to a maximum of 125 days in some of the more protected areas. At a number of stations at high

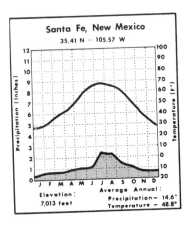

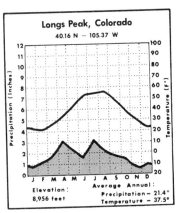

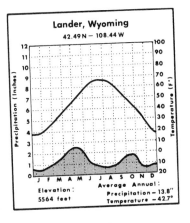

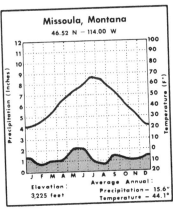

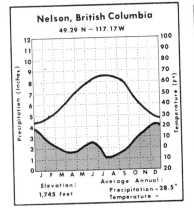

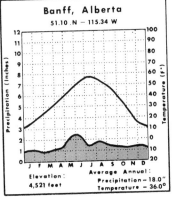

FIGURE 14-11. *Climatic graphs of the Rocky Mountain Region.*

altitudes in the interior, frosts or freezing temperatures are experienced in nearly every month of the year.

Natural Vegetation

The Rocky Mountains are high, sharp, and rugged, their tops usually mantled with bare rocks. Timber line corresponds with air temperature zones. Tree species are controlled in their distribution almost wholly by the degree of isolation of the site, by the resultant temperatures, and by the closely related surface conditions of moisture. In Yellowstone Park, for example, forests begin at 5,000 feet and disappear at 9,800 feet. On the Big Horn Mountains the limits of forest are 6,000 and 11,000 feet. In the lowlands bordering the Southern Rocky Mountains, greasewood, sagebrush and cactus are signs of aridity. The foothills are semiarid and dwarfed cedars and pinions appear as scattered clumps or groves of trees. Above the foothills, open stands of pine, aspen, and, a little higher, spruce and fir trees predominate. Still higher on the mountain slopes are belts of juniper and cedars and many low-flowering plants and shrubs. Beyond the tree line is a zone of grasses, mosses, and large areas of bare rock (*Fig. 14-12*).

Soils

Rocky Mountain soils vary greatly according to climate, elevation, and origin. The soils of the mountain valleys of Colorado, for example, are among the most fertile in Anglo-America. These soils contain rich amounts of the minerals needed by growing plants, and moderate amounts of humus. The high mountains have thin, immature soils called lithosols where there has been much moisture. Thin, grayish soils cover about half of the Rockies in Wyoming, especially in the southern and central sections. Strong, shallow soil, generally poor for farming, is found in most of the Central Rockies. As the range extends north through Alaska, the Rockies gradually become lower until they disappear in a series of ice-covered hills.

Settlement

The Rockies have a long history of settlement. Within 50 years after the discovery of the New World by Columbus, Spanish explorers seeking gold and fabled cities pushed north from Mexico to the borders of present-day Colorado. Francisco Coronado led the venture. There was gold in Colorado but the Spaniards failed to find it—and failed to occupy the land. They did, however, send several expeditions into the region in pursuit of Indians. These Spanish adventurers named many of the mountains and rivers of southern Colorado; the musical names remain as a permanent heritage from old Spain.

French fur traders, pushing westward in the early eighteenth century, reached the Colorado country. But their influence was slight and their stay brief.

Not until the beginning of the nineteenth century did Americans appear on the scene. Meriwether Lewis and William Clark crossed the Rockies in 1805. Captain Zebulon M. Pike made an unsuccessful attempt in late November, 1806, to reach the summit of the peak that now bears his name. Pike's expedition was followed by other government explorers, including, among others, Major Stephen C. Long,

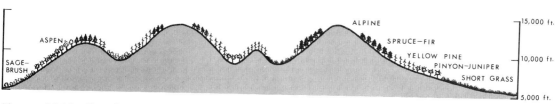

FIGURE 14-12. *Altitudinal zoning of vegetation in the Rocky Mountain Region.*

Lieutenant John C. Frémont, and Captain John W. Gunnison.

Trappers and hunters, such as Jim Bridger, Kit Carson, and Louis Vasquez, were the real trail blazers of the Rocky Mountain West. In search of beaver skins they followed the streams and penetrated the most secluded mountain valleys.

The fur trade brought the first visitors in numbers, for there was a ready market in England for beaver peltries for making hats. The traders and trappers, assisted by French rivermen, came up the Missouri. A few of them established fur-trading posts, set out traps, and traded with the Indians. Others journeyed overland across the wide plains (along a route soon to be known as the Oregon Trail), crossed the Continental Divide, and went down to the Green River, where beaver abounded. Still others followed the older route to Santa Fe.

The era of the trapper lasted only about 30 years. By 1842, less than four decades after Lewis and Clark trekked to the Columbia River, the trail-blazing period of the Rockies was at an end.

Mining development accounts for the first extensive settlement of the Rocky Mountain West. A prospecting party from Georgia under William Russell found placer gold during the summer of 1858 in the vicinity of what now is Denver, Colorado. Exaggerated accounts of the discoveries, when carried eastward, resulted in the Pike's Peak gold rush of 1859. Thousands of gold seekers hurried across the plains on foot, on horseback, in wagons, and even with handcarts and wheelbarrows. On reaching Cherry Creek and finding that the sands were not yellow with gold, many of the disillusioned adventurers started back for home. But on May 6, 1859, John H. Gregory discovered the Gregory Lode, a vein of gold-bearing quartz near present-day Central City, Colorado. This discovery was followed by others in rapid succession. Mines were quickly developed on the branches of Clear Creek, in South Park, and across the Continental Divide on the branches of the Blue River.

During the decade following the Pike's Peak gold rush, development was slow. Refractory ore was encountered in the mines; the Civil War claimed citizens for soldiers; and an Indian uprising threatened the existence of the territory.

After surviving the ordeals of the early years, Colorado made rapid progress in her second decade of settlement. Railways were completed to the heart of the territory in 1870; towns were founded; new mines were opened in the San Juan area; and immigration increased greatly. These factors brought about the admission of Colorado to the Union on August 1, 1876.

During the 1880's, growth continued on a grand scale. Leadville, Aspen, Ouray, and other mining regions poured forth their wealth. Towns began to flourish as smelters for the reduction of ores were erected. Gold, silver, copper, lead, and zinc were the chief minerals produced.

Mining

SOUTHERN ROCKIES

Mining activities in Colorado have created over $2 billion in mineral wealth so far, and mining continues to be a leading industry. Today zinc is in first place as an income producer, but lead still is mined from massive limestone replacements.

Molybdenum. Climax, near Leadville, Colorado, produces more than half of the U.S. molybdenum output (*Fig. 14-13*). Another molybdenum deposit has been opened about six miles from the town of Questa in the Red River mining district of Taos County in north-central New Mexico.

Uranium. A new era for the uranium industry began in 1956, looking beyond the military market to the permanent, long-range, industrial atomic power market. The uranium industry has developed a pattern similar to that of most other metal industries. It runs a full gamut in size of operations, from the small independent mine or group of small mines, to moderate-sized properties supporting a local

FIGURE 14-13. *The molybdenum mining and milling operations in Climax, Colorado. The deposits are at an elevation of 13,500 feet. (Colorado Dept. of Public Relations)*

custom mill, and to a large tonnage, integrated mining and milling operation. Western Colorado is one of the nation's principal sources of uranium (*Fig. 14-14*).

Coal. A large part of the total land area in Colorado and Wyoming is underlaid by coal deposits, the extent of which is unknown. Coal-bearing strata underlie the Wind River, Green River, and Big Horn River Basins.

Known reserves in the Big Horn Basin are in scattered, relatively small fields. There is both bituminous and subbituminous coal, but the major portion of the reserves is subbituminous.

The Wind River Basin coal deposits, in central Wyoming, are not continuous and are limited to small areas. The coal is subbituminous.

The Green River section is a roughly triangular area within which are found coal deposits ranging from subbituminous to high-volatile bituminous. This section is one of the most important coal-bearing areas in the Rockies.

No large-scale mining of coal has occurred to date within the Southern Rockies. By far the largest portion of coal production has been used by the railroads. Recently, however, diesel locomotives have put most of the coal-burners out of business. A much greater outlet appears

certain with new industries and a greater population demanding coal for domestic heating, for the generation of electric power, and for use in processing for chemical derivatives.

Oil shale. Oil shale is a fine-grained sedimentary rock containing organic matter that yields oil when distilled. It is distinguished from certain coals by its content of more than 33 per cent ash.

In this sedimentary rock, formed in past ages like other underground deposits, a solid substance called kerogen, or shale oil, is held. When shale oil is heated in a retort, it yields a liquid hydrocarbon resembling crude oil. Refining results in several valuable petroleum products—motor gasoline, jet fuel, and diesel fuel, for example. A ton of shale contains enough kerogen for 5 to 80 gallons of refined products.

The principal deposits of oil shale in the United States lie in Colorado, Utah, Nevada, and Wyoming. Some are in the Rocky Mountains, and some are in the plateaus to the west. The most important occurrences in the Southern Rockies are apparently limited to the central portion of the Green River Basin in Wyo-

FIGURE 14-14. *Waste dumps of uranium and vanadium mines near Naturita, Colorado. (Standard Oil Co. of New Jersey)*

ming, where exploratory wells have indicated the presence, at depths ranging from 300 to 3,000 feet below the surface, of 35 to 262 feet of shale that will produce 15 gallons of oil per ton.

Both mining and treatment of shale require processes different from those used in handling petroleum. Oil from shale is not competitive at present with crude oil, despite some recent claims made by the industry. However, the vast oil shale deposits are now considered a part of the nation's liquid fuel supply. Estimated reserves of recoverable petroleum from this source run as high as 300 billion barrels.

Petroleum. Wyoming has two major petroleum reserves—the Elk Basin field, containing 104 million barrels of proven crude oil, and the Oregon Basin, with 56 million barrels. The Elk Basin field extends into southern Montana.

CENTRAL ROCKIES

The Central Rockies contain such a wide variety of complex minerals that only the most important ones can be discussed here. These include: (1) the Butte-Anaconda district, Montana; (2) the Coeur d'Alene district, Idaho; and (3) the Kootenay district, British Columbia.

Butte-Anaconda district. The quest for gold brought a swarm of hardy prospectors into Montana after the discovery of rich placer deposits at Bannock in 1862. In the following years, the Alder Gulch strike, near the present site of Virginia City, attracted thousands more, who were rewarded during the next three years by more than $30 million in yellow treasure from the rich gravels. Last Chance Gulch (later to become Helena, the capital of Montana), Bear Gulch, Confederate Gulch, Blackfoot City, and other picturesque gold camps sprang up during the early 1860's.

The opening up of Butte, the richest hill on earth, in 1864, gave to Montana the title "Treasure State." The hill, first worked in 1864, made Butte a hell-raising camp, and then a city. Butte's copper workings yielded over $2.5 billion in 50 years. The city has 2,700 miles

of tunnels, and is described as "a mile deep, a mile high."

Most important of recent developments in Montana's mineral industry is the Anaconda Company's current expansion program that includes the construction of a multimillion-dollar copper ore concentrator and the expansion of deep-level mining.

Illustrative of the implications of this program, as far as Anaconda's Butte operations are concerned, is the revelation that copper, long the principal metal taken from Butte mines, is now being extracted from ores of grades as low as one-half of one per cent. This brings into operation tremendous mineable ore reserves that previously were of too low grade for production under existing mining methods and market conditions.

Trial open pit runs in small bodies of ore have proved satisfactory and now, after approximately 30 miles of exploratory drilling, a large section of the Butte hill, containing over 100 million tons of ore, is marked out for open pit operations. This section is called the Berkeley Pit, after an old mine shaft. Mining began here in December, 1955; to date more than 10 million tons of ore have been shipped to the smelter in Anaconda. Open pit operations will supplement underground mining, for as shafts go deeper, high-grade ores still are being found. The daily production from these sources is being increased as rapidly as possible along with that from surface mining.

Lead ores have been produced on a small scale as a by-product of manganese and zinc mining in Butte and at a number of small properties outside of Butte. The lead ores are composed principally of galena and are smelted at the American Smelting and Refining Company plant at East Helena.

Silver was the most important metal in the second stage of the development of the Butte district, and Montana is still a leading producer of silver in the United States. At present the silver is recovered almost entirely as a by-product of copper, lead, and zinc ores from the Butte district.

Coeur d'Alene district. Idaho has long been a leader in the production of minerals and the

Coeur d'Alene district, in the northern part of the state, is an important producer of silver, lead, and zinc. Silver mining began in 1884, starting a stampede into this area. Idaho is the leading producer of silver in the United States. It ranks second only to Montana in lead output and is third in zinc production (*Fig. 14-15*).

Kootenay district. Lode deposits—copper, lead and zinc—have been mined in the Kootenay district of southeastern British Columbia since the 1890's. The largest operator in the region is the Consolidated Mining and Smelting Company of Canada, Ltd. Its operation at Kimberley is the largest nonferrous metal mine in the Commonwealth.

The smelter at Trail, British Columbia, originally built to treat gold-copper ores from Rossland, is one of the leading lead and zinc smelters in the world. It treats concentrates and ores from mines in British Columbia, the Yukon Territory, Quebec, and from many different parts of the world (*Fig. 14-16*).

FIGURE 14-15. *The Bunker Hill-Sullivan zinc plant in Coeur d'Alene area of northern Idaho, the focal point of the vast mining industry of Idaho. (Idaho Dept. of Commerce)*

Agriculture

Physiography, as a direct and indirect agent, plays a dominant role in the agricultural development and utilization of the Rocky Mountain Region. This is especially significant in the distribution of land used for crops, pasture, and forests. The temperature and the amount of moisture both are affected directly by the physical features, and the different soil groups are linked closely with the topography, temperature, and precipitation.

FIGURE 14-16. *Metallurgical and chemical plants of the Consolidated Mining and Smelting Company at Trail, British Columbia, produce lead, zinc, silver, antimony, bismuth, cadmium, gold, and chemical fertilizers. (Consolidated Mining and Smelting Co.)*

SOUTHERN ROCKIES

In general, this subregion's agricultural enterprises may be divided into two groups, livestock and irrigation agriculture.

Livestock. The production of livestock is directly related to the condition of the range and therefore to the precipitation and general climatic conditions. Summer grazing takes place largely in the national forests. The park areas and some of the higher-altitude pla-

teaus are also used during the season. Ranches usually are located within the mountain valleys or on the edge of the Great Plains. Sagebrush plains and grassy slopes at higher elevations favor grazing activity. Winter feeding from locally grown summer forage in the protected valleys is the common practice. A transhumance system is practiced widely throughout the subregion (*Fig. 14-17*).

Grazing rights or permits are issued by the Forest Service on the basis of commensurability, that is, on the basis of the amount of privately owned land available to the applicant. Most ranchers keep both cattle and sheep. Cattle herds have increased considerably during the past decade, mainly because of market demand for beef and high selling prices. Normally, sheep outnumber cattle. According to ranchers, this is caused by the fact that sheep represent a "one-year crop"; that is, the lambs may be sold the year they are born, thus avoiding winter feeding. The mountain slopes are the summer ranges for the cattle, and the higher alpine meadows are especially suitable for sheep.

Irrigation agriculture. The irrigated lands are confined to a few watered valley favored by local relief and protection from winds and frost. The parallel arrangement of mountain ranges in northern New Mexico continues across Colorado, giving rise to several high basins and valleys.

Agriculture began during the mining period. Miners were forced to pay outrageous prices for food because, at first, the nearest agricultural-producing areas were as far away as 500 to 1,000 miles. The first settlers were literally forced to grow crops wherever water and level land were available. In this way, a string of small farms developed, and hay, wheat, oats, potatoes, and other staple crops were cultivated. These enterprises were privately financed. Later, as the area became more densely populated, states within the region began to construct irrigation projects in an attempt to increase the acreage under cultivation. Finally the Bureau of Reclamation entered the picture. Under its supervision sev-

FIGURE 14-17. *Beef cattle in a corral on a Wyoming ranch. Saddles in the foreground testify to the fact that machines have not entirely replaced the horse. (U.S. Dept. of Agriculture)*

eral large irrigation projects have made possible the reclamation of thousands of acres for intensive cultivation. One of the more spectacular developments is the Colorado-Big Thompson River Project. This diverts, by means of a 13-mile tunnel, 310,000 acre-feet of surplus water annually from the headwaters of the Colorado River on the western slope to northeastern Colorado on the eastern slope. Unlike most irrigation projects, the Colorado-Big Thompson is designed solely to provide additional or supplemental water for land already being irrigated.

The San Luis Valley in southern Colorado, a basin filled with alluvial fan deposits, is notable among the Rocky Mountain parks and valleys because of its size and importance in the local agricultural picture. Drained by the upper Rio Grande, it is about 100 miles long by 50 miles wide, and contains nearly 400,000 acres of cropland. Most of the crops grown are irrigated. The valley has over 3,000 artesian wells, but most of the irrigation water comes from streams, principally the Rio Grande. Because of the altitude, 7,500 feet in the center to 8,000 feet at the base of the mountains, only cool climate and frost-resistant crops are grown: hay (principally timothy, clover, alfalfa, and wild hay), potatoes, oats, wheat and barley, peas, and lettuce. Late lettuce is perhaps the most valuable crop in the valley.

The upper Arkansas Valley, much smaller and a little higher than the San Luis, lies to the north of that area, over a low divide. It has about 25,000 acres in crops, mostly hay and small grains, all irrigated, in addition to several hundred acres of lettuce.

Other notable irrigated basins in Colorado are South Park, Middle Park, and North Park. The land is used principally to supply winter feed (hay) for the cattle and sheep that graze in the national forests during the summer.

In Wyoming, there are the Laramie and Carbon Basins, the Wind River and Bridger Basins, and the Big Horn Basin. Over half the irrigated land is in hay, principally timothy and native hay; over one-fourth in pasture; and the remainder in grain, mostly wheat, with a few hundred acres in potatoes.

CENTRAL ROCKIES

Near the international boundary, division into ranges is largely by the following important valleys: the Columbia Valley, where the Columbia River flows south from Canada; the Purcell Trench, marked by Coeur d'Alene and Pend Orielle Lakes in Idaho; the Kootenay Lake in Canada; the Rocky Mountain Trench containing Flathead Lake and continuing south to include the Bitterroot Valley; and the broad north-south valley of the Missouri River south of Helena, Montana.

At places these valleys broaden into structural basins 10 to 25 miles wide. Otherwise the whole area is a deeply dissected upland whose skyline is 8,000 to 10,000 feet high on the east and south but declines a little toward the northwest.

Grazing and irrigation form the basis of all agricultural income in these valleys. Sheep and cattle are pastured on the mountain slopes in summer and winter fed from harvested grass hay and irrigated alfalfa. Field crops—beets and grains in Idaho and Montana and fruits in the Flathead Lake area of Montana and in the Kootenay Valley of Canada—also are major sources of the farmers' income.

Forestry

The Rocky Mountain forest is part of the Western pine region. Ponderosa, sugar, Idaho white, and lodgepole pines; Western larch; Engelmann spruce; white firs; and incense and red cedars are the most important species found there.

There are few forests in the Rocky Mountains that approach in density those of the Pacific Slope Region; nowhere in the Rockies are there individual trees as large as those on the slope. The trees of the Rockies usually grow most densely in the moist places at the foot of the ranges where the streams debouch, or in the ravines and gorges, or on the lower slopes. By far the most common deciduous tree throughout this region is the aspen, or quaking asp (often called cottonwood and, sometimes, poplar). This tree, almost worthless except for pulpwood, most commonly springs up to form dense thickets wherever the coniferous forest has been burned off. In various portions of the region there are scattered oaks, only here and there in sufficient quantity to be of importance. The black oak, the white oak, and a few other species dot the Southern Rockies subregion. The most densely forested portion of the region, however, is the Central Rockies subregion.

The establishment of national forests within the Rocky Mountain Region has withdrawn vast timberland tracts from commercial exploitation. Wilderness and wild areas in the national forests help preserve the natural beauty for all to enjoy. Timber stands also serve as protective watersheds, preventing floods and providing water for large-scale irrigation projects. These factors, combined with a small local population, distance from large consuming centers, inaccessibility and poor quality of timber, and transportation costs have greatly limited the lumber industry.

Exceptions occur in the states of Montana and Idaho, where there are better stands of timber; here they are consumed in large volume by the railroads and the various mining industries.

Recreation and Tourism

AMERICAN ROCKIES

The tourist industry adds millions of dollars to the revenue of the states in the American Rockies. Colorado, Montana, and Wyoming list their tourist industries among the first three income producers. Thousands of visitors from many parts of the United States and Canada, and from other parts of the world, journey to the Rockies to camp, hike, hunt, fish, and prospect, or simply to enjoy its many scenic wonders. Fortunately the United States government has set aside vast tracts for these purposes, administered by such agencies as the National Park Service, the Forest Service, the Bureau of Indian Affairs, the Bureau of Reclamation, and the Fish and Wildlife Service. Each of these government agencies performs valuable functions in maintaining and preserving the area's scenic beauty.

Rocky Mountain National Park. This park, embracing 405 square miles of spectacular scenery, is easily accessible the year round over broad, paved roads. The park contains 14 massive peaks, including 14,255-foot Long's Peak. In the wildlife sanctuary are hundreds of species of flowers and animals, including elk and deer. The Hidden Valley Winter Use Area offers excellent skiing. The town of Estes Park, alongside Lake Estes, at the park's eastern entrance, is a well-equipped, year-round resort area.

The Pike's Peak section. Centering upon Colorado Springs and Manitou Springs, this has long been an outstanding vacation area. Thrilling scenic drives include the Pike's Peak Highway and the Garden of the Gods to the north of Colorado Springs. The latter is an area where, because of folding and local faulting, red sandstone beds have been raised into a vertical position. Erosion has removed the weaker portions of sandstone leaving the stronger portions to be weathered into fantastic forms. The U.S. Air Force Academy, in Colorado Springs, is another popular tourist attraction.

Great Sand Dunes National Monument. This includes 46,034 acres of varicolored sands that lie in constantly shifting dunes and hills in the San Luis Valley, just west of the Sangre de Cristo Mountains.

Dinosaur National Monument. This monument in northwestern Colorado and northeastern Utah, includes more than 250,000 acres of country untouched by civilization. Impressive formations have been fashioned by the Green and Yampa Rivers, which flow through deep, narrow canyons with precipitous, delicately tinted sandstone cliffs. These canyons are dark and forbidding, with sheer walls that reach a height of 3,000 feet. The western section of the area, soon scheduled to be a reservoir contains great beds of dinosaur fossils.

Grand Teton-Jackson Hole. Grand Teton National Park, a large part of which is in Jackson Hole, is a wonderland of winter and summer beauty. The Tetons are a jagged, majestic range of peaks that jut above pine-covered mountains and valleys for 40 miles. Below the Teton Mountains are Jackson Lake, world famous for fishing and boating, Jenny Lake, and many other lakes and streams equally good for fishing.

Yellowstone National Park. Yellowstone lies to the west of the Absaroka Range. Much of the park is a basin with a floor some 2,000 feet lower than the surrounding uplands. Yellowstone, the largest of the national parks, is world famous for spouting geysers, steaming pools, mountains, canyons, streams, lakes, forests, and waterfalls. Fishing, horseback riding, boating, and relaxation in the midst of magnificent scenery are enjoyed by over a million visitors a year (*Fig. 14-18*).

Glacier National Park. This park lies in the most rugged section of the Montana Rockies. It has more than 60 glaciers, 200 sparkling lakes, forests of fragrant evergreens, fields of mountain wildflowers, wildlife of many varieties, and miles of good fishing streams.

Going-to-the-Sun Highway, a spectacular 50-mile drive running through the park,

crosses the Continental Divide at Logan Pass. Lofty peaks, sheer cliffs, dense forests, distant glaciers, meadows of brilliant blossoms, shimmering lakes, inquisitive bears, and proud mountain goats make up its changing panorama (*Fig. 14-19*).

Much of the park is accessible only by trail, and more than 1,000 miles of bridle paths and foot trails lead deep into the wilderness. The park, established in 1910, is the United States' section of Waterton-Glacier International Peace Park.

CANADIAN ROCKIES

The Canadian Rockies rival the Alps in beauty and grandeur. There are seven national parks in the Canadian Rockies: Jasper in northern Alberta, with an area of 4,400 square miles; Waterton Lakes in southern Alberta (120 square miles) adjoining the United States' Glacier National Park at the international boundary; four parks along the main line of the Canadian Pacific Railway through the Central Rockies and Selkirks—Banff, Yoho, Glacier, and Mount Revelstoke; and Kootenay Highway Park along the Vermillion-Columbia

FIGURE 14-18. *Lower Falls in Yellowstone National Park, Wyoming. (Union Pacific Railroad)*

FIGURE 14-19. *Citadel and Fusilade Mountains in Glacier National Park, Montana. In the foreground is Upper St. Mary Lake; glaciers mantle the peaks in the background. (National Park Service)*

section of the transmontane motor road. Of these, three parks—Banff, Yoho, and Jasper—merit further treatment.

Banff National Park. Banff was the first Canadian national park to be established and was originally named Rocky Mountains Park. It has an area of 2,585 square miles of high mountain territory on the eastern side of the Rocky Mountains, comprising the whole northerly watershed of the Saskatchewan River.

One of the special attractions of the park is the town of Banff, with its famous mineral hot springs; its two excellent bathhouses at the Cave and Basin and the Upper Hot Springs, respectively; its outstanding hotels, museum, and zoological garden; its golf course; and its many scenic drives. Here also are the headquarters of the Alpine Club of Canada, where Alpine climbers of international fame have stayed on their way to fresh climbing victories.

Of the scenic attractions in this great park, Lake Louise is probably the best known. Another tourist attraction is the Columbia Ice Field, which lies to the north of Banff.

Yoho National Park. At the Great Divide, the summit of Kickinghorse Pass, the traveler passes from Alberta to British Columbia and from Banff to Yoho Park. Seen from Kickinghorse Pass, Yoho is only a narrow cleft between heavily wooded mountain walls stretching north to the gleaming whiteness of Yoho Glacier. Yet that narrow opening is a valley 14 miles long and more than a mile deep, walled in by almost perpendicular mountains hung with primeval forest and crowned by enormous snowfields that creep down from the peaks in slow-moving rivers of ice or fall in tremendous cataracts (*Fig. 14-20*).

Jasper National Park. Jasper Park is on the main line of the Canadian National Railway,

FIGURE 14-20. *Yoho National Park, British Columbia. (Canadian Government Travel Bureau)*

about 240 miles west of Edmonton. It embraces a rich variety of river, lake, forest, and mountain scenery. Largest of the Canadian national parks, it contains the headwaters of the Athabaska River system, which flows into the Arctic Ocean. The park, an Alpine resort of great interest, offers golfing, tennis, boating, swimming, hiking, and riding.

Outlook

The Rocky Mountain Region has scarcely been tapped in terms of its ability to support a much greater population. It contains a wealth of minerals (especially metallics) in various stages of exploitation. Among the most plentiful are gold, silver, lead, zinc, and copper. Tungsten, molybdenum, uranium, vanadium, manganese, and radium are also produced, and there are enormous reserves (and some production) of phosphate rock, oil shale, petroleum, and bituminous coal. Cattle and sheep are grazed in enormous numbers (mainly in the United States portion) on winter ranges in valleys and plains, and on mountain pastures in the summer. Agriculture is of less importance, owing to the generally high altitude of most of the valleys of the Southern and Central Rockies, and the high latitude (and resultant short or nonexistent growing season) of the lowlands of the Central Rockies. Difficult terrain for logging and transportation, lack of local markets, and the comparatively low value of much Rocky Mountain timber have restricted commercial lumbering mainly to northern Montana and northern Idaho, although there are logging operations in many scattered areas.

The spectacular scenic beauty of the Rockies, particularly of the glaciated peaks of the northern United States and southern Canadian portions, have made the region one of the continent's great vacation lands. Greater leisure time in the years ahead and perhaps a considerably larger population will no doubt result in a more efficient use of the Rocky Mountain Region.

Selected References

CALEF, WESLEY, "Problems of Grazing Administration in the Basins of Southern Wyoming," *Economic Geography*, Vol. 28, April, 1952, pp. 122–127.

GARWOOD, JOHN D., "An Analysis of Postwar Industrial Migration to Utah and Colorado," *Economic Geography*, Vol. 29, January, 1953, pp. 79–88.

HARMISTON, FLOYD, "A Study of the Resources, People, and Economy of the Powder River Basin," *Wyoming Industrial Research Council Monograph*, Laramie, Wyo.: University of Wyoming Press, 1957.

HARTLEY, F. L., and BRINEGAR, C. S., "Oil Shale and Bituminous Sand," *The Scientific Monthly*, Vol. 84, June, 1957, pp. 275–289.

HAYSTEAD, LADD, and FITE, GILBERT C., *The Agricultural Regions of the United States*, Norman, Okla.: University of Oklahoma Press, 1955, pp. 218–232.

HELBURN, NICHOLAS, "Human Ecology of Western Montana Valleys," *The Journal of Geography*, Vol. 55, January, 1956, pp. 5–13.

HOFFMEISTER, HAROLD A., "Middle Park and the Colorado-Big Thompson Diversion Project," *Economic Geography*, Vol. 23, July, 1947, pp. 220–231.

JAMES, PRESTON E., *A Geography of Man*, Boston: Ginn & Co., 1959, pp. 391–410.

JENNESS, JOHN L., "Erosive Forces in the Physiography of Western Arctic Canada," *Geographical Review*, Vol. 42, April, 1952, pp. 238–252.

KIMBLE, GEORGE H. T., and GOOD, DOROTHY (eds.), *Geography of the Northlands*, New York: American Geographical Society, 1955.

LACKEY, EARL B., "Mountain Passes in the Colorado Rockies," *Economic Geography*, Vol. 25, July, 1949, pp. 211–215.

LONG, TANIA, "The Eskimos Meet the Twentieth Century," *The New York Times Magazine*, June 17, 1956, pp. 12–13.

McINNIS, WILMER, "Molybdenum—a Materials Survey," *Bureau of Mines Information Circular 7784*, April, 1957.

McKNIGHT, TOM L., "Recreational Use of the National Forests of Colorado," *The Southwestern Social Science Quarterly*, Vol. 32, 1951, pp. 264–270.

NELSON, J. G., and BYRNE, A. R., "Man as an In-
strument of Landscape Change: Fires, Floods,
and National Parks in the Bow Valley, Alberta," *The Geographical Review,* Vol. 46,
April, 1966, pp. 226–238.

O'BRIEN, BOB R., "The Future Road System of
Yellowstone National Park," *Annals of the
Association of American Geographers,* Vol.
56, September, 1966, pp. 385–407.

"Ranching in the Rockies," *Monthly Review* (Federal Reserve Bank of Minneapolis), Vol. 43,
October, 1961.

SOLOW, HERBERT, "Anaconda: One Face to the
Future," *Fortune,* Vol. 51, January, 1955,
pp. 89–95, 148–150.

SONNENFELD, J., "Changes in an Eskimo Hunting
Technology, An Introduction to Implement
Geography," *Annals of the Association of
American Geographers,* Vol. 50, June, 1960,
pp. 172–186.

STEAD, ROBERT J. C., "The Yellowhead Pass—
Canadian Rockies," *Canadian Geographical
Journal,* Vol. 36, 1948, pp. 51–65.

STERN, PETER M., "Alaska," *Focus,* Vol. 4, No. 1,
September, 1953, pp. 1–6.

WEIGERT, H. W., STEFANSSON, V., and HARRISON,
R. E. (eds.), *New Compass of the World,*
New York: The Macmillan Co., 1953, pp.
25–60.

WOLLE, M. S., *Stampede to Timberline: The
Ghost Towns and Mining Camps of Colorado,*
Boulder, Colo.: University of Colorado Press,
1949.

ZIERER, CLIFFORD M., "Tourism and Recreation in
the West," *Geographical Review,* Vol. 42,
July, 1952, pp. 462–481.

15 *Intermontane Basins and Plateaus Region*

The Intermontane Basins and Plateaus Region comprises a vast semiarid to arid territory (*Fig. 15-1*). It is an area of varied relief. There are partially dissected tablelands—lands of moderate to high relief, but with a large percentage of nearly level land that lies at a relatively high altitude in the Colorado Plateau. Plains with widely spaced hills and mountains, most of which lie at relatively low elevations, are the dominant landforms in Nevada, northeastern and southeastern California, and central and southeastern Oregon. In eastern Washington, southwestern Idaho, and north-central Oregon, lava plateaus, drained by the Columbia River system, predominate. Northward are the Interior Plateau of British Columbia, with a summit elevation of 3,500 feet above sea level, and the Yukon Plateau, a broad upland surface with a gently rolling topography (*Fig. 15-2*).

Land uses differ greatly from one part of the region to another depending upon local weather, terrain, mineral deposits and other resources, and geographical position. In general, the more arid areas support a grazing economy. Irrigation farming prevails in those favored valleys where water is available. Mining, health resorts, and recreational activities are found in areas suited to these enterprises.

Physiographically, this region may be subdivided into: Basin and Range, Colorado Plateau, Columbia Plateau, British Columbia Interior Plateau, and Yukon Plateau.

Surface Features

BASIN AND RANGE

This vast area, covering about 300,000 square miles, consists of isolated ranges separated from one another by basins. The ranges are the block-mountain type—blocks of the earth's crust separated by great faults and then tilted so that the upstanding edges form mountains. The mountains have been greatly worn down and their denudation has provided the material that fills the basins. The entire region is dry and covers most of the state of Nevada, western Utah, parts of Oregon and Idaho, northeastern and southeastern California, and portions of Arizona, New Mexico, and Texas. The Basin and Range may be further subdivided into the Great Basin, the Sonoran Desert, the Salton Trough,

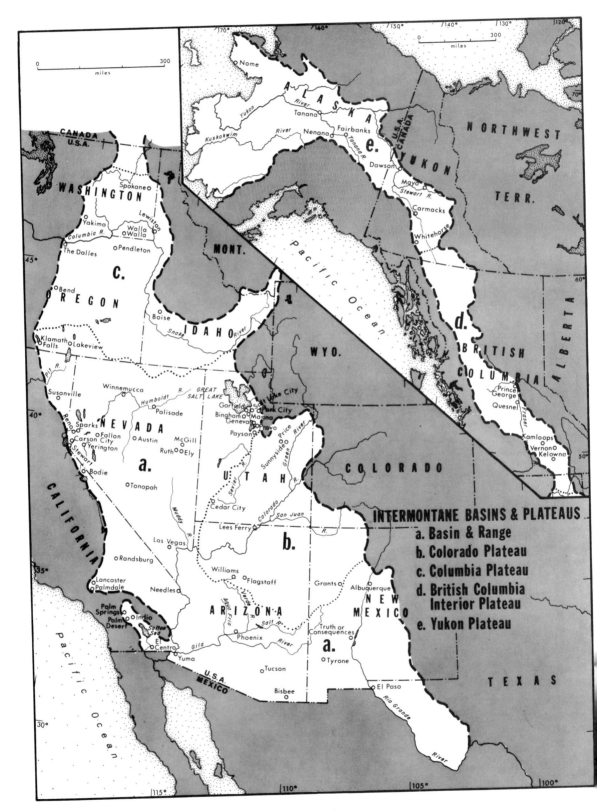

FIGURE 15-1.

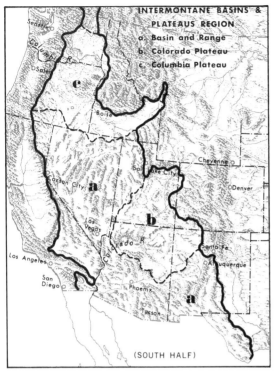

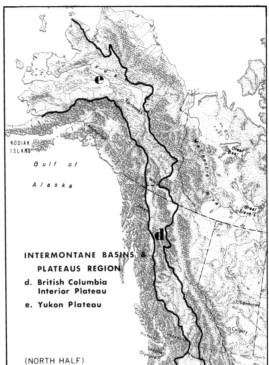

FIGURE 15-2. *The Intermontane Basins and Plateaus Region, physical relief.*

the Mexican Highland, and the Sacramento Mountains (*see Fig. 15-2*).

Mountains on the west (Sierra Nevada-Cascades) mark the boundary clearly. Between mountains the basins merge with the Columbia Plateau on the north, but the latter is almost free from mountains and generally has no detrital material. The eastern boundary against the Wasatch Mountains and the escarpment of the Colorado Plateau is generally clear. The boundary in New Mexico, which is not too definite, is against the Pecos section of the Great Plains Region, the latter being lower.

The Great Basin. This makes up about half of the Basin and Range subregion. This section centers in Nevada but extends into the adjoining states. The Oregon lake section is like the adjacent Columbia Plateau but is faulted into young block mountains 1,000 to 2,000 feet high made of formerly horizontal lavas. Some of the intervening lakes overflow regularly; some overflow occasionally; and others never overflow (*Fig. 15-3*).

The Nevada and Utah portions differ from the Oregon lake section in having older and larger block mountains, for the most part eroded to maturity. Their 50 to 100 ranges occupy fully half the area. Many are complexly deformed sedimentary rocks. It is as though an old folded mountain region were nearly base leveled, covered in places by lava, broken by new north-south faults—the new fault blocks being tilted into mountains—and then maturely eroded in a climate so arid that the intervening troughs were filled with waste that in a humid climate would have gone to the sea. Trees occur only on

FIGURE 15-3. *Block diagram of a part of the Steens Mountains in southern Oregon.*

the highest mountains (8,000 to 10,000 feet) or in occasional protected gorges. There is little soil on the mountains; bare rocks of bright colors are conspicuous (*Fig. 15-4*).

Some of these ranges are so eroded that their forms no longer suggest fault blocks, especially when it is remembered that the strata were complexly folded before the faulting. Their opposite sides may have equal steepness.

There are about 100 enclosed basins, generally with sinks. Some have salt lakes; a few, fresh lakes; and others, playas or salinas. In some cases alluvial fans from opposite sides meet. The depth of filling is sometimes 2,000 feet. Some basins are absolute deserts; some have sagebrush and bunch grass like the mountains. Generally, where cattle can find water there is also some grass.

In the glacial epoch, Lake Bonneville, in the eastern part of the Nevada Basin, rose 1,000 feet above Great Salt Lake and covered 20,000 square miles, overflowing to the Snake River. "Fossil" shorelines, cliffs, bars, deltas, and the like, are striking features of the present topography (*Fig. 15-5*). Lake Lahontan, in the western part, covered 8,440 square miles; it left similar shorelines but did not overflow.

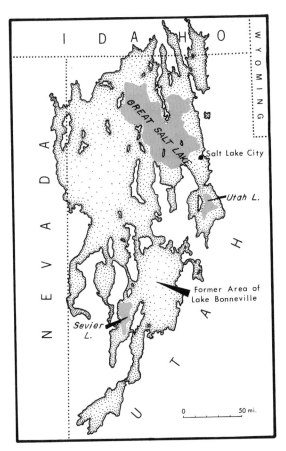

FIGURE 15-5. *Lake Bonneville and its remnant, Great Salt Lake.*

FIGURE 15-4. *A typical interior basin in Nevada, bounded by block-faulted mountains. Long alluvial fans may be seen sweeping down the sides of the upland area. (Photo-Art Commercial Studios)*

The northeastern part of California is an extensive tableland broken by numerous mountain ranges. Surface configuration bears almost universal evidence of former volcanic activity. Lava flows are visible wherever streams have cut valleys sufficiently deep to produce rapid erosion. Such flows also are apt to be apparent on the sides of the larger valleys; and the Pit River, the principal stream of the area, has eroded spectacular canyons through them.

The Sonoran Desert. This desert, which takes its name from the state of Sonora in Mexico, lies to the south of the Great Basin and extends southeastward to near Tucson, Arizona. Its western portion is the Mojave Desert, a region of interior drainage; the eastern portion is drained by the Gila River.

The Sonoran Desert is lower than the Great Basin. Its height varies from 2,000 to 4,000 feet on the north and east to 500 feet on the lower Colorado River. Its mountain ranges are small, occupying about one-sixth of the area and trending northwest-southeast. In the California portion are many bolsons (enclosed basins) with central alkali marshes (soda lakes, borax lakes, etc.), of which Death Valley is an example. The latter is the result of the down-faulting of a block whose floor is 282 feet below sea level (*Fig. 15-6*).

The Salton Trough. The trough is separated from the Sonoran Desert by the low Eagle and Chocolate Mountains. It is a great bolson, 2,000 square miles in extent, sloping toward Salton Sink, which is 241 feet below sea level. It was formerly an extension of the Gulf of California and was cut off by the growth of the delta of the Colorado River. It is emptied by evaporation when the river discharges into the Gulf of California on the south side of its delta. Occasionally, as in 1905-1907, the river flows down the north side of its delta and makes the Salton Sea.

The Mexican Highland. To the east of the Colorado River and south of the Colorado Plateau is the Mexican Highland. It is a northward extension of a great area of similar country in Mexico. It is not unlike the Great Basin, except that many of its drainage basins are connected, giving continuous slopes to the sea. It is so arid, however, that water flows down some of these slopes only at very long intervals. Some tributaries of the Gila River are dissecting old alluvial slopes into badlands. The Rio Grande flows through a series of bolsons, cutting 300 feet into their floors of detritus. It derives its water from an area north of central New Mexico. South of that for 600 miles it has no perennial tributaries. Irrigation in New Mexico uses most of the Rio Grande's water. About half the total area of this section is occupied by mountain ranges like those of the Great Basin; altitudes of 7,000 to 8,000 feet are common.

The Sacramento Mountains. Between the Rio Grande Valley on the west and the Pecos

FIGURE 15-6. *In this aerial view of Death Valley one may see the typical topography of fault-blocked ranges rising abruptly above flat-floored basins. Note the alluvial fan in the center. (Spence Air Photos)*

Valley on the east is a highland region comprising scarcely more than faulted plateaus tilted east, some of them 10,000 feet high. The plateaus are made rugged by mature dissection of the higher side, but they decline eastward and merge into the Pecos Valley.

COLORADO PLATEAU

The Colorado Plateau abuts against the Southern Rocky Mountains on the east and the Uinta Mountains on the north (*Fig. 15-7*). Elsewhere it is higher than its neighbors and is bounded by rough escarpments. As a whole the plateau is characterized by (1) horizontal rocks, (2) great elevation, and (3) deep canyons. Not much of its area is below 5,000 feet and it has some plateaus above 10,000 feet. There are hundreds of canyons, with Grand Canyon the deepest at 6,000 feet (*Fig. 15-8*).

The canyon lands of southern and eastern Utah are plateaus 6,000 to 7,000 feet high with several eroded domes and laccoliths. Intricate systems of deep canyons branch out from the Green, Muddy, Colorado, and San Juan Rivers, cutting the plateaus into isolated

FIGURE 15-7. *Cross-section of the Colorado Plateau (after Raisz).*

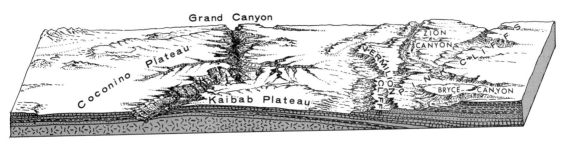

FIGURE 15-8. *Cross-section of a north-south section through the Grand Canyon of the Colorado (after Raisz).*

tablelands (*Fig. 15-9*). The Grand Canyon was eroded through nearly horizontal sedimentary rocks of unequal resistance; hence, there are many cliffs, benches, and platforms of varied colors.

COLUMBIA PLATEAU

South of the Canadian border and between the Central Rockies on the east and the Cascade Range on the west is a great plateau occupying a basin in Washington, Oregon, Idaho, and parts of Nevada, Montana, and Wyoming. The Columbia River has a long course in Canada and, after receiving the drainage from the Arrow and Kootenay Lakes, drains southward across the border and over this great plateau before being joined by the Snake River and turning west to cut through the Cascade Range. Originally the floor of the basin must have been interrupted by hills, mountains, and valleys, but in comparatively late geological time it was flooded again and again by great outpourings of very fluid basalt lavas. These now form horizontal sheets, in places several thousand feet thick, covering no

less than 250,000 square miles and burying all but the highest mountains.

The plateau has an average elevation of over 1,000 feet, but in places the lava beds have been broken by faults and the blocks tilted (*Fig. 15-10*). While the Columbia itself has cut a deep trench, the middle course of the Snake is through a spectacular canyon

FIGURE 15-9. *Intrenched meanders of the San Juan River in horizontal sedimentary strata. (Spence Air Photos)*

4,000 to 6,000 feet deep and 125 miles long—almost as grand as the Colorado canyon (*Fig. 15-11*).

Southeastern Washington and north-central Oregon are sometimes called the Columbia Plateau "proper" and distinguished from the other sections. The edge of this section in eastern Washington is 3,500 feet high. The slope is from all sides to where the Columbia River breaks through the Cascade Range. This section is older than the Snake River Plateau and considerably eroded. The streams are mainly in steep-sided valleys, here called "coulees." Between these the surface is generally rolling, partly because of erosion, partly because much of the soil is windblown. The low western part is underlain by sediments with a less fertile soil and very little rainfall because it is in the rain shadow of the Cascade Mountains. The glacier that came down the Okanogan Valley parallel to the Cascades blocked the Columbia and forced the latter to cut a deep gorge to the east—200 miles long and 400 feet deep. This it later abandoned, leaving the gorge (known as the Grand Coulee) dry except for a string of lakes. One of the longest dams in the world has been built across the Columbia River to create in the Grand Coulee a reservoir designed to irrigate more than a million acres of land (*Fig. 15-12*).

Southwestern Idaho and southeastern Oregon are in part underlain by lacustrine beds with some lava sheets interbedded. Near the Snake and its tributaries these soft beds are carved to maturity. The Owyhee Mountains farther south were never quite buried by lava.

FIGURE 15-10. *Lava flows folded into low anticlinal mountains in the western portion of the Columbia Plateau (after Raisz).*

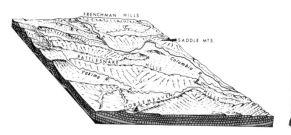

FIGURE 15-11. *The Grand Canyon of the Snake River, forming the boundary between Oregon and Idaho, is deeper than the mile-deep Grand Canyon of the Colorado River. Located in the midst of an extensive wilderness, this great gorge is difficult to reach. (Oregon State Highway Dept.)*

FIGURE 15-12. *Aerial view of Grand Coulee Dam and Lake Roosevelt. (Washington State Dept. of Commerce and Economic Development)*

They are now surrounded by an eroded lava plateau sloping away in all directions.

The Blue Mountain section consists of mountains of old rocks 9,000 feet high, standing above the lava and somewhat glaciated. The rest of this section, also called mountains, is a plateau surface that has been gently arched and deeply eroded and is locally mature.

The Harney section in central Oregon is arid country drained partially to salt lakes in its eastern part. Portions of it (with adjacent country to the south) are covered with volcanic dust or "sand" and are known locally as the "Great Sandy Desert."

BRITISH COLUMBIA INTERIOR PLATEAU

Between the Central Rockies and the Coast Ranges of Canada is a region of tablelands and low mountains that is called the British Columbia Interior Plateau. The average width of this plateau, which has a summit elevation of about 3,500 feet, is roughly 100 miles, although in some places it is 200 to 300 miles wide (see Fig. 15-2). In some respects it resembles the intermontane plateaus in the United States. To the north, the plateau gives way to a series of mountain ranges—the Stikine, Cassiar, Selwyn, and Mackenzie Mountains.

YUKON PLATEAU

Between the mountain system that borders the Pacific Ocean in Alaska and the Brooks Range (a continuation of the Rocky Mountain system in Alaska) is an area of rolling uplands. Here the summits show marked uniformity of elevation over broad expanses, although in places this pattern is interrupted by isolated mountains and ranges, including the Dawson, Big Salmon, and Pelly Mountains (Fig. 15-13). This broad upland takes its name from the Yukon River, the major stream that rises in the mountains to the south and empties into the Bering Sea.

Climate

In climatic characteristics this region shows great variety. Except in the high mountains, precipitation is light. More than 75 per cent of the total annual precipitation occurs during the winter or wet season. The mean annual precipitation varies from 25 inches or more in the higher mountains to 2 or 3 inches or less in the Mojave Desert and in Death Valley. At several places in the Imperial Valley and in Death Valley there have been periods of a year in which less than an inch of precipitation was recorded. In the mountains, on the other hand, very heavy rains have been recorded within short intervals of time (Fig. 15-14).

In general, the area is characterized by an abundance of sunshine, very little cloudy weather, wide variations in the length of the growing season in different parts of the region, considerable range of temperatures within a 24-hour period at any given point, low rela-

FIGURE 15-13. Cross-section of the Yukon Plateau (after Atwood).

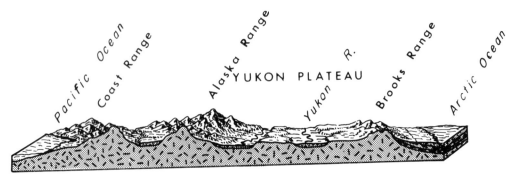

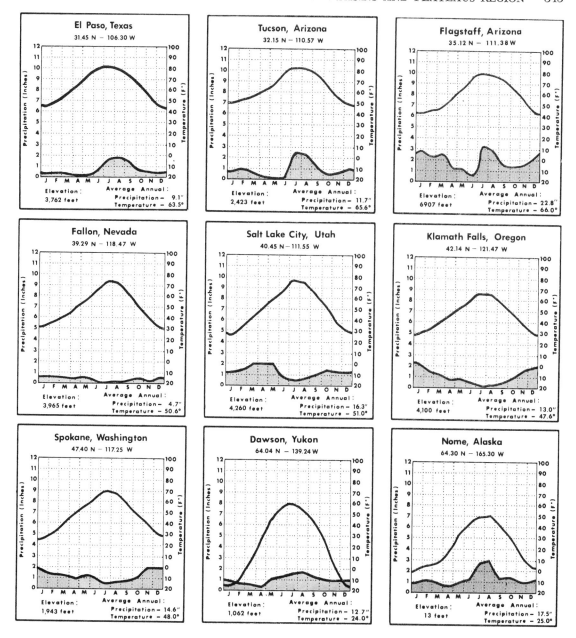

FIGURE 15-14. *Climatic graphs of the Intermontane Basins and Plateaus Region.*

tive humidity, scant annual precipitation, and very rapid evaporation of moisture from the surface of the ground. The prevailing winds are generally from the southwest and west.

The daily, monthly, and annual temperature ranges are wide in the desert region. In the Imperial Valley the summers are dry and hot; the winters are dry and moderately cold,

with occasional light rain. In Death Valley the air is relatively dry throughout the year; the winters are moderately cold, and the summers are the hottest in the United States.

Throughout the lower sections, mainly in southwestern Arizona, including the valleys of the lower Salt, Gila, and Colorado Rivers, where elevations are less than 3,000 feet above sea level, readings above 100° F. in the shade occur frequently during the long summer, which lasts from April to November. Because of the dry atmosphere, however, temperatures in the high 90's in these desert regions are more comfortable than those of 80° F. in the Atlantic and Gulf Coast states, where the principal cause of discomfort during periods of hot weather is excessive humidity rather than high temperature.

The southern section of Arizona has a delightful winter season, located as it is in the belt of maximum sunshine and minimum relative humidity for the entire United States. This part of the state has become a mecca for winter tourists and health seekers. The scenic and recreational areas in the mountain sections of the north and east have a pleasant summer climate, with cool, bracing nights and frequent showers.

In the higher areas, above 7,000 feet, temperatures average as low as they do in southern Minnesota, whereas in the lower elevations of the western and southern parts of the region, conditions are semitropical.

The most striking climatic features of the region are the high percentage of sunshine, the low rainfall in the valleys, and the high evaporation rate.

Precipitation, in addition to being generally low, is also extremely variable, following a pattern of successive wet and dry periods rather than a heterogeneous occurrence of single wet and dry years. This variability in precipitation is illustrated and confirmed by 80 years of weather records and over much longer periods by studies of changes in the levels of interior lakes and of tree growth. The above and below-average periods may be as short as 2 or 3 years, or as long as 20 years. The longer periods may be broken by single years of an opposite character.

Most of the precipitation occurs during the winter season; summer rainfall is very light. Storms with high winds rarely occur—and even more rarely do they cause appreciable damage. Thunderstorms do occur, but they are infrequent.

Natural Vegetation

A great diversity of vegetative types is to be found within the borders of the region because of differences in elevation, precipitation, temperature, length of growing season, and soil. Desert plant life—desert sage, scrub trees, cacti, salt tolerating shrubs, bunch grasses, and, at widely spaced intervals that follow the spring rains, sudden bright bursts of desert wild flowers—is characteristic of the lowlands (*Fig. 15-15*). Junipers and pinion pines grow on the flanks of some of the higher mountain ranges with which the Mojave Desert is dotted and in the no man's land northeast of the Salton Trough. Open stands of forest are found at the higher elevations in Arizona, New Mexico, and Utah. Beginning at 7,500 feet, Ponderosa pine is the common timber specie; at 9,000 feet, it gives way to the Douglas fir, white fir, and quaking aspen that grow up to about 10,500 feet elevation.

Soils

The Intermontane Basins and Plateaus Region has a wide variation of soil conditions and soil types. This is caused chiefly by a relatively large variety of parent rock from which the soils were derived, by variations in the climatic conditions that prevailed during

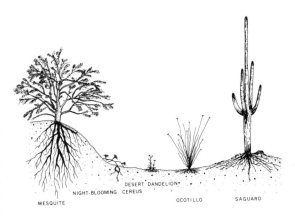

FIGURE 15-15. *Adaptations of root systems of selected desert plants.*

the soil forming periods, by the manner in which the soils were formed, and by variations in the age or maturity of the respective soil types.

Soils mantling the mesas, plateaus, and high plains within the region vary in texture from coarse gravel and sand, at one extreme, to clay loams, clay, and adobe, at the other. It is on this group of soils that nearly all of the dry farming is done. The silt loams and clay loams are best adapted to the production of small grains. Over much of this area the surface soils are shallow because they are underlain by caliche. The caliche varies in thickness from a few inches to many feet. In some places, where the topsoil has been eroded away, the caliche comes to the surface.

Soils that occcupy the slopes, alluvial fans, and escarpments form more or less continuous long areas asymmetrical in relief and broken here and there by erosion channels that continue the erratic deposition of colluvial material when flash floods occur. The surface soils of this group are quite variable. They are usually gravelly and in places stony. Their moisture-holding capacity is generally low because of the porous gravelly material in the subsoil. Most of the lands occupied by these soils are poorly adapted to crop production and for this reason have not been brought under cultivation.

The Sonoran Desert is a region of red desert soils because of its low rainfall, very hot summers, and mild winters. Organic matter and nitrogen are low. Agriculture is dependent upon irrigation.

Settlement

SOUTHERN SECTION

Folsom man lived in the American Southwest 20,000 years ago. Traces of his early agriculture are found in the region. High, almost inaccessible cliff dwellings still stand in evidence to yet another, much later prehistoric race (*Fig. 15-16*).

FIGURE 15-16. *The best-preserved cliff dwellings in the United States are found at Mesa Verde in southwestern Colorado. Built around A.D. 800, they were occupied until about A.D. 1200. (Colorado Dept. of Public Relations)*

Written history began when the Spaniards sent exploration parties northward from Mexico. The first traveler was a Franciscan priest named Marcos de Niza, who entered the territory in 1539. Later, others made their way into this land. The most famous of the explorers was Francisco Vasquez Coronado (1540-1542). Spanish priests followed to establish missions to bring Christianity to the Indians. The Spaniards introduced the use of metal tools, utensils, and weapons, and the wooden plow; they introduced most of the domestic animals found in the area today. They also introduced small grains, vegetables, tree fruits, and grapes.

From the date of the first colonization venture (1598) until Mexico gained her independence (1822), the region had virtually no outlet for her products and no source for obtaining supplies except through Chihuahua and Vera Cruz. During that period of more than 200 years, development was very slow; exports consisted mostly of sheep, wool, dressed deerskins, buffalo robes, furs, salt, and copper vessels. As a rule, the balance of trade was overwhelmingly against the region. The policy pursued was intended to keep the colonists short of funds and to prevent them from having outside commercial intercourse. As soon as Mexico obtained her independence, however, the commercial policies were changed; traffic over the Santa Fe Trail increased materially and a thriving commerce between the Missouri River points and Santa Fe soon developed. This continued from about 1825 to 1845.

The admission of Texas to the Union in 1845, the extension of the authority of the United States over the territory acquired as a result of the war with Mexico, and the discovery of gold in California in 1848, resulted in a great westward migration.

Permanent settlement in the Great Basin began with the arrival of the Mormon pioneers at what is now Salt Lake City in the summer of 1847. Modern irrigation in America dates from this period. Within two decades settlement spread to all parts of the region that could be irrigated easily. A permanent settlement was founded in Carson Valley in 1850.

CENTRAL SECTION

After the French and Indian War, Scottish, English, and American traders followed the watercourses on toward the north and west, seeking furs. A few years later, the Northwest Company of Canada was formed and the fur trade era began. David Thompson of the Northwest Company crossed the Rocky Mountains to the headwaters of the Columbia River, where in 1807 he built a trading post at Lake Windemere. In 1808, Simon Fraser explored the lower reaches of the Fraser River.

The Lewis and Clark expedition of 1804-05 was the most important single achievement in the annals of the exploration of the American West. This expedition demonstrated the practicability of an overland route to the Pacific and the wealth of furs available in the Northwest.

Travelers, missionaries, and some settlers crossed the plains under the protection of the fur traders. The decade of the 1830's was the period of missionary endeavor; the decade of the 1840's marked the arrival of permanent settlers with their families.

The discovery of gold in California in 1848 lured prospectors there. Shortly thereafter, gold seekers swarmed through all the western territories examining the stream gravels and sands. The Fraser River and Cariboo discoveries took thousands of American miners into British Columbia. Towns sprang up and river and overland freight supplied the miners' needs. Later, railroads were built and economic enterprises were established that encouraged more permanent settlement, e.g., grazing, lumbering, mining, irrigated agriculture, and manufacturing.

Mining

PRECIOUS METALS

It was the lure of gold and silver that prompted Coronado's famous expedition in search of the Seven Cities of Cibola. Mining continues to play a dominant role in the economy of the region. The value of precious metals, however, has been exceeded many times by that of industrial minerals.

Gold and silver, once the most sought after mineral prizes in the West, now are produced largely as recoverable by-product metals in large-scale copper, lead, and zinc mining operations, such as those at Bisbee, Arizona, and Bingham, Utah.

Gold. Gold occurs in a number of areas along the east flank of the central and northern parts of the Sierra Nevada Range. In the Diamond Mountain district, a few miles south of Susanville, California, gold is produced from quartz veins in granitic rocks and from stream gravels. More than $30 million worth of gold has been produced at Bodie, California, in eastern Mono County. The Randsburg district, which lies athwart Kern and San Bernardino Counties, contains the largest gold mines in southern California.

Rich placer ground was discovered in the Cariboo Mountains on the Quesnel River in 1861 and 1862. Gold was obtained so quickly by the thousands of individual miners working shallow gravels that the peak was reached in 1863.

Placer deposits have been worked in many parts of British Columbia. As early as 1880 many of the shallow diggings had been worked out. Miners turned to underground mining, and to hydraulic methods for the recovery of lower-grade ores.

Gold was reported in the Yukon by the Hudson's Bay Company in the 1850's; prospecting began in 1872. Fine gold was discovered on the bars of most of the main rivers. Hundreds of thousands of dollars in gold was recovered from Steamboat Bar on the Stewart River and from Cassiar Bar on the Lewes River. In the early 1890's, prospecting spread to the side streams, where coarse gold was disclosed. Klondike placer creeks were discovered in 1896; their amazing richness attracted miners from other parts of the Yukon. It was during this period that nearly all the known placer creeks in the Yukon were discovered, along with the deposits of the Whitehorse copper belt and the Mayo silver-lead district.

Silver. Lode mining in the Yukon has not yet attained the importance of placer mining, and most of the production has come from the Whitehorse and Mayo areas. The Whitehorse copper belt, discovered in 1897, is near the railway and therefore had advantages for early development. The Mayo silver-lead veins were found by placer miners in 1906. Mining began in 1913 and, with the exceptions of 1919 and 1920, some ore has been shipped each year from the camp.

INDUSTRIAL ORES

Copper. Copper is mined on a large scale in several states within the Basin and Range subregion. Arizona leads the nation in copper production. It is extracted from world famous

FIGURE 15-17. *The Bingham Canyon copper mine of the Kennecott Copper Corporation. The mine covers 1,050 excavated acres and resembles a huge football stadium. (Salt Lake City Chamber of Commerce)*

open-pit and underground mines such as Morenci, San Manuel, New Cornelia, Lavender Pit-Copper Queen, and Ray. These five operations yield nearly 70 per cent of the state's copper.

Utah is second to Arizona in copper production. Most of it is recovered at Bingham Canyon, Anglo-America's largest open-pit copper mine, located about 30 miles southwest of Salt Lake City (*Fig. 15-17*).

Only the large size and uniform mineralization of the ore body, which allow a large-scale and highly mechanized operation, make it economically possible to recover valuable metals from such low-grade material. Because of the low grade ore and the losses that occur, 309 pounds of waste and ore must be moved to obtain a pound of copper.

Ore is loaded into railroad cars and hauled by electric locomotives to the Copperton main assembly yard at the mouth of the canyon. There trains are made up for movement to the Arthur and Magna concentrating mills nearby. The concentrates are reduced to copper ingots at the American Smelting and Refining Company at Garfield, which is located a few miles to the north.

White Pine County, particularly in the Ely-Ruth-Kimberly-McGill sectors of east-central Nevada, was greatly favored by nature with very large copper ore deposits. Because both the Kennecott Copper Corporation and the Consolidated Coppermines Company have learned how to handle ores with a low copper content successfully and efficiently on a quantity production basis, copper mining in eastern Nevada has grown from a rather puny beginning to a position of great stability.

In contrast to Bingham Canyon, which is less than 30 miles from the well-developed transportation network serving metropolitan Salt Lake City, the Ely-Ruth district is separated from markets by barren desert. Consequently, exorbitant freight rates make the latter a marginal producer, and ore is shipped only when prices are high.

The Kennecott Copper Company has abandoned its famous Liberty Pit mine in northeastern Nevada after almost 60 years of operation because of its dwindling grade of ore. The company has shifted its mining to adjacent Tripp and Veteran Pits.

Yerington, Nevada, has become the center of impressive copper operations, its crater-like pit going down into a mountain of copper ore nearly two miles square. Tyrone, New Mexico, a former ultra-modern copper mining community, which has been a ghost town for four decades, may be on the verge of a rebirth since the Phelps Dodge Corporation is spending $100 million to reopen the mines.

Iron ore. Although iron ore deposits had been known to exist in several of the Western states for decades, they were of little significance until the beginning of World War II. At that time the need arose for iron and steel production in the West to supply Pacific Coast shipyards and factories with steel. Two integrated mills, one constructed at Fontana, California, and the other at Geneva, Utah, began to process local iron ore deposits.

The Kaiser Steel Corporation at Fontana operates Eagle Mountain, a source of iron ore 50 miles from Indio north of Highways 60 and 70. Since 1948, the mines at Eagle Mountain have shipped a steady stream of iron ore to the mills in Fontana in sufficient bulk to produce steel for 100 cars per day.

Large iron ore deposits are being mined west of Cedar City, Utah, at Iron Mountain and at Desert Mound. Average iron content runs approximately 54 per cent. Iron ore is shipped to the Geneva steel plant near Provo, Utah; the Colorado Fuel and Iron plant in Pueblo, Colorado; and the Kaiser Steel mill at Fontana.

Lead and zinc. These metals are found in association with copper-bearing ores. Their production varies widely, depending upon national demand, stockpiling policies, and the like. Bisbee, Arizona, is the major area of recovery in that state. Park City, Utah, is an important source of lead ore which occurs in bedded limestone. Lead ore is also recovered as a by-product of copper mining at Bingham.

Uranium. There is probably a considerable amount of uranium ore, both secondary and primary, in the Basin and Range subregion, but to date this region has not experienced bonanzas comparable to those of the Colorado Plateau. The most promising prospect at the present time is that of Apex Uranium, Inc., with a group of claims six miles south of Austin, Nevada, in the Toiyabe Range. The company has found and developed a large volume of secondary uranium ores on the surface and recently discovered a strong vein of primary ore at depth.

Open-pit mining is carried on in an old lake bed in the vicinity of Tonopah, Nevada, where a secondary ore of uranium is found associated with compacted sand, mud, and clay. Near Pyramid Lake north of Reno, the Homestake Mining Company of South Dakota is engaged in developing uranium ore. In Utah alone, over 100 companies are mining and shipping uranium ore to mills.

New Mexico is the nation's leading producer of uranium ore. At Grants, New Mexico, several mills concentrate ore from what is the nation's richest uranium district. The companies here are Anaconda, Homestake, Phillips Petroleum, and Kermac.

NONMETALLIC MINERALS

Clays, gypsum, feldspar, asbestos, barite, mica, pumice, and perlite are produced on a minor scale within the region. Since these minerals occur in great abundance in many parts of the nation and are relatively low in price, the region has been handicapped by adverse freight rates and its distance from industrial centers.

Salt is secured from the brines of Great Salt Lake by the solar process; the refined material is marketed for household, dairy, and stock purposes and is used in the manufacture of soda ash and other sodium compounds (*Fig. 15-18*).

Potash is produced from the brines underlying the Great Salt Lake Desert. It is increasingly important in commercial fertilizers and in the electrochemical industry. The process of recovery is comparable to that of salt from the lake. Potash is also available from enormous deposits of alunite with which Utah is favored.

Salines have been extracted continuously from Owens Lake since the early 1880's; commercial commodities obtained include trona or sodium sesquicarbonate, soda ash, and borax. Commercial deposits of potash, borax, boric acid, soda ash, bromine, and phosphoric acid are produced from Searles Lake.

MINERAL FUELS

Coal, natural gas, petroleum, and oil shale play an important role in the economy of the Intermontane Basins and Plateaus Region. They supply most of its energy and constitute a high percentage of the wealth derived from natural resources.

Coal. Utah ranks tenth among the states in coal production and first among the states west of the Mississippi. Its total output exceeds that of the other ten Western states. The bulk of Utah's coal is produced in two counties, Carbon and Emery. Reserves are estimated at 93 million tons. The coal is relatively hard, does not slack, and is blocky in structure. Most of it is highly volatile and

FIGURE 15-18. *The Bonneville Salt Flats west of Salt Lake City. (Salt Lake City Chamber of Commerce)*

noncoking, although there are several deposits of coking coal.

Approximately one-half the mined coal is marketed for commercial and residential heating in the Western states; the other half is mined for coking by U. S. Steel and Kaiser Steel for blast furnaces at Geneva, Utah, and Fontana, California. The chief mining centers are Price and Sunnyside, Utah.

Coal produced in the Yukon is used to meet local needs, which are small and uncertain. Coal comes from four localities: Rock Creek on the Klondike River, Coal Creek on the Yukon River, Carmacks, and the Whitehorse-Wheaton area. In the first two areas, lignite, and in the other two areas, good bituminous coal, have been found. Most of the output, however, has come from three mines near Carmacks, where production began in 1900. Tonnage is small, running less than 16,000 tons a year.

Coal mining is rapidly becoming one of the important elements of the mining industry in Alaska. In the last decade, military and civilian requirements for coal as a fuel for heating and for the generation of electricity have greatly expanded the market for locally produced coal. About one million tons are mined annually.

Although coal beds are present in many parts of the area, mines of more than local importance are to be found only in the Nenana coal field, about 75 miles southwest of Fairbanks. It contains high-grade lignite and sub-bituminous coal beds that range in thickness from 6 feet to more than 50 feet. The Geological Survey estimates known reserves at 850 million tons.

Petroleum. The Four Corners field, so named because it extends into the corners of four states—southwestern Colorado, southeastern Utah, northeastern Arizona, and northwestern New Mexico—holds great promise as an oil producing field. The pipeline from the Aneth field to refineries in Los Angeles, and the Texas-New Mexico pipeline from the Aneth field to Jal, New Mexico, provide the necessary outlets for crude oil from the highly productive Paradox Basin in the Four Corners field. Daily capacity of the two pipelines is 170,000 barrels.

The discovery in 1959 of oil and gas in the Yukon about 200 miles northeast of Dawson offers considerable hope for greater mineral exploitation. The discovery area is about 450 miles from Pacific tidewater. If found in commercial quantities, oil could be sent to the coast by pipeline for loading aboard tankers 12 months of the year.

Test drillings indicate that the oil is the type best suited for gasoline production. This is the first discovery of oil in the Yukon Territory and the first in the Far North since the Norman Wells oil field was discovered in the Northwest Territories in 1920. The rate of flow has not been determined; gas flow up to 10,000 cubic feet a day has been recorded.

Petroleum and natural gas deposits have been known to exist in Alaska for over a century. Their remote location from the rest of the United States, however, has prevented any large-scale exploitation to date. Within the past few years, however, there has been a great revival of interest in Alaskan petroleum and gas development. Several large companies and many smaller local companies have made explorations in likely areas.

Oil from shale. Shales containing 15 gallons of oil or more per ton occur in the 16,500 square-mile Green River area in Colorado, Wyoming, and Utah. The shale deposits, with an estimated oil content of several billion barrels, were laid down about 50 million years ago when the Green River area was covered by fresh-water lakes that were surrounded by hills.

Agriculture

The type of agriculture in any area represents an adaptation to the physical and economic environment. In the Intermontane Basins and Plateaus Region there are three general types of agriculture: (1) irrigated agriculture, (2) commercial grain farming, and (3) grazing. Although most farms belong entirely in one of these three categories, some are a mixture of two or of all three types.

General irrigated farms make up about 70 per cent of the total farms, although acreage of irrigated lands is relatively small. In addition, the supply of irrigation water is so inadequate in many cases that maximum crop yields are not obtained and the acreage of the most profitable crops is seriously curtailed. Most of the farms contain some grazing land, the major part of which is not irrigated because of this inadequacy of irrigation water. The grazing land is largely in pasture for dairy cattle and work animals.

IRRIGATED AGRICULTURE

With the building that began at the turn of the century of strategically situated dams along the region's major streams, the miner and the cowboy have had to make way for the less glamorous but economically more sound farmer. Several million acres of desert land have blossomed into one of the world's richest farm areas, bearing alfalfa, cotton, citrus fruits, melons, dates, and all kinds of vegetables. The chief irrigated districts are: (1) the Mesilla and Estancia Valleys in New Mexico; (2) the Salt, Gila, and Yuma Valleys in Arizona; (3) the Palo Verde, Imperial, Coachella, Borego, and Antelope Valleys in California; (4) the Bear and Sevier Basins and the Weber River-Utah Lake Basin in Utah; (5) the Truckee, Carson, Walker, and Humboldt River areas in Nevada; (6) the Long and Owens Basins in California; (7) the Columbia Basin Project and the Yakima and Wenatchee Valleys in Washington; and (8) the Okanogan (or Okanagan) Valley in Washington and Canada (*Fig. 15-19*).

Mesilla Valley. This is an irrigated area of the Rio Grande Valley in south-central New Mexico. Irrigation water is impounded in the Elephant Butte Dam, a federal reclamation

FIGURE 15-19. *Major irrigated areas of the Intermontane Basins and Plateaus Region.*

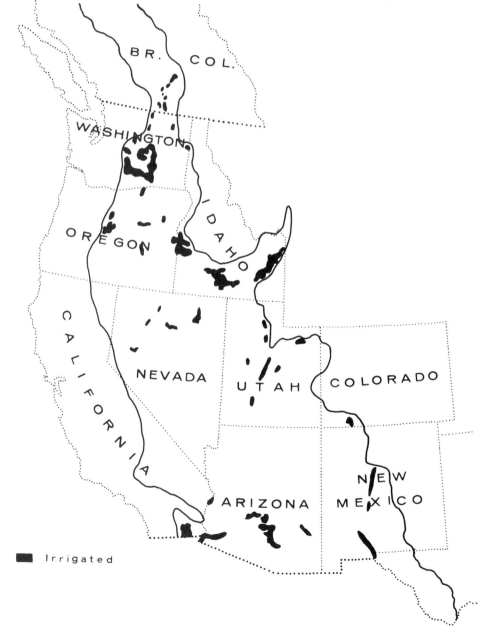

project located on the Rio Grande near Truth or Consequences, New Mexico.

The two principal crops produced in the valley are cotton and alfalfa. On most farms, cotton is the main crop and alfalfa is a leguminous rotation crop furnishing farm feed and cash income.

Livestock is not of major importance in the valley, but there is some dairying and livestock feeding. In recent years farmers have increased acreage of permanent irrigated pastures. This use of land offers opportunities for cheaper production of beef cattle and dairy products.

Estancia Valley. Located south and east of Albuquerque in Torrance County, New Mexico, this area specializes in the production of pinto beans and furnishes a good example of a situation in which physical conditions have reduced the alternatives available to farmers to a point where a single cash crop type of farming strongly predominates.

Salt, Gila, and Yuma Valleys. Water stored in eight reservoirs on the Salt, Verde, and Agua Fria Rivers supplies 465,000 irrigated acres in Maricopa County, making it one of the nation's wealthiest agricultural districts. Irrigation in the Salt River Valley dates to 1867, although a prehistoric tribe of Indians, the Hohokams, farmed by irrigation centuries before white men came to the valley. In 1911, Roosevelt Dam on the Salt River was completed, giving the valley its first dependable supply of irrigation water.

Cotton leads all other crops in acreage and value, followed by alfalfa, barley, grain sorghums, vegetables (winter lettuce, carrots, early potatoes, onions, cabbage, celery, cauliflower, and broccoli), and wheat.

Cattle feeding continues to increase. Several feedlots are located in the Salt River Valley in response to the growing demand in the Phoenix metropolitan area.

The Yuma Project, a federal irrigation development authorized in 1904, is located in California and Arizona, along both sides of the Colorado River. The Reservation Division, the California portion of the project, is made up of the Bard and the Indian sectors, which previously were served by a canal from Laguna Dam and now are supplied by the All-American Canal. In addition to lands in Arizona, the project covers a gross area of about 25,000 acres in California. The present irrigated area lies partly within the Bard Irrigation District, which was organized in 1927. Field crops of barley, oats, wheat, soybeans, corn, sorghums, and cotton, and major truck crops such as melons, lettuce, and tomatoes are grown in this area.

Palo Verde Valley. The Palo Verde Valley lies along the Colorado River in eastern Riverside County, California, and resembles the Imperial Valley in climate and agricultural pattern. The district embraces an area of 104,500 acres bordering and extending along the river for nearly 30 miles, and 17,500 acres of adjoining lands on the Palo Verde Mesa. Substantially two-thirds of the land in the district is now under irrigation, and the irrigated area continues to expand. Alfalfa hay and seed, melons, lettuce, cotton, grain, field corn, and sorghums are the principal crops.

Imperial Valley. The largest irrigation development in the desert area of southern California is that of the Imperial Valley.

The water storage capacity of the Hoover Dam safeguards the Imperial Valley against the danger of destructive spring floods and of summer water shortages alike. When the All-American Canal was completed in 1940, bringing Colorado River water to the valley entirely over American land, increased irrigated acreage and augmented hydroelectric power were made possible. Eighty miles long, 232 feet wide, and 21.6 feet deep, the canal feeds 1,700 miles of distribution canals that fan out from it.

The economy of the Imperial Valley is based squarely on agriculture; its industries are related almost entirely to the processing and packaging of food products. The valley specializes in the raising of winter vegetables and other crops that mature here earlier than in almost any other part of the United States. A very wide range of truck and field crops can be grown. Since only a minor fraction of the acreage is put in permanent crops, farming is rotated and flexible. Double cropping is common, about ten per cent of the total acreage being farmed in this way.

Farming is characterized by highly commercialized large-scale operations that utilize a considerable amount of machinery even by California's agricultural standards. Machines are used to prepare the fields, to plant them, to cultivate them, and to harvest many crops.

Imperial Valley products are shipped to all parts of the United States, chiefly by rail. They also find important local markets in the Los Angeles and San Diego metropolitan districts, for fine paved highways connect El Centro to Los Angeles, 210 miles away, and to San Diego, 118 miles distant.

Field crops are of the greatest importance in the area, if judged by value and acreage. They take up nearly 350,000 acres, or about 80 per cent of the cultivated land.

Alfalfa ordinarily covers about 40 per cent of the cultivated area each year, and it is used as a soil builder in almost every system of crop rotation. After two to four years of truck crops, flax, or grain, the land must be planted to alfalfa for the same number of years to restore its productivity. Since it is less profitable than flax or vegetables, alfalfa is generally maintained only to complete the rotation cycle. With climatic conditions in the valley favorable to its growth, alfalfa can be cut five to seven times a year.

Though cotton grows well in any part of the valley, it is concentrated chiefly in the north, where the Acala strains produce both the short- and long-staple varieties. A long growing season encourages the high yield per acre. Culture and harvest are both mechanized.

Sugar beets thrive on the local climate, yielding 50 per cent more per acre here than the national average. Harvested when southern California's sugar refineries would otherwise be idle, the sugar beet provides a good cash crop that fits well into the rotation farming of the region. Moreover, sugar beets can be grown successfully for at least two years on the same land.

Barley is sown throughout the valley and is the most important of the cereal crops. It can be grown alone and harvested as barley hay or can be combined with alfalfa to form winter pasture; it also can be cut in spring with the alfalfa to become mixed hay. The extremely hot weather, however, limits plantings to not later than the first of February.

Flax has been a major crop since its introduction in 1934; it now grows throughout the valley, which produces more flax per acre than any other region of similar size in the state or in the nation. Yield per acre exceeds the national average three or four times.

Minor field crops include various types of beans, corn, wheat, oats, clovers, safflower, vetches, and sorghums.

Truck crops, such as lettuce, carrots, cantaloupes, peas, tomatoes, and watermelons, grown in the fall, winter, and spring, prove highly profitable, for they can be shipped at times when they are not available in other regions. Some 40 to 50 per cent of the cultivated land is devoted to vegetables in any one rotation period.

The importance of the relation between livestock and agriculture in this desert area could scarcely be overemphasized, for the crop rotation essential to the maintenance of the fertility of irrigated desert land necessitates that one-third of the land always be planted in alfalfa, which assures an abundant supply of low-cost and high-quality feed. Into a situation of this kind livestock fit very naturally. Beef cattle are brought into the valley for fattening from all parts of the United States, but primarily from west of the Rocky Mountains. Until recently, this industry was limited entirely to autumn, winter, and spring fattening. Today, however, cattle feeding operates on a year-round basis.

Sheep are brought to the valley to be finished from their ranges. Some 350,000 sheep winter here every year and are marketed directly from the local green alfalfa or other pastures.

Southern California's dairying tends to locate near the centers of population. Some dairies in the valley, however, have installed the buildings and equipment essential to the production of Grade "A" milk and export the product. The long, hot summers decrease milk production, a factor that works a hardship on those breeders of purebred cattle who try to achieve a very high production from a limited number of selected cows. On the other hand, hay is cheaper in the valley than it is on the coast, and pastures are available on almost a year-round basis. Sorghum silage, available locally and very inexpensive, also cuts feed costs and makes the production of replacement stock economically profitable.

Coachella Valley. The Coachella Valley occupies the northern part of the Salton Basin, and has, for the most part, been developed since 1900. Its principal crops are early table grapes, dates, citrus fruit, vegetables out of season in other areas, and field crops.

Grapes make up the Coachella Valley's most important crop. Only the early table varieties are raised. The favorite and most extensively cultivated variety is the Thompson Seedless.

About 90 per cent of the date acreage in the United States is in the Coachella Valley. The relatively high temperatures, the fertile soil, and an abundance of water, have made the valley a natural environment for dates (Fig. 15-20).

Probably no activitiy in the Coachella Valley has experienced as rapid a growth as cattle feeding, which each year becomes a more important factor in the total economy. Cattle are brought here from Montana, Arizona, Texas, and New Mexico to be fed. The local operation proves that cattle can be fattened all twelve months and that scientifically designed shades, the use of cool water, and the feeding of balanced rations to obtain the greatest yield can stabilize the year-round aspect of the business.

Bear and Sevier Basins. The Bear River Basin embraces an area of nearly five million acres. Water is diverted directly from the Bear River or its major tributaries, the Logan and Little Bear Rivers, to irrigate some 240,000 acres of land, which include irrigated pasture.

FIGURE 15-20. *Two of the Coachella Valley's specialty crops, early sweet corn and dates. (Soil Conservation Service, U.S.D.A.)*

The Sevier River Basin includes most of the southwestern fourth of Utah. The river rises in the southeastern corner of the basin and flows northward. It breaks through the mountain range westward, circles back, and empties into Sevier Lake. The river and small streams, many of which either dry up completely or partially during the late season, are the main sources of irrigation water.

Weber River-Utah Lake Drainage Basin. This basin is located in north-central Utah. Within it are found the three largest cities of the state, most of the industrial activities, and the major part of the production from irrigation agriculture. The major streams that drain the area are the Weber River and its tributaries that empty into Great Salt Lake, and the Provo and the Spanish Fork Rivers that discharge into Utah Lake, which, in turn, empties into Great Salt Lake through the Jordan River.

Truckee Meadows area. Truckee Meadows, Washoe, Steamboat, Spanish Springs, Pleasant Valleys, and lands along the Truckee River down to Pyramid Lake are included in this area. Irrigation water comes from the Truckee River and its tributaries.

The urban influences of Reno and Sparks strongly affect the type of farming in this area.

The suburban fringes of these cities cover a large part of the agricultural land. Production of fresh milk is the major commercial enterprise, although several hundred acres are devoted to the production of vegetables for the local market.

Carson Valley area. Included within the Carson Valley area are Carson Valley proper, Jack's Valley, the irrigated lands around Carson City and Stewart, and the lands along the Carson River from Carson Valley to Lahontan Reservoir. It derives its water supply from the Carson River and its tributaries. Stock ranching is the prevailing type of farming. Dairying is quite well developed. The Lake Tahoe area offers a good summer market, and Reno is a year-round market.

Smith and Mason Valleys. The Smith and Mason Valleys are irrigated from the west and east forks of the Walker River. Livestock farming and ranching are by far the most important agricultural enterprises. These farms and ranches make up nearly two-thirds the total value of products for the area. Dairy and poultry enterprises are well developed, with a local creamery and a poultry dressing plant. This is also Nevada's principal potato-growing section.

Humboldt River area. The extensive area of irrigated lands along the Humboldt River includes Lovelock Valley, Paradise Valley, the middle river section from Winnemucca to Palisade, and the upper river area above Palisade.

The lands in the Lovelock Valley are leveled to permit irrigation by flooding methods. The Rye Patch Dam provides water for irrigation. Many of the farms in the valley are large and general farming methods are rather intensive. Alfalfa production and cattle feeding have long been the principal enterprises, although dairying has been developing slowly to meet the needs of a postwar population increase.

The production of beef cattle is the major farm enterprise in Paradise Valley. Crop production is favored and winter losses of livestock are reduced by a rather moderate climate. A limited amount of grain serves as a catch crop in good water seasons. Some fruits and vegetables are grown for the local market.

Long and Owens Rivers areas. Agricultural development on the Long and Owens Rivers drainage basin is confined to the eastern base of the Sierra Nevada Range. Livestock and livestock products, which include beef, sheep, wool, and dairy items, with hay as the only field crop of importance, are the mainstays of the local economy.

Wenatchee Valley. Although predominantly an apple producer, the apple crop of the Wenatchee Valley is supplemented by dairying, ranching, and a very minor marketing of field crops. Five per cent of the cling peach crop also is grown here.

Yakima Valley. This valley excels in the production of fruits and nuts—yielding about a fourth of Washington's apples, three-fourths of its peaches, and minor quantities of grapes, walnuts and filberts. Field crops are also important. Corn for grain leads, followed by spring wheat, winter wheat, and oats. Hops and potatoes are grown on a large scale.

Okanogan (Okanagan) Valley. This dry, hot, interior valley is ideally suited to irrigation farming of tree fruits and vegetables. Apples are the most important crop. Vernon is the chief exporting center of the valley (*Fig. 15-21*). Pears, cherries, plums and other small fruits are also important. Half the output of the Okanogan orchards is sold in Canada, although large quantities are also sold in the United States and overseas.

COMMERCIAL GRAIN FARMING

Wheat. Both soft red and hard white wheats are grown in the Columbia Plateau. The amount of precipitation is the chief factor that splits the region into the annual cropping and the summer fallow zones, which, in turn, can be divided into the dry farm area of 8 to 12 inches of annual precipitation and the area of intermediate precipitation, 12 to 18 inches.

The annual cropping system commonly is used in the zone that receives 18 to about 25

FIGURE 15-21. *The Okanogan Valley of British Columbia is a producer of apples, peaches, pears, plums, and cherries. (Canadian Government Travel Bureau)*

inches of precipitation yearly. Thus, in the areas of lower rainfall, crops are grown under a moisture stress; in this zone, the lack of moisture is seldom a major factor in crop growth. Precipitation ranges from about 20 inches in the Palouse Hills of eastern Washington and northern Idaho to a low of little more than 10 inches in the Big Bend area immediately east of the Columbia River. The growing season ranges from about 140 to 180 days, and both spring and winter wheat varieties are produced. It is not uncommon in this region to reseed to spring wheat the acreage of winter wheat that is winterkilled. But winter wheat is generally preferred because it yields better than spring wheat and because it provides some cover to retard erosion during the winter. The topography is undulating to rolling; in the Palouse area it is so rolling that track-laying tractors were adopted when farming operations were mechanized. Some of the cropland has slopes of 50 per cent or more.

Farther west, in the drier Big Bend section, wheat is grown exclusively on summer fallow. In the eastern parts where additional rainfall permits more alternatives, common practice has been to rotate fallow with wheat every two

or three years, primarily as a means of weed control.

Wheat from the Columbia-Snake Plateau yields a soft flour that is excellent for cakes and pastry; but this wheat must be balanced with a hard wheat, generally imported from Montana, for making bread. Soft white wheats suitable for pastry flour normally comprise about 90 per cent of the total wheat production. The hard red wheats are grown to a limited extent in the low precipitation areas.

Minor grains. Production of grains other than wheat is of minor importance.

Oats are grown mainly as feed grain and forage for livestock, but a small quantity is processed for human consumption. Oats are planted in the spring and mature in a shorter growing season than wheat.

Barley is in demand for feeding livestock; about 40 per cent of the annual crop is used for this purpose on the farms where it is grown. Barley is planted in the spring, using the same farming methods as for wheat, which it resembles closely.

Field corn is a minor crop because the weather during the summer is too dry for its growth. Rye does better than wheat on poor soil or inferior land and is sometimes planted for hay.

GRAZING

Range livestock ranching utilizes by far the major part of the land area of the Intermontane Basins and Plateaus Region. Ranch operations are built around the use of grazing land —mostly publicly owned and administered. However, many of the ranches, particularly the cattle ranches, have some cropland from which forage and feed crops are harvested to feed the animals through the winter. Some cattle and many sheep graze all year, a system that necessitates moving herds considerable distances from summer to winter grazing grounds. Since feeds suitable for fattening cattle or sheep are relatively scarce, most cattle and lambs are marketed out of the region as feeder animals. Exceptions to this practice may be found in the Phoenix area and in the Imperial Valley, where many feedlots have been established since World War II to meet the needs of a rapidly expanding population.

Precipitation ranges from an average of 8.5 inches in the extreme south-central and western portions of the area to more than 20 inches at the higher elevations.

The beef cattle industry is by far the most important of the ranch enterprises. Grazing is planned to take advantage of the seasonal growth of grasses and weeds. Breeding is carried on throughout the year, which results in calves being born the year round. As a result of the climatic conditions and ranch practices, the average weight of cows, the percentage of calf crop, and the weight of calves when weaned and sold are comparatively low.

Sheep ranching is on the decline in the Southwest, as it is in the rest of the nation. Competition with more intensive forms of agriculture, higher labor costs, and a scarcity of competent shepherds have plagued the industry.

The feeding capacity of much of the grazing land has been materially reduced by years of overstocking that has resulted in: (1) a weakening or deterioration of the vegetative cover; (2) an increase in both wind and water erosion; and (3) a decrease, where the overstocking is excessive, in both the quality and total pounds of livestock produced.

Water and Power Resources

The Rio Grande, the Colorado, the Columbia, and the Fraser are the four major river systems in the Intermontane Basins and Plateaus Region. Although all four of these basins have had some of their water power potential developed, only two—the Colorado and the Columbia—are involved in major development schemes. Multipurpose use planning for flood control, navigation, power generation, and recreation are part of the overall plan in these river basins.

COLORADO RIVER BASIN

The Colorado River drains one-twelfth of the area of the conterminous United States, or approximately 244,000 square miles. Though it has not been brought completely under control, the Colorado's vast system of dams, turbines, canals, and tunnels provides electricity for homes and industry and keeps millions of acres of farm land green in what used to be wasteland. Still, there is far from enough water in the Colorado to irrigate all the land, and an agreement had to be reached on sharing it among the seven states of the river basin. This came as early as 1922 with the signing of the Colorado River Compact, which determined a division of the water between the upper and lower basins at Lee Ferry, Arizona, a few miles below the Utah line.

Work on the main stem of the Colorado began in 1928 with the building of Hoover Dam (completed in 1935) across the Colorado River between Arizona and Nevada. Standing 726 feet above bedrock, it affords protection to the fertile valleys along the lower reaches of the river (*Fig. 15-22*). It also holds back Lake Mead, one of the largest artificial bodies of water in the world. Three other large dams

FIGURE 15-22. *Hoover Dam, one of the highest concrete dams in the world, has a hydroelectric capacity of 1,344,000 kilowatts, which can supply the domestic needs of 7.5 million people. (Bureau of Reclamation)*

have been completed below Hoover Dam: Imperial Dam near Yuma, Arizona; Parker Dam, 97 miles southeast of Needles, California; and Davis Dam, 50 miles north of Needles. The proposed Bridge Canyon and Marble Canyon Dams will complete the complicated network of dams and artificial lakes on the lower Colorado.

Work did not begin on the upper Colorado until 1956, when Congress authorized the construction of four major storage units. All have since been completed, and they make a combined storage capacity of approximately 34 million acre-feet and a manufacturing capacity of 1.3 million kilowatts. Glen Canyon Dam, near the Arizona-Utah border, is the key feature of the upper basin; its reservoir, Lake Powell, backs up into Utah almost 200 miles and has a

capacity of 28 million acre-feet of water. Farther upstream on the Green River tributary is Flaming Gorge Dam in the extreme northeast corner of Utah. The Blue Mesa Dam on the Gunnison River in west-central Colorado and the Navajo Dam on the San Juan River in northwestern New Mexico are slightly smaller and are devoted primarily to flood control, reclamation, and irrigation.

Seven other water projects are under construction on various tributaries of the upper Colorado. Four more are authorized and eventually a total of 40 projects will be constructed to catch and hold surface water in years of high runoff.

COLUMBIA RIVER BASIN

The Columbia River drains a basin of 259,000 square miles lying mostly in the Pacific Northwest of the United States. The remainder is in the province of British Columbia in Canada. About 220,000 square miles, or 85 per cent are within the United States and constitute about 7 per cent of the nation's area. The basin includes nearly all of Idaho, most of Washington and Oregon, the western part of Montana, smaller areas in Wyoming and Nevada, and the northwestern tip of Utah.

Half a century ago, the river raced freely to the sea. Now its torrential waters are slowed and harnessed by a series of huge dams in Washington and Oregon. King of them all is the Grand Coulee Dam, the first to trap the river flow from across the Canadian boundary. Downriver from Grand Coulee is Chief Joseph Dam, then Rocky Reach, Rock Island, Wanapum, and Priest Rapids Dams—all in Washington. Athwart the river where it forms the Washington-Oregon boundary are the McNary, John Day, The Dalles, and Bonneville Dams, the last of these being 140 miles from the sea. All these barriers waylay the rushing waters of the Columbia before they swing northward around the upper end of Oregon's coast range. Only then can they rush in freedom to the sea (Fig. 15-23).

The Snake River is the principal tributary of the Columbia. Rising in Yellowstone National

Park, Wyoming, it sweeps westward across southern Idaho, northward (joining the Idaho-Oregon boundary), and finally westward, south of the Columbia Plateau in Washington.

Six completed federal multipurpose projects on the Snake are Albeni Falls, Minidoka, Boise Diversion, Black Canyon, Anderson Ranch, and Palisades. Hells Canyon Dam on the Snake River between Idaho and Oregon, opened in late 1967, adds one-half of its 369,900 kilowatts to Idaho's total power development.

Forestry

The arid and semiarid landscape that dominates most of the Intermontane Basins and Plateaus Region excludes forestry over the greater part of the region. Logging is limited to the higher mountains and to the north. Only four areas are important commercially: (1) central Arizona; (2) the interior uplands of Washington, Oregon, and Idaho; (3) the British Columbia Interior Plateau; and (4) the Yukon Plateau.

The forests of Arizona are a valuable asset, providing a source of lumber, protection for water resources, a home for wildlife, and areas for recreation. Forest lands are found at altitudes of 5,000 to 11,500 feet. The mountain region contains the largest undisturbed area of Ponderosa and Jeffrey pine timber in the United States. Flagstaff, Williams, and McNary are important logging and milling centers.

The interior uplands of Washington, Oregon, and Idaho are forested predominantly in pine, of which the Ponderosa and Idaho white are the most important. Interspersed with the dominant species are Western larch, Douglas fir, sugar pine, Pacific white fir, and Grand fir. As a saw timber tree, Ponderosa pine is second in quality only to Douglas fir. As all spruces, true firs, and lodgepole pine can be pulped satisfactorily by any process, the vast, underdeveloped areas of these species in Idaho, eastern Washington, and eastern Oregon can be expected to support a sizeable pulp industry centered in favorable areas where water is available. Wallula and Millwood, Washington,

and Lewiston, Idaho, are pulp and paper mill centers.

About half of the timber cut in British Columbia comes from forest lands of the Interior Plateau. Douglas fir, Western hemlock, spruce, and Western red cedar are the leading commercial species. Pulp and paper mills are widely scattered throughout the area with plywood plants at Kelowna, Kamloops, Quesnel, and Prince George.

The forests of the Yukon are in the Boreal Forest region of Canada, in which not only the number of tree species is few, especially toward its northern border, but the area covered by forests and the rate of growth are relatively small. White spruce forms the bulk of the stands, mixed with aspen poplar, balsam poplar, and Alaska white birch. Difficulty of transportation and distance to market, in addi-

FIGURE 15-23. *The Columbia Basin Project.*

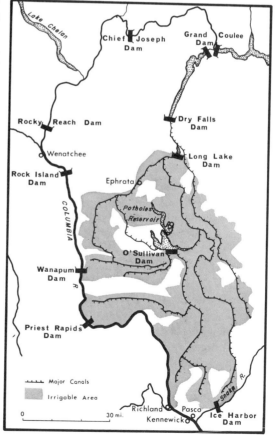

tion to poor timber species, are drawbacks to wide exploitation of this forest resource.

Manufacturing

Growth of manufacturing has, of necessity, been in those industrial enterprises whose products have low freight costs per unit to markets. Industries also have to turn out products that do not require large amounts of water in processing. Manufacturing must be relatively smoke-free. The electronics and aircraft components industries furnish the chief answers to these requirements. With products of this type, freight rates no longer are an overriding consideration and production is not necessarily market oriented. Along with these industries have come research laboratories, warehousing facilities, and growth in supporting industries. Food processing, an old established industry within the region, has grown considerably in recent years in response to the great increase in population.

Modern scientific and technological advances are responsible for the rapid growth in manufacturing in this region. Atomic and space research centers are located at Los Alamos, White Sands, Holloman, Kirtland, Sandia, and Albuquerque, New Mexico; Phoenix and Tucson, Arizona; and Palmdale and Lancaster in California's Antelope Valley. Los Alamos, a closed city high on a mesa, was the site of research for the first atomic bomb. At the giant Edwards Air Force Base dozens of civilian contractors work with the Air Force and the National Aeronautics and Space Administration on jet and satellite development. At Phoenix, Arizona, AiResearch Manufacturing Company, a division of the Garrett Corporation, specializes in electronics equipment. Motorola, Sperry-Rand, and General Electric also have electronics divisions here. Near Tucson, not far from the Mexican border at Fort Huachuca, is the U.S. Army's electronics proving ground.

Many industries have been attracted to the mushrooming desert electronics areas. The rapid population growth in Phoenix since 1950

has created a home market for many new firms to supply building materials and equipment to local contractors. Their products include such items as aluminum thresholds, lighting fixtures, concrete blocks, and prefabricated steel buildings.

El Paso is an important metallurgical center for smelting and refining copper, lead, and zinc ores. It is also a noted apparel center, utilizing low-cost female labor.

The Salt Lake City area is an important manufacturing center. Within 25 miles of Salt Lake City are large smelters operated by American Smelting, U.S. Smelting, and International Smelting, and two huge copper concentrating mills and a refinery operated by Kennecott.

Steelmaking in Utah began during World War II when the Defense Plant Corporation of the federal government built the Geneva plant, the first fully integrated mill in the West, on the shores of Utah Lake, to supply West Coast shipyards with structural steel shapes. The original plant cost more than $200 million and consisted of nine 255-ton furnaces. It was sold to the United States Steel Corporation in 1947 (*Fig. 15-24*).

FIGURE 15-24. *United Steel's Geneva Works, near Provo, Utah. This large, integrated plant features some of the West's most modern finishing facilities for steel and also produces a line of nitrogen chemicals and fertilizers. (U.S. Steel Corp.)*

Two basic factors brought this steel facility to Utah: (1) large local deposits of iron ore, coking coal, and limestone; and (2) location— it is equidistant from the Pacific Northwest, the San Francisco Bay area, and Los Angeles.

Finished steel products include plates, structural shapes, hot-rolled coils, and hot-rolled sheets. Nearby raw materials, available inexpensive water, good rail transportation, and skilled labor insure low-cost steel production. Coal is hauled 130 miles by rail from Sunnyside, Utah, in the southeast; iron ore is shipped by rail from Iron Mountain near Cedar City, 252 miles to the southwest; limestone and dolomite originate at the Keigley Quarry near Payson, some 30 miles to the south. Because local demand is small, most of Geneva's finished products are shipped via railroads to Pacific Coast markets. The corporation has integrated Geneva's economy with that of its Pittsburg, California, plant to make fuller use of its capacity.

Other important industries in the Salt Lake City area include sugar beet refining, flour milling and meatpacking. Chemical industries, petroleum refining from crude oil supplied via pipeline by oil fields of Colorado and Wyoming, and electronics also have been attracted to the area, owing to its strategic location, its industrial space available at reasonable cost, and a dependable labor supply.

The intermontane area of the Pacific Northwest is noted for aluminum refining at The Dalles, Oregon, and Spokane, Washington; food processing and canning at Walla Walla, Washington, and Pendleton, Oregon; and flour milling of Palouse wheat and saw-milling of nearby timber at Spokane.

Tourism

From an area to be shunned, the Intermontane Basins and Plateaus Region, in a few short years, has become the goal for a vast number of people seeking health, rest, and recreation.

The region displays many wonders. Lake Tahoe, straddling California and Nevada, is a major resort. The Grand Canyon, the Painted

Desert, Bryce Canyon, and Zion National Park are perhaps the best known, but Canyon de Chelly, Navajo National Monument, Saguaro National Monument, and the Petrified Forest in Arizona, Arches National Monument in Utah, and such spectacular engineering feats as Hoover Dam lure visitors to this area from many parts of the United States and the rest of the world.

Modern transportation has transformed the lowlands of this region into one of the West's most fascinating playgrounds (Fig. 15-25). The warm, sunny, and dry winter has created a tourist industry of major importance. The face of the land is dotted with new hotels and resorts—sometimes entire new communities.

One of the nation's famous desert resorts, Palm Springs, California, receives over a half-million visitors annually. Other resort cities of some note include Palm Desert, La Quinta, Cathedral City, North Palm Springs, and Desert Hot Springs, all in California's interior desert, and Phoenix and Tuscon, in Arizona.

Reno and Las Vegas, Nevada, with their gambling casinos and multimillion dollar resort hotels, featuring motion picture and television

FIGURE 15-25. *Modern highways transport tourists to resort areas through inhospitable country. This scene is in the Mohave Desert, about midway between Barstow, California, and the Nevada state line. (California Division of Highways)*

stars for entertainment, attract tourists from many parts of the nation.

The Salt Lake City area, with its history of Mormonism, its monuments and temples, its Great Salt Lake and Bonneville salt flats, and its superb setting at the foot of the Wasatch Mountains, attracts many visitors (*Fig. 15-26*). Winter sports, scenic grandeur, hiking, camping, hunting and fishing, and other such activities provide a great variety of recreational outlets.

Power dams on the Columbia River and its tributaries, such as Bonneville, John Day, McNary, and Ground Coulee, are major attractions in the Pacific Northwest. Overlooking these man-made engineering feats are majestic, eternally snow-capped volcanic peaks, i.e., Mt. Hood, Mt. Adams, Mt. Rainier, and Mt. Baker, among others, which provide an outlet for climbing and skiing, as well as spectacular vistas for the sightseer. Broad expanses of plateau stretch interminably to the far horizon, broken only occasionally by an iso-

lated mountain range or an erosional remnant. Sunny skies and clear, dry air impart added sharpness to the details of the landscape. Many rivers cut their way deep into the land and flow between steep-walled gorges. Urban attractions are offered by a number of interesting cities such as Spokane, Yakima, and Walla Walla in Washington, and Pendleton, Bend, and Lakeview in Oregon.

Outlook

The future of the Intermontane Basins and Plateaus Region still depends upon water. Fortunately, Anglo-America has accumulated more than a hundred years of experience in developing this valuable resource for the arid and semiarid regions of the West. The technical problems are largely conquered, or, at least, modern tools have brought them within sight of solution. Dams and reservoirs have proved effective in capturing stream flow. Yet,

FIGURE 15-26. *Aerial view of Salt Lake City, looking southeastward toward the 11,000-foot peaks of the Wasatch Range. (Utah Tourist and Publicity Council)*

impressive as these engineering feats are, they cannot by themselves solve all the inherent problems of aridity. New sources of water have to be discovered, greater storage facilities built, watersheds protected more completely, pollution and sedimentation of the streams reduced, and the many human and political problems resolved.

One of the best hopes at the moment for providing more water is to create patches in the desert for harvesting areas. Water harvesting is nothing new. The British obtain most of their water on Gibraltar by collecting runoff from the rocky slopes in corrugated iron aprons, as do the people in most of the Caribbean Islands.

Experts estimate that at least 90 per cent of the total rain that falls on the desert is lost by evaporation. A little goes for the support of plant life, but only a tiny fraction ever reaches the natural underground reservoirs, or aquifers. Experimenters are trying out various chemicals on large surfaces, as well as butyl rubber, aluminum foil, polyethylene, and several other plastics. Costs for different water repellents vary from 3 to 80 cents a square yard, and these repellents are capable of harvesting anywhere from 30 to 100 per cent of the rain falling on the covered area, depending upon atmospheric conditions and type of storm. This means that harvested water will cost more than three times what is now considered a reasonable price for water for irrigation purposes. But once harvested water is really needed, users will have no alternative.

With each advance in the struggle for more water, there has been a corresponding increase in population and a demand for still more water. Providing fresh water from saline sources at a cost comparable to that of natural supplies is at present unrealistic for the Intermontane region.

Perhaps the most dramatic, costly, and ambitious plan for bringing water to this region is the North American Water and Power Alliance (NAWAPA). NAWAPA provides for the collection of surplus waters from the Fraser, Yukon, Peace, and Athabasca Rivers, and other rivers of Alaska and western Canada. Through a complex system of canals, tunnels, rivers, lifts, aqueducts, and reservoirs, water would be distributed to the parched areas of Canada, the western United States, and northern Mexico.

Even if NAWAPA were completed by the year 2000, it probably would still fall short of supplying the total need for the arid West. For this and other reasons, some experts believe that the long-range solution is the curtailment, if not outright elimination of irrigated agriculture. They argue that, no matter how efficient irrigation becomes, it will never approach the values that are attainable for the use of the same water for other purposes, particularly for industry.

The arid West is viewed by some as a huge playground or sanctuary for those cramped up in cities most of the year. To them, the greatest challenge of the future is to preserve the region's scenery and outdoor recreational facilities. During the past 20 years the number of visitors to national parks, wilderness areas, and national monuments has multiplied tenfold. By the year 2000 such activities are expected to increase 20 to 30 times. As this happens, pressure to develop the public lands of the arid regions for further recreational use is inevitable. Water is, indeed, truly the key to the future of the Intermontane Basins and Plateaus Region.

Selected References

AHNERT, FRANK, "The Influence of Pleistocene Climates Upon the Morphology of Cuesta Scarps on the Colorado Plateau," *Annals of the Association of American Geographers,* Vol. 50, June, 1960, pp. 139–156.

BEATY, CHESTER B., "Origin of Alluvial Fans, White Mountains, California and Nevada," *Annals of the Association of American Geographers,* Vol. 53, December, 1963, pp. 516–535.

BROGAN, PHIL F., *East of the Cascades,* Portland, Ore.: Binfords & Mort, 1964.

CARTER, GEORGE F., "Man, Time, and Change in the Far Southwest," *Annals of the Association of American Geographers,* Vol. 49, September, 1959, pp. 8–30.

CLINE, GLORIA GRIFFEN, *Exploring the Great Basin,* Norman, Okla.: University of Oklahoma Press, 1963.

DUE, JOHN F., "The City of Prineville Railway and the Economic Development of Crook County," *Economic Geography,* Vol. 45, April, 1967, pp. 170–181.

FONAROFF, L. SCHUYLER, "Conservation and Stock Reduction on the Navajo Tribal Range," *The Geographical Review,* Vol. 53, April, 1963, pp. 200–226.

GRIFFIN, PAUL F., and YOUNG, ROBERT N., *California, the New Empire State: A Regional Geography,* Palo Alto, Calif.: Fearon Publishers, Inc., 1957, pp. 165–199.

HARRIS, DAVID R., "Recent Plant Invasions in the Arid and Semi-arid Southwest of the United States," *Annals of the Association of American Geographers,* Vol. 56, September, 1966, pp. 408–422.

HOLLON, W. EUGENE, *The Great American Desert,* New York: Oxford University Press, Inc. 1966.

KENNELLY, ROBERT A., "Cattle Feeding in the Imperial Valley," *Yearbook of the Association of Pacific Coast Geographers,* Vol. 22, 1960, pp. 50–56.

LEWIS, PEIRCE F., "Linear Topography in the Southwestern Palouse, Washington-Oregon," *Annals of the Association of American Geographers,* Vol. 50, June, 1960, pp. 98–111.

MACINKO, GEORGE, "The Columbia Basin Project: Expectations, Realizations, Implications," *The Geographical Review,* Vol. 53, April, 1963, pp. 185–199.

MEINIG, D. W., "The Mormon Culture Region: Strategies and Patterns in the Geography of the American West, 1847-1964," *Annals of the Association of American Geographers,* Vol. 55, June, 1965, p. 191–220.

NELSON, LOWRY, *The Mormon Village,* Salt Lake City, Utah: University of Utah Press, 1952.

POWELL, JOHN WESLEY, *Report on the Lands of the Arid Region of the United States with a More Detailed Account of the Lands of Utah,* ed. Wallace Stegner, Cambridge, Mass.: The Belknap Press of Harvard University Press, 1962.

RUHE, ROBERT V., "Landscape Morphology and Alluvial Deposits in Southern New Mexico," *Annals of the Association of American Geographers,* Vol. 54, March, 1964, pp. 147–159.

STEGNER, WALLACE, *Beyond the Hundredth Meridian,* Boston: Houghton Mifflin Co., 1962.

THOMAS, HAROLD E., "First Fourteen Years of Lake Mead," *Geological Survey Circular 346* (U. S. Department of the Interior), 1954.

TUAN, YI-FU, "New Mexican Gullies: A Critical Review and Some Recent Observations," *Annals of the Association of American Geographers,* Vol. 56, December, 1966, pp. 573–597.

———, "Structure, Climate, and Basin Land Forms in Arizona and New Mexico," *ibid.,* Vol. 52, March 1962, pp. 51–68.

WERTZ, JACQUES B., "The Flood Cycle of Ephemeral Mountain Streams in the Southwestern United States," *Annals of the Association of American Geographers,* Vol. 56, December, 1966, pp. 598–633.

WHITE, GILBERT F. (ed.), *The Future of the Arid Lands,* New York: American Geographical Society, 1957.

WILSON, ANDREW W., "Urbanization of the Arid Lands," *The Professional Geographer,* Vol. 12, November, 1960, pp. 4–7.

ZIERER, CLIFFORD M. (ed.), *California and the Southwest,* New York: John Wiley & Sons, Inc., 1956.

16 *Pacific Slope Region*

The Sierra Nevada-Cascade Ranges separate most of California, western Oregon, and western Washington from the Intermontane Basins and Plateaus Region. Partially screened off from the continental winds of the interior, these Pacific Coast areas enjoy a very mild climate for their latitudes. The marine effect may be seen in the profuse natural vegetation mantling the windward slopes of the Coast and Sierra Nevada-Cascade Ranges. The variety of agricultural crops—ranging from subtropical citrus and vine products to a vast array of deciduous fruit and nut crops, grains, and vegetables—exists as a result of both the long growing season and ample precipitation or available irrigation water.

Settlement patterns, land uses, and climates are sufficiently varied within the Pacific Slope Region to justify a division into: (1) the Sierra Nevada-Cascade Mountains and Valleys, (2) the Coastal Mountains and Valleys, and (3) the Pacific Border of British Columbia and Alaska (*Figs. 16-1, 16-2,* and *16-3*).

Surface Features

SIERRA NEVADA-CASCADE MOUNTAINS AND VALLEYS

The Sierra Nevada-Cascade Ranges form a continuous line of mountains 1,000 miles long, averaging 60 to 100 miles wide, 6,000 to 8,000 feet high in the northern half, and 11,000 to 14,000 feet or more in the southern Sierra Nevada. In general, these mountains rise abruptly above the Great Basin, the Columbia Plateau, and the Okanogan Valley, all of which belong to the Intermontane Basins and Plateaus Region.

Sierra Nevada section. This section extends south 400 miles from the 40th parallel. North of that all rocks are volcanic. The Sierra Nevada is mainly a granite batholith stripped of sedimentaries in its northern half. The remaining third is the "Gold Belt." Its rocks are folded and, in part, metamorphosed sediments called "auriferous slates" (but they are not all slate).

The whole range is an imperfect peneplain raised and tilted west with a great fault scarp on the east (*Fig. 16-4*). The descent on this side is at places 10,000 feet in 10 miles; hence, the crest is very near the east side. The general westward slope of the summit level is only 100 feet per mile in the northern part where the crest is 7,000 feet high. It may be 200 feet per mile in the southern part where the level crests are 11,200 to 12,500 feet high. Isolated monadnocks or broad remnants rise 1,000 feet above the peneplain in the northern part and 2,500 to 3,500 feet in the southern part, culminating in Mt. Whitney (14,495 feet). The north end of the range is triple,

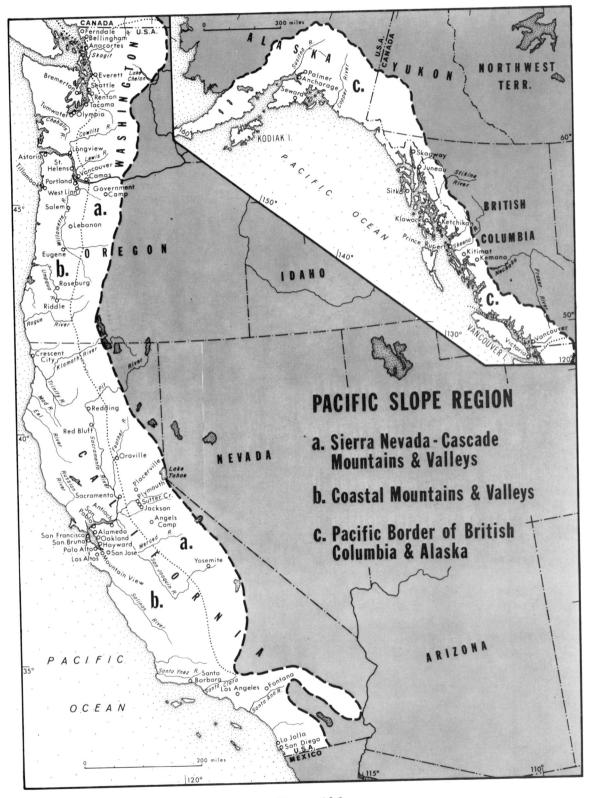

FIGURE 16-1.

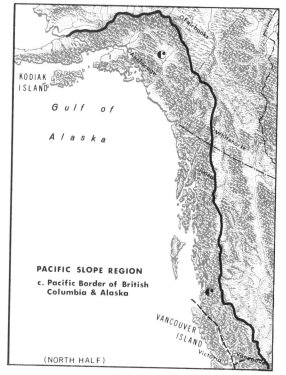

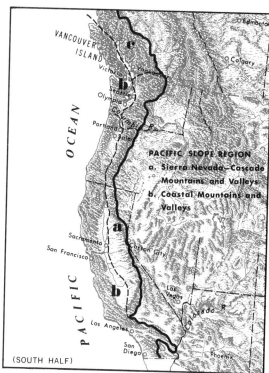

FIGURE 16-2. *The Pacific Slope Region, physical relief.*

FIGURE 16-3. *Cross-section of the Pacific Slope Region (after Raisz).*

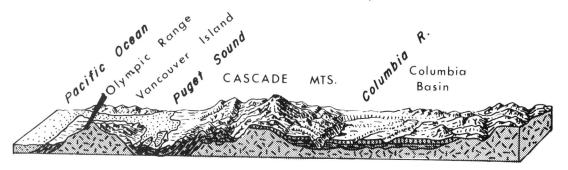

made so by parallel fault blocks tilted west. Lake Tahoe is a "moat," or trough, between upraised fault blocks.

The peneplain is cut by west-flowing streams, some of which have wide valleys trenched by canyons. Except near the foot of the mountains these valleys were modified by glaciers. The essential features of Yosemite Valley on the Merced River were thus produced. Many small glaciers survive. Lava flows in the northern part ran down old valleys, burying the auriferous gravels.

Southern Cascade section. This section extends north from the 40th parallel to southern Oregon, 150 miles. It is the narrowest part of the mountain belt and of very irregular height. It is not a "range" made by uplift but a belt of closely set volcanoes (120 in the first 50 miles at the south end) of all ages, from active to old and much eroded. Considerable areas are less than 5,000 feet high. The Pit and Klamath Rivers cross in canyons, but these canyons are cut in broad valleys whose floors are no higher than the Great Basin.

FIGURE 16-4. *The eastern scarp of the Sierra Nevada Mountains, Mono Valley, and Mono Lake. The lighter line along the base of the mountains marks the old shoreline of Lake Russell. (California Division of Highways)*

Lassen Peak (10,453 feet), near the south end, erupted in 1915, pouring forth steam and solid matter. Mt. Shasta (14,162 feet) is a typical conical volcano with a slope of 5 degrees near the base, 35 degrees near the summit, and an average slope of 15 degrees. It is beginning to be cut near the summit by ravines now occupied by glaciers (*Fig. 16-5*).

Middle Cascade section. Extending from southern Oregon almost to the latitude of Seattle, this section is a continuous range cut only by the Columbia River. Its southern part is similar to the southern Cascade section but its altitude is due to uplift (faulting and perhaps folding) instead of mere volcanic accumulation and more and more uplift. The altitude throughout is 6,000 to 7,000 feet. The northern part has a horizontal skyline like the Sierra Nevada but this gives out toward the south. Above this general level rise isolated volcanoes: Mt. Hood (11,245 feet), Mt.

FIGURE 16-5. *The volcano of Mt. Shasta. A number of glaciers are present on this peak. (Litton Industries, Aero Service Division)*

Adams (12,307 feet), Mt. Rainier (14,410 feet), and others.

Near the south end of this section is Crater Lake, 6,177 feet high, occupying the caldera of an old volcanic cone. Crater Lake is about six miles long, five miles wide, and 1,932 feet deep (*Figs. 16-6* and *16-7*).

Northern Cascade section. Situated in northern Washington and adjacent British Columbia, the northern Cascade section consists of metamorphosed Paleozoic rocks with granite batholiths. In general, they are carved into sharp peaks and rugged ridges of accordant height (6,000 to 8,000 feet) suggesting an uplifted peneplain deeply and maturely dissected by water and ice. The U-shaped valleys are very deep. In one of the valleys lies Lake Chelan, with a bottom 400 feet below sea level.

A series of volcanic peaks tower above the general summit of the northern Cascade section. The most noteworthy of these are Mt. Baker (10,750 feet) and Glacier Peak (10,436 feet).

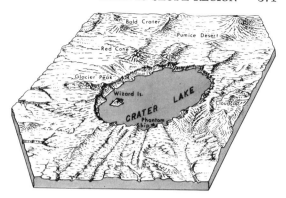

FIGURE 16-6. *A block diagram of Crater Lake.*

COASTAL MOUNTAINS AND VALLEYS

Along the Pacific Ocean coastline lie a series of rugged hills and mountains. Between ridges and ranges, and between these ridges and ranges and the ocean, are found small valleys and plains. It is here that the bulk of the population lives.

Between the coastal mountains and the Sierra Nevada-Cascades are an elongated series of north-south lowlands—the Central Valley of

FIGURE 16-7. *Crater walls that once supported a volcanic summit five thousand feet higher surround the blue waters of Crater Lake in southern Oregon. (Oregon State Highway Commission)*

California, the Willamette-Puget Trough, the Inside Passage (a submerged continuation of the Willamette-Puget Trough), and small valleys such as the Susitna and Matanuska, near the Pacific Coast of Alaska.

Los Angeles Lowlands (Santa Barbara to San Diego). The chief mountain ranges of this section are uplifted fault blocks and trend east-west. The San Bernardino Range still has a summit peneplain not reached by streams that dissect its slopes. All ranges west of it–San Gabriel and others–are maturely dissected. Altitudes of 5,000 to 7,000 feet are most common.

The so-called Los Angeles Basin, or "Valley of Southern California," embraces several connected basins south of these mountains and also a strip of coastal plain, less than 3,000 square miles in area, covered with alluvium from the mountains. Isolated granite hills rise through the alluvium from the uneven buried floor. The altitude ranges from sea level to 1,000 feet or more at the foot of the mountains where the alluvial slope is locally as steep as 300 to 500 feet per mile. All streams across these plains are "interrupted," having stretches of dry channel alternating with others of flowing water.

South of these lowlands the mountains again trend southeast. They are young fault blocks still preserving at their summits some of the original surface undissected. The Santa Ana and Santa Margarita Rivers are antecedent.

California Coast Range section. This is 400 miles long and 50 miles wide. Most crests are 2,000 to 4,000 feet high and rarely reach 5,000 feet. There are alternating parallel valleys with ranges of constant height as in the Appalachian Valley section, but less regular and more dissected. The main drainage is longitudinal. The rocks are mainly metamorphosed sedimentaries, folded and faulted along lines indicated by the ridges and valleys (*Fig. 16-8*).

Klamath Mountains. These mountains form a mountain knot connecting the Coast Ranges of Oregon on the north with those of Califor-

FIGURE 16-8. *The Santa Lucia Mountains, part of California's Coast Range, in Monterey County. In most cases, the mountains of the Coast Range come down to the Pacific Ocean. Only occasionally are there flat valleys or lowlands. (California Division of Highways)*

nia in the west and south, and meeting the Cascade Range at the northern end of the Central Valley of California. The Klamath section consists of intrusives and of old sedimentary rocks, folded and generally metamorphosed. Residual mountains on the main divides are named as separate "ranges." They rise 1,000 to 5,000 feet above the peneplain, or 7,000 to 9,000 feet above the sea, and have been moderately glaciated. Most of the area is occupied by broad valleys, 1,000 feet or more in depth; these are again trenched by narrow valleys, some of them canyons, 1,000 to 3,000 feet deep. Only here and there are narrow flats found at stream level.

Oregon-Washington Coast Range. This range extends from Oregon's Coquille River to Washington's Chehalis River and inland from the Pacific Ocean to the Willamette-Puget Lowland. It is mainly a gentle anticline of tertiary rocks. Dips are rarely steeper than 10 or 15 degrees. The crests indicate an almost maturely dissected peneplain 1,700 feet high at the north and 3,000 to 3,500 feet high at the south. A few monadnocks of volcanic rock rise above this horizon. A coastal plain only one or two miles wide at the south, increases in width to 20 miles at the north. All valleys crossing this coastal plain are drowned.

Olympic Mountains. These mountains, poleward from the Chehalis River, are much like the northern Cascades, having accordant crests at 4,500 feet, declining toward the edges. Up to that level forests are very dense. A higher central group of mountains 40 miles in diameter is bare and alpine. Mt. Olympus (7,954 feet) is the highest peak in the Olympic Mountains. A narrow strip of lowland surrounds the mountains.

Central Valley. The Central Valley of California is a great longitudinal trough about 450 miles long and 50 miles wide. Most of it is very flat and lies below 400 feet elevation except at the extreme south end. The valley slopes from all sides toward San Francisco Bay. Its surface is made up largely of alluvial slopes that are a little steeper near the moun-

tains, sloping in some places 100 feet to the mile. Small dissected areas (relief of 50 to 200 feet) occur near the mountains either on alluvial fans or older surfaces that were never buried. Two master streams, the Sacramento and the San Joaquin traverse the valley from the north and south respectively, converging and forming a great composite delta south of Sacramento (*Fig. 16-9*).

Willamette-Puget Trough. This is a continuous valley 350 miles long (within the United States) and 25 to 50 miles wide. Its general elevation in Washington is less than 500 feet; its northern portion is submerged in Puget and Queen Charlotte Sounds. Its southern end is the Willamette Valley in Oregon. The portion that drains into Puget Sound is deeply covered with glacial drift, much of it gravel. Many arms of Puget Sound are narrow, deep, steep troughs within a gravel outwash plain 200 to 300 feet higher. These arms are drowned preglacial valleys probably occupied by residual ice masses while the outwash plain was forming. Some

Figure 16-9. *A model of the Central Valley of California. The Coast Range is at the left and the Sierra Nevada is at the right. Mt. Shasta and Shasta Dam are in the left-center background. (Bureau of Reclamation)*

granite hills rise above the drift. The Willamette Valley is essentially an alluvial plain produced by the drowning of the former more rugged surface by enormous quantities of sediment brought in by tributary streams (*Fig. 16-10*).

PACIFIC BORDER OF BRITISH COLUMBIA AND ALASKA

Northward from the international boundary, the Coast Ranges of British Columbia extend for about 900 miles. They are about 100 miles wide and have a general summit elevation of from 7,000 to 8,000 feet. Deep canyons have been cut by streams such as the Fraser, Naas, Stikine, and Taku (*Fig. 16-11*).

The Coast Ranges of British Columbia and Alaska blend into the Nutzotin Mountains and then into the Alaska Range, which together form a great arc roughly parallel to the Gulf of Alaska.

FIGURE 16-11. *Mt. Rocher de Boule and Haguelget Canyon, near Hazelton, British Columbia. (British Columbia government photograph)*

FIGURE 16-10. *Mt. Hood stands high above the broad valley of Oregon's meandering Willamette River. More than half of Oregon's population lives in this fertile valley, which is the focal point of the state's commerce and industry and its major agricultural area. (Oregon State Highway Commission)*

Climate

Within the Pacific Slope Region are found six climatic realms (*see Fig. 1-16*). Of these climates, the Mediterranean subtropical, the marine west coast, and the subarctic predominate.

Most of California south of 40° N. latitude has a Mediterranean subtropical climate, characterized by cool, wet winters and warm-to-hot, dry summers (*Fig. 16-12*). Near the ocean, where sea breezes prevail, temperatures vary slightly from season to season. Santa Barbara, for example, has a January average of 58° F. and a July average of 71° F. San Diego has the same annual range but is nine degrees warmer. As one moves inland this slight fluctuation becomes more pronounced, since land not immediately associated with maritime air heats and cools at a faster rate.

Midday temperatures in the Central Valley (steppe and desert climates) during the high sun period are extremely high; maximums exceeding 110° F. occasionally occur, and extremes of 120° F. or above are not unknown (*Fig. 16-13*).

During winter months, night temperatures

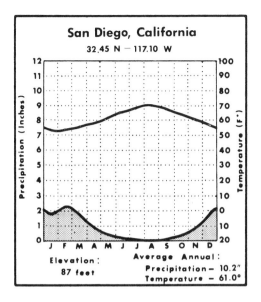

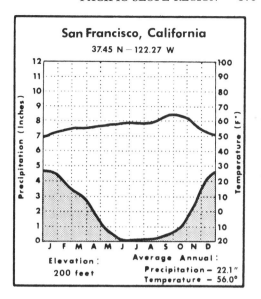

FIGURE 16-12. *Climatic graphs of the Mediterranean subtropical realm.*

FIGURE 16-13. *Climatic graphs of the steppe and desert realms.*

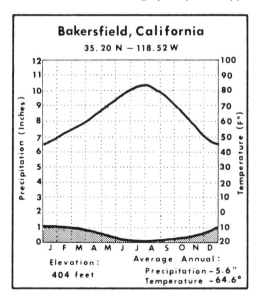

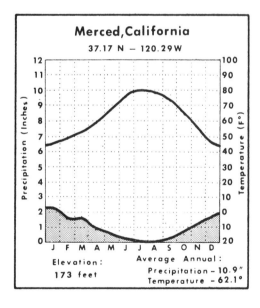

often fall to the freezing point or below, and frost sometimes forms. The days are comfortably warm throughout the winter and sunshine is abundant. During this period, radiation fogs of superficial depth are frequent in low-lying areas. These fogs usually dissipate soon after sunrise. Precipitation increases poleward along the coastal margins and inland on windward slopes. At San Diego, near California's south-

ern border, the annual rainfall averages 10.1 inches, while at Nellie, only 50 miles northeast, precipitation averages 48.2 inches. San Francisco, which lies near the northern coastal edge of the subtropics, receives an average rainfall of 22.1 inches annually.

The marine west coast climate, which extends from about 40° N. latitude to 60° N. latitude, has the greatest contrasts in precipitation of any part of Anglo-America. The area of extreme contrast is centered on the Olympic Peninsula, whose southwest-facing slopes may receive up to 200 inches of precipitation annually. A small area on the leeward, east-facing slope, which receives less than 10 inches per year is mantled by scrub vegetation.

Precipitation varies with latitude, nearness to the ocean, windward to leeward position, and other such factors (*Fig. 16-14*). On the average, more than 80 per cent of the precipitation occurs from October 15 to May 15. Relative humidity is high all year. It averages about 70 per cent in summer and about 90 per cent in winter. Much cloudiness, fog, and atmospheric haze prevail during the wet season (*Fig. 16-15*).

The average annual rainfall of the large cities is not great. Victoria has 30 inches, while the more exposed Vancouver receives 59 inches annually. Seattle gets 32 inches; Tacoma, 38 inches; Portland, 39 inches; and Salem, 40 inches.

Throughout this realm, winter rain and snow exceed summer precipitation. Extended periods of summer drought similar to the Mediterranean-type dry spells of California often occur. On the other hand, one may see

Mt. Rainier from Seattle only rarely in July and August.

During winter, snow has fallen everywhere within the realm, but rain is much more common in the lowlands. All the higher mountains receive copious blankets of snow, however. Annual snowfall is especially great in the mountains of Vancouver Island.

Temperatures are much modified by the proximity to the Pacific Ocean and by the year-round westerly winds that move predominantly maritime air over the region during all seasons. Readings in summer have gone above 100° F., while in winter the thermometer has dipped to below zero in every county. More common, however, are summers when it is never really too hot and winters when it is rarely bitterly cold.

In the Pacific Slope highlands, temperatures and precipitation rates vary with altitude, prevailing wind direction, and exposure. At a number of stations, freezing temperatures are experienced in nearly every month of the year (*Fig. 16-16*).

In the subarctic realm, climate is determined by latitudinal position, relief, and the direction, speed, and nature of air currents. Precipitation is not heavy anyplace (*Fig. 16-17*).

FIGURE 16-14. *Cross-section showing the general pattern of air circulation of water over Oregon.*

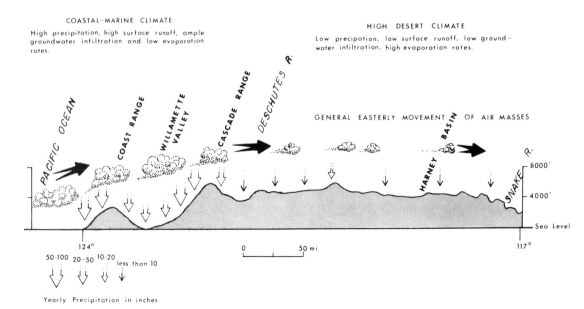

COASTAL-MARINE CLIMATE
High precipitation, high surface runoff, ample groundwater infiltration and low evaporation rates.

HIGH DESERT CLIMATE
Low precipation, low surface runoff, low groundwater infiltration, high evaporation rates.

Yearly Precipitation in inches

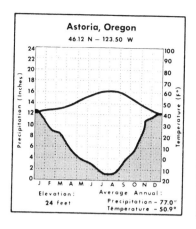

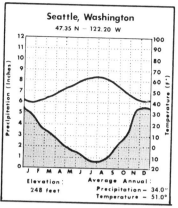

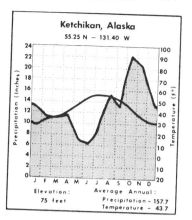

FIGURE 16-15. *Climatic graphs of the marine west coast realm.*

FIGURE 16-16. *Climatic graphs of highlands stations.*

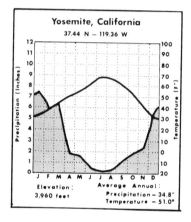

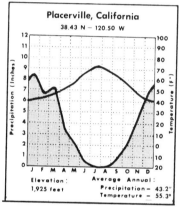

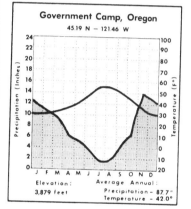

Natural Vegetation

The natural vegetation is as varied as the complexities of climates and landforms would lead one to suspect. In the Mediterranean subtropical realm, the dry and relatively untimbered mountain slopes are covered with a low evergreen scrub and brush thicket known as chaparral. Coastal sagebrush often occurs below the level of the chaparral. Plant growth is strictly limited in summer by drought conditions. The tree growths are, for the most part, of the deep-rooted variety whose leaves are small or thickened to decrease transpiration and conserve moisture during the dry periods. During the cool rainy season, the landscape is made brilliantly green by grass and shrubs,

but in the summer, the countryside becomes a dull yellow or brown. Many of the thick-leaved trees remain green all year round, for they are able to withstand drought by virtue of their extensive root systems, thick or corky bark, and special leaf structure. The myrtle, laurel, holly, madrona, scrub oak, greasewood, and manzanita, as well as a few forms of cactus, are characteristic vegetation of the realm.

The natural vegetation of the mild, rainy marine west coast realm is a heavy forest of coniferous trees. Great luxuriant forests of Douglas fir are continuous over much of western Washington and Oregon. Characteristic trees in addition to Douglas fir, which often forms 90 per cent of the forest, are giant cedar, Western hemlock, red alder, broadleaf maple,

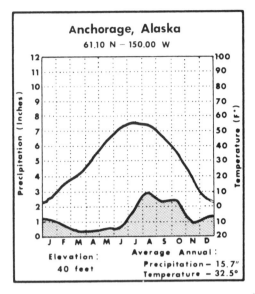

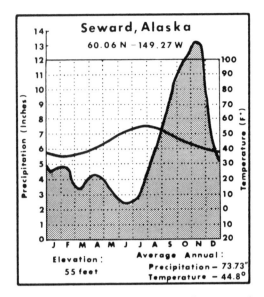

FIGURE 16-17. *Climatic graphs of the subarctic realm.*

and vine maple. The large trees are mostly evergreen conifers. The number of deciduous trees is relatively small. Broad-leaved evergreens are common. Toward the southern border, coastal redwoods are found in the fog belts (*Fig. 16-18*). Elsewhere, the lodgepole pine occupies the sandy coastal area.

The dominant types in British Columbia are Western hemlock and Western red cedar, with Douglas fir in the south and Sitka spruce in the north. The Douglas fir forest often has up to 100,000 board feet of timber per acre. Its most important uses are for residential construction and repair, plywood, pulp and paper, shingles, doors, and other such building needs.

Western hemlock is a wood of superior properties, and when properly manufactured and used, is excellent for many purposes. Western red cedar is one of the more durable species. Because it resists decay and insects, it is extremely desirable as lumber for siding and exterior paneling. Sitka spruce is an important source of lumber and is further manufactured into a wide variety of planing mill products.

Alaska's Panhandle, covered with conifers to an altitude of approximately 2,000 feet, occupies the so-called fog belt, usually less than 50 miles wide, along the shoreline of the Pacific. This coast forest, almost tropical in density, is predominantly a mixed stand of Western hemlock and Sitka spruce, with a small percentage of Alaskan cedar and Western red cedar in some localities. This is overtopped by scattered trees of the more light-demanding spruce, while underneath is a second story of somewhat suppressed sap-

FIGURE 16-18. *A grove of coastal redwood trees in northern California. (Georgia Pacific Corp.)*

lings of the more shade-resistant hemlock and cedar. At a still lower level are great clumps of blueberry, false azalea, the devil's club, and other woody shrubs.

The better areas of the coast forest are included in the Chugach and Tongass National Forests. The former consists principally of lands around Prince William Sound and on the eastern half of the Kenai Peninsula just north of Seward. The latter is in southeastern Alaska.

The natural vegetation of the Sierra Nevada Mountains, typical of the highlands climate in this region, is shown in profile in Figure 16-19.

Lumbermen classify the Sierra Nevada Mountains as pine region. Major species found there are the sugar pine, Ponderosa pine, Jeffrey pine, white fir, Douglas fir, and incense cedar.

Soils

Regional soils show great diversity. In California alone there are over 1,200 soil types.

The kind of parent material, the degree of mechanical or chemical weathering, or both, the amount of precipitation, the degree of slope, and other such factors greatly influence soil development. The soils of the marine terraces are usually light-textured, underlain by a dense claypan. They are shallow and tend to erode rapidly. The valley soils are light to coarse in texture, gravelly, and subject to flash floods and inundation. The mountain soils are mainly shallow and light textured; many of them are derived from granite materials. The larger valleys are floored with alluvium, and produce well under irrigation. The soils of the meadows are dark in color, of medium to heavy texture, and poorly drained. Glacial soils mantle the Puget Sound area of Washington and British Columbia.

The slope of the land affects not only the velocity of water runoff and the rate of soil erosion, but also the method of irrigation, the use of farm machinery, and other agricultural operations, all of which influence the use to which the land can be put.

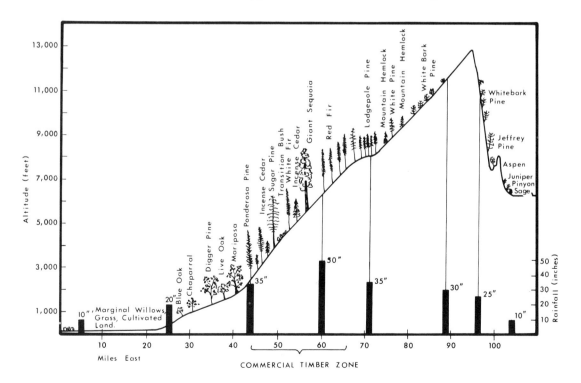

FIGURE 16-19. A profile of Sierra Nevada vegetation types.

Settlement

CALIFORNIA

A little more than four centuries ago, just 50 years after Columbus discovered America, the Spaniards first set foot on California soil. On September 28, 1542, a Spanish expedition under Juan Rodriguez Cabrillo discovered San Diego Bay and explored the coast as far as Point Reyes, stopping at Catalina Island, San Pedro Bay, the Santa Barbara Islands, and Monterey Bay. In 1579, Sir Francis Drake explored the coast and named the country New Albion.

The first of the Spanish missions was founded in 1769 at San Diego, and by 1821, 21 missions were in successful operation. In 1777, the Spaniards began the establishment of towns and, after the Mexican revolution in 1821, gradually increased and expanded their settlement efforts.

The first American emigrant wagon reached the state in 1826. When the Mexican War broke out, California was captured by American forces under Colonel Frémont and General Kearney. By the Treaty of Guadalupe-Hidalgo it was ceded by Mexico to the United States. On January 24, 1848, gold was discovered at Sutter's Mill, near Coloma. The news of this discovery led to an influx of settlers from many parts of the world. In 1849 the population exceeded 100,000. In that year, a constitution prohibiting slavery was adopted. In 1850 California was admitted as a free state under the compromise of that year. The completion of the Union Pacific Railway in 1869 placed her in closer communication with the rest of the Union, and since then her development has been rapid. California now leads the nation in population.

THE PACIFIC NORTHWEST

In 1543, Bartolomé Ferrelo, successor in command to Cabrillo, sailed up the coast as far north as Oregon. Sir Francis Drake explored and laid claim to the northern coast for England. Two centuries later, in 1775, the Spaniard Bruno Heceta landed on the Olympic Peninsula. In 1792, George Vancouver discovered, named, and explored Puget Sound. Many of the names he chose have remained unchanged, including Hood Canal, Mt. Baker, and Mt. Rainier.

In 1793, Alexander Mackenzie, of the Northwest Company, on his epochal journey from coast to coast, made his way into what is now British Columbia. Two years later, Spain renounced all claims to the region in favor of England. The United States denied British rights to the area. President Jefferson sent Meriwether Lewis and William Clark to explore the area, and they reached the Columbia in 1805.

During the period leading up to and during the War of 1812, the United States lost most of her European trade. Consequently, ships from New England, New York, and Chesapeake Bay ports began to look for trade in the Pacific. John Jacob Astor established a fort and fur post at Astoria in 1811. This began the era of the fur brigades, whose depots soon were scattered throughout the virgin wilderness. The British Hudson's Bay Company's men had gradually worked westward across Canada. A bitter rivalry developed between these great fur companies; the actual ownership of the vast territory of the Pacific Northwest was in dispute.

On June 15, 1846, the 49th parallel was defined as the international boundary. The United States portion was organized into the Oregon and the Washington Territories. Oregon was admitted to the Union in 1859; Washington, in 1889.

New Englanders began to settle in the Willamette Valley in 1832, and a Methodist mission was established at Salem in 1834. A regular migration route across the Great Plains and through the Rocky Mountains to the Columbia River was followed. Where it branched north, it was known as the Oregon Trail.

The first sawmill on Puget Sound was located at Tumwater in 1844. Settlers first came by boat from Oregon; later, they came by the Oregon Trail up the Cowlitz Valley. Soon other settlements were made. Fortunately, the lumber trade grew as the fur trade declined. Later, land was cleared and agriculture began. Many California gold seekers who were disappointed in their quest continued their journey into the Northwest, where they went into farming.

ALASKA

Colonization of Alaska began on August 3, 1784, with the establishment of a trading post at Three Saints Bay, Kodiak Island, by Grigori Shelekhov, a Russian. Shelekhov remained four years, firmly establishing the colony and setting up an outpost, named Fort Alexander, on Cook Inlet. He then returned to Russia to lay the groundwork for subsequent establishment of the crown-sanctioned Russian American Company. Almost all colonization for the next 50 years was under the auspices of this venture of the czars to emulate in Alaska what Great Britain had accomplished with its British East India Company.

The Russian American Company was formally chartered in 1799 by Alexander Baranov, a Russian merchant employed by Shelekhov to expand his fur-trading interests. When Baranov was replaced in 1818, he had succeeded in expanding Russian colonization of Alaska to 23 establishments.

Alaska was purchased from Russia by the United States in 1867. Eleven years later, two salmon canneries were established at Sitka and Klawak. From this beginning, new settlements sprang up in coastal regions as fishing became a multimillion dollar industry, employing thousands of workers.

The Klondike gold rush brought thousands of people to the Yukon and Alaska in 1896. Of those disappointed in prospecting, some remained to establish businesses, farm, fish, trap, cut timber, or live off the land by hunting. There was another influx of people in the period following World War II.

In 1958, a bill asking for statehood was approved. On January 3, 1959, Alaska was officially proclaimed the 49th state by the president.

Agriculture

CALIFORNIA

The size, variety, profitability, and commercialization of California agriculture are well known. California is the leading agricultural state in terms of value of production. Although it has only about three of every hundred acres of the nation's farmland, it produces roughly seven per cent of the nation's farm products (*Fig. 16-20*).

The wide range of climatic, soil, and water conditions makes it possible for farmers to raise over 80 kinds of vegetables, about 50 field crops, and nearly 70 fruits. The largest single income-generating farm crop in California is cotton (including lint and seed); it accounts for 11 per cent of the state's farm income. No single crop or individual group of farm products dominates California's agriculture, however. As much as 38 per cent of the state's farm income is derived from fruit and vegetable crops, in the production and marketing of which California leads all other states. None-

FIGURE 16-20. *Generalized types of agriculture in California (after Lantis, et al.).*

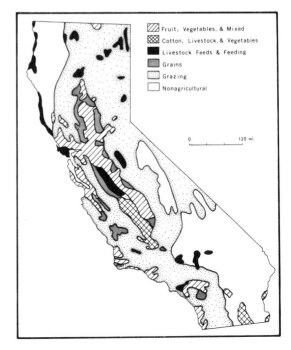

theless, each single product, if considered alone, represents only a minor portion of the state's farm income.

California leads the nation in production of grapes and wine, cantaloupes, carrots, lettuce, eggs, peaches, pears, prunes, rice, strawberries, tomatoes, turkeys, and beet sugar (*Fig. 16-21*). It stands second among the states in production of cotton, dry beans, oranges, onions, hay, barley, and sheep.

Although the rapid spread of urbanization has forced the retirement of huge tracts of the finest land from production since World War II, more land has been put to use to replace it. Thus the cropland acreage has remained nearly the same since the war. Productivity, however, has risen sharply; the attention of the world has been directed to the rapid mechanization, to the efficient, highly scientific soil treatment, and to the advanced use of fertilizer and selected seeds that have been typical of California farming.

Production costs in California run higher, but yields are correspondingly high; unit costs are fairly low. Marketing costs run higher than for many other types of agriculture. Much of the produce, particularly fruits and vegetables, must be specially packed for long-distance shipment. These shipments funnel

FIGURE 16-21. *"Dry" packing lettuce near Salinas, California, a familiar scene in California valleys. (Salinas Chamber of Commerce)*

through the big terminal markets in the eastern United States, where handling charges are high.

California's expansion in production is not due mainly to increases in acres planted, climate, exploding population, and other related factors; rather, the expansion is a part of the general farm revolution brought about by the discovery and use of better varieties of crops, of commercial fertilizers, by better control of plant and animal pests and diseases, and by the tremendous impact of irrigation.

Irrigation dates from the time of the Spanish missions, although it developed slowly until 1870. At that time, only about 60,000 acres were under irrigation. Now, some 8,000,000 acres—about a fourth of the national total—are irrigated, and the end is not in sight.

California's most important farming area lies in the Central Valley, where large land holdings of a few hundred to more than a thousand acres are operated as food factories. Capitalization is high, and the superintendents and foremen work from central administrative headquarters rather than from individual farms. The smaller operators usually concentrate upon the raising of one crop. This pattern, which is the result of such factors as distance from market, fluctuation of prices, and the uncertainty of yearly yields, has led to the formation of cooperatives designed to lower transportation costs by mass shipments to Middle Western and Eastern markets. Farmers' cooperatives also play a major role in California through their control of quality.

The northern part of the Central Valley is noted for general farming, field crops, and some dairying. Intensively cultivated truck crops are raised by efficient, large-scale methods in the Sacramento-San Joaquin Delta. The Sacramento Valley also markets sizable crops of peaches, prunes, almonds, pears, walnuts, olives, and some citrus fruits. Livestock, particularly cattle and sheep, are wintered in and around the Sacramento Valley, and summered either in nearby private rangelands or else in the mountain national forests. The pasturing of cattle on grain stubble and their feeding on a year-round diet of such crop residues as sugar beet tops are becoming increasingly important.

Its longer growing season has made the San Joaquin Valley more versatile agriculturally than the Sacramento. The largest enterprises in the San Joaquin are such field crops as grain, alfalfa, cotton, and sugar beets; fruit crops; nut crops; vegetables; dairying; and livestock feeding.

Almost every coastal valley produces a crop for which its soil and climate are especially suited. For example, the sheltered Santa Clara Valley yields prunes and apricots, the Santa Paula Valley produces lemons, the Napa Valley supplies grapes, and the Los Angeles Lowlands produce vegetables and citrus crops.

OREGON AND WASHINGTON

In the Willamette Valley, agriculture is highly diversified and the growing seasons are long. Most mid-latitude crops thrive there. Some specialty crops, truck crops, and pastures are irrigated, but most other field, fruit, and nut crops are grown without irrigation (*Fig. 16-22*). Supplemental irrigation during June, July, and August provides higher yields for most valley crops. In general, the valley produces grains, hays, forage, legume seeds, potatoes, tree fruits, and truck crops. Specialty crops include cherries, prunes, walnuts, filberts, strawberries, peppermint, and nursery products.

On the bottomlands along the coastal streams and valleys and on a few of the coastal terraces, a flourishing dairy enterprise has developed, based primarily upon mild weather and the luxuriant pasturage of fertile alluvial soils. These bottomland pastures, almost within sight of the sea—some of them below the level of high tide—are responsible for a type of farming somewhat like that of the Netherlands or Denmark. The land is in such demand for pasture that is is seldom plowed. Much of the milk produced is used for manufacturing cheese. Tillamook leads all other Oregon counties in this respect. Its famous Cheddar cheese is widely marketed in the Pacific Coast states. Tillamook dairies also

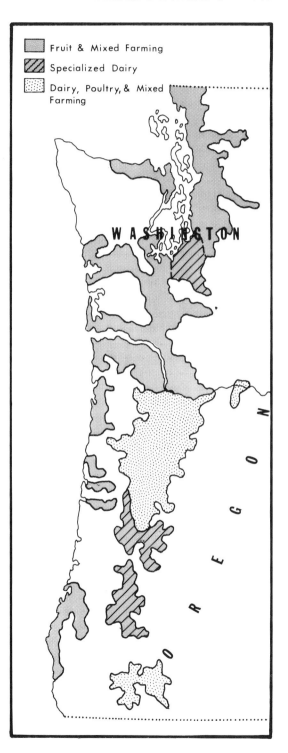

FIGURE 16-22. *Generalized types of agriculture in the Coastal Mountains and Valleys subregion of western Oregon and Washington (after Highsmith).*

supply fluid milk to Portland markets. Limited acreages are available for such specialty crops as bulbs, nursery stock, and small fruits and berries, including cranberries. The rearing of beef cattle, usually in small herds, has grown rapidly and is a year-round enterprise.

Agriculture in western Washington is a response to the proximity of large consuming markets and to climatic conditions. The mild oceanic climate provides an approximate growing season of 200 days in the farming areas. Rainfall varies greatly within short distances, but the greater part of the precipitation occurs between the months of October and May. As a result, pastures and cash crops are usually in need of moisture by the end of July.

Fertile land exists in the valleys, but it is so limited—and expensive—that the farmer is compelled to specialize in dairy and poultry enterprises, supplemented in many instances by truck crops, berries, fruits, nuts, and small grains. The average size of a farm in the area is 65 acres.

Conditions for dairying are generally very favorable. The marine climate of western Washington, with mild rainy winters and long cool summers, favors grazing and high milk production. Good pastures are found in the rainy lowlands. Many dairymen raise oats or other concentrated feed, but the region is not self-sufficient in grain; farmers import their grain from eastern Washington or farther away. Comparatively speaking, the costs for shelter and winter feeding are low. Where the cost of land is high, dairying tends to be replaced by intensive use of the land for small fruits, tree fruits, and vegetables.

Climatic and economic conditions favor poultry in western Washington. The mild winters help make possible high egg production at a time when areas in the Midwest and East produce at a much lower rate. Less favorable is the factor of feed, most of which must be imported. Many poultry farmers work in some other industry in addition to managing their farming enterprises. Poultry products find a ready market in Seattle and other Puget Sound cities.

This section ranks among the leading areas of the nation in production of strawberries and cranberries. Washington berry producers are usually first nationally in output of red raspberries, second in cultivated blackberries, third in strawberries and blueberries, and fourth in cranberries.

BRITISH COLUMBIA

Early settlers of British Columbia were of the gold-seeking and timber-cutting breed who for a long time paid little or no attention to farming. Consequently, it is only in comparatively recent years that agriculture has begun to grow in importance. Most of the land now under tillage lies in the river valleys, particularly in the Fraser Valley and on Vancouver Island. Agricultural statistics show that the most successful farms have been those engaged in mixed farming. In recent years, however, there has been a considerable increase in the number of such specialized establishments as dairy farms, tree fruit farms, poultry ranches, and seed and bulk farms. Immigrants from Holland and other areas are rapidly developing many sections of the area. Small holdings—berry and poultry farms of from three to ten acres where intensive cultivation is practiced—are popular near the larger centers. Cultivation under glass is featured in the vicinity of Victoria and Vancouver, and altogether there are over five million square feet of greenhouses. Successful dairy farms in the lower Fraser Valley vary in size from 40 to 100 acres.

ALASKA

Agricultural production in Alaska is confined to relatively small areas. The major area is the Matanuska Valley around Palmer, including a few farms around Anchorage and also a few in the adjoining Susitna Valley (*Fig. 16-23*). Other farming districts include the Kenai Peninsula, the Southeast, the Southwest and West.

In the Matanuska Valley, dairying is the most important farm enterprise, followed by potatoes. The growing season ranges from 100 to 120 days. In the Kenai Peninsula, milk, beef, swine, and poultry are produced for local consumption. On Kodiak and the Aleutian Islands, stock raising (sheep and cattle) is the leading agricultural enterprise. Wool is shipped to the conterminous United States. Some beef is shipped to Anchorage; the remainder is consumed locally.

Forest Industries

CALIFORNIA

Since the days of the Gold Rush, lumbering has been economically important in the Sierra Nevada Mountains. The first sawmills were established shortly after the discovery of gold to provide rough lumber for miners' shacks and other purposes. Lumber continued to play an important part in the development of the mines and also in the agricultural, industrial, and residential aspects of life in California.

Although the industry is gradually shifting to the north coastal area of California, the Sierra Nevada Mountains are still the second largest lumber-producing area in the state.

Fortunately, the forested mountain slopes lie fairly close to Central Valley communities so that accessible timber can be hauled down to market at a distinct profit. Only a small portion of the cut reaches the coastal cities, which are more cheaply supplied by the coastal forests of northern California and southern Oregon.

Three-fifths of the timber stands are government owned. Most of this commercial forest land is within the national forests. Timber companies, railroads, recreation areas, ranchers, farmers, and individual residents own the rest of the timberlands.

All along the Redwood Highway, from a point about 120 miles north of San Francisco to beyond Crescent City and far back into the hidden recesses of the Coast Ranges, there are scores of small sawmills, many of them 24-hour operations. Recently, however, larger and less wasteful operations have come to be the prevalent type.

The north coastal area contains more than a quarter of California's commercial forest land and produces at least 35 per cent of its salable timber. From the standpoint of growth potential, this is one of the outstanding timber areas of the world. It is known as the Douglas fir-

FIGURE 16-23. *The Matanuska Valley, Alaska's major agricultural area. (Alaska Agricultural Experimental Station)*

redwood subregion to lumbermen. Stands of fir grow at elevations of 5,000 to 6,000 feet; they are divided equally between public and private ownership.

The redwood of the Coast Ranges attains an average height greater than that of the Sierra species, sometimes reaching 350 feet. These redwoods are well suited for building materials and have been adapted to many uses, right down to their bark and sawdust. The redwood industry is among the most important in the state; the species ranks third as a source of California lumber, and accounts for nearly a fifth of the total volume produced.

OREGON AND WASHINGTON

The Cascade Range forms a barrier to coastal storms. Precipitation ranges from 40 inches in the lower foothills to as high as 130 inches in the mountains. On the eastern slope, precipitation is greatly reduced, for the air has lost a considerable portion of its moisture on the west. These physiographic and climatic conditions affect the forest growth. On the western slope, four primary species dominate —Douglas fir, West Coast hemlock, Western red cedar, and Sitka spruce—to produce some of the most luxuriant forests in the United States. Species found in lesser volume are silver fir, noble fir, and white fir. On the eastern slope, precipitation is sparse and temperatures fluctuate widely. Ponderosa pine predominates there, but Western larch, white fir, lodgepole pine, and Sierra juniper are also important. Douglas fir, West Coast hemlock, Western red cedar, Sitka spruce, and Ponderosa pine are the principal commercial trees of the Cascade Range.

In the days of cheap timber and forest products, very little attention was paid to the replenishment of the forest. The last 15 years have brought about a significant increase in the value of both timber on the stump and its manufactured products. This has encouraged Cascades forest owners to establish tree farms and adopt other long-range, scientific forestry practices (*Fig. 16-24*).

FIGURE 16-24. *In the Pacific Northwest, Douglas fir trees are harvested by clear cutting of selected patches on commercial tree farms (top). Logs are dragged to a loading area by high-lead cables and tractors. There a shovel loader stacks them on logging trucks carrying up to sixty tons of logs apiece (bottom). (Weyerhaeuser Timber Co.)*

BRITISH COLUMBIA

Douglas fir, Western hemlock, spruce, and Western red cedar are the leading commercial tree species in British Columbia. Sawmills there manufacture about 55 per cent of the lumber produced in Canada. Sixty-five per cent of Canadian exports of planks and boards and 16 per cent of Canadian exports of pulp and paper originate in this area.

ALASKA

Alaskan coastal forests offer the most immediate and important prospect for resource development in that state. The state's two national forests lie along the coast from Portland Canal to Cook Inlet. The Tongass National Forest—16,073,200 acres, containing about 78 billion board feet of commercial timber—covers most of southeastern Alaska. The Chugach National Forest—4,810,200 acres with an estimated 7 billion board feet of commercial timber—includes the coastal area surrounding Prince William Sound and the eastern half of the Kenai Peninsula. This timber is about 74 per cent hemlock and 20 per cent spruce, with small quantities of Western red cedar and Alaska cedar, all close to tidewater.

Outside capital is interested in southeastern Alaska's timber. American Viscose and Puget Sound Pulp and Paper formed the Ketchikan Pulp Company in 1954 and constructed a $52 million dissolving plant at Ward's Cove, Alaska, six miles northwest of Ketchikan. The company has a 50-year cutting contract in the Tongass National Forest.

The Ketchikan mill is the opening wedge to a great industrial development of the area's resources. Other lumber companies with capital investment in Alaska's forests are: (1) Pacific Northern Timber of Portland, Oregon; (2) Alaska Pulp of Japan; and (3) Georgia Pacific Plywood.

Fisheries

California leads the nation in both volume and value of fishery products. Los Angeles is the center of the fishing industry. Fishermen catch more than 70 kinds of seafood off the California coast. The wholesale markets of San Pedro handle most of the fresh fish trade. Tuna is the major commercial species caught, with a value of more than $75 million annually. Salmon fishing, which began on the Sacramento River in 1864, is second to tuna in value. Sardines stand second to tuna in volume.

Other commercially important fish caught off the California coast include anchovies, rockfish, sole, and white sea bass. Shellfish include abalone, crabs, oysters, shrimp, and squid.

Fishery resources are the basis for one of the major industries in the Pacific Northwest and Alaska (*Fig. 16-25*). Salmon are the most valuable of the fish caught. Pacific salmon are

FIGURE 16-25. *A salmon purse seiner working near one of the many islands off the coast of Alaska. Fishermen must work long hours during the short summer season to balance out the slack winter season. Boats range from elaborate vessels with large crews, capable of cleaning and processing the catch, to small ships such as the one in this photograph. (E. P. Haddon, U.S. Fish and Wildlife Service)*

anadromous; that is, they are hatched in fresh-water streams, descend to salt water and attain most of their growth there, and then return to the streams to spawn. Five species of salmon are native to the region—chinook, sockeye, coho, pink, and chum. All are so high in food value and so admirably suited to the process of canning that an enormous trade has developed. Halibut, herring, and crab also bring in a considerable revenue each year. Other commercial catches include tuna, cod, sole, clams, oysters, and whales. This area of the Pacific is one of the world's great fishing grounds.

Mining

CALIFORNIA

In the state of California, minerals are a multibillion dollar industry. The discovery of gold at Sutter's Mill in 1848 ignited excitement that amounted to a national furor. Within a few months would-be miners were swarming through every creek and gulch from the Co-sumnes River to the Mokelumne River, from the edge of the Central Valley to the crest of the Sierra Nevada.

Mining camps sprang up rapidly in the placer and surface mining areas—lawless, hard-living boom towns such as Drytown, Fiddletown, Plymouth, Volcano, Sutter Creek, Jackson, Grizzly Flats, Chili Bar, Fairplay, Angels Camp, and Cherokee Flat (*Fig. 16-26*). Deep mines came later; the Argonaut, Kennedy, Oneida, Keystone, and Lone Star were a few. From these mines and others in the mother lode came the gold that was to finance the growth of America for the next century. Then, almost as suddenly as it had begun, the Age of Gold ended.

Most of the gold that comes from California today is taken from river beds by dredges—large floating power shovels that scoop up gravel from the river bottom, run it through the concentrating machines mounted upon the floating barge, and shoot the unwanted gravel out the rear to be stacked in large piles along the shore.

FIGURE 16-26. *Kennedy tailing wheels in the Sierra Nevada Mountains. Such relics of gold mining days are found throughout the Sierras along California's Gold Highway 49. (Mary Hill)*

In recent years, petroleum and natural gas have accounted for more than 80 per cent of the total value of mineral production. Despite its huge output, California's liquid fuels industry cannot meet the demands of the consumers within the state. Crude petroleum and gasoline, and other refinery products must be imported each year in constantly increasing quantities by ocean tanker and pipeline. Natural gas is imported by pipeline from as far away as Canada. This demand stems from a combination of ever-rising population, lack of solid fuels, and the requirements of more than 10 million motor vehicles registered in the state.

In addition to the mineral fuels, output is high in the so-called industrial groups of the nonmetals, such as cement, clay, gypsum, lime, sand and gravel, miscellaneous stone, and talc. In the saline group, borates, iodine, salt, sodium carbonate, and sodium sulfate are important. Metals mined include tungsten, iron ore, chromite, manganese, and quicksilver.

PACIFIC NORTHWEST AND ALASKA

The mineral deposits in this section are insignficant when measured against those of the intermontane states or interior British Columbia. Oregon nickel is being mined and smelted at a 28.5 million-dollar plant at Riddle, south of Roseburg, by the Hannah interests, who are working with the government under a defense subsidy. This plant supplies 5 per cent of the nation's requirements. Near Portland, Oregon, there are large deposits of laterite containing alumina, iron, silica, titanium, and other minerals. Some of the deposits are reported under lease to the Aluminum Company of America. There are 25 or 30 limestone mines and a doubling of limestone output is expected because the area produces less than half the amount it now needs for pulp and paper operations, for sugar refining, and for the cement industry. Large bodies of high-grade bituminous coal are located on Vancouver Island at tidewater. Sizeable deposits of iron ore have been known for many years, but it was not until very recently that these were opened to any extent. The major operation is on the east coast of Vancouver Island; this ore is shipped to Japanese furnaces.

Deposits of gold and silver are known to exist in almost every region of Alaska. Petroleum and natural gas are being produced in a number of areas. Cook Inlet waters near Anchorage contain at least four major oil fields, and there are real prospects that several others exist there. Many large, permanent, all-weather drilling platforms have been, or are being, positioned in the waters of the inlet. The Panhandle is known to have such important minerals as iron, lead, zinc, copper, nickel, and tungsten. Mineral deposits of the Gulf of Alaska coast include copper, coal, platinum, tin, and mercury.

Water

CALIFORNIA

Water is California's most precious asset, and also her most precious need. Without an ample supply of this vital resource, her fertile fields would lie fallow, her cities and towns would wither, and her industry and commerce would be stunted.

California's chief rivers are the Klamath and its principal tributaries—the Shasta, Trinity, and Salmon—which flow northwest; the Sacramento and San Joaquin, with their many tributaries, which drain the Central Valley and discharge into San Francisco Bay; and the Colorado, which forms the California-Arizona boundary. Within the state's borders are also a number of smaller rivers, including the Smith, Mad, Eel, Russian, Pajaro, Salinas, Santa Maria, Santa Ynez, and Santa Clara. These and many others empty directly into the Pacific Ocean.

California's leading water problem is not a deficiency of water; rather, it is the availability of the proper amount of water at the time and place it is needed. Most of the state is subject either to flooding or drought, some areas to both.

The problem is three-sided: seasonal, geographical, and ecological. The greatest runoff occurs in the winter and early spring, the lowest during the summer growing season. Also there is a variation from year to year. One year the state may be drenched; the next, parched. Approximately 72 per cent of its water resources are found in the northern third of the state, whereas 75 per cent of the demand is in the remaining two-thirds. While the north coast is the only area having a general surplus of water, the Central Valley, with its skyrocketing population and its expanding agriculture and industry, accounts for more than half the total water usage in the state.

Among the units initially proposed by the state to meet its water needs were Shasta Dam (on the Sacramento River a few miles north of Redding), a series of canals to convey the stored water released from the delta area southward to the San Joaquin Valley, and a power transmission system to carry the hydroelectricity generated by a powerhouse at the dam. With federal help from the Bureau of Reclamation, this led to the Central Valley Project, which has now developed into the most extensive artificial water transport systems in the world (*Fig. 16-27*).

Latest feature of the CVP is a unique federal-state joint-use project, the San Luis unit. This complex of dams, reservoirs, pumping plants, and canals will distribute irrigation water to reclamation project farms and also will function as a vital link in the 500-mile-long conveyance system to transport state water to extreme southern California.

Meanwhile, as a feature of its Feather River Project, the state completed the highest dam in the United States, 765-foot Oroville Dam on the Feather River. Aqueducts, including the joint-use San Luis Canal, will carry the water regulated by Oroville from the San Francisco Bay Area as far south as Los Angeles and San Diego to help supply municipal and industrial water for those cities.

The burgeoning energy requirements of California are being met with hydroelectric power transmitted from the Northwest by means of the Pacific Northwest-Southwest Intertie, the most important achievement in

FIGURE 16-27. *Friant Dam and the Friant-Kern Canal. This canal is the main irrigation artery for the rich San Joaquin Valley agricultural empire. It is part of the Central Valley Project. (Bureau of Reclamation)*

the history of electric power development in the United States. Consisting of four major lines from the Columbia River to southwest terminals, and four shorter interconnections, this system is being built jointly by federal and nonfederal public power agencies and private utilities.

Hoover, Parker, and Davis Dams on the Colorado River supply California with more than 90 per cent of its generated power. Privately owned power plants include the Pacific Gas and Electric Company's steam-electric plant at Moss Landing, the Contra Costa County steam-electric plant at Antioch, the Big Creek hydroelectric plant in the Sierras, and the Etiwanda steam plant near Fontana.

OREGON AND WASHINGTON

This area has historically met its power requirements almost entirely by hydroelectric means. Its mountainous nature, along with its heavy precipitation, gives the area a large hydroelectric potential. The Skagit, Snoqualmie, White, Green, Lewis, Chelan, Clackamas, Umpqua, and Rogue Rivers in the northern and central Cascades are power suppliers. These streams have their highest flow in winter and early spring and complement the summer maximum flow of the Columbia River. Power plants built on the lesser rivers have the effect of stabilizing seasonal power on the Columbia. Already six of the world's greatest power developments—Grand Coulee, Chief Joseph, McNary, The Dalles, Bonneville, and John Day—have been completed on the Columbia (*Fig. 16-28*).

BRITISH COLUMBIA

This area has developed only about one-fifth of its water power resources. Despite this, it ranks third among Canadian provinces in hydroelectric development, with about 1.7 horsepower per capita, compared with an average of 1.0 horsepower for all of Canada. The major portion of the power is used to supply the demands of the forestry, chemical, metallurgical, and other industries.

One of the outstanding examples of power development for a special industry is the huge Kitimat Project of the Aluminum Company of Canada. The Kitimat Project includes a huge mountain-canyon dam that reverses the eastward flow of the Nechako River, backs the water into a 150-mile-long reservoir, and sends it into a 10-mile tunnel drilled through the Coast Mountains. The water drops more than 2,500 feet from the tunnel to a power plant at Kemano. The power plant, built inside the mountain, generates power for the Kitimat smelters 50 miles away (*Fig. 16-29*).

ALASKA

Hydroelectric power is one of the three bulwarks of Alaska's industrial future. Like the other two—forestry and mining—its potential is not fully measured. Low-cost hydroelectric power is important to serve a growing population, but it is even more important as a base for industry. The most conspicuous opportunity in this line is the Taiya Project, a proposal by the Aluminum Company of America for development of 800,000 kilowatts of power and a huge new aluminum plant near Skagway. The Eklutna Project, near Anchorage, is the largest hydroelectric development to date and furnishes much of Alaska's power.

FIGURE 16-28. *The Dalles Dam in Oregon is one of several multipurpose dams across the mighty Columbia River. (Oregon State Highway Commission)*

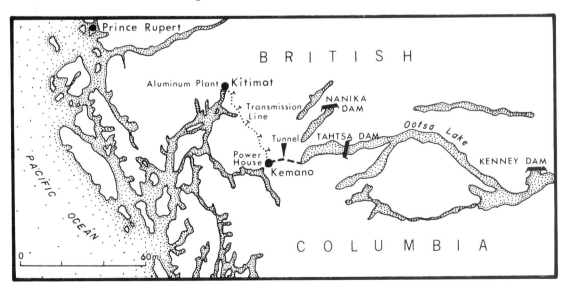

FIGURE 16-29. *The Kitimat Project in British Columbia.*

Manufacturing and Commerce

The Pacific Slope Region, stretching from San Diego to the Aleutians, has a wide variety of raw material resources for processing—forest products, petroleum, grain, fish, fruit, and other such resources. Proximity to the Pacific Basin, excellent transportation facilities, good harbors, skilled labor, and a large consumer market are but a few of many reasons why industries are attracted to the region.

California has experienced an industrial growth unequaled by any other part of the United States. The boom has included all major types of American industry except textiles. Transportation equipment, steel, chemicals, food products, household furnishings, clothing, and construction, to name only a few, have all grown. From La Jolla north to San Francisco Bay, a new kind of industrial landscape has emerged—pleasant, clean, soothing and often luxurious. In this process a new industrial way of life has been created. There are three primary reasons for this: (1) The state's industrial growth has come within the last generation. There is no huge capital investment in old plants that must be worked off before new ones are to be built. (2) The weather permits an architect almost unlimited use of glass and greenery. His roof design need not be inhibited by planning for possible snow load. Heat loss in winter is such a minor consideration that big window walls can be installed to give that "outside feeling" to a man operating a steel lathe. (3) The new look has been stimulated by the emergence of industries—primarily electronics—where raw materials, processes, and end products lend themselves to it.

Five major manufacturing districts may be identified in the Pacific Slope Region: southern California, the San Francisco Bay Area, Portland, Seattle-Vancouver, and Prince Rupert-Kitimat.

SOUTHERN CALIFORNIA

Since this area has neither coal nor accessible iron ore deposits, its industrial develop-ment remained negligible until sources of power were developed during the early years of this century. These sources of power included natural gas, the generation of hydroelectricity, and, most important af all, the local petroleum industry.

The period of modern development may be said to have begun with the establishment of Los Angeles as the world's motion picture center during the early 1900's; the industry was attracted there by the mild climate and by the wide range of natural settings easily available. With the development of the petroleum industry in the 1920's, the industrial boom got under way.

The southern California consumers' market today numbers approximately 12 million persons. Elsewhere in the western United States, an additional market of 20 million can be reached. This massive domestic market, coupled with a growing volume of international trade, has made a southern California branch or regional facility a necessity for many Eastern and Midwestern firms. Furthermore, it has led to the establishment and development of numerous industries of national stature headquartered in southern California. Many of these have established branch facilities in other parts of the country.

The area is recognized as the nation's leading aerospace center. In terms of "value added by manufacture" (the value of products shipped less the cost of materials, supplies, fuel, electricity, and contract work), the aerospace industries of aircraft, electronics, missiles, and scientific instruments contribute a little more than a third of southern California's total manufacturing output.

Other major manufacturing groups include processed foods, nonelectrical machinery, fabricated metals, chemicals, printing and pub-lishing, and apparel and fabricated textiles (*Fig. 16-30*). Other products of major importance that are assembled or manufactured locally include: automobiles; tires and other rubber and plastic products; heating and plumbing equipment; pumps and compressors; stone, clay, and glass products; petroleum products; and furniture and fixtures.

FIGURE 16-30. *The steel plant of Kaiser Steel Corporation at Fontana, California. This 1,800-acre plant some 45 miles east of Los Angeles supplies a large share of the market for steel in the West and Southwest. (Kaiser Steel Corp.)*

There are over 300,000 individual business enterprises of all types located in the state of California; of this number, 62 per cent, or nearly 200,000 ,are located in southern California. In addition to the mild climate and abundant natural resources, the attraction of southern California for industrial investment is nourished by a number of factors. Chief of these are: (1) a continuing rapid population growth, (2) a highly skilled labor force in space-age manufacturing, (3) excellent educational systems and research capabilities that emphasize research and development, and (4) the managerial, technical, scientific and professional skills force that modern industry demands.

SAN FRANCISCO BAY AREA

San Francisco Bay itself is the linking factor of this key area, the second largest metropolitan center of California. Occupying a strategic position on the coast, and being the best natural harbor, the bay forms the chief trans-portation route for the agricultural wealth of the Central Valley. From the bay these goods are distributed to other parts of the state, to the nation, and throughout the world (*Fig. 16-31*).

Despite industrial and residential dispersion, San Francisco is still the heart of the Bay Area. The city forms the center of a hybrid economic pattern, halfway between the nucleated urban sprawls of the East and the vast low-density sprawl of Los Angeles. It is supplemented by strings of suburban communities, some north of the bay, some down the southern peninsula, each of which preserves its social, if not its geographic, identity.

The city is not only the undisputed financial and insurance capital of the West, but ranks second in the nation in these fields after New York City. Seven of the nation's 100 largest commercial banks have their home offices here; and the 12th Federal Reserve District, with headquarters in the Federal Reserve Bank of San Francisco, is third in the nation

FIGURE 16-31. *San Francisco and her two great bridges are shown in this aerial photograph. Part of the Bay Bridge to Oakland is in the foreground; the Golden Gate Bridge is at the upper right. The broad Pacific Ocean lies beyond the Golden Gate. Some of the 45 deep-water piers that serve San Francisco can also be seen. (San Francisco Chamber of Commerce)*

in volume of business as measured by bank debits. Nearly three-quarters of the fire, marine, and casualty insurance companies authorized to transact business in California have their headquarters in the city.

Many of the large manufacturing firms that have main offices or distribution and warehouse facilities in San Francisco produce part or all of their products in plants located either within the metropolitan area or within the state. Industry forms an integral part of the city's economy. Investment in new companies and expansion of existing facilities amounted to over $100 million in the past five years. Tidelands in the southern part of the city provide industry with hundreds of acres contiguous to excellent freeways and railroads. Food processing ranks first in the city's industrial economy, producing such items as canned fruit, vegetables, seafood, beer, soft drinks, coffee, and dairy products. Fabricated metals

are second: tin containers, rolled steel products, and builders' hardware. Some 334 firms engage in the making of apparel and allied products. Paper and paper products, chemicals, and transportation equipment also rank high in terms of product value and numbers of workers employed.

San Francisco's future as a central city might be compared to that of New York City's Manhattan. Having grown at the same period and in the same way as did the large Eastern cities, San Francisco is more like them than such post-1900 boom towns as Seattle, Portland, Los Angeles, and San Diego.

Two-thirds of all the people in the San Francisco Bay Area live in cities within a 50-mile radius of San Francisco, half of them in 12 contiguous central cities.

The Peninsula. San Francisco and the Peninsula form an uninterrupted 50-mile urban strip. Much of this growth has occurred since World

War II, with four out of every ten persons newly settled in the region since 1940 (*Fig. 16-32*). Concern for maintenance of their residential character prompted city planners of the Peninsula to seek industries that do not produce noise, offensive odors, and smoke. Electronics concerns were encouraged, and there are dozens of plants devoted to electronics in the area between San Bruno and Palo Alto.

On land belonging to Stanford University in Palo Alto, a light industry tract has been opened. This industrial park already contains electronics manufacturers, research laboratories, a film processing laboratory, textbook publishers, and others attracted by the climate, the favorable location, and the research opportunities offered by the nearby university.

The East Bay. A study of the East Bay industrial expansion reveals two advantageous characteristics: a tendency toward diversification rather than toward a single industry, and a preponderance of small industries employing 100 men or less, partially balanced by a number of big industries.

Today the East Bay extends in a narrow, 25-mile-long strip of solid urbanization from San Pablo to Hayward, and the fringes of its central city, Oakland, now merge with what were once outlying towns. The war years were undoubtedly chiefly responsible for rapid expansion in the East Bay, for it was then that military installations began to provide major employment opportunities.

Petroleum makes up three-fifths of all the cargo passing through the Golden Gate, feeding four huge refineries in the area. The chemical industry, closely allied to petroleum products and concentrated in the same general area, also has mushroomed (*Fig. 16-33*).

PORTLAND

Lumber and lumber products, food processing, metalworking, textiles, chemicals, and electronics are the dominant industries in metropolitan Portland. Although Oregon has attracted many national concerns since World War II, most of the state's new industries were

FIGURE 16-32. *Aerial view of an area near San Jose, California. Over vast stretches of the Santa Clara Valley, a major transformation from agricultural to intensive residential land use has taken place. (California Division of Highways)*

FIGURE 16-33. *The Standard Oil Company refinery in Richmond, California. Crossing San Francisco Bay here is the Richmond-San Rafael Bridge. Richmond is one of California's most important refining centers. (Standard Oil Co. of California)*

organized and developed by local people. A significant factor concerning these new industrial plants is that a large proportion of them are turning out products not formerly made in the state or in the Pacific Northwest—aluminum, shingles, irrigation systems, electronic devices, and many other household and industrial products.

Lumber industries. One-fifth of the lumber produced in the United States comes from Oregon, where more than eight billion board feet are cut annually. Although much of the lumber is shipped out of the area in a rough or semifinished state, the manufacture of highly finished wood products, such as doors, roof trusses, plywood, and furniture, is taking place (*Fig. 16-34*).

The Portland area is the center of Crown Zellerbach's operations, and 14 tree farms in the area furnish an estimated nine billion board feet of timber to other companies' paper mills at Camas, West Linn, St. Helens, and Lebanon.

FIGURE 16-34. *Oregon's greatest industry is lumbering. Six to eight billion board feet of timber are produced annually. Logs are usually towed down the rivers, as shown here at the mouth of the Umpqua River at Reedsport. (Oregon State Highway Commission)*

Food processing. Food processing employs about one-sixth of the industrial workers. Fruits and vegetables are frozen and canned in freezing and canning plants in the Willamette Valley. Many canning and freezing plants at Astoria process salmon, halibut, sardines, tuna, oysters, and shrimp. Cheddar cheese made in Tillamook County is marketed in many Far West cities.

Metalworking. Including the production of primary metals, metalworking has become the leading employer of the Portland metropolitan area. The variety of products includes: merchant's tools, heating apparatus, automotive trucks and trailers, factory lift trucks, foundry products, and specialized machinery for lumber, food, and chemical plants.

Electronics. Most of the electronics plants are centered around the larger industrial areas. Typical of these new plants is that of the Tektronix Company in Beaverton, Oregon, which manufactures oscilloscopes and other scientific equipment.

SEATTLE-VANCOUVER

Puget Sound's manufacturing base rests heavily upon four industry groups—transportation equipment, lumber, food, and minerals.

Transportation equipment. Aircraft, shipbuilding, and railroad equipment lead in the transportation field. The Boeing aerospace industry dwarfs all others in the Pacific Northwest. A highly competent staff of scientists and engineers implements the Boeing Company's immense and imaginative research and development program, a prime factor in the company's pre-eminent position in the aerospace industry.

With Boeing's Renton facilities occupied by the 707 commercial jets and the 727 and 737 programs, and with its Everett facilities (about 30 miles north of Seattle) scheduled to handle construction of the 747 jumbo jet, there exists now a modern industrial megalopolis that sprawls from just north of Tacoma to just south of Everett.

Shipbuilding centers include Seattle, Bremerton, Tacoma, Bellingham, and Vancouver. With its many deep-water harbors, the area offers alternative location possibilities for the manufacturer (*Fig. 16-35*). The naval shipyard at Bremerton is the largest on the Pacific Coast.

Lumber. More than a third of the value of all manufactured products comes from wood pulp and paper, sawed lumber, veneer, plywood, and various products manufactured from wood. With one of the world's best climates for growing timber and with natural waterways to permit economical transportation of bulky logs, the Puget Sound area has long been an important manufacturer of lumber and wood products.

Greater Vancouver's industrial activity centers on pulp and paper plants, although metalworking, chemicals, and aluminum fabricating industries are becoming increasingly important.

Food. Food processing industries include canning and freezing of fruits, berries, vegetables, and seafood; flour milling; meat packing; grain mill products; and prepared mixes and other packaged products.

Mineral processing. Mineral processing industries are an important sector of the economy. Copper is smelted at Tacoma. Steel is made from imported ores at Seattle. Tacoma, Vancouver, and Longview have either aluminum reduction plants or aluminum rolling mills. Industrial chemicals of mineral origin, such as uranium compounds, also are processed. Crude petroleum shipped from California and Alaska is refined at Ferndale and Anacortes.

PRINCE RUPERT-KITIMAT

Prince Rupert, 500 miles northwest of Vancouver near the mouth of the Skeena River, is a grain shipping and fishing port with large drydocks, fish processing plants, and a large cellulose factory operated by the Celanese Corporation. An ice-free port, it is a vital link in the trade between Alaska and the conterminous United States.

FIGURE 16-35. *The Lake Washington Floating Bridge is the eastern gateway to Seattle, the industrial and commercial center of Washington and a major port. (Seattle Chamber of Commerce)*

Kitimat is the site of a large aluminum refining plant operated by the Aluminum Company of Canada.

Recreation and Tourism

The Pacific Slope Region may have a wider array of scenic wonders and tourist attractions than any other area in Anglo-America. Mild climates, bold, rugged mountain peaks, beautiful mountain lakes, innumerable hiking trails, many campsites, freshwater streams stocked with sport fish, and seashore vistas all combine to make this region a wonderland for the vacationer.

California has surpassed all other states as a tourist attraction. The historic gold mining region, the matchless scenery of the Sierra

Nevada, and a climate favorable to both summer and winter sports lure thousands of visitors to the state, many of whom remain as permanent citizens. Yosemite National Park, Sequoia National Park, Kings Canyon National Park, and Lake Tahoe are but a few of the many outstanding recreational areas in California (*Fig. 16-36*).

In contrast to these natural parks and lakes, many of southern California's famous attractions are man-made, ranging from the Rose Bowl Parade to Disneyland and Knott's Berry Farm.

San Francisco, one of the world's most beautiful and civilized cities, counts tourism as its major industry. The Bay Area also offers superb recreational facilities to those interested in hunting, fishing, camping, or simply the enjoyment of scenery. Development of these recreational facilities has been greatest in the coastal redwood belt and along the lower reaches of the Russian River, largely because these regions are accessible from the densely populated San Francisco Bay Area and from the Sacramento area.

The Pacific Northwest has infinitely varied scenery on a majestic scale. Lush meadowlands lead to snowy mountaintops rising from green foothills, park-like valleys, and deep canyons. The coastal scenery is incomparably fine (*Fig. 16-37*). The insular system of the Puget Sound extends for its entire length. The hunter, camper, boater, fisherman, or ski enthusiast can find much to enjoy. There are seashores and inland waters. There are mountain peaks to scale and glaciers to traverse. There are hundreds of miles of trails through alpine forests and meadows. One can ski on snowfields or on the waters of the lakes, or drive to vantage points to view lovely vistas.

Outlook

By any measure, the broad shift of Anglo-America is westward. The land, water, min-

FIGURE 16-36. *Yosemite Valley, California. This U-shaped glacial valley, famed for its waterfalls and big trees, attracts visitors from all over the world. (National Park Service)*

FIGURE 16-37. *Seastacks and rocks capped by surf dominate this coastal section in northern Oregon. (Oregon State Highway Commission)*

erals, and mild climates are the magnets which continue to lure people to the Pacific Coast. These, combined with man's ingenuity, provide countless new opportunities and a graceful way of life that is difficult to duplicate in any other region of Anglo-America.

California, indeed, has become the promised land for millions of Americans. But, in many ways, the golden promise of California lies in the future. Although faced with many problems in the conservation, development, and wise use of her resources, California's citizens bring an indispensable resource of their own to the task ahead: their determination to succeed. The state is extraordinarily endowed in resources both above and below the land and sea, in natural beauty, and in the imagination of her people.

The Pacific Northwest is an area rich in land, water, timber, fish, and wildlife, as well as being tremendously endowed with scenic beauty, historical significance, and great recreational opportunities. Living in a great timberland originally teeming with valuable fur-bearing animals, the people of the Pacific Northwest have become progressive and diligent guardians of their wealth, working to insure the future of their area. Already, however, technology and the fruits of industrialization are beginning to be felt in a steady urbanization that is changing a tranquil existence into a hurried, crowded, polluted megalopolis. It is conceivable that by the year 2000 the Puget-Willamette Lowland might be one almost-solid urban core.

Selected References

ALLEN, EDWARD W., "Fishery Geography of the North Pacific Ocean," *The Geographical Review,* Vol. 43, October, 1953, pp. 558–563.

ASCHMANN, HOMER, "The Evolution of a Wild Landscape and its Persistence in Southern California," *Annals of the Association of American Geographers,* Vol. 49, Supplement, September, 1959, pp. 34–56.

BYRNE, JOHN V., "An Erosional Classification for the Northern Oregon Coast," *Annals of the Association of American Geographers,* Vol. 54, September, 1964, pp. 329–335.

CARTER, GEORGE F., "Man, Time, and Change in the Far Southwest," *Annals of the Association of American Geographers,* Vol. 49, Supplement, September, 1959, pp. 8–30.

FIELDING, GORDON J., "The Los Angeles Milkshed: A Study of the Political Factor in Agriculture," *The Geographical Review,* Vol. 44, January, 1967, pp. 1–12.

FREEMAN, OTIS W., and MARTIN, HOWARD H. (eds.), *The Pacific Northwest, an Over-all Appreciation,* New York: John Wiley & Sons, Inc., 1954.

GREGOR, HOWARD F., "Regional Hierarchies in California Agricultural Production: 1939-1954," *Annals of the Association of American Geographers,* Vol. 53, March, 1963, pp. 27–37.

————, "Spatial Disharmonies in California Population Growth," *The Geographical Review,* Vol. 63, January, 1963, pp. 100–122.

————, "The Changing Plantation," *Annals of the Association of American Geographers,* Vol. 55, June, 1965, pp. 221–238.

GRIFFIN, PAUL F., and CHATHAM, RONALD L., "Population: A Challenge to California's Changing Citrus Industry," *Economic Geography,* Vol. 34, July, 1958, pp. 272–276.

————, "Urban Impact on Agriculture in Santa Clara County, California," *Annals of the Association of American Geographers,* Vol. 48, September, 1958, pp. 195–208.

GRIFFIN, PAUL F., and YOUNG, ROBERT N., *California, the New Empire State: A Regional Geography,* Palo Alto, Calif.: Fearon Publishers, Inc., 1957.

HIGHSMITH, RICHARD M. (ed.), *Atlas of the Pacific Northwest,* 3rd ed., Corvallis, Ore.: Oregon State University, 1962.

LANTIS, DAVID, STEINER, RODNEY, and KARINEN, ARTHUR, *California: Land of Contrast,* Belmont, Calif.: Wadsworth Publishing Co., 1963.

McGOVERN, P. D., "Industrial Development in the Vancouver Area," *Economic Geography,* Vol. 37, July, 1961, pp. 189–206.

MARTS, M. E., and SEWELL, W. R. D., "The Conflict Between Fish and Power Resources in the Pacific Northwest," *Annals of the Association of American Geographers,* Vol. 50, March, 1960, pp. 42–50.

MATHEWS, W. H., "Two Self-dumping Ice-dammed Lakes in British Columbia," *The Geographical Review,* Vol. 45, January, 1965, pp. 46–52.

NELSON, HOWARD J., "The Spread of an Artificial Landscape over Southern California," *Annals of the Association of American Geographers,* Vol. 49, Supplement, September, 1959, pp. 80–99.

POMEROY, EARL, *The Pacific Slope,* New York: Alfred A. Knopf, 1965.

PRICE, EDWARD T., "The Future of California's Southland," *Annals of the Association of American Geographers,* Vol. 49, Supplement, September, 1959, pp. 101–116.

RAUP, H. F., "Transformation of Southern California to a Cultivated Land," *Annals of the Association of American Geographers,* Vol. 49, Supplement, September, 1959, pp. 58–78.

STEINER, RODNEY, "Reserved Lands and the Supply of Space for the Southern California Metropolis," *The Geographical Review,* Vol. 46, July, 1966, pp. 344–362.

THOMAS, WILLIAM L., JR., "Man, Time, and Space in Southern California," *Annals of the Association of American Geographers,* Vol. 49, Supplement, September, 1959, pp. 1–7.

THOMPSON, KENNETH, "Riparian Forests of the Sacramento Valley, California," *Annals of the Association of American Geographers,* Vol. 51, September, 1961, pp. 294–315.

WOOD, WALTER A., "The Icefield Ranges Research Project," *The Geographical Review,* Vol. 53, April, 1963, pp. 163–184.

17 *Canadian Shield, Arctic Lowlands, and Arctic Islands Region*

The Canadian Shield, Arctic Lowlands, and Arctic Islands Region comprises the remotest section of Anglo-America. These are lands of extreme climates and sparse population. Great distances separate them from the more densely settled regions of Anglo-America, but the air age has brought them into world prominence because of their strategic position in the North Polar area. Joint United States-Canadian defense operations have established radar networks and bases in the Far North. Other than military and mining activities, however, a subsistence economy largely prevails (*Figs. 17-1* and *17-2*).

Surface Features

CANADIAN SHIELD

The Canadian Shield, embracing about one-half of the total area of Canada, is a roughly horseshoe-shaped terrain of some 1,850,000 square miles, having Hudson Bay as its approximate center. The Shield continues into the United States west and south of Lake Superior. Far back in geological time the Shield contained many ranges of high mountains, but these have been mainly worn down to a surface of moderate relief consisting of hills, ridges, and valleys containing innumerable lakes and streams (*see Fig. 1-6*). Most of the surface is from 600 to 1,200 feet above sea level, but higher uplands form such well-known features as the Laurentian Mountains north of Montreal and the Haliburton Highlands in southeastern Ontario. The Shield is a complex assemblage of Precambrian rocks that, as a whole, represent at least five-sixths of the long duration of geological time. Most of the rocks have been subjected to more than one and, in some cases, several periods of orogeny, resulting in intricate structures, intense metamorphism, widespread igneous intrusions, and alteration of much ancient sedimentary rock to granite and related material.

In detail, the topography is hummocky, consisting of ridges and hills separated by depressions commonly occupied by lakes or muskegs. The hundreds of lakes are of many sizes and shapes with very irregular shorelines and nu-

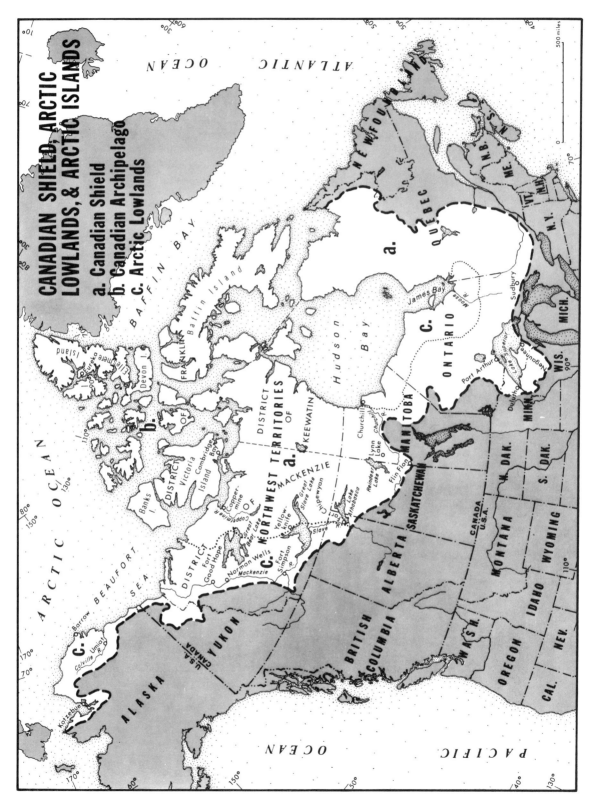

CANADIAN SHIELD, ARCTIC LOWLANDS, & ARCTIC ISLANDS

a. Canadian Shield
b. Canadian Archipelago
c. Arctic Lowlands

FIGURE 17-1.

FIGURE 17-2. *The Canadian Shield, Arctic Lowlands, and Arctic Islands Region, physical relief.*

merous islands. Over wide areas the land only here and there rises as much as 100 feet above the level of the immediately adjacent lakes. In other places differences in local relief amount to more than 1,000 feet. The lakes owe their origin to the work of the continental ice sheet that spread during the Pleistocene period.

The low relief was produced by continuous erosion in late Precambrian time, action that eventually leveled the mountain belts that had been produced earlier by folding.

The last great event in the geological history of the area was the spread of a continental ice sheet mass in Pleistocene times. This had its focal point west of Hudson Bay, from which center it advanced in all directions. Erratics and morainal material left by the ice are scattered over the entire area.

CANADIAN ARCHIPELAGO

The Arctic islands comprise approximately 549,000 square miles of land. From east to west the archipelago extends from the southern tip of Baffin Island to the northwest corner of Banks Island—a distance of about 1,860 miles. In a north-south direction it extends from approximately 61° N. latitude in Baffin Island to Cape Columbia on the north coast of Ellesmere Island in latitude 83° 39'—a distance of 1,550 miles (*Fig. 17-3*).

One of the principal topographic features of the Canadian Archipelago is the mountain range that extends in a north-south direction from Labrador across Baffin, Devon, Ellesmere, and Axel Heiberg Islands. This range, which in some sections reaches elevations of 8,000 or

FIGURE 17-3. *The settlement at Grise Fiord, on the southern coast of Ellesmere Island, a predominantly mountainous island. (Northern Affairs photograph)*

even 10,000 feet, strongly affects the climate of the rest of the archipelago, because it acts as a mechanical barrier for the free flow of air from one side to the other. This is strikingly illustrated by the annual mean temperature, which at Bache Peninsula on the east coast of Ellesmere Island, in latitude 79° N., is 4° F.; whereas at Eureka, on the west side, in latitude 80° N., it is −4° F. At Bache Peninsula the total annual precipitation is 5.19 inches, but at Eureka it is only 1.74 inches.

Two major gaps or breaks occur in this mountain range; the first in Hudson Strait, which separates Ungava-Labrador from Baffin Island; the second in Lancaster Sound, which separates Baffin Island from Devon. Lancaster Sound and its westward projection through Barrow Strait, Viscount Melville Sound, and M'Clure Strait—just south of the 75th parallel—are other major topographical features that divide the archipelago into well-marked northern and southern parts. The southern part is divided by Boothia Peninsula into an eastern and western section. The principal topographical feature of the eastern section is Baffin Island; Banks and Victoria Islands dominate the western section. In the northern half of the archipelago, Ellesmere and Devon form a natural topographic northern extension of the eastern Arctic; to the west the islands comprising the Sverdrup and the Parry groups form a more or less natural topographic unit (*Fig. 17-4*).

ARCTIC LOWLANDS

Arctic Coastal Plain. The Arctic Coastal Plain is a smooth plain rising imperceptibly from the Arctic Ocean to a maximum altitude of 600 feet at its southern margin. The coastline makes little break in the profile of the coastal plain and shelf, and the shore is generally only 1 to 10 feet above the ocean; the highest coastal cliffs are only 50 feet high. The plain is poorly drained and consequently is marshy in summer. It is crossed by rivers that rise in the highlands to the south. Rivers west of the Colville River meander sluggishly in valleys incised 50 to 300 feet; those rivers east of the Colville cross the plain in braided channels and are building deltas into the Arctic Ocean.

The entire land area is underlain by permafrost at least 1,000 feet thick. The permafrost

FIGURE 17-4. *The Arctic Archipelago in summer. Note the floes of ice between stretches of open water. Only partial melting occurs, even during the warmest period. (Canadian Dept. of National Defense)*

table (base of zone of summer thaw) is one-half to four feet below the surface. A network of ice-wedge polygons covers the coastal plain.

Mackenzie Lowland. This lowland includes the belt between the Cordilleran area on the west and the Canadian Shield on the east. It begins on the Slave River, embraces the basin at the west end of Great Slave Lake, and continues down to the Arctic Coast. On the Slave River its elevation is about 700 feet, and from there northward the surface slopes gradually to the Arctic Ocean. North of the Nahanni River, the Mackenzie Lowland is divided into parts by the long, narrow ridge of the Franklin Mountains—a western portion varying in width from 20 to 80 miles through which the Mackenzie flows, and an eastern portion occupying all but the eastern part of the drainage basin of Great Bear Lake (*Fig. 17-5*). The highest summit is Mt. Clark in the Franklin Range, with an elevation of between 3,000 and 4,000 feet.

FIGURE 17-5. *Wrigley, a settlement on the Mackenzie River in the Northwest Territories of Canada, is located in a typical plains area, with forest vegetation. (National Film Board of Canada)*

Hudson Bay-James Bay Lowlands. This lowland is found west and south of Hudson Bay. The section between the Moose River of Ontario and the Churchill River of Manitoba is underlain by sedimentary rocks, and is, therefore, not part of the Canadian Shield. North of Churchill River the Precambrian rocks are nearly all buried under glacial or marine deposits. Both sections are poorly drained. Streams wander slowly across this surface, after having dropped through many rapids across the Shield.

Climate

This region, as might be expected, lies predominantly in the realms of the polar continental and subarctic climates. That portion near the Great Lakes is in the humid continental short summer realm (*see Fig. 1-16*).

The temperatures in the Mackenzie District are more moderate than its latitude would suggest. Charts of summer temperatures show the 55° isotherm, which passes just a few miles north of Port Arthur, Ontario, as swinging northward to include the Mackenzie Valley as far as Fort Good Hope and the Arctic Circle. The low-lying parts of the area forming the Mackenzie Valley proper are favored with an exceptionally agreeable climate, doubtless influenced by the presence of large bodies of water, the forest covering the land areas, and the general low altitude. A three-month period of daylight is experienced in all parts of the Mackenzie District (the twilight continuing throughout the short time the sun is below the horizon), and north of the Arctic Circle the midnight sun is a feature of note. At Fort Simpson, the average possible number of hours of sunshine daily during the summer season is nearly 18. Because of these favorable conditions, many gardens are cultivated in the district at missions, Indian agencies, and trading posts.

Precipitation in most parts of the Northwest Territories is normally under 10 inches a year, except in the Mackenzie Valley west of Great Slave and Great Bear Lakes, where it varies from 10 to 20 inches. Moisture is retained longer than in southerly regions, for low temperatures reduce the amount of evaporation, and the permanently frozen subsoil prevents underground drainage (*Fig. 17-6*).

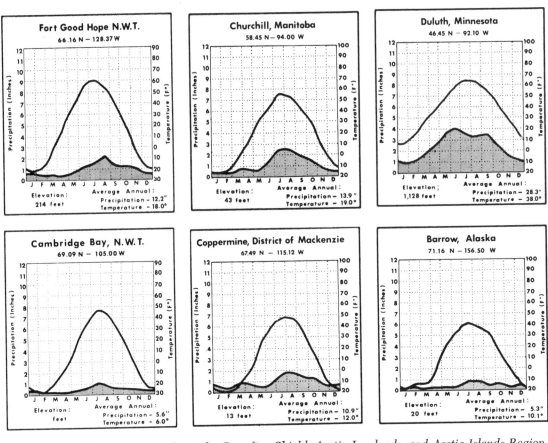

FIGURE 17-6. *Climatic graphs of the Canadian Shield, Arctic Lowlands, and Arctic Islands Region.*

There is a marked distinction between the climates of the eastern and western Arctic regions of Canada, a distinction most clearly manifested in July. Along the Arctic Circle the average temperature in July ranges from about 42° F. in southern Baffin Island to about 60° in the northern Mackenzie Valley. On the lower portion of Ellesmere Island and throughout the Parry Islands the average temperature is less than 40°. If the isotherm of 50° in July is taken as the criterion of a northern summer, then there is no summer north and east of a line that begins on the Labrador Coast, touches the southern end of Ungava Bay, and passes across Hudson Bay from the Belcher Islands to Eskimo Point, then northwestward to the mouth of the Coppermine River and along the Arctic Coast to the mouth of the Mackenzie River.

In midwinter all the Arctic territory is sub-ject to periods of great cold, and these periods are associated with the slow outflow of prob-ably shallow, but extremely dry and cold domes of surface air from the area west of the Parry Islands and Victoria Island. These masses move up the Mackenzie Valley to spread out over the Canadian prairies before showing much tendency to drift eastward. As the year advances, the eastward compon-ent of motion becomes much more important than the southward component, so that in midsummer the eastern Arctic continues to be dominated by wintry conditions, while the western Arctic is increasingly influenced by air masses modified over Alaska and the North Pacific. In fact, air masses that have been recently modified in more southerly latitudes of the continent frequently affect the weather of the western Arctic. As a consequence, the highest temperature in Baffin Island averages about 65° F., while on the Arctic Circle in the Mackenzie Valley it is 85° or higher.

Precipitation in the Arctic Lowlands is slight; the mean annual precipitation is 4.2 inches at Barrow, Alaska, and 5.4 inches at Umiat, 175 miles to the northeast. Half the precipitation is represented by rain that falls during the months of July, August, and September. Annual snowfall is about 29 inches at Barrow and 33 inches at Umiat (*Fig. 17-7*).

Natural Vegetation

Portions of the Canadian Shield lie within the great transcontinental coniferous forest that merges on the north into the Arctic barren grounds. It stretches northward in the east only to the head of Ungava Bay but slopes steeply northeastward to reach the delta of the Mackenzie River. White spruce favors upland sites, with aspen and paper birch as common associates throughout nearly the entire area. Black spruce favors low-lying wet muskegs where it is commonly associated throughout the area with tamarack. The ground cover is usually sparse, even in relatively open areas since the thick layer of old, very slowly

decaying needles of past years provide little encouragement for seedlings to root. Shrubs and herbs are typically acid-loving. Characteristic shrubs of the area include junipers, various currants and gooseberries, honeysuckles, and elderberries (*Fig. 17-8*).

Vegetation in the Arctic lands is subjected to severe conditions—dry, short, cool summers and an exceedingly thin soil mantle over the frozen ground, smooth rock, or debris of mechanical denudation, as the case may be. Plants obtain only a small part of their moisture directly from precipitation, which is not even at its maximum in summer. The greater part of their moisture comes from the snow melting on the slopes, from the thawing ground, and from the coastal fogs, which, especially for lichens and mosses, are an important form of humidity and, at the same time, a protection against evaporation and loss of heat. As a result of the small amount of moisture, plant life is developed in xerophytic forms; it is characterized by small leathery leaves, a tendency to succulence, hairlike coverings, tussock formation, low stature, and, often, very short stems. Bushes and even grasses are characterized by one-sided growth, because the windward side dries up. Much-

FIGURE 17-7. *Point Barrow, Alaska, during the winter. This area is characterized by long, cold winters and very short, cool summers. (Official U. S. Navy photograph)*

FIGURE 17-8. *River scene in the Northwest Territories. Note the coniferous vegetation. (Canadian Government Travel Bureau)*

exposed surfaces carry only lichen coverings. As a result of the shortness of the summer, which in some places lasts only two months, most plants are perennial, sprouting leaves and buds in the autumn and blossoming rapidly the following June.

The dominant vegetation over large areas consists of carpets of moss and lichen, known as "barren grounds"; grasslands, however, also exist to an extent that led to the coining of the expression "Arctic prairies." Generally, of course, plant life in the Arctic is characterized by a dearth of species. Many of the species occur again and again, such as the willows, the reed and wool grasses, and heath plants.

Soils

Podzol soils occupy a large portion of the Canadian Shield; the remainder consists of bog soils, permafrost, and others. The podzols develop beneath coniferous forests, under the influence of the downward movement of water carrying organic acids formed by the decom-

position of forest waste. The process of podzolization is reflected outwardly in the soil profile by the development of a whitish, leached horizon. The aluminum and ferric hydoxides and other products of mineral decomposition that are washed out of the leached horizon are partly carried away in the ground waters and partly retained in the lower horizon. The soils are classified as weak, medium, and heavily podzolized by the degree of development of the podzolized horizon. The majority of podzolized soils show a degree of peat formation, in which the humus horizon acquires a more or less clearly defined soil structure and accumulates plant food elements.

Bog soils are formed where there is a persistent excess of moisture. A characteristic of bog soils is the accumulation of organic matter in the surface horizon.

Permafrost, or permanently frozen ground, is a common phenomenon in the subarctics. Permafrost is covered by a layer of soil of varying thickness, called the active layer, which usually contains much moisture and varies in temperature with the seasons. This layer freezes every winter; a warm summer may thaw it down to the upper surface of the permafrost, and a cool one may not. There are two types of permafrost. Some is solid, the soil being frozen to great depth without a break; some, commonly found on the periphery of a solid layer, has alternating frozen and unfrozen layers, the latter being kept from freezing by the ground water that constantly or periodically circulates through it. The local distribution of permafrost is determined largely by subsurface drainage and surface insulation. Permafrost usually lies in shallowest depth in areas mantled with peat, organic silt, or a dense mat of living vegetation; it lies at greatest depth beneath bare gravel or in exposed bedrock.

Arctic soils are sterile because of the cold climate, the short summer, and consequent low soil temperatures. Vegetation everywhere is sparse, dwarfed, and starved. Organic decay by bacterial action is greatly reduced, so the soil is deficient in nitrates, phosphates, and other materials needed by plants. Where these nutrients are present, Arctic plants respond with lush and luxuriant growth. Thus, bird cliffs, animal burrows, muskox meadows, owl perches, goose nesting grounds, and places near present or past human habitation—even near animal dung or skeletal remains—are often marked from afar by rich green vegetation, which contrasts strikingly with the otherwise drab and gray landscape.

Lowland areas are underlain by unconsolidated sediments as much as several hundred feet thick. The fill generally consists of 10 to 20 feet of silt, muck, and peat over thick layers of gravel. In some areas, however, the lowland fill consists almost entirely of fine-grained sediments and includes only scattered lenticular gravel. Aprons of alluvial gravel mantled with only a few feet of silt and peat occur along some coastal margins. Most upland ridges are mantled by a few feet of windblown silt beneath which lies frost-rived bedrock rubble; on some ridges the rubble is exposed. The fine-grained mantle thickens in saddles and on slopes, reaching a thickness of several scores

of feet on the lower slopes. Swales and minor valleys generally consist of 2 to 6 feet of gravel overlain by silt, muck, and peat. The flood plains of larger valleys generally are underlain by 5 to 30 feet of gravel and a few feet of silt.

Subsurface materials are perennially frozen nearly everywhere except beneath and near lakes, channels of perennial streams, some ocean beaches, and hot springs. The frozen layer ranges in thickness from 15 to more than 260 feet; in most places, subsurface materials probably are frozen to depths of at least 200 feet.

The surface layers of the soil thaw to depths of one to ten feet, depending on the surface material, vegetation cover, and exposure. In general, the depth to which the soil thaws during the summer increases according to the amount of coarseness of surface material and the sparseness of vegetation. The depth of thaw is less on steep north slopes than on steep south slopes; the difference is imperceptible, however, on slopes of less than 15 degrees.

Settlement

ALASKA

The Arctic Lowland, the habitat of the Eskimos of Alaska, is as harsh an area for human life as the planet has to offer. Windy, treeless wastes where temperatures are well below zero in winter and under 50° F. in the short, cold summer, present what seems to be an almost insurmountable challenge to the ingenuity of man.

Yet this area had a remarkable, flourishing culture about two thousand years ago. The Stone Age remains discovered on the Point Hope Peninsula indicate that these people had considerable artistic ability. Among the artifacts that have been found on Point Hope are hunting implements of stone, jade, bone, and ivory, as well as articles that were plainly intended for use in war. A rigorous people, they scoured the land and the sea in their activities.

These prehistoric peoples were succeeded by the Eskimos, who were in the Alaskan Arctic when the Russians began exploring the region in the middle of the eighteenth century. Living along the coast in permanent villages, the Eskimos found a reasonably plentiful supply of salmon, some berries, great flocks of ducks, geese, and other shorebirds, numerous ptarmigan, and a few wandering caribou. The Eskimos would scarcely have survived, however, had they not been able to develop their hunting at sea and on the ice to a high degree. In these activities they are unsurpassed. In sturdy craft made of driftwood covered with skins, armed only with harpoons, these people succeeded in subduing 60-ton bowhead whales. The whale, the seal, and the walrus were the mainstay of their economy (*Fig. 17-9*). Clothing was made entirely of skins from the reindeer, ground squirrel, seal, eider duck, cormorant, and murre.

Reindeer were introduced from Siberia at the turn of the century. Lapp herders accompanied the reindeer, and many of them settled and intermarried with the Eskimos. Reindeer roundups still take place. Every part of the animal is used for food or clothing.

The kayak is a seaworthy canoe from 10 to 20 feet long and about 2 feet wide. It is made of seal or walrus skin tightly stretched over a framework of wood or bone, decked over except for the round hole in the middle in which the occupant sits. It is propelled by a double-bladed paddle (*Fig. 17-10*). The umiak, also built of seal or walrus hides carefully stitched so that they are watertight, is a deckless vessel that is large enough to carry several passengers and considerable freight. It is a sturdy craft and can be readily pulled up over the ice or shelving beach. An outboard motor is a frequent present-day adjunct to the umiak.

Eskimos are generally of small stature, with round heads, small and well-formed hands and feet, and broad faces with somewhat Oriental features. The men hunt and do some fur trapping. All the household duties are performed by the women—they cook, make and mend clothing, repair kayaks and umiaks, pitch tents in summer, and dry fish and meat and store them for winter.

Of the total indigenous population of about 43,000, about 22,800 are Eskimos, 5,700 Aleuts, and 14,500 Indians. They live in widely separated villages scattered along the 25,000-mile coastline and the great rivers of Alaska. Among these peoples, the village, varying in population from 30 to 1,000, is the most important social unit (*Fig. 17-11*).

Alaskan Eskimos and Indians are no longer primitive peoples. Although many still hunt and fish for part of their food, many are air-

FIGURE 17-9. *An Eskimo woman of Arctic Alaska splitting a walrus hide. (U. S. Fish and Wildlife Service)*

FIGURE 17-10. *An Eskimo kayak is waterproofed by an Arctic Eskimo craftsman. (Alaska Travel Division)*

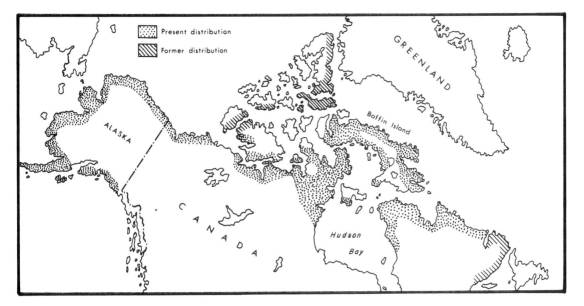

FIGURE 17-11. *Areas of Eskimo culture.*

plane pilots, welders, mechanics, carpenters, storekeepers, teachers, office clerks, and state senators and representatives. Where electricity is available, many Eskimo and Indian homes today have washing machines and other appliances.

CANADA

Indians. Roughly 7,500 Indians dwell within the Canadian portion of the region. About 4,000 of them live in the valley of the Macken-zie River. The principal Indian tribes are the Chipewyan, Beaver, Sekani, Slave, Yellow-knife, Dogrib, Hare, Hahani, and Kutchin or Loucheux.

Intertribal raids among the Indians came to an end about a century ago, and they began to congregate about the posts and settlements of the fur traders, who tried, not very success-fully, to elevate as chiefs the most influential and reliable hunters and to give them a limited authority over their own countrymen. Missionaries were also very active.

Through most of the nineteenth century, social and economic changes threatened to bring about the extinction of the Indians. Alcoholic excesses and diseases previously unknown, particularly smallpox, tuberculosis,

and influenza, reduced their number from what was estimated by some authorities to be 13,000 to one-third of that total.

In recent years, exploration, settlement, and mining activities have led to a demand for In-dian guides, canoe men, and packers, and have resulted in increasing the Indians' dependence on flour, beans, bacon, and other imported food supplies. From the earliest times, too, many white traders and trappers have taken Indian women as wives, and have modified the whole outlook and manners of the tribes among whom they have resided. So extensive, indeed, has been this intermarriage that today in the whole area there are probably few In-dians of pure stock.

It is confidently felt that increasing settle-ment and a great development of the resources of the Northwest Territories will open up new avenues of employment for the Indians, lower their heavy infant mortality rate, and, through a general improvement in living conditions, arouse in them new vigor and new ambitions for the future.

Eskimos. Eskimos inhabit the entire Arctic Coast of Canada from the Yukon-Alaskan boundary to the eastern limits of Canadian territory, the more southerly islands of the

Arctic Archipelago, and some of the islands of Hudson Bay and James Bay. About 5,400 Eskimos are in the Northwest Territories, and most of these live in the Franklin and Keewatin Districts. There are also about 1,800 Eskimos in northern Quebec, formerly the Ungava District of the Northwest Territories (*see Fig. 17-11*).

There are no Eskimo tribes; the term "tribe" is associated with North American Indians. The Eskimos of the eastern Arctic live and travel in bands or groups of two or more families, and each band or group usually contains some outstanding individual who acts as leader.

Contact between the bands is limited mainly to communication with those hunting or trapping in adjoining areas. Each band secures its livelihood in its own district, which has no definite boundaries. Bands move about to match the movement of game and the changing seasons. In bad seasons it may become necessary to look for new hunting grounds, but Eskimos are very likely to return to the old district when they think conditions have improved. The hunting and trapping grounds of eastern Arctic Eskimos are along the coast, the sea furnishing the greater part of their requirements for food, fuel, and clothing.

The Eskimo of the eastern Arctic lives in a snowhouse, or igloo, in winter and a tent in summer. Sealskin, canvas, sacking, pieces of board, stone, and even glazed glass may be used to make up the tents or houses.

Travel in summer is by boat; in winter, by dog sled (*Fig. 17-12*). The usual type of cruising boat is the open whaleboat to which a sail is attached. Other types are also brought in on order by the trading companies and are equipped, when the owners can afford it, with gasoline engines. Eskimos are mechanically inclined and with a little coaching quickly learn to operate and keep in repair complicated marine engines. They know thoroughly the districts in which they hunt and trap, and the actions of the tides, currents, and ice; they frequently go out to sea under conditions that would keep other men ashore. The smaller, one-man kayak is still used extensively by the

FIGURE 17-12. *A dog team and sled in northern Manitoba. This is still the only dependable form of surface transportation in the Canadian Arctic during the winter season. (R. Harrington, Hudson's Bay Co.)*

Eskimos and is probably the outstanding article of equipment made by these remarkable people.

Coastal Eskimos of the western Arctic move out on the ice to sealing grounds, where many of them live in igloos. These sealing camps may be from 5 to 20 miles out on the ice and are frequently used as bases for trapping operations. In summer those who own whaleboats go to the whaling grounds where they fish for white whale. A successful whaling season means prosperity for all. The flesh of the white whale is used for both human consumption and for dog food. Oil extracted from the blubber is stored in barrels or sealskin bags for use as part of every meal in the winter. Those who have no whaleboats live in tents in summer and do their fishing and whaling from the shore.

For generations Eskimos of the Canadian Northland have wrested a living, mated, and reared families in a country where only a hardy and intelligent race could survive. They are slowly assimilating a certain amount of civilization while still retaining their independence, pride, and ability to care for themselves.

Fur Enterprises

Alaska and Canada support a thriving fur industry. A combination of bitterly cold winters and frost cover protection provides ideal natural environmental conditions for fur-bearing animals.

Before outsiders first ventured into Alaska, the Eskimos and Indians of the interior relied almost exclusively upon hunting and trapping for their survival. The fur trade was the lure that encouraged early explorations. Large numbers of people, mostly Indians and Eskimos, still depend directly upon this resource for their physical and economic well-being. Fur-bearing animals are an important source of income. Blue, red, and white fox, mink, muskrat, beaver, marten, and lynx are the leading animals trapped (*Fig. 17-13*).

The Canadian fur trade had its beginning in the seventeenth century when the Hudson's Bay Company received its charter. The trapping of fine furs is still, and is likely to remain, the chief occupation of most of the native population. Trading posts are scattered throughout the region. From the viewpoint of value, white fox pelts lead. Chief among the other furs of economic importance are red fox (in its three color phases—red, cross, and silver), beaver, lynx, marten, and muskrat. Smaller numbers of ermine, otter, wolf, wolverine, bear, and others are also obtained.

Ontario has several hundred fur farms. Mink make up 90 per cent of the animals; the remainder consist chiefly of chinchillas and foxes. The most important animals trapped are beaver, muskrat, and mink. The cutover country of upper Michigan, northern Wisconsin, and northern Minnesota supports fur industries; fox, mink, weasel, muskrat, and beaver are caught there. Fur farming is also important.

Forest Products

Pulp and paper manufacturing is an economic mainstay of the upper Great Lakes area of the United States and in the Canadian provinces of Ontario and Quebec. There are enormous stands of red, black, and white spruce; balsam fir; white, red, jack, and pitch pine; Eastern hemlock; and poplar. These trees are ideally suited for making pulpwood. Forest industries are the largest consumers of electricity and the largest industrial buyers of goods and services.

Quebec produces more than one-third of all Canada's pulp and paper products. Within its boundaries are stands of 50 million cubic feet, or about half of Canada's coniferous trees. In addition to this supply of raw material, Quebec has an unexcelled system of waterways to carry logs to the mills and to supply the mills with the hydroelectric power to run the machines that make the paper.

Ontario's pulp and paper is exported mainly to the United States. The forest resources of Ontario provide a number of important products: lumber, veneers and plywood, laths, shingles, fuel wood, ties, poles, posts, and mine timbers (*Fig. 17-14*).

The place of pulp and paper as Canada's principal manufacture is a reflection of the country's forest lands. Forests, mostly softwood, cover over 1.5 million square miles, or

FIGURE 17-13. *Indian trappers from the Mackenzie District return home on snowshoes with the animals that were caught in their traps. (National Film Board of Canada)*

FIGURE 17-14. *Millions of tons of lumber have been formed into "teardrop" log booms on this Ontario waterway. Note how the "teardrops" dwarf the huge freighter loading logs by crane. (Canadian Government Travel Bureau)*

more than 40 per cent of Canada's land area, of which some 600,000 square miles are productive and accessible. Canada's newsprint capacity is nearly five times greater than that of any other country, and the industry accounts for about 51 per cent of the world's total production.

Agriculture

Agricultural endeavors in the region are limited not by a single climatic factor, but rather by a refractory combination of climatically related features: a cool, short, irregular growing season; infertile podzol soils; poor drainage; and permafrost. The bitterly cold winters do not necessarily preclude farming, but the summer growing season is short and the weather is often raw. Crop failures are frequent. The podzol soils of these northern areas are deficient in soluble plant foods, low

in colloids, poor in structure, and highly acidic. Heavy manuring and liming are necessary to sustain agriculture, but the cost of such operations is scarcely justified in low-yield areas.

Farming is of little importance in the Canadian subarctics except in meeting local requirements. So far, it has been confined chiefly to the efforts of scattered missions and a few individuals, primarily in the Mackenzie River Valley. Some of these efforts have been highly successful, even though they are conducted on a small scale.

Mining

The Canadian Shield has a wealth of minerals that makes it an important producer of raw materials. Iron ore is mined in several places, but its greatest concentration occurs in the upper Great Lakes area. Mining activities began in 1845 near Negaunee, Michigan. Lake

Superior ore has been the backbone of United States industry ever since. Minnesota's Mesabi iron was discovered in 1890. Most of the high-grade hematite ore (64 per cent iron content), originally estimated at 2.5 billion long tons, has been consumed. Open-pit mining methods and short rail hauls to the Great Lakes ore fleet, which moves the ore at low cost to distributing points along the lakes, account for both the importance of this ore body to American industry and its rapid depletion. Other sources of iron ore in Minnesota include the Vermillion Range, opened in 1865 and worked by underground mining methods, and Cuyuna, opened in 1904. Marquette, in Michigan, and Menominee and Gogebic, in Michigan and Wisconsin, complete the list of Lake Superior iron ore ranges in the United States. Along the Canadian border are two iron ore districts, Michipicoten and Moose Mountain, lying partly in Minnesota and partly in Ontario, near Atikokan. Steep Rock, Ontario, 140 miles north of Duluth, is the site of a large iron ore body whose reserves are estimated at more than 60 million tons.

Copper is mined in the Keweenaw Peninsula of Michigan. Though dwarfed by the West's large-scale exploitation of low-grade ores, Michigan's shaft copper mines are important locally, despite their relatively small yield.

Limestone is quarried at Calcite, Michigan. It is used as a flux stone in the iron and steel industry as well as for cement, concrete, road building, and fertilizer.

Asbestos is extracted in Quebec. Gypsum and nepheline syenite are mined in Ontario. Petroleum has been recovered from Norman Wells, in the Mackenzie River Valley, since 1920. Radium-bearing ores and silver ores were discovered at Echo Bay, on the eastern side of Great Bear Lake, in 1930. Gold was discovered at Yellowknife in 1935 (*Fig. 17-15*). Copper, nickel, lead, and zinc are being mined in several areas. Uranium, platinum, cobalt, and tungsten also exist, along with deposits of tantalum, columbium, and beryllium. The Sudbury district of Ontario is the source of over 85 per cent of the noncommunist world's nickel output. The Athabasca oil

FIGURE 17-15. *The Consolidated Mining and Smelting Company's gold mine at Yellowknife, Northwest Territories. In operation since 1938, the mine presently employs 250 people. (Consolidated Mining and Smelting Co.)*

sands in northern Alberta are believed to contain some 100 to 300 billion barrels of oil. In Flin Flon, Manitoba, the Hudson Bay Mining and Smelting Company mines copper, zinc, and cadmium (*Fig. 17-16*). Farther north, at Lynn Lake, Sherritt Gordon Mines, Ltd., is recovering nickel, copper, and cobalt. East of Flin Flon, at Mystery and Moak Lakes, the International Nickel Company is developing a nickel deposit that may prove to be second only to the Sudbury district of Ontario. Ontario produces all of Canada's magnesium, calcium, and platinum, most of its cobalt, over 90 per cent of its nickel, 55 per cent of its gold, and 45 per cent of its copper.

Manufacturing

Most of the Alaskan and the Canadian portions of this region are sparsely populated. None of the major industries—forestry, fishing, mining, or water power—will support dense populations over wide areas. The only important manufacturing district of the region is

FIGURE 17-16. *Flin Flon, Manitoba. The Canadian National Railroad built a line 87 miles long from The Pas to Flin Flon in 1928 to open the area to mining operations. A hydroelectric plant at Island Falls, Saskatchewan, on the Churchill River, supplies power for the zinc recovery plant and the copper smelter in Flin Flon. (Hudson Bay Mining and Smelting Co., Ltd.)*

along the northern and western parts of Lake Superior.

The bulk of Lake Superior ore clears through the vast loading docks at Duluth and adjacent Superior (*Fig. 17-17*). Most of the ore shipments are from Superior, where the Great Northern Railway has the world's largest group of ore docks, capable of loading 24 freighters in as many hours.

Duluth (population 106,884) has an iron and steel industry based on local iron ore and coal from Pennsylvania and West Virginia borne as return cargo following the unloading of ore at the eastern end of the Great Lakes. It is the shipping outlet for one of the greatest grain producing areas in the world, extending west almost to the Pacific. Duluth's elevators can store 46 million bushels, and the port annually clears around 100 million bushels of wheat and other cereals. In addition, it ships large quantities of balsam wood and other forest products, wool, flax, shingles, fabricated iron and steel, and various other items that make up the so-called "package freight" business, as distinguished from the bulk traffic—ore, coal, and grain. Waterborne commerce of Duluth-Superior is second only to New York.

A whole day by train from the twin ports of Duluth and Superior on the American side are the Canadian twins, Fort William and Port Arthur. Wheat is by far the major commodity here, filling the 92-million-bushel elevators at the lake front and flowing eastward to the St. Lawrence at the rate of 200 to 300 million bushels per year, with a small quantity going west to Duluth for transshipment to various mills in the United States. In exchange, Fort William and Port Arthur take in supplies of every description for the vast hinterland—nails, binder twine, barbed wire, canned goods, clothing, mining and agricultural machinery, and other equipment.

Outlook

Mineral wealth and forest products will continue to attract capital from the middle latitudes. As industrial minerals now supply-

FIGURE 17-17. *Loading iron ore at a Duluth ore dock. The ore is dumped from railroad cars into dockside bins, from which it pours down chutes and into the ship's hold. Approximately 13,000 tons of ore is loaded in four hours. (Standard Oil Co. of New Jersey)*

ing the world's manufacturing regions are depleted or become too costly to recover, man will turn more and more to the natural resources of this region. New manufacturing establishments also may be expected to arise in some of the mining districts, especially as market-oriented industries develop there to meet local demands. The enormous coniferous forests will continue to provide man with lumber, paper pulp, newsprint, and countless new wood products developed through chemical research. Living costs in the high latitudes are bound to remain high so long as the inhabitants desire the comforts of the middle latitudes. Most of man's food, clothing, manufactures, and the like are produced outside the region. Transportation is expensive because of the distance from populated centers and because of the many handicaps to surface movement of goods. No doubt any development of the region on a large scale will be greatly

limited because of man's preference to dwell in greater numbers in the more favored climatic realms of the middle latitudes.

Selected References

"An Introduction to the Geography of the Canadian Arctic," *Canadian Geography Information Series No. 2*, Ottawa, 1951.

BANK, THEODORE, *Birthplace of the Winds*, New York: Thomas Y. Crowell Co., 1956.

BERTRAM, G. C. L., "Pribilof Fur Seals," *Arctic*, Vol. 3, No. 2, August, 1950, pp. 75–85.

BLACK, ROBERT F., "Aeolian Deposits of Alaska," *Arctic*, Vol. 4, No. 2, September, 1951, pp. 89–111.

BROWN, R. J. E., *et al.*, "The Mackenzie River Delta," *The Canadian Geographer*, No. 7, 1956.

"Canada Counts Its Caribou," *The National Geographic Magazine*, Vol. 102, August, 1952, pp. 261–268.

CARNES, WILLIAM G., "Novice North of Nowhere: An Adventure in the Landscape of America's Arctic," *Landscape Architecture*, Vol. 46, No. 1, October, 1955, pp. 19–25.

CRAIG, ROLAND D., "The Forests of Canada," *Economic Geography*, Vol. 2, 1926, pp. 394–413.

DEBENHAM, FRANK, "The Ice Islands of the Arctic," *The Geographical Review*, Vol. 44, October, 1954, pp. 495–507.

GRUENING, ERNEST, *The State of Alaska*, New York: Random House, 1954.

HULLEY, CLARENCE C., *Alaska, 1741-1953*, Portland, Ore.: Binfords & Mort, 1953.

JORDAN, G. F., "Redistribution of Sediments in Alaskan Bays and Inlets," *The Geographical Review*, Vol. 52, October, 1962, pp. 548–558.

KIMBLE, G. H. T., and GOOD, DOROTHY (eds.), *Geography of the Northlands*, New York: American Geographical Society, 1955.

LA FAY, HOWARD, "Dew Line, Sentry of the Far North," *The National Geographic Magazine*, Vol. 114, No. 1, July, 1958, pp. 128–146.

LANTIS, MARGARET, "The Reindeer Industry in Alaska," *Arctic*, April, 1950.

McDERMOTT, GEORGE L., "Frontier of Settlement in the Great Clay Belt, Ontario and Quebec," *Annals of the Association of American Geographers*, Vol. 51, September, 1961, pp. 261–273.

MOORE, W. ROBERT, "Alaska, the Big Land," *The National Geographic Magazine,* Vol. 109, No. 6, June, 1956, pp. 776–805.

"Oil in Northern Alaska," *Polar Record,* Vol. 6, July 1953, pp. 815–816.

PORSILD, A. E., "Plant Life in the Arctic," *Canadian Geographical Journal,* Vol. 42, 1951, pp. 121–145.

"Resources of the Arctic," *Focus,* Vol. 2, February, 1952.

ROWLEY, DIANA (ed.), "Arctic Research: The Current Status of Research and Some Immediate Problems in the North American Arctic and Sub-Arctic," *Special Publication No. 2* (Arctic Institute of America), 1955.

RUMNEY, G. R., "Settlements on the Canadian Shield," *Canadian Geographical Journal,* Vol. 43, 1951, pp. 116–127.

STAMP, L. D., and HARE, F. K., *Physical Geography of Canada,* Toronto: Longmans, 1953.

STANTON, WILLIAM J., "The Purpose and Source of Seasonal Migration to Alaska," *Economic Geography,* Vol. 31, No. 2, April, 1955, pp. 138–148.

VANDERHILL, BURKE G., "Observations in the Pioneer Fringe of Western Canada," *The Journal of Geography,* Vol. 57, December, 1958, pp. 431–440.

WAHL, E., *This Land, a Geography of Canada,* Toronto: Oxford University Press, 1961.

18 *Hawaiian Archipelago Region*

The Hawaiian Archipelago is a chain of volcanic islands near the center of the northern Pacific Ocean (*Fig. 18-1*). The larger islands form a group about 375 miles long at the eastern end of the chain and lie entirely within the tropics. Their isolation and their great diversity of soil, relief, drainage, and climate have led to the development of a unique and extremely varied flora. Many of the native species are found nowhere else.

The Hawaiian Islands, though not usually considered a part of Anglo-America physically or culturally, warrant inclusion in this treatment because the entry of Hawaii into the United States as the fiftieth state ties this island archipelago closer both politically and economically to the rest of the nation.

The main group of the Hawaiian Islands, eight relatively large islands lying between 18° 55′ and 22° 16′ N., and between 154° 49′ and 160° 15′ W., is near the northern limit of the tropics, due south of the Alaska Peninsula, and directly west of Yucatan. From Honolulu it is 2,089 miles to San Francisco and 4,420 to Sydney, Australia. The total area of the main group is 6,435 square miles, slightly more than that of Connecticut and Rhode Island combined. A series of about 15 small, uninhabited, and seldom visited islands, lying to the northwest of the main group, terminates not far from Midway Island.

Surface Features

The Hawaiian Islands are the summits of a submarine range of volcanic mountains 2,000 miles long. Elevations have built up from the ocean floor, some 18,000 feet below sea level, to a maximum height of nearly 14,000 feet above sea level—a total of 32,000 feet. Formation of the islands occurred at various periods; the western end of the chain is the oldest and the eastern end is the youngest. Decided contrasts in the effects of weatherings and erosion, found within short distances, are caused by the marked local variations in rainfall and the resultant vegetation. Kauai, the oldest and most northwesterly of the larger islands, is badly cut up by gorges and ravines, while Hawaii, the youngest and most southeasterly, shows much less evidence of erosion. Since its volcanoes are not yet extinct, Hawaii is still in a formative stage (*Figs. 18-2* and *18-3*).

Nearly half the area encompassed by the state of Hawaii, including the greater part of all the islands except Hawaii, lies within five miles of the ocean. Approximately one-fourth

419

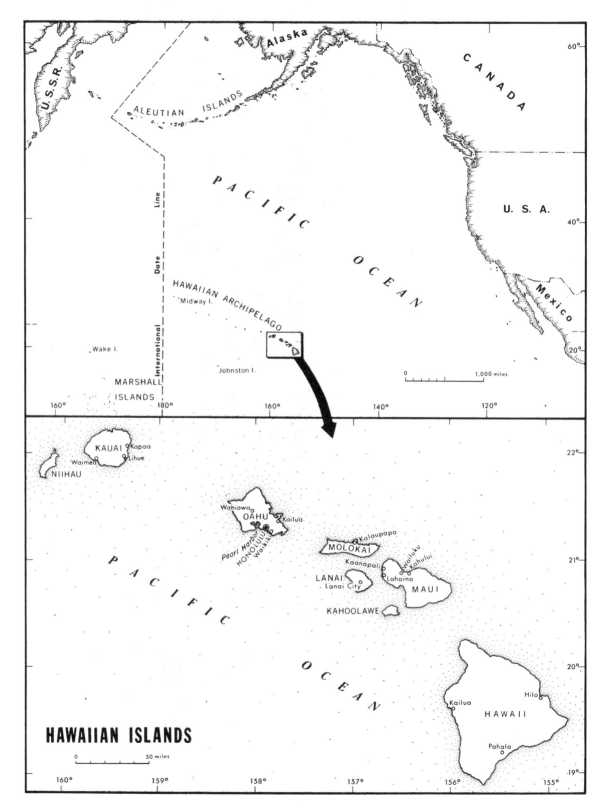

FIGURE 18-1.

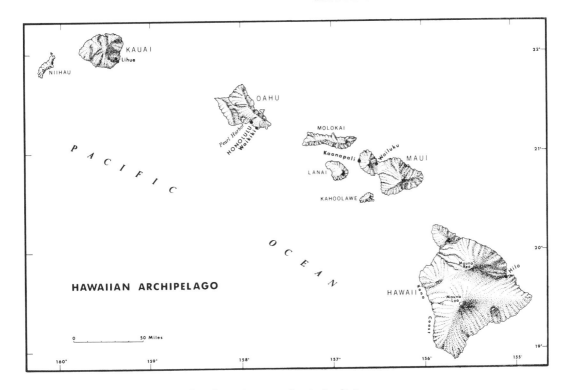

FIGURE 18-2. *The Hawaiian Archipelago Region, physical relief.*

FIGURE 18-3. *Eroded volcanic domes of the Hawaiian Islands (after Lobeck).*

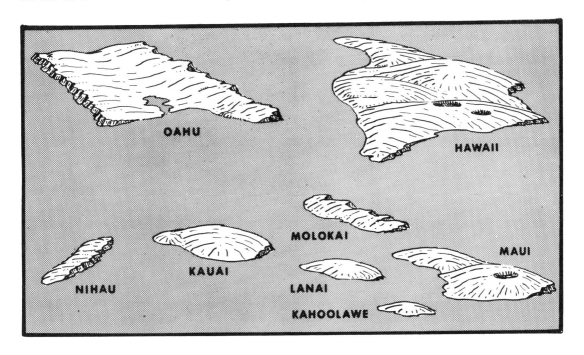

the land is at an elevation of less than 650 feet, one-half below 1,950 feet, and one-fourth above 4,500 feet. All but a small percentage of the population lives in the areas with elevations of less than 650 feet. On each of the islands there is a considerable percentage of land that cannot be utilized for cultivation.

Hawaii, the largest island, from which the group takes its name, has an area of 4,090 square miles. The other seven principal islands in order, are Maui, 728 square miles; Oahu, 604 square miles; Kauai, 555 square miles; Molokai, 260 square miles; Lanai, 141 square miles; Niihau, 72 square miles; and Kahoolawe, 45 square miles.

Climate

The climate of the Hawaiian Islands is unusually pleasant for a tropical area, the result principally of the marked marine influence and the persistent trade winds. Considering the latitude of the islands there is relatively little uncomfortable heat. The discomfort that is occasionally experienced usually occurs when the trade winds are temporarily displaced by light variable or southerly winds that are accompanied by comparatively higher humidities. The outstanding climatic features of the islands are the dominant trade wind influences throughout all seasons, the remarkable variation in rainfall over adjacent areas, and the uniform temperatures.

During the summer season the trade winds blow with a high degree of persistency. As a result, uncomfortable periods are usually delayed until fall. Rains most frequently fall at night. Thunderstorms are infrequent and practically never severe. Hail seldom occurs. Occasionally, local storms are accompanied by winds of sufficient force to do limited damage, but severe storms such as hurricanes or tornadoes are rare. So-called thick weather is almost unknown to the extent of seriously interfering with shipping and is usually confined to mist and rain rather than fog. Except for rare one- or two-day disruptions of interisland airplane schedules, interference to shipping or travel because of bad weather is almost unknown.

The strongest influence in the pressure pattern underlying the general circulation of air over the Hawaiian Islands area is the persistent and semipersistent high-pressure cell known as the Pacific High. The clockwise circulation around this cell, coupled with a slight deflection of the surface winds away from the high pressure, result in the northeast trades that are the dominant winds of the area.

KONA WEATHER

The word "kona" is of Polynesian origin and means *leeward*. It refers to the southerly winds and accompanying unpleasant weather on the normally leeward slopes of the principal Hawaiian island that, because of the wind shift, have temporarily become the windward slopes.

The konas, which occur most frequently during the months of October through April, provide the major climatic variations of the Hawaiian Islands. During these storms heavy rainfall, cloudiness, and accompanying high humidity can be expected on the lee sides of coasts and slopes that under the usual wind pattern receive less cloudiness and may have almost no rain. Near gales may occur, especially near points where the air tends to funnel into sharp mountain passes located near the coasts.

PRECIPITATION

The complicated rainfall pattern over the islands results chiefly from the effects of the rugged terrain on the persistent trade winds. Frequent and heavy showers fall almost daily in windward and upland areas, while rains of sufficient intensity and duration to cause more than temporary inconvenience are infrequent over lower leeward areas (*Fig. 18-3*).

More rain falls from November through April over the islands as a whole than from May through October. It is not unusual for an entire summer month to go by without measurable rain falling at some points on the

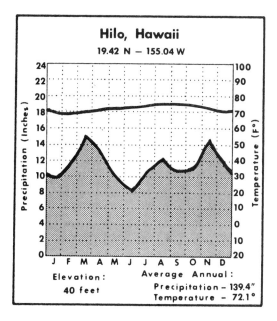

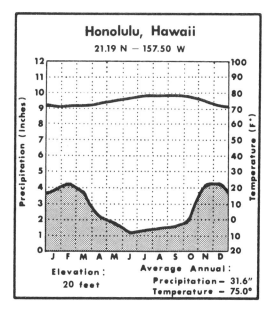

FIGURE 18-4. *Climatic graphs of the Hawaiian Archipelago Region.*

Maui isthmus; at times considerably longer dry periods may occur in that locality.

From windward to leeward slopes, instances of pronounced and sudden decline in rainfall may be found. This is well illustrated in central Kauai, where at the summit of Mt. Waialeale (5,075 feet), the average annual amount of rain is over 450 inches, while about 15 miles southwest, on the leeward side, it is less than 20 inches.

Not only does rainfall vary greatly within short distances, but monthly amounts received at a station over a period of years may also show a phenomenal range. Most stations, even many where the annual normal precipitation is 100 inches or more, occasionally have a dry period when the monthly total is less than 1 inch. Conversely, some of the driest points, where the annual average rainfall is 20 to 30 inches, may occasionally have an amount approaching or surpassing the annual normals during a single wet month, or sometimes even within a period of a few days.

TEMPERATURE AND HUMIDITY

Elevation is the major control factor in determining temperatures, although location,

whether in a leeward or windward position, is also a noticeable factor. The maximum temperatures reached during the day in leeward districts are usually higher than those attained in windward areas. The daily range is also greater over leeward districts where, because of less cloudiness, the maximum temperatures are higher and the minimum temperatures usually lower.

August and September are the warmest months and January and February are the coldest. At Honolulu there is an average monthly range between a low of 72° F. in January and February and a high of 78.5° in August. The extreme range of temperature at Honolulu for a recorded 34-year period is from a low of 57° F. for January to a high of 88° recorded in August and September. This spread of only 31 degrees between the extreme high and extreme low temperatures is small when compared with ranges at Pacific Coast ports of the conterminous United States.

All coastal areas are subject to the relatively high humidities associated with a marine climate. Humidities, however, vary considerably, from high percentages over and near the windward slopes to low percentages on the leeward side of the higher elevations.

Natural Vegetation

The pattern of rainfall and the uniform temperature gradient produce several strikingly different climates that are clearly reflected in the distribution of the natural vegetation. Areas that receive 20 inches or less of rainfall annually have a sparse coverage of drought-resistant shrubs and a coastal fringe of trees. Where rainfall is limited to between 20 and 40 inches annually and occurs below 3,000 feet, the natural cover is xerophytic shrub, with some trees. Places that receive between 40 and 60 inches of rainfall have a natural cover of mixed open forest and shrubs, subdivided into a lower tropical phase below 2,500 feet and a middle latitude phase above 2,500 feet. Belts that receive 60 inches or more of rainfall a year have mixed forest, subdivided into a low, a middle, and a high phase, the latter extending in places to 7,000 feet (Fig. 18-5).

Hawaiian flora includes majagua, a small tropical tree yielding a durable fiber; banyan, a partly epiphytic tree whose branches send out numerous aerial roots that grow down to the soil and form props or additional trunks; fern; and algarroba plants (carob with edible beans or pods), sometimes called St. John's bread. Mango, breadfruit, banana, coconut, ohia, and guava trees are widespread throughout the western, tropical portions of the island chain.

Soils

The soils of Hawaii are derived almost entirely from volcanic material. Differences in character result from the nature of such material, its age, depth, and the rainfall and temperature under which the soil-forming processes took place. Residual soils derived from lava vary from essentially undecomposed material to deeply weathered lateritic clays. Soils derived from volcanic ash are common, particularly in the uplands. They range in depth from a shallow covering to deep layers. Such soils are usually friable and are productive when they have sufficient depth for any kind of use.

The deepest deposits of topsoil lie in the valleys between mountain peaks. This porous soil allows much rain to soak into the ground, providing good resources for the storage of underground water. But the many mountainsides have only thin coverings of topsoil. Great barren areas of lava rock cover many parts of Hawaii.

Settlement

No one yet knows when Hawaii was first inhabited, and there is a continuous program of research conducted by Honolulu's Bishop Museum to shed further light on the subject. For many years it was believed that the Polynesians first arrived in Hawaii from Tahiti

FIGURE 18-5. *Cross-section of the island of Oahu illustrating the interrelationship of topographic position, rainfall, vegetation, soils, and land use (after Hunt).*

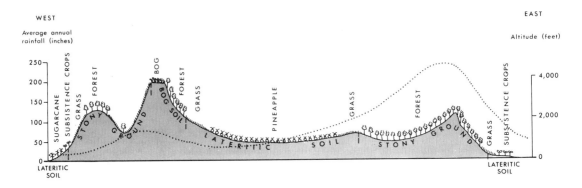

sometime around A.D. 1000, but new discoveries have suggested that the true date may be closer to A.D. 124.

Present-day researchers believe that the Polynesians who conquered the Pacific in their double-hulled canoes came originally from Southeast Asia. Tahiti is believed to be one center of Polynesian development, but there is some evidence indicating that Hawaii was first settled by people from the Marquesas Islands.

The discovery of Hawaii by the western world occurred in 1778, when British explorer Captain James Cook sighted Oahu. In January, 1779, Cook was slain in a fight with the Hawaiians at Kealakekua on the Island of Hawaii. Cook originally called the archipelago the Sandwich Islands, after his patron in England, the Earl of Sandwich, and for many years the islands were so known in the western world.

In early times each island had a king, but under Kamehameha I the islands were formed into one kingdom. Kamehameha I died in 1819 and was succeeded by his son, Liholiho, who adopted the name of Kamehameha II on his accession. His reign was famous for the abolition of idolatry and the system of taboo throughout all the islands.

George Vancouver, an English navigator who arrived with Cook in 1778, returned in 1792 and again for several weeks in 1794. Vancouver made sincere attempts to convert the islanders during these visits. He succeeded so well that during his last visit (1794), he was requested by Kamehameha II and his chiefs to send religious teachers to them from England. The first Christian missionaries to visit the islands, however, came from New England in 1820. The missionaries were well received, and the work of instruction was at once begun, as the king saw the necessity of introducing a new religion to take the place of the one he had abolished.

Over the years, the American missionary families and later American arrivals gained more and more power and wealth in the islands. When, under the reign of Queen Liliuokalani, they saw their position threatened, they fomented a revolution (1893). A provisional government was then formed and overtures were made for annexation to the United States. As these were not favorably received, the Republic of Hawaii was proclaimed July 4, 1894, with a constitution modeled after the Constitution of the United States.

The election of William McKinley in 1896 brought a more sympathetic attitude to the White House regarding annexation, and the outbreak of the Spanish-American War in 1898 quickly brought matters to a head. Hawaii's strategic military importance in the Pacific was recognized. Particular consideration was given to its potential threat to the United States if another great power were to occupy the islands. By joint resolution of Congress, the islands were officially annexed, and formal transfer of sovereignty was made on August 12, 1898. The new possession was quickly organized as a territory, and Sanford B. Dole was appointed its first governor, taking office June 14, 1900. The first territorial legislature convened on February 20, 1901. Hawaii officially entered the American Union as the 50th state on August 21, 1959.

THE PEOPLE OF HAWAII

Hawaii's people are unusual for two reasons. First, it is a young population—about half are under 25 years of age. Second, everyone in Hawaii is a member of a racial minority group —no single racial group constitutes more than about a third of the population.

Hawaii's history has resulted in a multiracial society admired for the degree of harmony and assimilation that has been achieved. Here the various peoples of Asia have followed a pattern similar to that set by European immigrants in other areas of the United States. The second and third generations have become thoroughly Americanized, and have produced a full quota of successful professional and technical people. They sit in the state legislature, and in Congress. They are doctors, lawyers, judges, teachers, scientists, artists, and musicians.

In ancestry, they include Anglo-Saxon, Japanese, Chinese, Hawaiian, Spanish, German, Korean, Puerto Rican, Filipino, Portuguese, Indian, Samoan, and Negro. Yet they are American, nearly all of them born under the American flag and educated in American schools. While ancestral languages are still spoken in Hawaii, English is by far the dominant tongue. Since World War II, one out of three marraiges in Hawaii has been interracial, which has contributed to making Hawaii's population extremely cosmopolitan (*Fig. 18-6*).

Hawaii's 760,000 people are concentrated largely in the city-county of Honolulu that encompasses the Island of Oahu. Eighty-two per cent of the state's entire population lives on Oahu.

FIGURE 18-6. *Hawaiian, Portuguese, Chinese, and English ancestries give a unique beauty to this Hawaiian girl. Japanese and Caucasians each make up about a third of the racial-ethnic groups of the state. Large numbers of Filipinos, Chinese, and people with partial native Hawaiian ancestry are also present in the islands. (Hawaiian Visitors Bureau)*

Approximately 63,000 servicemen are stationed in Hawaii. They are included in the resident population together with 73,000 civilian dependents. All but a few hundred servicemen and dependents live on Oahu, where the major military bases are located.

Agriculture

Few visitors to Hawaii realize that behind the beckoning beaches and the enchantment of the Waikiki "miracle mile" lies a complex and fascinating island world of agriculture, perhaps the most sophisticated that man has developed anywhere.

The remarkable growth and appeal of tourism has tended to obscure the fact that agriculture is still the most basic activity in the 50th state. In terms of agricultural production, two crops—sugarcane and pineapples—are outstanding. Although these have lost their once all-dominant position in the islands' economy, they have remained dynamic under the prodding of competition and continue to account for the bulk of income derived from agriculture.

SUGARCANE

The four largest Hawaiian islands, Kauai, Oahu, Maui, and Hawaii, produce roughly one-fifth of the sugar grown on American soil. The 26 plantation companies farm about 229,000 acres and provide year-round employment to some 12,500 people in the islands. These far-flung plantations produce more than a million tons of cane sugar each year, about seven per cent of which is grown by nearly 950 small, independent growers, mostly on the island of Hawaii (*Fig. 18-7*).

To a greater extent than in any other sugar producing area, Hawaii has replaced grueling hand work with specially-adapted machinery. Subsoilers break the earth to a depth of as much as two feet in irrigated fields. After plowing, the fields are smoothed and clods broken up with huge disc plows. After the fields are surveyed for alignment of irrigation furrows and to prevent soil erosion, the ponderous

FIGURE 18-7. *A sugarcane plantation, with a sugar mill in the background. (Bank of Hawaii)*

machines move in. They dig furrows, drop the seed cane in the furrow at proper intervals, add fertilizer, and cover the seed, all in one operation. Cane sugar requires a growing period of from 22 to 24 months to mature.

The sugar industry, established in 1835, has expanded to the point where there is simply no more acreage available for cultivation. But its tremendous research arm—the Hawaii Sugar Planters' Association Experiment Station—has increased yields to levels several times that of any other sugar producing area. The only hope for expansion of Hawaii's sugar industry is to get higher yields per acre, but yields are already very high compared to other cane sugar-producing areas. The average yield of sugar per acre is 10.64 tons in Hawaii, 2.38 tons for United States beet sugar, 1.76 tons for Louisiana cane, 2.61 tons for Florida cane, and 3.26 tons for Puerto Rican cane.

Most of the islands' sugar is refined at Crockett, California, and marketed in the Western states. Since most of the sugar beet producers are also located in the West, Ha-

waiian sugar must compete in a surplus area. For this reason the price that Hawaii's plantations receive for their sugar is below the price paid by Eastern refiners. It is not economical to market the sugar in the Middle West or East to take advantage of higher prices because of the high transportation cost. Only sugar that cannot be sold in the West is sent to Eastern markets.

PINEAPPLES

Hawaii is the world's largest grower and canner of pineapples, accounting for about 45 per cent of all commercial production. Second to sugarcane as an agricultural crop, pineapples do not compete with cane fields for space since they are grown largely on nonirrigated land, at higher elevations, or in rain-shadow locations. Thus, the two crops are complementary to each other in the economy of the state (*Fig. 18-8*).

Pineapples occupy 77,000 acres, and are grown on five islands, Kauai, Oahu, Molokai, Lanai, and Maui; they are the one product of the company-owned island of Lanai. Seventeen pineapple plantations, plus fruits grown by small farmers, support nine large canneries.

Hawaiian pineapple has had to compete not only with other fruits but also with increasing production of cheap foreign pineapple. The industry has been able to maintain its share of the national market by producing a high-quality product. Since 1935, the per capita consumption of pineapple has declined from 3.9 pounds to 3.3 pounds annually, while per capita consumption of all canned fruits rose from 13.4 to 23.3 pounds.

Against this kind of adversity, a less resourceful industry would have wilted out of existence long ago. Hawaiian growers and producers are meeting these threats through research—by further improving the quality and yield of fruit, by developing new products, by better marketing practices, and by seeking ways to reduce costs.

Hawaii enjoys freedom from competition in the huge mainland market, which absorbs about 95 per cent of the output. Great strides

FIGURE 18-8. *Pineapple fields in Hawaii. At the peak of the harvest, 23,000 people are employed in harvesting and canning pineapples, the state's largest crop. (Hawaii Visitors Bureau)*

have been made in the marketing of fresh pineapple over the past few years. Dole Company, the largest canner, has been so successful in promoting fresh pineapples all over the nation that it is now certain a permanent new market has been created.

OTHER CROPS

Other agricultural crops include fruits, vegetables, nuts, flowers, and coffee. Although fruits and nuts account for only one per cent of Hawaii's agricultural products, their importance is increasing yearly. Products include bananas, papayas, macadamia nuts, cantaloupes, oranges, tangerines, avocados, and watermelons.

Hawaii is the only state in the Union that grows coffee. Called Kona coffee after the area where it is grown, the industry takes advantage of small productivity of quality coffee by tapping the premium and gourmet markets. Quality control has been instituted through incentive payments, and the cooperative of coffee farmers will market only quality coffee

in instant and vacuum packs, rather than sell it for use as a blend. The coffee is all grown commercially on small farms (operated mainly by persons of Japanese descent) on about 6,000 acres in the highlands of the Kona coast of Hawaii.

Specialty fruits that show new promise of export potential are guava and passion fruit. Pacific Hawaiian Products Company, a subsidiary of R. J. Reynolds Tobacco Company, is increasing production of these fruits for use in its Hawaiian Punch drink. Other companies are using more of these two fruits either as straight juices or as blends.

Flowers, especially anthuriums (which sprout a single flower-petal that is flattish and brilliantly colored), are receiving more attention as export possibilities today. The state is engaged in marketing research on the islands' blossoms. Since the early 1950's, orchids from Hawaii have been common in the Eastern United States.

The University of Hawaii College of Tropical Agriculture has started looking into several commodities it feels have the best possibility for export income. Papaya has received top priority. The objective is to double yields and to find ways to prolong freshness through irradiation. In five years, shipment of this fruit to the mainland has climbed from one million pounds to five million pounds. Introduction of air shipments in 1961 helped greatly to expand the mainland market, allowing the grower to ship riper fruit and giving the grocer a more salable product.

LIVESTOCK

Beef cattle, poultry, and swine are produced for local markets. Poultry and egg producers and the dairy industry have improved their positions with modern methods. The cattle industry is beginning to see better results from modern pen feeding. To meet competition from abroad, farmers are banding into cooperatives and developing the large corporate-type farms that have been so successful in the growing of sugarcane and pineapples.

The rearing of beef cattle is a ranch industry. More than 400 ranches, half of them on the island of Hawaii, occupy over a million acres, or 77 per cent of the total agricultural land. The Parker Ranch (262,000 acres) extends along the eastern, southern, and western slopes of Mauna Kea and west to the Pacific. Nearly 40,000 head of cattle graze on the Parker Ranch, said to be the second largest in the United States. The slaughtering of cattle is concentrated in Honolulu (*Fig. 18-9*).

Manufacturing and Commerce

Most of Hawaii's manufacturing is concentrated in the city-county of Honolulu on the island of Oahu. In addition to sugar mills and pineapple canneries, many companies produce a variety of food products, including Hawaiian and Oriental food specialties. More than 60 garment manufacturers produce Hawaiian sportswear and other clothing. Many of the garments are made from textiles that have been screen printed in Hawaii.

FIGURE 18-9. *The Parker Ranch on the island of Hawaii is one of the world's largest cattle ranches. Note the typical vegetation in the background. (Hawaii Visitors Bureau)*

Durable goods include home and office furniture, plastics, adhesives, packaging materials, pumps, and air conditioning equipment. Heavy manufacturing is limited. It consists of: (1) an oil refinery opened early in 1960; (2) two cement plants; (3) an aluminum extrusion plant; (4) a steel mill, opened in 1959, which makes reinforcing rods and is based upon imported scrap and local markets; and (5) a concrete pipe plant (*Fig. 18-10*).

Figure 18-10. *The multimillion dollar Permanente Cement Company plant at Waianae, Oahu, has an annual production capacity of 1.7 million barrels of cement. (Permanente Cement Co.)*

The maritime commerce of Hawaii consists basically of exporting raw sugar and pineapple products to the mainland United States and importing from it food, manufactured goods, lumber, building materials, and feeds. Tourism also ranks high. Within the islands, the original sugar processing companies have gone beyond their function of serving the plantations; they are now engaged in varied commercial activities, such as insurance, shipping, retailing, and wholesaling (*Fig. 18-11*).

Fisheries

Hawaii is situated in the midst of a vast mid-ocean fishery capable of sharp expansion. The skipjack tuna offers the best potential for immediate exploitation. The fishing fleet, manned principally by persons of Japanese extraction, supplies local markets and a tuna cannery. More tuna is imported from Japan and elsewhere for packing.

Tuna are present the year-round in Hawaiian waters. The live bait method involving the use of small living fish to attract a school of fish, usually tuna, is the chief means employed by the island fishermen. Once the tuna are in a feeding frenzy, they are hooked by fishermen using a pole and line with a barbless hook attached.

Other methods of catching fish should be explored, including the longline technique, troll fishing, traps and gill nets, and the Norwegian bluefin purse seine. Construction of modern, fast, and efficient fishing boats financed on a matching fund basis between private industry and government is imperative if Hawaii is to compete with the Soviet Union and Japan.

Recreation and Tourism

Tourism in Hawaii is a brisk, booming industry. The state has one of the best-organized visitor promotion services in the world. The jet age has more than doubled the state's tourist industry. The main tourist area continues to be the Waikiki Beach section of Honolulu, although developers are becoming increasingly aware of the untrammeled beauty of the neighboring islands. Excellent hotel facilities, lush tropical scenery, a perfect climate, fine restaurants, and wonderful beaches are attractions that few other areas can match (*Fig. 18-12*).

Complete destination areas, rather than individual hotels, now are being built. These destination areas usually involve golf courses, accommodations in all price ranges, airstrips, shopping centers, residential sections, and mountain-to-seashore activities.

A 20-mile stretch along Maui's west coast, where the climate is dry and warm and the rainfall slight, already is being developed. In the middle of this coastal strip is Kaanapali

FIGURE 18-11. *The central business district of Honolulu, Oahu. In the background are the Koolau Range and the ocean. (Bank of Hawaii)*

FIGURE 18-12. *Halekulani Beach, with Diamond Head in the background. (Halekulani Hotel)*

Beach, the first large destination center to be built outside of Waikiki. By 1980, it will be a complex of 15 hotels with a total of 3,400 rooms.

Resort development of an even greater magnitude is on the drawing boards for the vast Kona Coast of Hawaii. A dozen or more hotels already dot this shoreline. The biggest impact by far in this coastal area has been made by the Mauna Kea Beach Hotel, an elegant resort that draws heavily from America's East Coast. The immediate success of this luxury hotel has spurred a flurry of master planning for thousands upon thousands of undeveloped acres in nearby areas.

Outlook

Federal spending for armed services installations, exports of sugar and pineapple, and tourism rank as the most important sectors in Hawaii's present economy. Hawaii's central location at "the crossroads of the Pacific" places it in a strategic position. Honolulu is the only important port equally accessible to all the major markets on the rim of the Pacific Basin. It is the closest point to the ton-mile center of transpacific trade. The potential of this geographic position means Hawaii should not be measured in terms of the state's 760,000 people and more than 700,000 annual visitors alone. Another measurement is the surrounding Pacific market that Hawaii-based operations can serve, including Asia, Oceania, Australia, New Zealand, South America, and North America. The latter is one of the basic reasons for the establishment of new trading companies and branch manufacturing, distribution, and marketing outlets in Hawaii. National and international concerns would do well to consider this avenue for the development of new Pacific and Asian markets.

With the vigor of the present day economies

of Japan, Taiwan, Australia, and New Zealand, and rising aspirations in other developing areas of Asia and the Pacific, a great increase in the volume of trans-Pacific trade is anticipated. Hawaii could play a major role in bringing together buyers and sellers from East and West, assisting them in their trading and financial arrangements, and providing them with display, exhibition, and test market facilities.

Selected References

ADAMS, ANSEL, and JOESTING, EDWARD, *An Introduction to Hawaii*, San Francisco: Five Associates, Inc., 1964.

BRYAN, E. H., JR., *The Hawaiian Chain*, Honolulu, Hawaii: Bishop Museum Press, 1954.

DAY, A. GROVE, and STROVEN, CARL, *Hawaii and Its People*, New York: Duell, Sloan & Pearce, 1960.

DURAND, LOYAL, JR., "Hawaii," *Focus*, Vol. 9, May, 1959.

————, "The Dairy Industry of the Hawaiian Islands," *Economic Geography*, Vol. 35, July, 1959, pp. 228–246.

EISELEN, ELIZABETH, "Geographic Problems of Our Fiftieth State," *The Journal of Geography*, Vol. 59, March, 1960, pp. 132–135.

GOSLINE, WILLIAM A., and BROCK, VERNON E., *Handbook of Hawaiian Fishes*, Honolulu, Hawaii: University of Hawaii Press, 1960.

GRIFFIN, PAUL F., "Some Geographic Aspects of the California and Hawaiian Sugar Industry," *The Journal of Geography*, Vol. 53, November, 1954, pp. 325–336:

Hawaii: Patterns of Island Growth, Honolulu, Hawaii: Bank of Hawaii, Department of Business Research, 1958.

JONES, STEPHEN B., "The Weather Element in the Hawaiian Climate," *Annals of the Association of American Geographers*, Vol. 29, March, 1939, pp. 29–57.

LIND, ANDREW W., *Hawaii's People*, Honolulu, Hawaii: University of Hawaii Press, 1955.

MALO, DAVID, *Hawaiian Antiquities*, Honolulu, Hawaii: University of Hawaii Press, 1951.

MELLEN, KATHLEEN, *An Island Kingdom Passes; Hawaii Becomes American*, New York: Hastings House, 1958.

NORBECK, EDWARD, *Pineapple Town: Hawaii*, Berkeley, Calif.: University of California Press, 1959.

"On Oahu," *Bulletin* (Standard Oil Company of California), Vol. 39, October, 1960, pp. 18–23.

PEARCY, G. ETZEL, "Hawaii's Territorial Sea," *The Professional Geographer*, Vol. 11, November, 1959, pp. 2–6.

STEARNS, HAROLD T., "Geology of the Hawaiian Islands," *U. S. Geological Survey Bulletin No. 8*, Honolulu, Hawaii, 1946.

WILSON, JAMES N., "Pineapple Industry of Hawaii," *Economic Geography*, October, 1948, pp. 251–262.

Index